BOTTOM LINE YEAR BOOK 2020

BY THE EDITORS OF

Bottom Line
PERSONAL

BottomLineInc.com

Bottom Line Yearbook 2020

Copyright © 2019 by Bottom Line Inc.

10 9 8 7 6 5 4 3 2 1

ISBN 0-88723-824-6

Bottom Line Books® publishes the advice of expert authorities in many fields. These opinions
may at times conflict as there are often different approaches to solving problems. The use
of a book is not a substitute for legal, accounting, investment, health or any other professional
services. Consult competent professionals for answers to your specific questions.

Offers, prices, rates, addresses, telephone numbers and websites
listed in this book are accurate at the time of publication,
but they are subject to frequent change.

Bottom Line Books® is a registered trademark of Bottom Line Inc.
3 Landmark Square, Suite 201, Stamford, CT 06901

BottomLineInc.com

Bottom Line Books® is an imprint of Bottom Line Inc., publisher of print periodicals,
e-letters and books. We are dedicated to bringing you the best information from the most
knowledgeable sources in the world. Our goal is to help you gain greater wealth,
better health, more wisdom, extra time and increased happiness.

Printed in the United States of America

Contents

PART TWO • YOUR MONEY

7 • MONEY MANAGER

PART FOUR • YOUR LEISURE

13 • TRAVEL TIME

14 • FUN FINDS

PART FIVE • YOUR LIFE

15 • CAR CARE

16 • HAPPY HOME

17 • HOUSEHOLD HACKS

18 • LIFE LESSONS

Preface

We are happy to bring you our *2020 Bottom Line Yearbook*. Here you will discover numerous helpful and practical ideas for yourself and for everyone in your family.

At Bottom Line Books, it is our mission to provide all of our readers with the best information to help them gain better health, greater wealth, more wisdom, extra time and increased happiness.

The *2020 Yearbook* represents the very best and the most useful Bottom Line articles from the past year. Whether you are looking for ways to get the most from your money or ensure the retirement of your dreams…prevent a stroke before it happens or lose weight more quickly…get your marriage back on track or end those bad habits that have plagued you for years, you'll find it all in this book…and a whole lot more.

Over the past 39 years, we have built a network of thousands of expert sources.

When you consult the *2020 Yearbook*, you are accessing a stellar group of authorities in fields that range from natural and conventional medicine…to shopping, investing, taxes and insurance…to cars, travel, security and self-improvement. Our advisers are affiliated with the premier universities, financial institutions, law firms and hospitals. These experts are truly among the most knowledgeable people in the country.

As a reader of a Bottom Line book, you can be assured that you are receiving reliable, well-researched and up-to-date information from a trusted source.

We are very confident that the *2020 Bottom Line Yearbook* can help you and your family have a healthier, wealthier, wiser life. Enjoy!

The Editors, *Bottom Line Personal*
Stamford, CT

1

Health Highlights

Is That Symptom Serious? How to Tell and What to Do

oogle is *not* your friend when you're investigating a mysterious new symptom. Do you rush to a doctor...or try to wait it out?

What doctors know: The vast majority of symptoms that bring people to doctors' offices turn out to be minor—or at least manageable. But unless you've had years of medical training, you won't know what's serious and what's not. Some seemingly "minor" symptoms really *do* need to be checked out...others can be ignored...and some should send you racing to the ER. *Common symptoms—and what to do...*

LIGHT-HEADEDNESS

It usually means that your brain isn't getting enough blood. That sounds scary, and it can be—but not always.

Relax if you sometimes feel light-headed when you get out of bed or stand up from a seated position, particularly when the sensation lasts a few seconds or less and isn't so severe that you feel like you're going to pass out. All it means is that your change of position is forcing blood to move against gravity—there's a slight lag before your blood pressure compensates and the brain gets enough blood and oxygen.

Exception: Light-headedness that occurs every time you stand up...lasts more than a minute...or forces you to sit/lie down could be due to *orthostatic hypotension*, a large drop in blood pressure that's often caused by dehydration...side effects from certain medications (such as beta-blockers and diuretics)...or bleeding (from an ulcer, for example) that may or may not have been detected. You'll want

Christopher Kelly, MD, a physician at Columbia University Medical Center in New York City. His research has been published in *The New England Journal of Medicine* and other professional journals. He is coauthor, with Marc Eisenberg, MD, of *Am I Dying?!: A Complete Guide to Your Symptoms—and What to Do Next.*

to see a doctor the same or next day. *Note:* If you're bleeding and feel light-headed, go to the ER.

Make an appointment if you have worsening light-headedness during exercise. I worry most when a patient is age 50 or older and gets light-headed during mild exertion. This could indicate that the heart isn't supplying enough blood to the muscles—which can occur because of *aortic stenosis*, a stiffening of the main valve that separates the heart from the aorta, the large vessel that conveys oxygen-rich blood to your entire body—or weakening of the heart muscle from blockages in the arteries (*atherosclerosis*). Your doctor will probably recommend an ultrasound and possibly a stress test or other tests to assess the health of your cardiovascular system.

Call an ambulance if you feel light-headed and your heart is racing out of control. You could be experiencing a rapid and irregular heart rhythm, such as *atrial fibrillation* or *ventricular tachycardia*, that can be deadly without quick treatment. After you call 911, lie down while you're waiting for an ambulance and elevate your feet.

HEADACHES

They're among the most common symptoms that bring people to doctors' offices and ERs. They're painful but usually not serious—with some exceptions.

Relax when headaches feel like a band of pain around your skull…improve with rest and medication, such as *acetaminophen* (Tylenol) or *ibuprofen* (Advil)…and tend to occur at high-stress moments in your life. They're probably just tension headaches, thought to be caused in part by muscle spasms in the scalp. They rarely last long and aren't a problem for most people.

Make an appointment if your scalp hurts when you brush your hair, your jaw tires quickly while chewing and you're age 50 or older. It could be *temporal arteritis*, an uncommon autoimmune disease that affects the temporal arteries that carry blood to the head. It can eventually cause severe pain and/or vision loss.

Temporal arteritis can usually be diagnosed with blood/imaging tests, although a biopsy of the affected artery may be needed. *Treatment:* Oral steroids (such as *prednisone*) taken for a few months to a year or more. High-dose intravenous steroids may be given at the time of diagnosis. The condition can't be cured, but drugs will stop the pain and reduce the risk for complications.

Call an ambulance if the headache pain is sudden and among the worst you've ever had—like an ice pick stabbing into your head. It could be a *subarachnoid hemorrhage*, a ruptured blood vessel in the head. It may be accompanied by neck pain, nausea or vomiting. About one in eight people don't live long enough to get to a hospital. Get help immediately!

FATIGUE

The causes of fatigue run the gamut. But if you feel constantly run-down—even when you get enough sleep—there's probably something wrong.

Relax if you've started a new medication. Fatigue is a common drug side effect, even among drugs that people don't associate with sedation. *Common offenders:* Blood pressure medications—such as *atenolol* (Tenormin), *metoprolol* (Lopressor) and additional beta-blockers—along with pain relievers, antihistamines and many antidepressants.

My advice: Talk to your doctor if you notice fatigue after starting any new drug. In most cases, all you'll have to do is switch to a different drug or take a lower dose. Also, remember that there are numerous causes of fatigue, including stress.

Make an appointment if you're also suffering from constipation…have gained weight…and often feel cold. These are symptoms of *hypothyroidism*, an underactive thyroid gland. It's easily diagnosed with simple blood tests. Most people will get back to normal when they start a thyroid-replacement medication, such as *levothyroxine* (Synthroid).

Other possibilities: Sleep apnea, in which breathing intermittently stops and starts during sleep—and prevents you from getting a good night's rest. People with sleep apnea usually aren't aware of it, but their partners often complain about loud snoring and/or gasping. It's clinically diagnosed with a sleep test.

Progressively worsening fatigue combined with weight loss can be a red flag for cancer. This, too, warrants a visit to your doctor.

Call an ambulance if you *suddenly* experience bone-deep fatigue that's accompanied by any degree of mental confusion. There are multiple life-threatening conditions that can cause sudden, severe fatigue/confusion, including a brain infection, stroke or sepsis.

6 Heart Disease Prevention Myths: Aspirin, Omega-3s, Statins and More

Erin D. Michos, MD, MHS, associate director of preventive cardiology at Ciccarone Center for the Prevention of Heart Disease at The Johns Hopkins University School of Medicine in Baltimore.

Heart disease remains the number-one killer of both men and women in the US today, so prevention is paramount. But conflicting news stories make it tough to figure out what to do. Should you take a baby aspirin…a fish oil supplement…a statin? Since everyone is different, is the risk for some people actually overblown? *Here's what's true about preventing heart disease…what's false… and how to know what you should do…*

MYTH: **A baby aspirin a day keeps heart disease away.** A number of recent studies conducted at major medical research institutions have confirmed that most healthy people without known heart disease shouldn't be taking daily aspirin to prevent heart attacks. The ARRIVE trial looked at more than 12,500 men (age 55 or older) and women (age 60 or older) who were at moderate risk for heart attack, while the ASPREE study included more than 19,000 healthy, low-risk adults over age 65. Both studies were designed to determine whether a daily low-dose aspirin would prevent a first heart attack or stroke. Not only did

the low-dose aspirin not reduce that risk in either study—it also increased the risk for major gastrointestinal bleeding. Even more alarming, in ASPREE, the group randomly assigned to take aspirin experienced more deaths from cancer.

Important: Aspirin still is recommended for patients who have had a heart attack already to prevent a second one. But if you're healthy and popping a daily aspirin, my advice is to ask your doctor about stopping your aspirin.

MYTH: **Over-the-counter omega-3 supplements prevent heart disease.** A recent review of major studies found that over-the-counter supplements did not reduce the risk for heart disease or stroke in the general population.

But one type of high-dose omega-3 prescription drug may help certain patients. *New research:* The REDUCE-IT trial, conducted at Harvard Medical School, studied Vascepa, a purified form of *eicosapentaenoic acid* (EPA) given in a high dose (4,000 mg) to patients already treated with statins who were at high risk for cardiovascular disease or diabetes and who had high triglyceride levels. In early results, Vascepa reduced cardiovascular events such as heart attacks and strokes by 25% over five years. (The full results will be presented at the American Heart Association annual meeting in November 2018.) While this may turn out to be an effective prescription for certain patients, these results shouldn't prompt healthy people to take over-the-counter fish oil supplements.

MYTH: **The higher your level of HDL "good" cholesterol, the more protected you are from heart disease.** HDL is the so-called "good" cholesterol because it helps remove "bad" LDL cholesterol from your bloodstream. And studies have found that people with high HDL seem to have lower risk for heart disease. But new research casts doubt on whether it's truly protective. *Example*: No drug therapies that boost HDL have been shown to reduce heart disease risk.

And too high a level of HDL actually may be harmful. Two recent studies have shown an association between very high levels of HDL (above 80 mg/dL) and increased heart attacks and death from all causes. We don't know why this is, but it may be that very high HDL indicates that your HDL is not functioning properly. Until more is known, focus on the heart disease risks that you can control, such as increasing physical activity, optimizing body weight and keeping triglycerides, LDL cholesterol, blood pressure and blood sugar under control.

MYTH: **If your cholesterol is too high, you need a statin.** Actually, some people with high cholesterol don't benefit from a statin—and some people with low cholesterol actually do. While high cholesterol, especially "bad" LDL cholesterol, is a major risk factor for heart disease, it's not the whole story. Many other factors matter—age, gender, race, blood pressure, family history and whether you smoke, have diabetes or are sedentary. So doctors evaluate your overall risk factors for heart disease to help determine whether to treat you with a statin. They do so by calculating your 10-year risk of having a heart attack or stroke. A score of 7.5% or higher means that a statin is "recommended"—whatever your cholesterol number.

Even if your score is 7.5% or higher, however, you still may not need a statin. Why? The calculator, developed by the American Heart Association and the American College of Cardiology, may overestimate risk, some studies find.

What to do: If your score is high, ask your doctor about a *coronary artery calcium (CAC) scan*, which detects calcium deposits in arterial plaque. If your CAC score is zero, there's no need for a statin. If it's high (typically 101 or above), that means you have a high risk for heart disease, and a statin generally is recommended. What if it's in the middle, between one and 100? That's a decision to make with your doctor, considering your other risk factors—along with your personal preference about whether you want to start taking a statin.

MYTH: **Reducing inflammation is a healthy goal, but we don't know whether it will reduce heart disease risk.** Actually, we do. Cardiologists have suspected for some time that chronic inflammation—a state in which your immune system is in overdrive—can fuel the development of clogged arteries

(atherosclerosis)…and trigger plaque to rupture and cause a heart attack. But we didn't know until recently whether tamping down inflammation could really help prevent heart attacks and strokes.

Now we know that it can. Last year, the CANTOS study, conducted at Brigham and Women's Hospital in Boston, showed that *canakinumab*, a type of drug called a monoclonal antibody that reduces inflammation, reduces the risk for a new heart attack or stroke by a significant 15% in people who already have had a heart attack.

While the drug still is experimental (and likely will be very expensive if/when it's FDA-approved), the good news is that we already know how to substantially reduce chronic inflammation with healthy habits. These include not smoking…keeping your waist size no more than 40 inches for men and 35 inches for women, regardless of your body weight… eating a Mediterranean-type diet…exercising regularly…getting six to eight hours of sleep every night (the sweet spot for heart health)… and reducing stress (meditation, yoga).

MYTH: **Unless I have diabetes, my blood sugar levels won't affect heart health.** Blood sugar that's consistently even just a little above normal means that you have prediabetes. As a result, you're not only at greatly increased risk for diabetes but also heart disease. It's a wake-up call to improve your lifestyle, including weight loss (often losing 10 pounds is enough

---

TAKE NOTE...

Forehead Wrinkles Warning

People with the most and deepest horizontal forehead wrinkles had nearly *10 times* the risk of dying from heart disease as those with no wrinkles, according to a 20-year study of 3,200 adults ages 32 to 62.

Theory: Some of the factors that lead to premature skin aging and wrinkles also are linked to aging of the arteries and atherosclerosis.

Yolande Esquirol, MD, PhD, associate professor of occupational health at Centre Hospitalier Universitaire de Toulouse, France.

to bring blood sugar back to normal)…increasing dietary fiber…eliminating sugar-sweetened drinks and processed meats…and exercising. Simply by taking a 30-minute daily walk, you can reduce the risk that prediabetes will turn into diabetes by 30%.

Home Blood Pressure Monitoring Solves a Big Problem

Many patients don't take blood pressure medicine as they should. But when they see a high blood pressure reading at home, they are more apt to take their medicine. In a pilot study of 2,550 adults with previously uncontrolled hypertension, 79% quickly achieved blood pressure control and required fewer doctor visits over the next six months.

Roy Champion, MSc, BSN, a quality-assurance nurse at Scott & White Health Plan, Temple, Texas. His study was presented at the 2018 American Heart Association's Joint Hypertension Scientific Sessions.

Women: Avoid These Heart Attack Traps

C. Noel Bairey Merz, MD, director, Barbra Streisand Women's Heart Center, Linda Joy Pollin Women's Heart Health Program and Preventive and Rehabilitative Cardiac Center at the Smidt Heart Institute, all at Cedars-Sinai Medical Center, Los Angeles. She also is chair of the National Institutes of Health–sponsored Women's Ischemia Syndrome Evaluation (WISE) initiative, which is investigating methods for more effective diagnosis and evaluation of coronary artery disease in women.

The message is finally sinking in—men are not the only ones who have heart attacks.

However: Common medical mistakes are putting *millions* of middle-aged and older women at risk for a heart attack, the number-one killer of American women, with nearly 300,000 deaths every year.

To find out what women can do to protect themselves, we spoke with C. Noel Bairey Merz, MD, a renowned women's heart specialist.

AN OVERLOOKED PROBLEM

A common scenario illustrates the problem women face. Let's say a woman sees a doctor and complains about persistent chest pain. The doctor orders an *angiogram*, a test that detects the plaque in the major arteries of the heart that can decrease or stop blood flow, triggering a heart attack. But the angiogram shows no blockages, so the doctor tells the woman she doesn't have heart disease. A week later, she has a heart attack.

Many women experience angina, which is marked by frequent and intense chest pain, even when they do not have blockages in the major arteries of the heart—the leading cause of heart attack in men. In women, the pain also can be caused by *coronary microvascular dysfunction* in the tiny arteries around the heart.

This condition poses a similar threat to a woman's heart as a blockage in the major arteries. But standard heart tests—such as an angiogram or an electrocardiogram (which detects abnormal heart rhythms and poor blood flow)—*don't* detect coronary microvascular dysfunction.

Troubling recent finding: Researchers from the Barbra Streisand Women's Heart Center, Smidt Heart Institute at Cedars-Sinai in Los Angeles asked 340 women who complained of chest pain but had no blockages in major coronary arteries to have a cardiac MRI, a highly detailed imaging scan of the heart. According to the research, the MRI found nearly one in 10 (8%) of the women had *already* suffered a heart attack—in most cases, previously undetected.

Other sobering research: In a study conducted by researchers at the Yale School of Public Health, 62% of women having a heart attack were found to have three or more non–chest pain symptoms (see box on page 6) —and more than half of those women said their health-care provider did not think the symptoms were heart-related.

7-STEP PLAN

Because women with heart disease are routinely undertreated, it's crucial to develop a strategy to effectively diagnose the condition—and, if it's present, to effectively treat it. To do this, partner with your physician. *Here's what you need to know...*

***STEP #1:* Take heart disease seriously.** It kills more women than any other disease—more women than *all* cancers combined. If you've got one or more risk factors for heart disease, ask your primary care physician for a cardiovascular workup (see below). Those risk factors include high blood pressure, high LDL cholesterol, smoking, excess body weight, a sedentary lifestyle, a poor diet (one that emphasizes sugary, fatty processed foods) and a family history of heart disease.

***STEP #2:* Get a second opinion.** Perhaps your physician has conducted tests and told you that you don't have heart disease—but you have symptoms that make you suspect you do, such as shortness of breath or unexplained chest pain or pressure. Get a second opinion from a doctor who will listen to your concerns. It could be an internist or a cardiologist. Second opinions are covered by most health insurance and—given the seriousness of heart disease—it's a prudent action.

***STEP #3:* Get the right stress test.** If your risk factors put you at high risk for heart disease, your doctor may order a stress test, also called a *treadmill test, exercise electrocardiogram, graded exercise test* or *stress electrocardiogram.* This test—in which you exercise at increasingly intense levels while hooked up to electrodes that measure the electrical activity of your heart—determines blood flow to your heart and can detect abnormal heart rhythms.

Other options include a *stress echocardiogram* or *nuclear stress test*, both of which also generate images of the heart and can more accurately determine blood flow...and the *dobutamine* or *adenosine* stress test, a drug-based test used in people who are unable to exercise. If you have any questions about the right stress test for you, consult a cardiologist.

More from Dr. C. Noel Bairey Merz...

Red Flags Women Should Watch For...

Most women who are having a heart attack don't experience crushing chest pain, the "classic" heart attack symptom found in most men. *Instead, a woman might have...*

- **Sharp or burning pain or pressure in the chest.**
- **Pain or pressure in the neck, jaw, throat, abdomen or upper back.**
- **Shortness of breath.**
- **Indigestion and heartburn.**
- **Nausea and vomiting.**
- **Extreme fatigue.**
- **General upper-body discomfort.**

Doctors frequently fail to recognize these symptoms as red flags for heart attack. The result is that heart disease and heart attacks are often misdiagnosed in women.

***STEP #4:* Ask about a stress cardiac MRI or cardiac PET scan.** These tests have become more widely available only in the last 10 years. They are more sensitive, so they improve the detection of more subtle and female-pattern abnormalities in *smaller hearts*—which means they help women more than men. Either test would be particularly important in women with persistent chest pain and an abnormal stress test.

***STEP #5:* If you're having unexplained heart symptoms, ask your doctor to investigate less common forms of heart disease.** One uncommon condition is *spontaneous coronary artery dissection*, a tear in the artery wall. This condition, which can lead to heart attack, is more often detected in younger women (half the time during or shortly after pregnancy), who have symptoms such as unexplained chest pain.

The other is *stress-related cardiomyopathy* (also known as "broken heart syndrome"), which can cause chest pain and shortness of breath. It is caused by severe mental stress or shock, such as the death of a spouse, or a near-miss automobile accident. The condition is usually treatable, and most patients recover, although recurrence can happen in 5% to 10% of cases.

STEP #6: Demand standard therapy. Studies show that women with diagnosed heart disease are significantly less likely than men to be treated with standard therapy. If you've been diagnosed with heart disease, talk to your physician about lifestyle changes (including smoking cessation, diet and exercise), along with the drugs you may need—such as low-dose (81 mg) aspirin to prevent artery-clogging blood clots, a statin to lower high cholesterol and medication to reduce blood pressure.

STEP #7: Go to the ER. If you're having any of the symptoms of a heart attack that are common in women (see box at left), the emergency room is where you belong. And once you're there, don't let anyone tell you that you're *not* having a heart attack. Instead, insist on getting the *troponin test*, which detects protein in the blood generated by damaged heart cells…in other words, by a heart attack. This simple test—a sample of blood is all that's required—generates results in 15 to 20 minutes and provides incontrovertible evidence as to whether you are or aren't having a heart attack.

Important: Call 911 instead of driving yourself, and take a low-dose aspirin if you suspect that you are having a heart attack.

How to Stop a Stroke *Before* It Happens

Bruce A. Perler, MD, MBA, a practicing vascular surgeon at Johns Hopkins Medicine and the Julius H. Jacobson II, MD, Endowed Chair in Vascular Surgery at Johns Hopkins University School of Medicine, both in Baltimore. Dr. Perler is author of nearly 200 peer-reviewed medical journal articles and textbook chapters and has edited several textbooks, including *Rutherford's Vascular Surgery and Endovascular Therapy.*

Feeling perfectly healthy? Chances are, your doctor still orders certain tests—called "screening tests"—that check for conditions such as colon cancer or osteoporosis that might be lurking and could be treated.

So why not a screening test for stroke risk? We know that people living in the US have nearly 800,000 strokes each year and that 80% to 90% of those strokes are caused by blood clots. Many of these strokes originate from clogged carotid arteries—large arteries in the neck that feed blood to your brain. Like the arteries that feed your heart, these can be narrowed by plaque buildup as you age.

This may surprise you: There is a test that can detect such blockages. It's a simple ultrasound of your neck that costs about $70 to $300 (depending on where you live) and sometimes is covered by insurance.

However, no major medical group advises checking the carotid arteries of *all* adults—due to concerns that many questionable results will turn out to be wrong, leading to needless worry, costly follow-up testing and risky surgeries.

But some medical groups, such as the Society for Vascular Surgery, the American Heart Association and the American Stroke Association, think it makes sense to test certain people who are at increased risk for a stroke from a clogged carotid artery.

The danger: Without testing, too many people, while clinically asymptomatic, will unknowingly suffer one or more symptomless "silent strokes"—small, repeated insults to the brain caused by inadequate blood flow, which over time can lead to decline in cognitive function. Unsuspecting people with blockages also may ignore signs of transient ischemic attacks, or TIAs (also known as "ministrokes")—brief attacks that produce passing stroke symptoms that may last only for a few minutes, such as weakness of an arm or leg, brief loss of vision or difficulties speaking. Ministrokes can be the precursor to a bigger and permanently damaging stroke. Still other people will get no warning before a stroke that leaves them disabled or dead, further adding rationale for the screening test.

SHOULD YOU GET SCANNED?

While guidelines from medical groups vary, many doctors—including myself—say that you should consider a potentially lifesaving scan of your carotid arteries if one or more of the following apply to you...

● **A "bruit" in your neck is detected by your doctor.** This abnormal sound, detected by a stethoscope during a routine physical exam, can indicate a narrowed artery—especially when it's accompanied by other stroke risk factors, such as high blood pressure. *Note:* Your doctor should listen for a bruit on *both* sides of your neck. In some cases, patients actually can hear a "whooshing" sound in their ears.

● **You are over age 65 and have multiple stroke risk factors,** such as smoking, elevated cholesterol, high blood pressure and/or diagnosed coronary artery disease.

● **You have been diagnosed with peripheral artery disease (PAD).** This narrowing of the leg arteries can cause leg pain, particularly when walking. If the arteries feeding your limbs are clogged with plaque, the arteries in your neck may be, too.

● **You have worrisome results from an ankle-brachial index test.** With this test, your doctor compares your blood pressure readings at your ankle and upper arm. The test can indicate PAD, so it's recommended for people with suspicious symptoms in their legs, including pain, numbness or weakness, but also is sometimes used as a broader screening tool for artery health.

● **You have had symptoms of a ministroke.** This might include weakness or numbness on one side of your body or slurred speech. Even

if the symptoms lasted for just a minute or two, they are serious. People who have a ministroke are at high risk for a bigger stroke, most often in the first few days, but also in the months and years ahead. *If you have possible ministroke symptoms in the future:* Treat them as a medical emergency, and call 911 right away.

Important: If you decide, in consultation with your doctor, to get a carotid ultrasound, make sure that you get the gold-standard test, called a *carotid duplex ultrasound*, from a laboratory accredited by the Intersocietal Accreditation Commission (IAC). The test, which requires no preparation, can take up to 30 to 60 minutes. You will be asked to wear loose-fitting clothing that allows the technician to access your neck. If there is significant plaque in a carotid artery, the lab report should say how extensive the blockage is and describe the characteristics of the plaque in a way that will help your doctor assess your risks.

WHAT'S NEXT?

If your carotid scan shows no significant blockage, continue taking steps to lower your stroke risk—control blood pressure and cholesterol, maintain a healthy body weight and don't smoke.

What if your carotid testing indicates trouble? *Here are the rules of thumb...*

● **If less than 50% to 60% of your artery is blocked and you have no symptoms,** you will likely be advised to continue or add medications that reduce your stroke risk, such as a statin for high cholesterol, aspirin to reduce clotting and medication to lower your blood pressure. If you smoke, you will have a powerful new reason to quit.

● **If your blockage is 60% or more but you have no symptoms,** surgery (called a *carotid endarterectomy*) to remove the plaque may be needed, depending on the severity of the narrowing and the character of the plaque...or if there has been increased narrowing over time. If surgery is not indicated, drugs and lifestyle changes are recommended, and scanning should be repeated every six to 12 months to watch for progression.

● **If you have a blockage of 50% to 99% and symptoms, the choices are clearer.** Un-

---

STROKE ALERT...

Diet Drink–Stroke Link

A new study found an association between artificially sweetened beverages and a high risk for heart attack, stroke and death among postmenopausal women. Those who drank two diet drinks daily were 29% more likely to have heart disease, 31% more likely to have a clot-caused stroke and 16% more likely to die from any cause than those who drank less than one a week (or not at all).

Yasmin Mossavar-Rahmani, PhD, RD, CDN, associate clinical professor of epidemiology and population health at Albert Einstein College of Medicine, the Bronx, New York, and lead author of a study published in *Stroke*.

less you have a condition, such as severe, noncorrectable coronary artery disease, heart failure or severe chronic obstructive pulmonary disease (COPD), that makes such procedures too risky, endarterectomy or a stent to open your clogged artery likely will be offered. Stenting is considered more appropriate for symptomatic patients who are too high risk for endarterectomy.

Caution: These procedures can reduce your long-term stroke risk, but they both carry risks of causing an immediate stroke or death by dislodging plaque and sending it to your brain.

My advice: If you are considering one of these procedures, look for a highly experienced surgeon and hospital—and ask for their complication rates. With a top-notch team, stroke or death rates following endarterectomy or stenting should be no more than 2% to 3% for asymptomatic patients…and no more than 5% to 6% for symptomatic patients.

Are You Stroke-Ready? It Could Be the Difference Between Life and Death

Michael Frankel, MD, professor of neurology at Emory University School of Medicine, and chief of neurology and director of the Marcus Stroke and Neuroscience Center at Grady Memorial Hospital, both in Atlanta. His team played a major role in the DAWN trial, published in *The New England Journal of Medicine* in January 2018. This study provided critically important data showing the benefit of thrombectomy within 24 hours of stroke onset.

O f course, no one wants to suffer a stroke. But about 800,000 times a year someone in the US has one. Most often, it's an acute ischemic stroke—blood flow to the brain is interrupted, starting a cascade of damage that can lead to death or disability.

The good news: Today's stroke is not your grandfather's stroke. Your chances of surviving and thriving have increased dramatically, thanks to recent advances. To have the best chance of recovering from a stroke, you need to act quickly—and smartly. *Here are four mistakes that can make the difference between life and death…*

MISTAKE #1: **Not recognizing stroke symptoms.** A stroke often causes multiple symptoms, but some people have only one. However, to spot one or more stroke symptoms, you need to recognize them.

Most people can name at least one of the many stroke symptoms. Classic symptoms include a droopy face on one side…numbness or weakness of the face, arm or leg (especially on just one side)…and trouble walking or balancing. *But there are other symptoms that are also important to watch for…*

- **Trouble seeing in one or both eyes.**
- **Sudden confusion.**
- **A severe headache that has no known cause.**
- **Sudden, unexplained dizziness.**

Helpful: If you think someone near you may be having a stroke, think FAST. *The letters stand for…*

F: **Face.** Ask the person to smile to see if one side of the face droops.

A: **Arms.** Ask the person to raise both arms to see if one drifts downward or can't be moved at all.

S: **Speech.** Ask the person to repeat a simple phrase and listen for slurring or other difficulties.

T: **Time.** If you see *any* of these signs, call 911 right away—and make note of the time. Medical personnel will want to know when the symptoms started.

MISTAKE #2: **Ignoring a stroke symptom that lasts only a few minutes.** You may have had (or witnessed) a transient ischemic attack, a so-called TIA or "ministroke." That can be a warning that a bigger stroke is coming. You should still call 911.

Important: If you witnessed a person who had possible stroke symptoms, be sure that the hospital team has your cell phone number so you can be reached to confirm what you observed in the patient.

MISTAKE #3: **Getting a ride to the hospital.** In a medical emergency, you may be tempted to wait to see what happens or have someone drive you to a hospital or doctor's office. With a possible stroke, this is a *very* bad idea. Instead, call 911 and tell the operator you are seeing or having possible stroke symptoms. Don't worry about being wrong.

Emergency medical workers will assess you and look for other conditions (such as low blood sugar, low blood pressure or a seizure) that could mimic a stroke. They can start treating such conditions right away. If the emergency crew suspects a stroke, they will call ahead to the nearest appropriate hospital so the medical team can prepare.

MISTAKE #4: **Going to any hospital.** With a stroke, it does matter what hospital you go to—and that's another reason to call 911.

Under an accreditation system that's maintained by The Joint Commission, hospitals can get certifications that range from "acute stroke ready" for those with basic supports in place…to "primary stroke centers" for those offering more advanced care…to "comprehensive stroke centers" for those offering the most advanced state-of-the-art care.

A new approach: According to new guidelines from the American Heart Association/American Stroke Association (AHA/ASA), if the patient is having severe stroke symptoms, emergency personnel can travel an additional distance (up to 15 minutes) to reach a comprehensive stroke center. In some regions, the distance may need to be longer. And in some states, medics are required to take patients to the hospital of their choice, while other states leave this decision to emergency personnel. Medics are trained to make the best hospital choice for the patient's needs.

GETTING THE RIGHT TREATMENT

If you are taken to the hospital as a possible stroke patient, ideally you will arrive with a loved one who can describe the onset of your symptoms and share your medical history.

Important: Keep a cell phone number for a family member in your wallet—this is critical so that someone who knows you well can give medical information if you are alone and cannot speak for yourself.

If the hospital team determines that you may be having symptoms of an acute stroke,

you will receive brain imaging—most often in a CT machine, ideally within 20 minutes of arriving at the hospital.

If your scan rules out bleeding in or around your brain (a hemorrhagic stroke) and you meet other criteria—including onset of your stroke no more than three to four-and-a-half hours earlier—you will get immediate intravenous treatment with a clot-busting medication called a *tissue plasminogen activator*, or tPA, to break up the clot in your brain, limiting damage and potential disability.

BEYOND tPA

There's now an alternative to tPA called *mechanical thrombectomy*. This procedure physically removes the blood clot. It is sometimes done after or instead of clot-busting drug treatment. In some cases, you will need to be transferred to another hospital, by ambulance or helicopter, to get it.

Under guidelines from 2015, the procedure had to start within six hours of your initial stroke symptoms. This was a problem for people far from well-equipped and well-staffed hospitals or who woke up with symptoms (a so-called "wake-up stroke") or had stroke symptoms of uncertain duration.

Now: The treatment window has been expanded. Studies show that some patients with blockage in a major artery leading to the brain can benefit from thrombectomy 16 to 24 hours after the stroke began.

Again, doctors will try to determine whether you are in that time window by asking when your symptoms started (or when you were last seen symptom-free). Patients also are screened with advanced brain-imaging tests to find those who still have large areas of brain tissue healthy enough to benefit from restored blood flow.

Diabetes Meds Linked to Dangerous Infection

Common diabetes medications are linked to a dangerous infection called *Fournier's gangrene*. *SGLT2 inhibitors*, which include

Jardiance and Invokana, reduce blood glucose by stimulating its excretion in the urine. When sugary urine leaks and remains on the skin in the groin area, the tissue can become irritated and infected. Always practice good hygiene, but if you have redness or swelling of the genitals, call your doctor. These symptoms can worsen quickly and lead to serious problems such as blindness, kidney damage and heart disease.

Gerald Bernstein, MD, director of the Diabetes Management Program, Friedman Diabetes Institute, Lenox Hill Hospital, New York City.

The Upside of Diabetes

In a recent study, the partners of more than 180,000 people newly diagnosed with diabetes were significantly more likely to change their health behaviors for the better when compared with people whose partners did not have the disease. Specifically, partners of people with diabetes were about 50% more likely to take a weight-management class. They also were more likely to participate in glucose, lipid and blood pressure screening and get a flu shot.

Julie Schmittdiel, PhD, research scientist, Kaiser Permanente, Oakland, California.

Melanoma:
The Major Good News

Marianne Berwick, PhD, distinguished professor, department of internal medicine, University of New Mexico School of Medicine, and former chief, Division of Epidemiology, Biostatistics and Preventive Medicine, University of New Mexico Comprehensive Cancer Center, both in Albuquerque. She is author or coauthor of more than 200 scientific papers on melanoma published in leading medical journals.

Many adults grew up during the sun-loving era of the 1950s, '60s and '70s. *Now:* It's believed to be partially responsible for the *quadrupling* of melanoma cases over the past several decades. More than 9,000 Americans die from the disease each year.

Patients and doctors also are paying more attention to skin changes that might be cancer—and spotting melanoma earlier.

Major good news: Early-stage melanoma is usually *cured* by lesion-removing surgery. The five-year survival rate for early-stage melanoma is 99%. But even stage III melanoma, cancer that has spread to nearby skin or lymph nodes, has a five-year survival rate of 63%. Stage IV melanoma, in which cancer has metastasized or spread to other sites in the body, has a five-year survival rate of 20%—but even for these advanced cases, new therapies designed to contain or reverse the disease are extending lives. *Here's what's new...*

DIAGNOSIS

Examination of *all* the skin on your body by a savvy dermatologist at least once a year—and a biopsy of any suspicious moles—is still the best first-line of defense against melanoma. Be alert to the "ABCDE" warning signs for melanoma (see box on page 12). Bring any skin changes to your doctor's attention immediately (even if it isn't time for your yearly skin check).

Diagnostic danger: Melanoma is tough to diagnose, particularly in its early, or "thin," stage, when the mole is less than one-millimeter thick.

My advice: If your doctor tells you that you have melanoma, ask to have your biopsy slide sent to another pathologist for a second opinion. Check first with your insurance provider to see if that's covered and if you need preauthorization.

Also important: Most people think of melanoma as a brown or black spot that is changing. But *amelanotic melanoma* is pale and reddish and has a poor prognosis because it's usually detected after it has spread.

What to do: Alert your doctor to both dark and light unusual skin changes.

New option: If you have a suspicious lesion, you may be able to avoid surgical biopsy. Ask your doctor about having genetic testing instead, such as the Dermtech Pigmented Le-

11

sion Assay (PLA). It is highly accurate in distinguishing malignant melanoma from benign nevi, and may be covered by your insurer.

NEW THERAPIES

New therapies are brightening the previous grim outlook for advanced melanoma.

For example, several recently approved oral drugs inhibit a genetic mutation called *BRAF* that drives approximately 40% to 60% of melanomas. These drugs, which slow the growth of tumors and extend life, include *vemurafenib* (Zelboraf) and *dabrafenib* (Tafinlar).

A new class of drugs called *MEK inhibitors—trametinib* (Mekinist), *cobimetinib* (Cotellic) and others—inhibit the MEK protein, which helps speed the growth and spread of melanoma tumors.

New development: Combining dabrafenib and trametinib more than doubles average survival for advanced melanoma from five months to 11 months. Unfortunately, these drugs do have side effects, ranging from headaches and fatigue to kidney and heart problems—and even, ironically, *basal cell carcinoma*, another type of skin cancer. Also, although they can slow and shrink tumors and extend life for months, even years, the cancer eventually returns.

What to do: Make sure your oncologist tests your tumor for genetic mutations.

Immunotherapy—drugs such as *pembrolizumab* (Keytruda), *nivolumab* (Opdivo) and *ipilimumab* (Yervoy) that stimulate the immune system to fight cancer—is another new way to treat advanced melanoma. But the drugs work only in a small percentage of patients, control cancer for a limited time, are very expensive and have a range of debilitating and even deadly side effects.

New development: Combination immunotherapy—such as the immunotherapeutic drug Keytruda with cellular therapy, which uses immune cells such as *interleukin* or *interferon*—is showing better results in clinical trials. FDA-approved interferon and interleukin-based treatments for melanoma include *aldesleukin* (Proleukin), *interferon alfa-2b* (Intron A) and *peginterferon alfa-2b* (Sylatron).

> **TAKE NOTE...**
>
> ## ABCDE Warning Signs of Melanoma
>
> Asymmetry...irregular Borders...more than one or uneven distribution of Color...Diameter larger than one-quarter inch...Evolution, such as changes in color and/or size.

FEWER SURGICAL COMPLICATIONS

Once melanoma is diagnosed, a *sentinel-lymph-node biopsy* can determine whether it has spread to nearby lymph nodes. Often, all lymph nodes in an area are removed if cancer is found in the sentinel lymph node. However, removing all the lymph nodes in an arm or a leg can cause *lymphedema*—permanent, painful swelling of the limb that limits activity and can lead to frequent infections.

New scientific finding: Less extreme surgery is just as effective, according to a study conducted at 63 medical centers and reported in *The New England Journal of Medicine*. *Details:* 1,900 patients with melanoma that had spread to at least one lymph node either had all their lymph nodes in the area of the affected node immediately removed...or had only the affected lymph node or nodes removed, while the other nodes in the area were tracked with ultrasound. If melanoma occurred in a new node, the other lymph nodes were removed. After three years, the two groups had the same survival times. But patients who had all their lymph nodes removed had *four times* the risk for severe swelling in the affected arm or leg.

Men and Melanoma

Men taking aspirin daily for heart health have almost twice the melanoma risk of men not taking aspirin. But the benefits of taking aspirin likely outweigh the higher melanoma risk. Men taking aspirin should be sure to use sunscreen, avoid tanning beds and have regular skin checks. Women taking aspirin do not have increased melanoma risk.

Reason: Unknown, but it may be because men produce fewer protective enzymes than women.

Beatrice Nardone, MD, PhD, research assistant professor in dermatology, Feinberg School of Medicine, Northwestern University, Chicago, and senior author of a study published in *Journal of the American Academy of Dermatology.*

Important Drug Increases Sun Sensitivity

The drug *azathioprine* treats inflammatory bowel disease, arthritis and vasculitis, and it is used to prevent organ rejection in transplant patients. A new study found links between azathioprine and squamous cell carcinoma, a common skin cancer. Azathioprine was known to give patients increased sensitivity to UVA light, which increases skin cancer risk. The new study does not mean that people should stop using azathioprine—the conditions it treats are potentially life-threatening. It does mean that sun protection, regular skin exams and early diagnosis of skin cancers are important for patients using azathioprine.

Charlotte Proby, MD, professor of dermatology, School of Medicine, University of Dundee, Scotland, and leader of a study published in *Nature Communications.*

Skin Cancer and Parkinson's Linked

A new study backs up past speculation that there is a link between the risk for Parkinson's disease and the risk of developing the skin cancer melanoma. The research found that people who have melanoma are about four times more likely to develop Parkinson's disease and vice versa. Study authors suggest that those who develop melanoma might benefit from counseling about their likely higher risk of developing Parkinson's. In addition, those with Parkinson's, or a family history of the disease, may benefit from more proactive melanoma screening.

Study of nearly 4,000 people by researchers at Mayo Clinic, Rochester, Minnesota, published in *Mayo Clinic Proceedings.*

Big Breakthroughs in Lung Cancer

Timothy Burns, MD, PhD, assistant professor of medicine in the department of medicine, Division of Hematology/Oncology, at UPMC Hillman Cancer Center in Pittsburgh, where his laboratory focuses on discovering targeted therapies for lung cancer. His scientific papers on lung cancer have appeared in *Nature Genetics, Oncogene, Cancer Research, Molecular Cancer Research, Cancer* and many other medical journals.

Lung cancer kills more Americans—both smokers and nonsmokers—than colon, breast and prostate cancers *combined.* But the good news is, treatment options are now extending the lives of many people affected by this formidable disease.

Latest development: Recently announced treatment breakthroughs provide new hope for people with *non-small cell lung cancer* (NSCLC)—the type of malignancy responsible for 85% of all lung cancers.

THE NEW HEAVY HITTERS

•**Immunotherapy.** Some of the newest treatments for NSCLC are *immune checkpoint inhibitors*—drugs that energize the immune system to kill cancer cells by blocking one of two cancer-promoting proteins, PD-1 and PD-L1. These drugs include *pembrolizumab* (Keytruda), the immunotherapy treatment credited with saving the life of former President Jimmy Carter when melanoma spread to his brain… *nivolumab* (Opdivo)…*atezolizumab* (Tecentriq)…and *durvalumab* (Imfinzi).

Typically, these drugs are used only as *second-line therapies* for patients with advanced disease who haven't responded to other types of treatments, such as chemotherapy. But several studies presented at the 2018 annual meeting of the American Association for Cancer Research show that immunotherapy can work as a *first-line therapy* for people with advanced NSCLC, improving survival.

New scientific findings: A combination of the immunotherapy drug pembrolizumab and chemotherapy worked better than chemo alone as a first-line treatment for patients with metastatic NSCLC—69% were still alive after one year in the combo group, with only 49% alive in the chemo-only group, according to a one-year study published in *The New England Journal of Medicine*.

In a similar one-year study, patients with stage IV lung cancer were given either chemotherapy or two immunotherapy drugs—nivolumab and *ipilimumab* (Yervoy), which blocks CTLA-4, a protein similar to PD-1. Those treated with immunotherapy were 42% less likely to have their disease progress than those who received other treatment.

Meanwhile, research focusing on the use of immunotherapy *without* chemotherapy as a first-line treatment—reported at a recent meeting of the American Society of Clinical Oncology—also delivered positive results. The stage IV NSCLC patients getting pembrolizumab lived four to eight months longer than those getting chemo. Only 18% of the immunotherapy patients suffered severe side effects, such as inflammation of the lung, liver or colon, versus 41% of those in the chemo group.

Takeaway: With the impressive results of these studies, first-line treatment with an immunotherapy drug with or without chemotherapy is now the standard-of-care for most cases of advanced NSCLC. If a test of your tumor tissue shows that you have a high PD-L1 activity—and one-third of patients with NSCLC do—then single-agent immunotherapy might be the best *first* treatment for you with or without chemotherapy. Patients whose tumor does not express high levels of this marker still benefit from the combination of immunotherapy with chemotherapy in the majority of cases. Talk to your oncologist.

• **Gene-modulating drugs.** This type of therapy uses drugs to turn off one of several genetic mutations (oncogenes) that can drive lung cancer. As estimated 10% to 20% of NSCLC patients have the *epidermal growth factor re-ceptor* (EGFR) mutation, which is treated with drugs such as *erlotinib* (Tarceva), *afatinib* (Gilotrif), *gefitinib* (Iressa) and *osimertinib* (Tagrisso). An estimated 5% have the anaplastic lymphoma kinase (ALK) mutation, which is treated with drugs such as *crizotinib* (Xalkori), *ceritinib* (Zykadia), *alectinib* (Alecensa) and *brigatinib* (Alunbrig).

These oral drugs are so powerful that they can, in rare cases, extend life by five years or more. However, the newer and more effective of these drugs—such as alectinib for ALK—has been used as a *second-line therapy*. Now this treatment paradigm is changing.

New scientific findings: In a study published earlier this year, more than 500 NSCLC patients with an EGFR mutation got either osimertinib as a *first-line* treatment or the previous standard therapy (erlotinib or gefitinib). After 12 months, those taking osimertinib had a 54% lower risk for disease progression or death. In April 2018, the FDA approved osimertinib for first-line treatment of metastatic NSCLC.

In a study of more than 300 metastatic NSCLC patients with the ALK mutation, the disease progressed or death occurred in 41% of those receiving alectinib (a newer more effective drug) compared with 68% receiving crizotinib, an older drug, after about a year and a half. The alectinib group also had fewer side effects. Patients receiving alectinib had control of their tumors for almost three years, on average.

Takeaway: If you are diagnosed with NSCLC, get tested to find out if you have a genetic mutation driving the disease. If you do, talk to your oncologist about the best gene-targeting drug for you—patients with these mutations often do not benefit from immunotherapy.

THE LIQUID BIOPSY OPTION...

The gold standard for biopsies in NSCLC is a tissue biopsy—removing a portion of the tumor and testing it—to identify the specific type of cancer and genetic mutations that inform treatment decisions.

Problem: In many cases, a tissue biopsy isn't possible—for example, the position of the tumor in the lung or other organ may make it too difficult to biopsy, or the patient may have emphysema.

Solution: A liquid (blood-based) biopsy can be used when a tissue biopsy is not an option. The FDA approved liquid biopsy for lung cancer in 2016. A recent study published in *JAMA Oncology* suggests that combining liquid biopsies with tumor biopsies can improve the chance of finding a targetable mutation. Ask your oncologist if this is right for you. FoundationOne and Guardant360 are the two most widely used liquid biopsies.

"Dirty Bomb" Stops Deadly Cancer Spread

Cancer deaths are mainly caused by metastasis, the spread of cancer cells to other organs. In animal studies, a new compound (*metarrestin*)—described as a "dirty bomb against cancer"—significantly reduced the spread of breast, prostate and pancreatic cancers.

Science Translational Medicine.

GOOD TO KNOW...

Avoid Eating at This Time to Reduce Cancer Risk

Dining too close to bedtime may increase risk for cancer. Women who ate at least two hours before bedtime had 16% lower risk for breast cancer, compared with women who ate right before going to sleep. For men, the same two hours between dinner and bedtime cut the risk for prostate cancer by 26%. Sleeping soon after eating may affect how food is metabolized, and that may lead to increased cancer risk.

Manolis Kogevinas, MD, PhD, head of the Cancer Research Program at ISGlobal in Barcelona, Spain, and lead author of a study published in *International Journal of Cancer.*

Your Bones Are in Danger—and Osteoporosis Isn't the Only Threat

Neil Binkley, MD, professor in the divisions of geriatrics and endocrinology at University of Wisconsin (UW) School of Medicine and Public Health, Madison. He is director of the UW Osteoporosis Clinical Research Program and associate director of the UW Institute on Aging. Aging.wisc.edu

We have been told that the best way to prevent fractures is to prevent or treat osteoporosis with diet, exercise and, if needed, medications. But that approach has not been successful.

For people with osteoporosis, medications do prevent many spinal fractures—but fewer than half of hip and other fractures, according to a major study published in *The New England Journal of Medicine.* And many people who fall and break bones don't even have osteoporosis.

Example: An overweight or obese person may have good bone density (from carrying that extra weight) but still get fractures. Unless he/she has the muscle strength to carry that extra weight, mobility issues—such as difficulty getting up off the toilet or climbing stairs—can lead to falls that cause fractures. Rather than hip fractures due to weakened bones, they tend to get ankle or lower-leg fractures.

In the end, it's preventing fractures—from any cause—that really matters. Many of us think that if we break a bone, our friendly orthopedic surgeon will put it back together and life will go on as usual. But after age 50—and especially after age 65—a fractured bone can threaten independence and quality of life. And that's what we fear most about aging—losing independence…not being able to drive…and winding up in a nursing home. The classic example is a hip fracture, which often sends people to nursing homes and is linked to a shorter life span. But breaking an ankle, an arm or even a wrist can make daily life harder at home…and make it tougher to be mobile.

More from Dr. Neil Binkley...

This Exercise Prevents Falls

One of the simplest and most effective exercises—and one that you can do almost anywhere—is the Chair Rise. Do this daily to strengthen the muscles in your thighs and buttocks, which can help keep you steady on your feet and prevent falls...

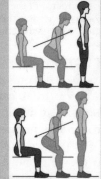

- **Sit toward the front of a sturdy chair,** with your knees bent and feet flat on the floor, shoulder-width apart.

- **Rest your hands lightly on the seat on either side of you,** keeping your back and neck straight and chest slightly forward.

- **Breathe in slowly.** Lean forward and exhale as you stand up—feel your weight on the front of your feet.

- **Pause for a full breath in and out.**

- **Breathe in as you slowly sit down.** Try not to collapse down into the chair. Rather, control your lowering as much as possible.

- **Breathe out.**

Repeat for a total of 10 to 15 stand/sits. Rest and breathe for a minute, then do another set of 10 to 15. You may need to work up to this level over several days or a few weeks. The goal is to get to the point where you can complete two sets without using your hands at all.

To find out what is really needed to prevent fractures, we spoke with geriatrician and endocrinologist Neil Binkley, MD. He started with a simple question—"What causes most fractures in older people?"

The answer: Falling.

Here's how to prevent falls—and the fractures that could end your independence...

- **Eat for muscle strength, not just bones.** Getting enough calcium and vitamin D—standard elements of osteoporosis prevention—still is important. But pay close attention to calories and protein, too. These are essential to maintaining muscle strength—and that's as important as strong bones in preventing

fractures. After all, when our muscle strength declines, we fall. And when we fall on weak bones, guess what? They break.

Protein needs are based on your body weight. To calculate your individual needs, multiply your body weight by 0.45. For a 150-pound woman, that's 67 grams a day...for a 185-pound man, 83 grams. To get a sense of what that looks like, a three-ounce serving of tuna or salmon contains about 22 grams of protein and an egg contains six grams, on average. Aim to include good sources of protein—seafood, lean meat, poultry, eggs, nuts, seeds, soy and legumes such as beans and peas—at every meal.

For some older people, a waning appetite also can mean that they just don't eat enough calories. If you're not eating enough, a registered dietitian can help find practical ways to help you get enough protein and calories each day.

- **Get strong—and balanced.** Now that you're nourishing muscles, make them work. Exercise helps keep your bones and muscles strong, so it's vital for lowering your fracture risk. The best exercise is the one that you'll actually do, whether it's walking, biking, swimming or team sports. Beyond general fitness, exercises that improve core strength and balance are key to fall prevention. *Suggestions...*

- Join a tai chi class. This ancient Chinese set of gentle, slow-moving exercises strengthens lower limbs and improves balance. Several studies have found that practicing tai chi regularly significantly reduces fall risk in older adults.

- Yoga may help, too. It can strengthen bones, and while it is less well-studied for fall prevention, it has been shown to improve balance and mobility in older people.

- **Take fall-prevention classes.** One popular, evidence-based program is Stepping On, a seven-week, two-hours-per-week workshop, first developed in Australia, that now is offered in 20 US states. It is geared to healthy adults over age 65. One study, published in *Journal of the American Geriatrics Society*, reported that people who participated in Stepping On had 31% fewer falls over the next 14 months, compared with a similar group of people who didn't go through the program. To find programs like this in your area, check with the National Council on Aging's Falls Prevention website (go to NCOA.org/healthy-aging/falls-prevention).

•**Consider physical therapy.** If you've fallen and have been injured—even if you didn't break a bone—you're waving a red flag that a fracture could be in your future. A physical therapist can do a formal strength-and-balance assessment…show you exercises to strengthen muscles, bones, walking posture and balance…and help you find classes in your community.

•**Make your home safer.** A key part of fall prevention is taking a look at what you can do to make it less likely that you'll trip and fall…

•Do you have night-lights in your home? Consider putting a night-light in your bathroom for those middle-of-the-night trips.

•Are there throw rugs that you might slip on? Get rid of them!

•Is there clutter on the floor or stairs that you could stumble on? Declutter!

•Do you need to get on a chair or step stool to reach things on high shelves? Put everyday items on lower shelves that are easy to reach.

•Is it hard to get in and out of your bathtub without slipping? Consider installing grab bars or replacing your tub with a walk-in shower.

Some of your safety changes may need to be in your own behavior—such as drinking less alcohol. That's a fall risk that many older people don't consider. And don't forget to get your vision checked regularly. If you can't see it, you can trip on it.

•**Review your medications.** Some medications (prescription or over-the-counter) or medication interactions can cause dizziness, light-headedness or low blood pressure, which can increase the risk of falling. Key medications to be aware of include antihistamines, sleep aids, pain pills, antidepressants and antianxiety medications. In addition, some medications, such as glucocorticoids (steroids taken for inflammatory and autoimmune conditions) contribute to bone loss. If you are taking medications that increase your fall risk, talk to your doctor to see if you can reduce

the dose, find an alternative—or modify how you take it, such as only at bedtime.

It's not that strong bones aren't important—they are a key part of a fracture-prevention plan…but only one part. If your doctor has prescribed a diet, exercise program or medication for you to prevent or treat osteoporosis, continue following those instructions. Osteoporosis medications often are prescribed based on an individual's estimated risk for fracture. For individuals at high fracture risk, the benefits of reducing that risk far outweigh the risk of side effects. But just taking medications is not enough.

Now you know what else you need to do to protect yourself.

What You Need to Know About the Latest Shingles Vaccine

Lindsay C. Strowd, MD, assistant professor of dermatology at Wake Forest Baptist Health in Winston-Salem, North Carolina. Her research has appeared in *Journal of the American Academy of Dermatology*, *The American Journal of Dermatopathology* and other professional journals.

Shingles is one of those dreaded conditions that you may not think too much about—until it's your turn to endure the ravages of this painful viral infection.

Recent development: The latest vaccine provides better protection than the previous one. But despite all the attention it's getting, many people are still unaware of some key details.

Reality check: Because some people—vaccinated or not—still do develop shingles, you also need to know how to best treat the condition and use self-care measures to curb the suffering.

THE SHINGLES VACCINE

The first vaccine for adult shingles, Zostavax, was FDA approved in 2006. It was found to prevent shingles in about half of people who received the single shot.

What you may not realize: Shingles is much more than a skin rash. It's a viral infection that *starts* with a rash but usually doesn't stop there. The rash can be intensely painful and can lead to severe nerve pain that's potentially permanent. And in some cases, shingles can increase stroke risk.

Shingrix, the shingles vaccine that was FDA approved in late 2017, is about 97% effective against shingles during the first year. Its effectiveness wanes over time, but experts predict that it will continue to reduce infections by about 85% over four years. Research has shown that it's particularly effective in older adults, who face the highest risk for shingles.

What you may not realize: The new vaccine is also recommended for those who were previously vaccinated with Zostavax. Even if you've already received the older vaccine, the CDC recommends getting the new one. *Also important:* Just because you've already had shingles, it doesn't mean you're off the hook—you can get shingles more than once. *Other key facts to know about the new vaccine...*

• **It requires two doses instead of one.** While the original shingles vaccine was given in a single dose, Shingrix requires two doses—given about two to six months apart.

• **It's pricey.** Shingrix is about $280 for both shots total, roughly the same cost as the single-shot original vaccine. Most insurance, including Medicare, is expected to cover the new vaccine, but you'll want to check before getting the shots.

• **There's some discomfort from the shot,** which involves mainly arm swelling and localized pain—this is typical with most injections. But about half of patients age 70 and older report more bothersome side effects, including widespread muscle pain, fatigue and/or headaches. Most side effects are temporary and last about 24 to 48 hours.

• **The vaccine's duration is uncertain.** Most vaccines lose their protection over time. The older shingles vaccine seems to lose some of its protection after about five or six years. Shingrix has not been used long enough to determine exactly how many years of protection it will give. And patients may need re-

vaccination at some point after the original vaccination series.

• **Shingrix uses killed viruses, while Zostavax uses live viruses.** Those with impaired immune systems cannot receive live vaccines. If you have been told in the past that you cannot get the shingles vaccine due to an impaired immune system, ask your doctor about Shingrix.

• **Shingrix can be given starting at age 50,** while Zostavax was given to those age 60 and older.

My advice: Everyone age 50 or older and any adult with an impaired immune system should ask a doctor about getting the new vaccine.

THE SHINGLES TRAP

About 90% of adults had chicken pox (*varicella-zoster virus*) early in life. Once you've been exposed to this virus, it retreats to the nervous system and lies dormant. The virus can reactivate later in life, usually after age 50, and cause shingles.

Sometimes shingles will be reactivated during periods of extreme stress on the body—for example, during a bad illness. People with weakened immune systems—the elderly... those with chronic diseases...and/or patients taking immune-suppressing medications for conditions such as rheumatoid arthritis or lupus or using chemotherapy drugs—are at greater risk of developing shingles.

How to Survive Sepsis

Steven Q. Simpson, MD, professor of medicine at University of Kansas, Kansas City, and chief medical officer of the Sepsis Alliance, Sepsis.org. He was among the authors of the *2016 International Guidelines for Management of Sepsis and Septic Shock.*

When it comes to medical emergencies, we all know that heart attack, stroke and asthma attacks are among the most serious. But there's a medical emergency that most people don't know about even though it kills 270,000 people in the US each year. That's one death every two minutes…and more deaths than those caused by prostate cancer, breast cancer and AIDS *combined*.

This runaway killer is known as sepsis. It is a life-threatening condition that occurs when the body goes into overdrive to fight an infection, such as pneumonia, the flu or even a urinary tract infection.

Sepsis causes a deadly cascade of events when the chemicals that the immune system releases into the blood to fight infection trigger inflammation throughout the body that leads to tissue damage, organ failure and death. If not recognized and treated promptly, sepsis can worsen—and kill—within a matter of days…or even hours.

Latest development: New efforts are under way to help people identify sepsis more quickly and get the right treatment promptly so they can survive this devastating illness.

What you need to know to protect yourself and your family…

THE DANGER SIGNS

While anyone who is battling a bacterial, viral or fungal infection can develop sepsis, the old and very young are at particular risk. So are people with chronic diseases such as diabetes, cancer, chronic obstructive pulmonary disease (COPD) and kidney disease.

Sepsis is commonly misdiagnosed because its symptoms—including fast breathing (greater than 20 breaths per minute—the normal rate is 12 to 20)…a racing pulse (above 90 beats per minute)…the chills…pale, clammy skin…and extreme fatigue—can be mistaken for any number of health problems such as heart attack, stroke, pulmonary embolism, exacerbations of chronic lung disease or heart failure.

Misdiagnosis also can occur because there is no definitive test for sepsis—it is diagnosed based on a checklist of signs and symptoms.

To help people identify the red flags of sepsis, the Sepsis Alliance has created the *TIME* acronym…

Temperature: It can be either above normal (such as 100.4°F or higher) or below normal (such as 96.8°F or lower). Severe chills or burning fever are common.

More from Dr. Steven Q. Simpson…

Avoiding Sepsis

The key to preventing sepsis is to prevent infection. *To do this…*

• **Get recommended vaccinations,** including yearly flu shots and vaccination against pneumonia. *Also:* Sepsis can occur with shingles if the skin becomes infected with bacteria. This is an additional reason to consider getting the shingles vaccine.

• **Practice good hygiene.** Wash your hands frequently and thoroughly (for at least 20 seconds).

• **Clean any cut, scrape or burn quickly** and apply antiseptic or antimicrobial cream. If a wound shows signs of a worsening infection—redness, swelling, red streaks radiating up the arm or leg—seek immediate medical attention.

Note: Sepsis is not generally contagious, but some infections that cause sepsis are, such as plague or meningococcal meningitis.

Infection: It may be obvious, such as the flu or an abscess, or there could be less obvious signs and symptoms, including intense pain in some part of one's body, profound weakness or loss of appetite for both food and water.

Mental decline: People with sepsis are often confused or disoriented. They may be very sleepy and hard to rouse.

Extremely ill: Sufferers often experience intense, sharp pain in the chest, belly or elsewhere. They may be short of breath. Many survivors recall, "I felt like I was going to die."

If you think you may have sepsis, seek immediate medical attention. If your doctor isn't available, call 911 or get to an emergency room.

Important: Whether you're seeing your own physician or an ER doctor, make sure he/she knows your concerns. *Ask straight out:* "Could this be sepsis?" Don't be shy about pushing for tests for impaired organ function such as creatinine for kidney function, lactate (lactic acid) level, platelet count, bilirubin and liver enzyme studies.

Keep in mind that the diagnosis of sepsis is missed completely about half of the time—and a delay in treatment can be fatal. Untreated sepsis can rapidly turn into shock, in which blood pressure plummets and tissues are starved for oxygen and nutrients. For every hour that treatment is delayed, the likelihood of septic shock increases.

NEWEST TREATMENT OPTIONS

The latest sepsis practice guidelines, jointly issued by American and European critical care medicine societies, more strongly emphasize the urgency of sepsis diagnosis and treatment.

Under these guidelines, a main goal is to eradicate infection with antibiotics that cover a wide variety of bacteria. Equally important is raising blood pressure to restore delivery of oxygen and nutrients to the organs and normalize their ability to function. This means intravenous fluids and, if needed, vasopressor drugs, such as *norepinephrine*, that stimulate the heart and tighten blood vessels to improve function.

Drugs to reduce immune system activity, once a mainstay of treatment, are no longer standard, reflecting a better understanding of the complex biology involved. Instead, researchers are exploring the use of anti-inflammatory drugs early in the condition's course and immune-stimulating drugs later.

Another change involves medical centers' adoption of highly organized procedures to bring optimal treatment to their patients in the shortest time.

For example, in New York State, which mandates this approach, patients who were diagnosed and treated for sepsis after three hours (and up to 12 hours) of an exam were 14% more likely to die in the hospital than those treated within three hours, according to a 2017 study published in *The New England Journal of Medicine*.

To be alert for possible sepsis: If you have a loved one in the ICU, ask the doctors every day if there are signs of infection, especially if the person is on a mechanical ventilator.

LINGERING AILMENTS

Scientists are discovering increasing evidence that the effects of sepsis can linger. Up to half of survivors suffer "post-sepsis syndrome" (PSS). Physical aspects of PSS reflect damage to vital organs and other tissues. There can be impaired breathing and liver and kidney function, which are often irreversible. Gangrene due to tissue death caused by infecting organisms can necessitate amputation. Fatigue and muscle and joint pain are sometimes disabling.

Recent discovery: The long-term *mental* impact has only recently been recognized. This may include insomnia, hallucinations, panic attacks, poor concentration, impaired memory and even post-traumatic stress disorder (PTSD).

While the reasons for such mental effects are not yet known, it's believed that sepsis may disrupt the protective blood-brain barrier, leaving the brain vulnerable to damaging inflammation.

Medications used in the ICU—especially sedative agents, including benzodiazepines such as *midazolam* (Versed)—also may have negative effects on mental functioning, sometimes lasting for years.

Much remains to be learned about PSS, but it seems likely that quick action early in the course of sepsis could cut the risk.

See Better Than Ever! New Treatments for Cataracts and Glaucoma

Robert Abel, Jr., MD, an ophthalmologist at Delaware Ophthalmology Consultants in Wilmington and founder/medical director of Medical Eye Bank of Delaware. Dr. Abel is a recipient of the Senior Achievement Award given by the American Academy of Ophthalmology. He is a board member of Vision to Learn, a nonprofit group that offers eye screenings and eyeglasses to students in low-income communities, and author of *The Eye Care Revolution*.

When you're nearly blinded by oncoming headlights or can't read the menu in a candlelit restaurant, you've officially entered the world of "age-related vision loss."

For many people, such vision loss starts in their 40s or 50s. By age 65, about one-third of Americans will have vision loss due to common conditions such as *presbyopia* (trouble focusing close up)…or more serious eye problems such as cataracts or glaucoma.

Latest development: New advances are rapidly improving treatments for cataracts and glaucoma—especially when the problem is caught early.

Here are the breakthroughs to consider—and what to watch out for…*

CATARACTS

Cataracts are caused by a clouding of the lens that results in such symptoms as blurry vision, cloudy vision, poor night vision and even double vision. The preferred treatment is cataract surgery—a procedure that's become increasingly effective in recent years. *Latest advances…*

• **Extended depth of focus lens.** With cataract surgery, a surgeon can remove the cloudy, vision-impairing lens of the eye in a matter of minutes and replace it with a clear corrective lens. But until recently, the replacement lens would only enhance either near or far vision in each eye.

This meant that doctors might treat one eye for near vision and the other eye for seeing at a distance…or they might use a "multifocal" implant that offered *some* improvement in both near and far vision. Most people simply choose to correct for far vision and use reading glasses the rest of the time.

The new extended depth of focus (EDOF) lens is an important advance because it can correct distance vision while also improving your ability to see up close. For eye surgeons, it's one step closer to the holy grail—the ability to completely reverse age-related vision loss without the need for glasses. With EDOF, you might actually see better than you ever did.

Drawbacks: The new lenses are expensive. If your insurance doesn't pick up the tab, you can expect to pay $1,500 to $2,500 more *per eye* than you would for traditional replacement lenses.

*The treatments included in this article may not be covered by insurance. Check with your insurer for details.

Even though the new lenses are better for brightness, contrast and seeing colors—and they do improve vision at in-between distances—you still might need reading glasses in some cases.

Best for: Active middle-aged and older adults who want to avoid wearing glasses.

• **RxSight Light Adjustable Lens.** The FDA approved an artificial lens in 2017 that can be adjusted *repeatedly* after cataract surgery—important because slight errors in lens manufacturing (or eye changes that occur during healing) can skew the vision-correcting effects.

This adjustable lens contains a unique material that shifts in response to UV light. If your vision isn't optimal after the surgery, your doctor can fine-tune it with three or four laser treatments that modify the curvature of the lens, delivered about three weeks after the procedure.

The lens can provide vision improvements that are comparable to vision-correcting procedures such as LASIK. But for now (despite the FDA's approval), the lens has not yet become widely adopted and is mainly available for patients who are participating in ongoing studies.

Best for: Any cataract surgery patient who is looking for precise vision correction that is permanent.

GLAUCOMA

Glaucoma results from fluid buildup that damages the eye's optic nerve, potentially causing vision loss and even blindness. Depending on the extent of the disease, treatment has traditionally included medication (such as eyedrops or pills)…laser surgery (to help make sure that fluid drains out of the eye)…or conventional surgery (to create an opening for fluid to leave the eye). *Latest advances…*

• **iStent.** Because most types of glaucoma are accompanied by excessive fluid buildup (often leading to high pressure within the eye), one of the main treatments is to surgically install a stent (or a related device called a shunt) to improve drainage and keep eye pressure low.

The iStent is a game-changer. It's the first FDA-approved device that can be implanted *during* cataract surgery for patients who have mild-to-moderate open-angle glaucoma, which accounts for at least 90% of all glaucoma cases. The device, which is about one-third the size of a grain of rice, creates a permanent opening to improve fluid drainage.

Previous devices worked similarly, but they required the surgeon to open a flap of skin from outside the eye, install the stent, then close things up. The iStent doesn't require a separate procedure when performed with cataract surgery.

Bonus: Patients who have the stent often can reduce their dependence on pressure-reducing medications, which tend to be less reliable and may cause side effects, including extremely low pressure. It's a phenomenal development!

Best for: Any glaucoma patient who is undergoing cataract surgery.

• **Pressure-reducing eyedrops.** More than 95% of adults with glaucoma use eyedrops (at least initially) to reduce glaucoma-causing fluid buildups.

About half of patients require two or more eye medications—and patients using multiple drugs are less likely to follow dosing instructions. The most commonly used medications are *prostaglandin analogs* (PGAs), which improve the functioning of the drainage pathway known as the *uveoscleral outflow*.

What's new: *Latanoprostene bunod* ophthalmic solution (Vyzulta), approved by the FDA in 2017. Unlike other PGAs, it increases the outflow of fluid through both the uveoscleral pathway and the *trabecular meshwork* (an area of tissue near the base of the cornea). In studies, it lowered intraocular pressure more than the older drugs…and the dual action means that some glaucoma patients can use only one eyedrop.

My take: All of the PGAs, including Vyzulta, can cause inflammation and red or puffy eyes. For this reason, I believe that glaucoma patients will often do better with other (non-PGA) eyedrops or laser treatments.

Best for: Vyzulta can be a reasonable choice for advanced glaucoma patients who must use eyedrops but are resistant to other products and are not significantly troubled by mild eye inflammation.

Stress Can Cause Vision Loss

Muneeb Faiq, PhD, a post-doctoral researcher at New York University School of Medicine in New York City and coauthor of a review of psychosomatic ophthalmology, published in *EPMA Journal (European Association for Predictive, Preventive and Personalised Medicine)*.

At your eye exam, your doctor tells you that there is a buildup of pressure in your eyes—the only treatable risk factor for glaucoma. Unless the pressure is relieved, typically with drugs and/or surgery, you could lose your vision. So you get a prescription for eyedrops, which you will use for the rest of your life.

But there is another risk factor that your eye doctor may not mention—stress. Chronic stress bathes your body in the hormone *cortisol*, which raises pressure in your eyes. Controlling your stress may help you control that pressure—and help prevent glaucoma.

Stress is an underappreciated contributor to a wide range of eye conditions including *optic neuropathy*—damage to the optic nerve from, for example, diabetes. Stress even may play a role in myopia (nearsightedness). How? Stress-induced spasms of the tiny muscles in the eye can alter the thickness of the lens.

Research shows that stress reduction not only can prevent the onset of some eye diseases in susceptible people but also reduce the severity of the diseases, improve response to treatment and lead to better outcomes.

So how do you treat stress that could steal your vision? Same as you should any stress—meditation and mindfulness-based stress-reduction techniques, proper diet and good sleep. At a minimum, reducing stress helps you manage an eye condition after it's diagnosed—but it also may help you avoid one in the first place.

Fall in Love with Your Hearing Aids

Barbara E. Weinstein, PhD, professor of audiology and head of the Audiology Program at City University of New York Graduate Center in New York City, where she specializes in hearing loss in older adults, hearing screening, handicap assessment and evidence-based practice. She is author of the textbook *Geriatric Audiology*.

Few individuals welcome the idea of getting hearing aids. Some are too embarrassed to wear them, while others are put off by the high cost. Whatever the reason, about three-quarters of the roughly 30 million American adults who could benefit from these remarkable little devices don't get them…and most who do get them postpone the decision for close to 10 years.

So you might assume that the battle is won when a holdout takes the plunge and *does* get hearing aids. But that's not always true. Nearly 13% of new hearing-aid users wind up tossing the devices in a drawer. And up to 25% of new users wear them for less than two hours a day, depriving themselves of their full benefit.

Why do so many new hearing-aid users falter? One underappreciated trap is that it can take weeks or even months to get accustomed to the sounds (and the feel) of new hearing aids. So it's crucial to not let the initial discomforts put you off.

Proper use of hearing aids can enrich your relationships and social life…possibly guard against accidents that can occur if you don't hear warning signals…and prevent falls that can be precipitated by walking while struggling to understand what someone is saying. Improved hearing may even help protect your brain health because you can better communicate with your family and friends and remain engaged.

For the latest advice on getting the most from hearing aids, we spoke with Barbara E. Weinstein, PhD, a leading authority on hearing loss. Whether you're a new hearing-aid owner or your hearing aids are collecting dust in a drawer, here's what can help…

HEARING AND THE BRAIN

People cite a number of reasons for not wearing their hearing aids. Some complain that they hurt their ears. Others notice that the sounds they hear don't seem natural…or that they're bothered by sounds they hadn't noticed before.

While new hearing aids *do* take some getting used to, they are definitely worth the effort. For one thing, emerging evidence suggests that the part of the brain that processes spoken language (the temporal lobe) may be subject to atrophy and volume declines when not stimulated. This means that people with an impaired hearing mechanism who wait too long to correct their hearing may not benefit as much from hearing interventions.

Even scarier risk: In a study by a group of researchers at Johns Hopkins who tracked 639 adults (ages 36 to 90), mild hearing loss was linked to twice the risk for dementia…and moderate-to-severe hearing loss increased the risk between three- and fivefold.

ADJUSTING TO CHANGE

It's easier to get used to hearing aids in your younger years, so don't wait until you're adjusting the TV volume to wall-shaking levels. The most important part of successful aging is staying socially engaged—and you can't do that when you can't hear or communicate with others. *Secrets to adjusting to your hearing aids…*

SECRET #1: **Wear them all day.** Depending on the degree/duration of your hearing loss, it might have been years since you've heard the sound of your own footsteps…water running in the sink…or the clatter of dishes. The "new" sounds can be distracting—even disturbing—until you get used to them.

My advice: Wear your new hearing aids all day, even when you first get them. We used to advise patients to use them for just a few hours a day at first, but we've found that people often do better with full-on exposure. Just know that it may take days, weeks or even months before background sounds truly fade into the background.

SECRET #2: **When it's too loud, make adjustments.** You'll probably find that most sounds—even the ones you want to hear—are uncomfortably loud at first. Some hearing aids have volume controls, which you can adjust, but it will take your brain time to adjust even to the lower settings. If sounds are too loud, be sure to return to your hearing-aid provider to make the necessary adjustments, as hearing aids have many features that can be adjusted.

My advice: As mentioned above, it's important to wear your hearing aids all day. You might want to make an exception, however, for unusually noisy environments—for example, in the subway, at a concert or at the airport. High-volume venues won't always be an impediment, but they can be a turnoff during the adjustment period.

If the sound of your own voice is disturbing, ask your audiologist if the devices need adjusting. Turning down the volume might not do it. An audiologist can make adjustments—to the sound frequencies, for example, or the shape of the earpiece (known as the mold)—that will often help.

Important: To become comfortable with their hearing aids, most people require one or two additional visits for adjustments, which are typically included in the price of the hearing aids.

SECRET #3: **Cut through the clutter.** People with normal hearing may struggle to hear conversations when there's a lot of background noise, but it is worse for those with hearing loss. Even inexpensive hearing aids typically have a noise-cancellation feature that enhances higher frequencies (typical of speech) while suppressing lower frequencies (from background noise). The setting is often adjustable—learn how to use it.

My advice: If adjusting noise cancellation doesn't help, ask an audiologist to make changes in the "output" and/or "gain." Gain is the power of the signal that affects amplification, and output is the level of "sound pressure" that's produced by the combination of incoming sounds and the gain added by the hearing aid.

SECRET #4: **Master the controls.** Hearing aids keep getting smaller, which means that the controls also are getting smaller—too small, in many cases, for people (especially those with big fingers or limited hand mobility) to easily adjust.

My advice: Don't buy a hearing aid just because it has a zillion adjustable features. They won't do you any good unless you have the finger dexterity (and the technical savvy) to master them. An audiologist can help you decide which features you absolutely need—and those you can do without.

Helpful: Many hearing aids use Bluetooth wireless technology, which allows them to be adjusted by an app that appears on the screen of your smartphone. This is a great feature if you have one of these phones and you're willing to use it as a remote control. An audiologist talked my 93-year-old cousin into getting this feature…but in order to use it, she had to buy her first smartphone, which she didn't know how to use and actually found annoying.

SECRET #5: **Learn how to fix whistling sounds.** The squealing/whistling sounds that you'll sometimes hear are a type of feedback. It doesn't mean that there's a problem with the electronics. Most hearing aids have "feedback interceptors" that suppress whistles, but they don't eliminate them entirely.

My advice: Ask your audiologist if you need a tighter-fitting ear mold. Squeals and whistles occur when amplified sound from the hearing aid leaks out of the ear…gets picked up by the microphone…and then returns to the ear as a whistling noise.

SECRET #6: **Don't put up with ear discomfort.** Many people complain that their hearing aids are uncomfortable. They may find themselves constantly pulling/adjusting the ear mold to reduce discomfort, but the frequent back-and-forth adjustments only make the irritation worse.

My advice: You can get a hearing-aid lubricant/cream from an audiologist, online or at pharmacies. Brands include Westone Oto-Ease and Audiologist's Choice anti-itch cream. They're particularly helpful if you happen to have dryness in the ear canal.

Worth a try: If you continue to have problems, your audiologist might need to fashion an ear mold/tip that fits more comfortably.

This is one advantage of buying locally. I don't discourage patients from buying hearing aids online, but this type of adjustment can be done only by a local professional.

Video Games May Protect the Brain

Older adults who played Super Mario 64, a 3-D logic-and-puzzle game, for 30 minutes a day, five days a week, for six months, had increased volume of gray matter in the brain's hippocampus and cerebellum regions—and their short-term memory improved. The effects were not seen in people who took piano lessons for six months or in a control group that did neither activity. Gray matter normally atrophies as people age. Learning new things may help slow the atrophy—but the reason for the specific effectiveness of the video game in this study remains unknown.

Gregory West, PhD, associate professor of psychology, Université de Montréal, Canada, and coauthor of a study published in *PLOS ONE*.

A Brand-New Form of Medical Treatment Helps Stroke, Depression, More

James Giordano, PhD, professor in the departments of neurology and biochemistry and chief of the Neuroethics Studies Program of the Pellegrino Center for Clinical Bioethics at Georgetown University Medical Center, Washington, DC. ClinicalBioethics.Georgetown.edu

Meredith Hutter Chamorro, a certified Yoga Tune Up teacher with advanced training in restorative yoga, Stroudsburg, Pennsylvania. SheSwingsOnAStar.com

Its name means "wandering," but it is far from aimless. It travels from the brain down each side of the neck, through the chest and deep into the gut. It helps regulate an astounding number of the body's essential functions—including breathing, heart rate, blood pressure, perspiration and digestion.

It's the *vagus nerve*, and it's turning out to be a key to wellness—and to fighting disease. Yogis call it the "Buddha Nerve" because the core benefits of meditation—calm and a sense of balance—stem from activating it. But it also now is the basis of cutting-edge medicine.

To understand the "vagus revolution," we reached out to James Giordano, PhD, a world-renowned neuroscientist at Georgetown University…and Meredith Hutter Chamorro, a restorative yoga teacher whose work focuses on improving vagus nerve function.

WHY THE VAGUS NERVE MATTERS

The vagus nerve plays a key role in stimulating the *parasympathetic* nervous system. This is your body's "rest-and-digest" response—a counterbalance to the "fight-or-flight" mechanisms of the sympathetic nervous system. An activated parasympathetic system means that we're calmer, have lower blood pressure, digest food better and produce less inflammation.

We need both systems, but health depends on how well we *balance* them. That's known as "vagal tone." If you have high vagal tone, you relax quickly after a stressful moment. In that state, your body is better at regulating blood glucose levels and cholesterol so that, over time, you're at less risk for cardiovascular disease, stroke and diabetes. You're also less anxious and better able to manage your emotions. Conversely, low vagal tone is associated with increased risk for depression, gastrointestinal disorders and heart disease.

ELECTRIFYING MEDICINE

Vagus nerve stimulation (VNS) is fast becoming a new form of medical treatment. According to Dr. Giordano, it can be done in two ways—invasively, in which a device that is surgically implanted in the chest (with electrodes in the neck) sends very mild electrical pulses at regular intervals to the vagus nerve…or noninvasively, through the use of a handheld device that a patient applies to the neck. *Exciting research findings…*

• **Epilepsy.** VNS originally was developed to treat epilepsy patients who did not respond well to antiseizure medication. It gets more effective the longer it is used—in one study conducted at New York University Langone

25

Medical Center, the frequency of seizures decreased by 36% in six months...58% in four years...and 75.5% in 10 years.

• **Parkinson's disease.** VNS allows some patients to get longer-lasting effects with lower doses of drugs. This is important because drugs used to treat Parkinson's tend to become less effective as the disease progresses, and increasing the doses can have debilitating side effects.

• **Migraines.** These headaches often begin in the back of the head where there's a branch of the vagus nerve. Several recent studies have found that by using a handheld stimulator over the nerve in the neck when symptoms begin, sufferers can decrease pain—and, in some cases, nip a migraine in the bud. In early 2018, the Food and Drug Administration cleared one such device—*gammaCore*—for home treatment of migraines. It's not cheap—$600 a month (although the company offers a co-pay assistance program) and may not be covered by insurance, although the company is working to expand coverage. The device requires a prescription.

• **Depression.** A landmark study published in *The American Journal of Psychiatry* followed 795 treatment-resistant depression patients for five years. Nearly half (43%) of those who used medication and therapy plus an implanted VNS device experienced remission of their depression—compared with only 26% of those who had only medication/therapy.

• **Anxiety, stroke and cognitive health.** VNS also is proving to be helpful in reducing anxiety disorders including post-traumatic stress disorder (PTSD). Some stroke patients benefit from VNS, as do some head-injury patients. Early research suggests that improving vagal tone (see below to learn how) may help people with cognitive issues improve alertness, focus, decision making and memory.

8 WAYS TO WORK OUT YOUR VAGUS

While medical advances are exciting for people with certain conditions, every one of us can take steps now to improve our vagal tone and vitality. Yoga instructor Meredith Hutter Chamorro uses several approaches to improve vagal tone in her clients. *Try these every day...*

• **Deep diaphragmatic breathing.** Breathing through your nose, inhale deeply into your belly and exhale slowly. Control your exhale so that it lasts longer than the inhale—like letting air out of a tire. During the inhale, you'll massage the vagus nerve, and during the exhale the diaphragm releases around the vagus nerve, improving its functioning.

• **Massage.** Grab a squishy exercise ball—I use one that is about nine inches in diameter—and lay with your tummy on it. Don't use a firm ball because this exercise should feel comfortable with no pain. Do some diaphragmatic breathing, and try slowly rolling from side to side on the ball. This helps release tension in your core muscles, making it easier to take deep, diaphragmatic breaths.

• **Cold water.** Stimulate your vagus nerve simply by splashing cold water on your face. When your body adjusts to cold, your fight-or-flight response declines and your rest-and-digest system kicks in.

• **Singing and humming.** These vocal activities produce vibration in the neck, which stimulates the vagus nerve in a beneficial way.

• **Gargling.** Grab a glass of water each morning, and gargle to contract the muscles in the back of the throat, which stimulates your vagus nerve and digestive tract. For the most benefit, gargle continuously until your eyes start to tear up—another vagus function.

• **Yoga.** Add "toning your vagus nerve" to your long list of reasons to do yoga. The practice incorporates diaphragmatic breathing, chanting and stress reduction.

• **Meditation.** All types of meditation are good for the vagus nerve. My favorite is compassionate, or "Loving-Kindness," meditation. Rather than letting your mind wander, you direct your good thoughts to other people. As positive emotions increase, so does your vagal tone.

• **Laughter.** Laughing reduces muscle tension in the face, neck and diaphragm that can cause bottlenecks in vagus signals. It also requires diaphragmatic movements and has been shown to improve vagal tone. Watch funny movies and comedy shows, and tell jokes with your friends—laughter really is great medicine!

2

Medical Matters

6 Germ Hot Spots in Your Doctor's Office

There's a secret that doctors know but don't always talk about—one of the most germ-laden places to visit may be a medical office.

While doctors, nurses and medical assistants have gotten more conscientious about washing their hands, millions of Americans still develop health-care related infections every year. As you'd expect, hospitals are among the most germ-laden places, but even routine doctor visits can present risks.

Troubling development: Bacteria that can lead to life-threatening *Clostridium difficile* infection (commonly referred to as "*C. diff*"), a diarrhea-related illness that once was found almost exclusively in hospitals and nursing homes, has been linked to visits to doctors' and dentists' offices, according to a 2015 study published in *The New England Journal of Medicine.*

If you know where the germs are most likely to hide out in medical offices, there are simple steps you can take—beyond hand-washing—to reduce your risk of picking up microorganisms that spread colds, flu and other diseases.

IN THE WAITING ROOM

Even though it's impossible to find a germ-free doctor's office (or really any place that people frequent), you shouldn't let that stop you from seeing your physician if you're sick or need a checkup. *When you go, just be sure to follow these steps to avoid germs that lurk in these common hot spots…*

• **Dirty pens.** Patients are accustomed to the pen-and-clipboard check-in ritual, but have

Miryam Z. Wahrman, PhD, professor of biology at William Paterson University in Wayne, New Jersey, where she specializes in microbiology, hand hygiene and the interactions between bacteria and environmental surfaces. She is author of *The Hand Book: Surviving in a Germ-Filled World.*

you ever wondered what lives on the clipboard pen? It's been touched by *hundreds* of germy hands, including those of people who are seriously ill. If your check-in involves an electronic tablet, many fingers have touched that as well.

Test swabs taken from doctors' offices show that the average writing implement harbors vast quantities of pathogens—far more than door handles, the armrests of the waiting-room chairs or the doctor's computer keyboard. Because people grip pens with unwashed hands...put them behind their ears...or even in their mouths, pens are also germier than the clipboard you get at check-in.

My advice: Carry your own pen for filling out forms in your doctor's office, signing receipts and to use anywhere you might need to give your signature—at the supermarket, department stores, etc.

•**Germy magazines.** The well-thumbed magazines on a waiting-room table can carry whatever germs were on the previous reader's hands...or were sprayed like an aerosol from a sneeze or cough.

My advice: Bring your own reading material to the doctor's waiting room. Our research, conducted at William Paterson University, found that germs can survive for weeks or even months on paper.

•**Other patients.** Pediatrician offices often have "sick" and "well" areas in the waiting rooms. This hasn't become common practice for doctors who treat adults—perhaps because adults tend to be more careful about hygiene than young children, covering sneezes and coughs and using tissues—and few doctors have waiting rooms big enough to accommodate separate areas.

My advice: Don't sit near patients who are coughing or sneezing, wiping their noses or are otherwise *visibly* ill. If possible, schedule routine visits so that you're not in the office during flu season. And definitely keep up with vaccines, including those for flu and pneumonia.

Helpful: Consider wearing a face mask in the doctor's office, particularly during flu season. Experts used to think that the flu virus was mainly transmitted through coughing and sneezing and by touching contaminated surfaces. But we now know that these *infectious aerosols*, airborne droplets produced by coughs or sneezes, can hover in the air for *hours*. New research shows that these aerosols are also transmitted simply during normal breathing.

You can buy surgical-style face masks in pharmacies...or ask for one at the front desk if your doctor's office provides them for patients who could be contagious. They don't provide a perfect barrier, but a snug-fitting mask will help protect you from other patients—and protect them from *you*. Even though you may feel self-conscious wearing one, the other patients will appreciate it if they think you're the one who is sick.

THE DOCTOR

•**Handheld devices.** Doctors routinely carry cell phones, tablets or other electronic devices when they make their rounds or see patients in the office. They use them to take notes, check your medical history and look up drug information—and unwittingly to pass germs, in some cases, from one patient to the next.

Shocking research: In a study published in *Online Journal of Health and Allied Sciences*, 75% of the cell phones carried by health professionals were contaminated with disease-causing germs, including *methicillin-resistant Staphylococcus aureus* (MRSA) and other dangerous pathogens. Equally concerning was that more than half of the health-care workers said that they never cleaned their phones... and 87% admitted that they didn't wash their hands after using them.

Even if your doctor is conscientious about handwashing, the device will reinfect his/her fingertips every time it's touched.

My advice: Ask your doctor to wash his hands after touching the device—and *before* touching you. Gloves can help, but only if they're new. You can say to your doctor, "I see that you just touched your tablet. Would you mind putting on a new pair of gloves?"

•**Contaminated stethoscopes.** The stethoscope is the classic emblem of medical care. It's also one of the most contaminated.

Scientific evidence: When researchers measured bacterial concentrations both on stethoscopes and on the hands of doctors who used them, in 71 out of 83 cases, the stethoscopes carried more germs than any part of the doctors' hands except for the fingertips, according to a study in *Mayo Clinic Proceedings*.

Unless a stethoscope is wiped down with alcohol after every use, assume that you're being exposed to bacteria or viruses from the patients who came before you.

My advice: Doctors have gotten better about cleaning their stethoscopes with alcohol wipes, but they may forget...so remind them!

•**White coats.** Most doctors wear a white coat and keep it on all day. It's not as clean as it may look.

Research published in *American Journal of Infection Control* found that 23% of physician white coats carried disease-causing microorganisms, including, in some cases, antibiotic-resistant MRSA.

GREAT ADVICE...

For a Much Better Doctor Appointment

To get more value when seeing your doctor...
•**Write down your concerns,** and refer to your notes during the visit.
•**Prioritize**—decide on your main concerns and discuss the most important one first.
•**Bring a list of all your medicines, prescription and over-the-counter,** so your doctor can look for interactions and no-longer-needed drugs.
•**Take notes during the visit.** You might not remember everything your doctor says, especially if you're not feeling well.
•**Take advantage of available help.** The office may have specialists who can help with your specific issues—a dietitian for weight-loss concerns, for example.
•**Expect some face-to-face quality time with your doctor**—doctors must enter data during a visit for electronic recordkeeping, but if your doctor focuses only on the screen and not on you, consider finding another doctor.

Roundup of experts on health care, reported at *Consumer Reports*.

My advice: Whether or not the doctor is wearing a white coat, be aware of what the doctor touches before he touches you. He should don his gloves right before examining you. If the doctor adjusts his necktie (another germ hot spot) or gets something from a pocket, he should put on a clean pair of gloves. Politely ask your doctor to use an alcohol pad to swab skin areas that have been accidentally brushed with a necktie or jacket sleeve.

When the appointment is over, feel free to give your doctor a fist bump instead of a handshake...or, better yet, just a friendly smile. He will respect your nod to the latest trend in hand-hygiene practices!

After your appointment: Don't forget to wash your hands before leaving the doctor's office—ideally, with soap and water for 20 seconds, but with an alcohol-based hand sanitizer if a sink is not readily available. Research has shown that hand jewelry—and particularly rings, which are rarely removed—is a common cause of bacterial contamination (and transmission), so scrub well, including on and around rings.

Grab a clean paper towel on your way out of the restroom and use that as a barrier when you open doors and push elevator buttons. Then throw it in the trash on your way out of the building.

The Truth About Online Doctor Reviews

Roy Benaroch, MD, adjunct assistant professor of pediatrics at Emory University School of Medicine, Atlanta. He has written about physician-rating services at PediatricInsider.com.

Online review websites might help you choose a hotel, restaurant or contractor—but doctor-review websites such as Healthgrades, RateMDs, Vitals or Zocdocs aren't likely to help you find a good doctor. *Here's why...*

•**They don't reflect scientifically valid patient reviews.** A study published in *Mayo*

Clinic Proceedings found that physicians with negative online reviews were no more likely to have negative scores on patient-satisfaction surveys than their colleagues.

•**They don't reflect physician quality.** A study published in *Journal of Medical Internet Research* compared online physician ratings with postsurgical mortality rates for cardiac surgeons. *Result*: No correlation. Indeed, some surgeons with high online ratings had high mortality rates, too.

How do these sites leave inaccurate impressions? One factor is that what patients like isn't always best for them.

Example: A doctor who is quick to prescribe antibiotics may have patients who feel satisfied and listened to. They'll write favorable reviews, but this doesn't necessarily mean that they got good care. And negative reviews very often cite such things as communication with the front desk, appointment access, waiting time, billing, even parking—not physician quality. *These things matter, too, but if you want to find someone who is good at being a doctor, there are better ways…*

•**Take the old-fashioned route.** Ask friends and neighbors in your community.

•**Ask the same of health professionals you know**—your current physicians and their nurses/assistants…your physical therapist and your pharmacist.

•**Network among people with similar health concerns.** *Example*: If you have multiple sclerosis, ask for doctor recommendations on message boards at the website for the National Multiple Sclerosis Society.

Doctor vs. Nurse Practitioner

Trisha Torrey, founder of EveryPatientsAdvocate. com, Leesburg, Florida.

There's nothing illegal about a medical practice changing your provider from a doctor to a nurse practitioner (NP) or physician's assistant (PA) for an appointment, but you should be told in advance.

Why this might happen: Maybe the doctor is sick that day, is overbooked or had an emergency, among other reasons.

What to do: When you make an appointment, tell the scheduler who you want to see and confirm that he/she will be available. Also ask the scheduler to let you know ahead of time if a change needs to be made.

Note: The quality of care provided by an NP or a PA has been shown to be equal to (or sometimes better than) what you'd get from a medical doctor if it's a routine visit or it's a basic and acute problem such as the flu or a rash. And many people actually prefer to see an NP or a PA due to better availability, extra time for questions and perhaps lower costs. However, it's best to see your doctor if you're having unusual symptoms or you have a chronic condition that needs constant monitoring and you're not being seen by a specialist.

Stay with Your Doctor

Patients ages 62 to 82 with the highest continuity of care had 12% fewer hospitalizations for preventable conditions—such as asthma and pneumonia—than those who had the least continuity of care.

Study by researchers at Health Foundation, London, UK, of more than 230,000 patients, published in *The BMJ*.

When Requesting Medical Records…

Be specific when requesting your medical records—call your provider or visit its website to specifically request what you want. You can expect records within 30 days—the time set by federal law—but be understanding if a provider tells you more time is needed. If you experience unexplained delays, ask to speak to someone higher up in a practice or hospital—and if necessary, file a complaint with the federal Office of Civil Rights (HHS.gov/ocr).

Study about requesting medical records by researchers at Yale University, New Haven, Connecticut, published in *JAMA Network Open*.

Your Doctor May Get Drug Company Perks

Rebecca Shannonhouse, editor in chief, *Bottom Line Health*, BottomLineInc.com.

When it comes to high-paying jobs in the US, physicians rank at (or near) the top. But some doctors are more than well paid—they pull in tens of millions of dollars a year.

How do they do it? The answer lies largely with pharmaceutical and medical-device companies that pay certain doctors boatloads of money for speaking, research and consulting.

If you are wondering whether your own, say, family practitioner or dermatologist is getting any freebies, look around his/her office. Check for pens, notepads and coffee cups emblazoned with industry logos. These are mere tokens compared with the megabucks some doctors get. But even these small perks could make a difference.

A report in *JAMA* found that about half of US doctors received industry payments (including gifts). And even though most doctors swear that they can't be "bought" for the price of a steak dinner or a sleek coffee cup, research shows otherwise.

For example, generic drugs are virtually identical to brand-name counterparts, and cost 80% to 85% less. Yet doctors who receive money and/or gifts from drug companies are less likely to prescribe the generics.

When hospitals impose restrictions—such as banning free meals and drug samples—brand-name prescriptions decline. This suggests that small gifts do matter.

Curious about your own doctor? To see whether your doctor receives money from industry sources, check the ProPublica database at Projects.ProPublica.org/docdollars. You may be surprised by what you find!

Is Your Medication the Cause of Your Pain or Numbness?

Janice F. Wiesman, MD, FAAN, clinical associate professor of neurology at New York University School of Medicine in New York City and adjunct assistant professor of neurology at Boston University School of Medicine. She is author of *Peripheral Neuropathy: What It Is and What You Can Do to Feel Better*.

When your foot goes numb after a few hours of couch time or you wake up at night with a tingling (or even painful) arm crooked beneath your head, you're experiencing what people with neuropathy live with…every day.

Peripheral neuropathy is a mysterious condition. Many patients never discover what is causing their nerve-related numbness, pain, tingling or other sensations.

Often-overlooked culprit: The medicine cabinet. After diabetes, medication is one of the most common causes of neuropathy. Dozens of medications—even those that you would think are totally safe—can cause nerve

TAKE NOTE...

FDA Warning on MRI Dye

A recent FDA warning notes that the metal *gadolinium*, commonly injected during an MRI scan to improve image quality, can linger in the brain, skin and bones for years. While it has not been directly linked to adverse health outcomes in people with normal kidney function, some patients have complained of pain, burning sensations and weakness after injection.

If you're scheduled for an MRI, especially if you get repeated scans: Don't avoid the dye, but do ask whether it is required.

Janet Woodcock, MD, director, Center for Drug Evaluation and Research, FDA, Silver Spring, Maryland.

damage that's often slow to appear and equally slow to heal...if it ever does. *What you need to know...*

THE LEADING CULPRITS

Nerve-related side effects, known as *drug-induced neuropathies*, are tricky to identify because they often appear months or even years after starting a medication—although there are exceptions.

Example: Some of the drugs used in chemotherapy are notorious for causing neuropathy. These cases are easy to identify because the symptoms show up quickly—typically within a week or a few months of starting the chemotherapy. Up to 75% of cancer patients given the chemotherapy drug *vincristine* (Oncovin) will experience neuropathy. *Paclitaxel* (Taxol), discussed later, is another common offender.

In general, about one-third of patients who have drug-induced neuropathy will completely recover when they stop—or at least lower the dose of—an offending drug. One-third will stay the same, and another third might get worse. *Drugs to suspect...*

•**Statins.** Cholesterol-lowering statins—including *atorvastatin* (Lipitor), *rosuvastatin* (Crestor) and *simvastatin* (Zocor)—are among the most commonly prescribed medications in the US. According to research published in *Neurology*, statin users were four times more likely to develop neuropathy than people not taking statins.

Experts aren't sure why statins often cause neuropathy. The good news, however, is that most people with statin-related nerve symptoms will recover when they stop taking the drug, though it may take months in some cases. But how do they manage their cholesterol without the medication?

My advice: Switching to a different statin might be the solution—but it's impossible to predict if (or when) a new drug will cause similar problems. To help control your cholesterol levels, your doctor should advise you to exercise more and eat a lower-meat (or even vegetarian) diet.

Even if you can't completely control cholesterol with lifestyle changes, diet and exercise can lower it enough that you might be able to take a lower statin dose—important because the higher the statin dose, the greater the risk for neuropathy. *Note*: Case reports have shown that people taking supplements containing red yeast rice, a naturally occurring statin, have also developed neuropathy.

•**Antibiotics.** A number of antibiotics can lead to neuropathy. *Ciprofloxacin* (Cipro) is a widely used broad-spectrum antibiotic. Along with other drugs in this class, known as fluoroquinolones—such as *levofloxacin* (Levaquin) and *moxifloxacin* (Avelox)—it's a common cause of nerve symptoms.

Important: If you notice neuropathy symptoms while taking one of these drugs, don't ignore them. The discomfort usually involves tingling and/or numbness that starts in the feet, moves up to the knees and then starts to affect the hands and fingers.

My advice: If you experience such symptoms, promptly contact your doctor. Ask him/her whether you can switch to a safer antibiotic, such as *penicillin, tetracycline* or *doxycycline*. Neuropathy symptoms usually subside when a person goes off a fluoroquinolone but, in rare cases, may not.

In my opinion, Cipro or another fluoroquinolone antibiotic should be used only when you have an infection that won't respond to one of the safer antibiotics mentioned above.

Nitrofurantoin (Macrobid) is an antibiotic that's used both to treat urinary tract infections (UTIs) and to help prevent recurrent UTIs in patients who are particularly susceptible, such as nursing home patients and those with spinal cord injuries using urinary catheters.

Unlike most other drug-induced neuropathies, the ones caused by Macrobid usually occur quickly—within a week, in some cases. The discomfort usually begins in the feet and legs and moves upward (as described earlier) and can be irreversible if the drug isn't stopped quickly enough.

Most UTIs can be treated with newer, safer drugs or drug combinations, such as *trimethoprim* and *sulfamethoxazole* (Bactrim or Septra). Patients should tell their doctors immediately if they notice neuropathy symptoms, such as numbness, tingling, etc., to determine whether they can be switched to a different antibiotic.

• **Taxol.** About 30% to 40% of cancer patients who are treated with chemotherapy will develop neuropathy. Taxol, commonly used for breast cancer, is a common offender because many women take it for years after their initial diagnosis and treatments.

Important finding: More than 40% of women taking Taxol or similar drugs continued to experience numbness and/or tingling in their hands or feet two years after starting treatment...and 10% rated the discomfort as severe, according to a report in *Journal of the National Cancer Institute*. Neuropathy symptoms should subside when Taxol is changed or stopped, but this might take months or years.

You're more likely to get foot tingling/numbness (the so-called "Taxol toes") or other symptoms, such as sensations of burning in a hand or loss of touch sensation, if you're also obese... have a preexisting history of neuropathy...have had a mastectomy...or if a large number of your lymph nodes harbored cancer cells.

My advice: Be sure to tell your oncologist (if he doesn't ask) if you've had neuropathy in the past. You might be advised to undergo treatments that have about the same survival benefit but are less likely to have this side effect.

• **Amiodarone (Cordarone).** This medication is one of the most frequently prescribed for heart-rhythm abnormalities (arrhythmias).

Up to 10% of patients who take Cordarone over a period of years will develop neuropathy...and some will develop *optic neuropathy*, which can cause blurred vision, abnormalities in the visual field (such as "halo vision") or even progressive (and painless) vision loss.

Note: Certain other drugs, including Cipro, the cancer medication *tamoxifen* (Nolvadex) and the erectile dysfunction drug *sildenafil* (Viagra), also can cause optic neuropathy.

My advice: Tell your doctor right away if you notice visual symptoms after starting any of these medications. "Ocular toxicity" usually begins within one year, with vision changes occurring in as little as six months. The vision changes usually will clear up once you stop the drug and switch to a different one, but in rare cases they may not.

• **Phenytoin (Dilantin).** This antiepilepsy drug is sometimes used, paradoxically, to treat neuropathic pain. Up to half of patients who take Dilantin for 15 years develop neuropathy. Many patients experience neuropathy sooner.

Neuropathies caused by the drug tend to be minor. These might include diminished (or absent) tendon reflexes in the legs that are barely noticeable, although some may observe that they're a bit unsteady when they walk.

My advice: Be sure to tell your doctor about your neuropathy symptoms. If they are mild, he may feel that the benefits of the drug outweigh the risks. More likely, your doctor will advise switching to one of the newer (but more expensive) antiepilepsy drugs, such as *lamotrigine* (Lamictal) or *topiramate* (Topamax), which do not cause neuropathy. If the medication is changed, neuropathy symptoms may or may not subside.

Very Common Drugs That Rob Your Body of Nutrients

Hyla Cass, MD, integrative physician in private practice in Los Angeles. She is author of several books, including *8 Weeks to Vibrant Health* and *Supplement Your Prescription: What Your Doctor Doesn't Know About Nutrition*. CassMD.com

If you're taking a prescription medication every day, it may be interfering with your nutrition—and your doctor may not know it. This problem is so common that I wrote the book *Supplement Your Prescription: What Your Doctor Doesn't Know About Nutrition*.

Fortunately, you can protect yourself. When I treat patients who are taking prescription medications, I almost always prescribe specific nutritional supplements to head off deficiencies that the drugs can cause.

Important: These are the minimum doses for my standard nutritional prescriptions. You may benefit from higher doses, which you should discuss with your health-care provider.

METFORMIN

If you take the diabetes medicine *metformin* (Glucophage, Glumetza, Fortamet), it can deplete vitamin B-12. Metformin also may deplete the body of the antioxidant and cardiovascular protector coenzyme Q10 (CoQ10). A study published in *Archives of Internal Medicine* showed that people with diabetes taking metformin had B-12 levels that were, on average, less than half the levels of people not taking the medication. Metformin also depletes folate (vitamin B-9). You most often will see this vitamin supplied as folic acid, which is then metabolized in the body to folate. (It also can be supplied as methylfolate for poor metabolizers of folic acid.)

Daily supplements needed…

- **Vitamin B-12 (1,000 mcg)**
- **Folic acid or methylfolate (400 mcg)**
- **CoQ10 (100 mg)**

CORTICOSTERIODS

Corticosteroids include *prednisone, prednisolone, betamethasone, budesonide, triamcinolone, cortisone* and *methylprednisolone*. While these anti-inflammatory drugs often are prescribed for short-term use to manage conditions such as allergic rashes, people with certain autoimmune conditions such as rheumatoid arthritis, Crohn's disease, ulcerative colitis and lupus often take them indefinitely. The nutrients they can deplete include calcium, folate, magnesium, potassium, selenium, vitamin D and zinc.

Daily supplements needed…

- **Calcium (600 mg).** *Note*: Most of your calcium should come from food.
- **Folate (400 mcg)**
- **Magnesium (400 mg)**
- **Potassium (99 mg)**
- **Selenium (100 mcg)**
- **Vitamin D (1,000 IU)**
- **Zinc (25 mg)**

ACE INHIBITORS

If you take an ACE inhibitor blood pressure drug such as *benazepril* (Lotensin), *enalapril* (Vasotec), *lisinopril* (Prinivil) or *ramipril* (Altace), it can deplete zinc.

Daily supplement needed: Zinc (25 mg).

CALCIUM CHANNEL BLOCKERS

Calcium channel blockers for high blood pressure such as *amlodipine* (Norvasc), *diltiazem* (Cardizem), *felodipine* (Plendil), *isradipine* (DynaCirc), *nicardipine* (Cardene), *nisoldipine* (Sular) or *verapamil* (Calan, Covera-HS, Isoptin, Verelan) deplete potassium.

Daily supplement needed: Potassium—the average daily requirement is 4.7 grams (4,700 mg), best obtained through eating potassium-rich foods including bananas, cooked spinach and many other fruits and vegetables. Supplements top out at 99 mg (found in your multi), while pharmaceutical supplements are higher but also contain a lot of unneeded chemicals. Have your potassium blood level checked, and go by your health practitioner's recommendation.

BETA-BLOCKERS

If you take a beta-blocker for high blood pressure and/or heart disease, it can deplete CoQ10.

Daily supplement needed: CoQ10 (100 mg).

STATINS

If you take a statin to reduce cholesterol, it can deplete the body of CoQ10, which is vital for heart health.

Daily supplement needed: CoQ10 (100 mg).

ANTIBIOTICS

If you take an antibiotic even for a short time, it can deplete the nutrients biotin, inositol, vitamins B-1 (thiamine), B-2 (riboflavin), B-3 (niacin), B-5 (pantothenic acid), B-6 (pyridoxine), B-12 (cyanocobalamin) and vitamin K—and interfere with the beneficial bacteria in your gut. *Also:* Fluoroquinolones (any antibiotic that has a generic name that ends with the suffix "-floxacin," including the well-known *ciprofloxacin*, aka Cipro) can deplete calcium and iron. Tetracyclines (ending with the suffix "-cycline") can deplete calcium and magnesium. Trimethoprim-containing antibiotics (Trimpex, Proloprim, Primsol) can deplete folic acid.

Penicillins (ending with the suffix "-cillin") can deplete potassium.

Daily supplements needed...

• **You needn't worry about how to find and take all those nutrients!** The doses of magnesium, calcium and other nutrients contained in a good multivitamin/mineral supplement should cover your needs for these nutrients during a course of antibiotic therapy.

• **Additionally, find a high-potency B-complex supplement that contains close to these ingredients and doses:** B-1 (25 mg), B-2 (25 mg), B-3 (50 mg), B-6 (50 mg), folic acid (400 mcg to 800 mcg), B-12 (10 mcg), biotin (50 mg) and B-5 (50 mg). A "B-50" formula generally will provide these levels.

• **B-12 (1,000 mcg),** taken in sublingual tablets for better absorption.

• **Vitamin K (30 mcg to 100 mcg)**

• **After a course of antibiotics,** take a probiotic supplement to restore the beneficial bacteria in your gut. Choose one that contains at least one billion live organisms per daily dose and includes both *Lactobacillus acidophilus* (*L. acidophilus*) and *Bifidobacterium bifidum* (*B. bifidum*).

BETTER WAY...

Talk About Your Meds!

Two-thirds of adults (ages 50 to 80) who take at least one prescription drug have not discussed drug interactions with their pharmacists or health-care providers within the last two years. Most of the 1,690 people surveyed had multiple doctors, and one in five bought medications from several pharmacies.

Why it matters: When drugs interact with one another (or with supplements, food or alcohol), it can decrease or increase a medication's potency...lead to side effects such as kidney problems...or, in rare cases, cause death.

Preeti Malani, MD, professor of internal medicine, University of Michigan, Ann Arbor.

When Your Medication Makes You Gain Weight

Jack E. Fincham, PhD, RPh, professor of pharmacy administration at Presbyterian College School of Pharmacy in Clinton, South Carolina. He is a panel member of the FDA Non-Prescription Drug Advisory Committee and Peripheral and Central Nervous System Drugs Advisory Committee.

Medications that you take to improve your health—including, paradoxically, some of the same drugs that are used to treat obesity-related illnesses—could be adding inches to your waistline.

Shocking fact: It's estimated that more than 500 widely used medications have weight gain as a possible side effect. It doesn't happen to everyone, but be suspicious if you notice that you've gained a few pounds (or more) soon after starting a new medication. In some cases, the extra pounds drop off if the drug is stopped—but not always.

Take action: If the scales start creeping upward, tell your doctor. In many cases, switching to a different type of medication—or even another drug in the same class—can help. If the medication is working well, you can instead ask your doctor about taking a lower dose. In some cases, this may stem the weight gain but still have a therapeutic effect. *Among the common suspects...*

• **SSRI antidepressants.** The emotional and physical tolls of depression are widely recognized. But most people don't realize that the risk for obesity could jump by as much as 58% if you're depressed...and, in a cruel twist, the most popular drugs for treating depression can cause even *more* weight gain.

Up to 25% of patients who take antidepressants, including the *selective serotonin reuptake inhibitors* (SSRIs), notice that they've gained weight. It's common for drugs such as *paroxetine* (Paxil) and *sertraline* (Zoloft) to trigger weight gain that totals 10 pounds or more.

*Always check with your doctor before stopping a prescribed medication or changing the dose. Making such changes without a physician's advice can cause serious side effects.

It is possible that the drugs' effects on serotonin, a neurotransmitter involved in mood, changes both appetite and the body's ability to metabolize nutrients. People who feel better after treating depression also may find that they're enjoying life (and food!) more than they did before. Weight gain mainly occurs in patients who have taken the drugs for more than six months.

My advice: Ask your doctor about switching to *venlafaxine* (Effexor XR) or *nefazodone* (Serzone). These antidepressants are effective but unlikely to cause weight gain. Another popular antidepressant, *bupropion* (Wellbutrin), can cause some people to lose weight.

• **Antihistamines.** You're unlikely to gain weight by taking an occasional antihistamine (for example, during allergy seasons—spring, summer and/or fall), but people who regularly take drugs such as *fexofenadine* (Allegra) or *cetirizine* (Zyrtec) often gain weight. It's believed that drugs used to block the effects of histamine may trigger brain changes that boost appetite.

Important finding: In a 2010 study published in *Obesity*, patients who took antihistamines daily to treat allergies had larger waist circumferences and higher insulin levels than those who didn't take these drugs.

My advice: If you think an antihistamine is affecting your weight, ask your doctor about switching to a nonsedating antihistamine, such as *loratadine* (Claritin). You won't have the drowsiness that can occur with older antihistamines (such as Benadryl). You'll likely have more energy and might burn more calories.

• **Diabetes drugs.** If you've been diagnosed with type 2 diabetes, there's a good chance that you're taking one of the *sulfonylureas*, a class of drugs that includes *chlorpropamide* (Diabinese) and *glyburide* (such as Micronase). They're useful drugs because they stimulate the pancreas to secrete more insulin, but they may cause weight gain.

Patients who take these drugs, which also can change how the body metabolizes carbohydrates and sugar, gain, on average, a total of about four pounds.

My advice: Talk to your doctor about *metformin*, a *biguanide* medication that helps improve the body's sensitivity to insulin and lowers the amount of sugar produced by the liver. This drug is less likely to cause weight gain and even could help obese people lose extra weight.

As an alternative, consider one of the newer, self-injectable drugs that have similar effects. *Liraglutide* (Victoza) is taken once daily… another injectable drug, *dulaglutide* (Trulicity), is taken once a week. The drugs closely mimic the body's natural insulin responses—and make weight gain less likely.

• **Tamoxifen (Nolvadex, Emblon, others).** It blocks the effects of estrogen on breast cells and is used for the treatment and prevention of breast cancer. Some studies have found that women who take it can gain a total of 20 pounds or more within one to three years.

When you're dealing with cancer, weight is probably not your greatest concern—but the extra pounds can increase your risk for diabetes and other health problems.

Important: It's not entirely clear if tamoxifen directly causes weight gain. Women with cancer often deal with depression, which could negatively affect their eating habits and activity levels. Other drugs that are used in cancer treatments, such as steroids, also can lead to weight gain.

My advice: As much as you can, try to make a healthy lifestyle—wholesome foods, regular exercise, etc.—part of your cancer care. If you're doing well on a brand-name version of tamoxifen, keep taking it. The drug has a *narrow therapeutic index*, which means that even slight variations in blood levels—which can occur when you switch to a generic—can decrease the effectiveness and/or cause weight gain or other side effects.

Tamoxifen usually is taken for five years, but some patients may be able to stop it after two to three years and use an aromatase inhibitor drug instead. Two of these drugs, *anastrozole* (Arimidex) and *exemestane* (Aromasin), are associated with less weight gain.

• **Divalproex sodium (Depakote)**. This drug, also known as valproic acid, is commonly prescribed for seizures, bipolar disorder and migraine prevention. It often increases appetite as well as cravings for fast-food fats and carbohydrates.

Important finding: A 2007 study published in *Seizure* found that about 24% of men and 44% of women gained significant amounts of weight (14 pounds, on average) after taking the drug for a year or more.

Other antiseizure drugs may also be used as mood stabilizers. Two of these medications, *carbamazepine* (Tegretol) and *oxcarbazepine* (Trileptal), may lead to weight gain, but a third drug, *lamotrigine* (Lamictal), is less likely to have this side effect. In fact, it may result in weight loss.

Lithium, another drug used to treat bipolar disorder, might (or might not) cause less weight gain than Depakote.

My advice: If you're taking Depakote, ask your doctor if other mood-stabilizing medications will work for you. If there is no viable substitute, exercise and a healthy diet are essential while taking this drug.

• **Atypical antipsychotics.** They can be life-saving medications for patients with schizophrenia or other psychiatric disorders, but they're known for causing serious weight gain. The drugs affect *dopamine* and *leptin*, substances in the body that impact both food cravings and appetite.

The older drugs for treating psychiatric conditions are known to cause *dystonic reactions*, such as involuntary muscle movements. The newer atypical drugs, including *clozapine* (Clozaril) and *olanzapine* (Zyprexa), don't generally have this unpleasant side effect, but about one-third of patients gain 10 to 30 pounds within the first year.

My advice: Never stop taking an antipsychotic medication without your doctor's advice—the mental health consequences can be severe. *Helpful*: Talk to your doctor about how to control weight gain when you first start taking the drug. Research has shown that patients who talk to their doctors about their weight concerns when beginning any

ANTIBIOTIC ALERTS...

Kidney Stone Danger

People taking *sulfa antibiotics* (such as Septra and Bactrim) were more than twice as likely to develop kidney stones within three to 12 months as those not taking oral antibiotics, according to an analysis of 286,000 children and adults covering 21 years.

Four additional classes/types of antibiotics also increased kidney stone risk but to a lesser degree—*cephalosporins* (Keflex)...*fluoroquinolones* (Cipro)...*nitrofurantoin* (Macrobid)/*methenamine* (Hiprex)...and *broad-spectrum penicillins.*

Gregory Tasian, MD, pediatric urologist, Children's Hospital of Philadelphia.

Beware This New Antibiotic Danger

Fluoroquinolone antibiotics, such as *ciprofloxacin* (Cipro) and *levofloxacin* (Levaquin), double the risk for an aortic aneurysm or dissection, according to four studies reviewed by the FDA. Patients most at risk for this potentially deadly complication include those with a history of aortic aneurysm or high blood pressure.

If you are prescribed a fluoroquinolone: Ask your doctor if it is right for you. In some cases, such as pneumonia, the benefits may outweigh the risks.

Robert Steven Gold, RPh, affiliate instructor of clinical pharmacy, Purdue University, West Lafayette, Indiana, and author of *Are Your Medications Making You Sick?*

new medication—and who follow up with healthier eating and other lifestyle changes—often can lose weight and/or keep it off during treatment.

However, with any drug that causes weight gain, you may need the medication to treat a specific medical condition. Once the condition is under control, you then can focus on weight loss if needed.

Are Too Many Medications Making Your Life Worse?

Barbara Farrell, PharmD, assistant professor in the department of family medicine and an adjunct assistant professor in the School of Pharmacy, both at University of Waterloo, Canada. She was named Pharmacist of the Year by the Canadian Pharmacist Association in 2011 and is cofounder of the Canadian Deprescribing Network. Follow her research team on Twitter (@deprescribing). Deprescribing.org

It happens for the best of reasons. Your cardiologist, say, prescribes one medication, then you see your endocrinologist and get another, and your rheumatologist gives you another—and the doctors don't talk to one another. Each is trying to help you—but collectively, they could be hurting you...possibly badly.

Polypharmacy—taking a combination of medications that does more harm than good—is a national epidemic, and it's getting worse. The truth is, our medical system is a lot better at prescribing medications than at stopping ones that are no longer needed—*deprescribing*. Yet doing so, carefully and under medical supervision, reduces the adverse side effects and often improves health. Would it help you to deprescribe?

A SNEAKY MULTIPLICATION

Polypharmacy can happen before you know it. *Case in point*: Many medications, regardless of the conditions they're prescribed for, can have depression as a side effect. They include certain blood pressure drugs...heart drugs...drugs for heartburn (proton pump inhibitors)...even painkillers. The more of these drugs you take, the higher your statistical risk of developing depression.

Polypharmacy also is associated with a host of other adverse effects including an increased risk for falls and cognitive impairment that can lead to emergency room visits and hospitalization. The problem often gets worse as you get older—you're not only likely to need more medications, but your body's ability to process those medications declines. A drug or dosage that was appropriate when initially prescribed might no longer be safe or appropriate. However, polypharmacy can happen *at any age*.

A "MIRACULOUS" RECOVERY

You now understand polypharmacy. For an idea of how deprescribing can work, consider this case study...

The woman sat slumped over in her chair—and then slid out onto the floor when she tried to stand. She had been diagnosed with dementia and was on the waiting list for a long-term-care facility, where she seemed likely to live out her remaining days. Instead, 10 weeks later, she was walking and living an active life. Her long-term-care stay had been canceled—her doctors realized that she did not even have dementia!

What changed? A medical team reviewed this woman's case and discovered that she was taking 32 prescription medications each day—and together, the medications that had been prescribed to help this woman instead were ruining her life. The review team gradually eliminated 15 of those drugs and reduced the dosages of several others.

For most, polypharmacy's effects are subtler. And to determine whether it's happening to you, you probably will need to press your doctor or doctors. Most physicians are far more likely to write prescriptions than to review and eliminate them. That's slowly changing, but for now it's up to you to take the lead. *Here's how...*

• **Make a medications list.** It's a good idea to put all your prescription drugs, over-the-counter medications, vitamins and other supplements in a bag and bring them to your doctor and ask for a review. But also bring a list of each of these, including dosages, to help your doctor review them accurately and quickly. Group drugs together on the list by their purpose—heart drugs, pain drugs, etc.

• **Call your doctor's attention to medications that are likely to be problematic.** Certain kinds of prescription drugs, if used long term, are particularly likely to cause problems...

• Sleeping pills

• Blood sugar drugs (especially sulfonylurea drugs)

• Blood pressure drugs (especially if they lead to low-pressure episodes)

• Narcotic pain drugs

• Heartburn/GERD drugs (proton pump inhibitors)

• Ask your doctor—or doctors—to review all your medications. You might start a conversation this way—"I read an article about the dangers of polypharmacy, and I want to take a serious look at all of the medications I am taking..." For any particular medication, you might ask, "Is this prescription and dosage a problem to take for as long as I've been on it? Is it appropriate for my age? Could I be on a lower dose?" If you see several specialists, have this conversation with each one.

• If you are prescribed medications after a hospital stay, follow up with your own doctor. According to a study of elderly patients discharged from 11 Veterans Affairs medical centers, 44% were prescribed one or more unnecessary drugs.

And even if the medications are appropriate for you at discharge, ask your doctor—or the hospital pharmacist—which ones you can stop taking a few weeks or a month later.

AVOID FUTURE UNNECESSARY PRESCRIPTIONS

To reduce your odds of being given unnecessary prescriptions in the first place...

• If you develop a new health problem, raise the possibility that drugs are causing it. Ask, "Could this be a side effect of any of the drugs I'm currently taking or the combination of drugs?" It might not be, but you'll ensure that your doctor considers that possibility.

• Ask the following questions about any new medication—how long should you take it...how will you know whether it's working... and what side effects should you watch for.

• Explore lifestyle changes that can reduce the need for certain prescriptions. *Example*: Consider relaxation techniques before resorting to sleeping pills. Jot down your questions before you see your doctor.

• Talk to your pharmacist. With any new prescription, raise the question of polypharmacy with your pharmacist. If he/she has a concern that your doctor did not bring up, ask

him to call your doctor's office to resolve the situation.

Helpful: Use the same pharmacy for all your prescriptions. That increases the odds that the pharmacist will spot potentially problematic drug interactions even before you ask about them.

• Be aware of the risks of stopping certain medications too quickly. Discontinuing certain prescription drugs can cause side effects—and some can be dangerous. This is especially true for certain classes of medications including antidepressants, blood pressure drugs called beta-blockers and sleeping pills. But there are others, too. So don't reduce or stop any drug without guidance from your doctor...and if a doctor does recommend ending a drug, ask whether it needs to be tapered and, if so, ask for detailed instructions on how to do that properly.

The OTC Painkiller Trap: Most People Don't Know What's Safest

Leslie Kernisan, MD, MPH, clinical instructor, division of geriatrics, University of California, San Francisco. Board-certified in both geriatrics and internal medicine, she is founder of BetterHealthWhileAging. net, a website that provides practical information for older adults and family caregivers. She has a geriatric consultation practice in the Bay Area and writes about geriatrics and new technologies at GeriTech.org.

Many people assume that over-the-counter (OTC) drugs are less likely to cause dangerous side effects than their prescription counterparts. But that's not always true—especially when it comes to pain-relieving medications.

The nonsteroidal anti-inflammatory drugs (NSAIDs), a class of painkillers that includes *ibuprofen* (such as Advil and Motrin), *naproxen* (such as Aleve) and aspirin, cause more than 100,000 hospitalizations and 7,000 to 16,500 deaths each year.

Acetaminophen, the active ingredient in products such as Tylenol, Panadol and others, is generally safer than NSAIDs. But even this drug, the most popular painkiller worldwide, can cause liver damage and liver failure at too-high doses.

The problem: It's common for people who have chronic pain—whether it's from a bad back, persistent headaches or a bum knee—to take *multiple* doses daily and continue using the drug month after month, greatly increasing the dangers. This is particularly true for older adults, who metabolize drugs differently than younger people and are more likely to have health conditions (such as impaired kidney function) that increase the risks even more.

A SAFER CHOICE

You've likely heard that acetaminophen isn't helpful for painful conditions that involve inflammation, such as arthritis and joint injuries. Studies generally find that NSAIDs are a bit more effective than acetaminophen for arthritis pain, which is one of the main reasons that older adults use OTC painkillers. Still, since acetaminophen is so much safer (when used at recommended doses) than NSAIDs, I almost always advise older adults to try acetaminophen first.

Important: Acetaminophen stops being safe when people exceed the recommended dose. This can happen when people think that they need a higher dose...or when they (often unknowingly) use other products that contain it.

Acetaminophen is an ingredient in dozens of OTC medications, including sleep aids (such as Tylenol PM) and cold and flu remedies (NyQuil and Theraflu). It's also used in some prescription painkillers (such as Vicodin). If you don't check ingredient labels, you could wind up taking far more than the recommended limit of 3,000 mg per day. (Aiming to take less than 2,000 mg per day is even safer.)

To prevent liver damage, people with a history of alcohol abuse—or those who drink alcohol frequently—definitely shouldn't take more than 2,000 mg daily. I advise patients who take daily doses of acetaminophen for long-term problems (such as arthritis) to ask their doctors if their liver enzymes should be checked—either occasionally or regularly.

USE CAUTION WITH NSAIDs

NSAIDs, such as ibuprofen and naproxen, are *never* my first choice because they fre-

quently cause stomach/intestinal bleeding... increase blood pressure...and lead to kidney damage in those who already have impaired kidney function.

Sobering caution: In 2015, the FDA strengthened existing label warnings on non-aspirin NSAIDs to alert consumers about the increased risk for heart attack and stroke, which can occur even in the first weeks of using one of these drugs—especially when taken at higher doses...and in people with and without heart disease.

Caveat: Because some people get more relief from an NSAID than from acetaminophen, it's sometimes reasonable to accept the risks of using an NSAID for a short time, such as a few days to a week. But even then, I am cautious about recommending them for patients who take blood thinners (NSAIDs have a blood-thinning effect) or have impaired kidney function or other health problems.

My advice: It's probably OK for older adults to take an *occasional* NSAID if they feel acetaminophen doesn't provide enough relief...but these drugs are not safe for daily use. People with arthritis or other long-term conditions should talk to their doctors about nondrug ways to manage pain, such as weight loss, physical therapy, exercise and cognitive behavioral therapy—all of which have been proven to be effective.

More from Dr. Leslie Kernisan...

The Topical Option

If you feel that you need an NSAID for pain relief, using a topical cream or gel reduces some of the risks. Topical NSAIDs used for musculoskeletal pain are effective, according to a Cochrane (a nonprofit group that evaluates medical treatments) review.

My advice: If your stomach can't handle oral NSAIDs—and acetaminophen doesn't seem to work—a topical drug (including OTC topical aspirin, such as Bengay, Aspercreme and other products with salicylate listed on the label) might be worth a try. Some people may also get relief from capsaicin cream.

WHAT ABOUT ASPIRIN?

Doctors today almost *never* recommend aspirin as a pain reliever. Even at low doses (81 mg), it increases the risk for GI bleeding and for cerebral hemorrhage…and the risks for complications are higher among older adults and those with high blood pressure or other chronic diseases.

Aspirin is most likely to cause bleeding and other side effects when it's taken at doses of more than 100 mg daily for months or longer. But even low doses, as mentioned above, can be risky. Because of these risks, I try to discourage patients from taking aspirin as a pain reliever.

Exception: If you've had a heart attack or stroke, your doctor might advise you to take a daily aspirin (typically 81 mg) to prevent blood clots and a subsequent heart attack/stroke. The benefits of this so-called *secondary prevention* are believed to outweigh the risks.

However, experts no longer recommend aspirin for *primary prevention* (preventing a first heart attack/stroke) except for certain high-risk patients—for example, someone who has received a stent or has diabetes and another risk factor such as smoking or high blood pressure. Unless a person is at relatively high risk for a cardiovascular event, the risk of bleeding from a daily baby aspirin is generally higher than the chance of avoiding a heart attack or stroke due to this therapy.

Are You Addicted to Painkillers? It's Easy to Cross That Line

Mel Pohl, MD, chief medical officer of Las Vegas Recovery Center in Nevada, where he played a key role in developing the center's chronic pain recovery program. Certified by the American Board of Addiction Medicine and a distinguished fellow of the American Society of Addiction Medicine, Dr. Pohl is coauthor of several books, including *The Pain Antidote* and *Pain Recovery.* LasVegasRecovery.com

---

H ere's a common scenario—you've had surgery…or you threw your back out carrying groceries. To help you get over that distressing hump, your doctor prescribes an opioid painkiller—a class of drugs that includes *morphine, codeine* and *hydrocodone* (Vicodin) and newer heavyweights such as *oxycodone* (OxyContin) and *fentanyl* (Duragesic).

But a few weeks or even months later, the pain is still nagging you. Your doctor agrees to refill your prescription. Considering the daily drumbeat of scary statistics related to painkiller use and abuse, you'd think it wouldn't be so easy to get a steady supply of these drugs.

But it often is, and the consequences are dire. In the US alone, more than 42,000 deaths from drug overdoses in 2016 were blamed on opioids. This translates into 115 Americans dying *each day* from an opioid overdose. A large percentage of these opioid users begin using the drug to treat pain.

DRIVING HOME THE DANGERS

Pain is a very real problem. More than one in four Americans have suffered from pain that lasts over 24 hours, according to the National Center for Health Statistics, and chronic pain is the most common cause of long-term disability.

But new research drives home the startling fact that opioids—once introduced—are habit-forming. A 2017 study involving 1.3 million noncancer patients showed that 12% of people prescribed an initial six-day supply of an opioid painkiller were still taking the drug a year later. Those odds doubled to 24% if a 12-day supply was prescribed. When a month-long course of opioid pain medication was prescribed, 30% were still taking a painkiller a year later.

Clearly, short-term prescriptions can create long-term problems if we don't pay close attention to our use of these medications. It's surprisingly easy for a person to inadvertently become dependent on these drugs…or even addicted.

DEPENDENCE VS. ADDICTION

In the world of addiction treatment, there are subtle but important differences between dependence and addiction. The distinction helps guide treatment decisions. *What each means…*

• **Dependence** is the steady use of a drug that stops short of addiction. It happens when you find yourself taking higher and higher doses of a painkiller over time to achieve the same level of relief from a physical condition. This is known as tolerance. As the cycle progresses, you become physically dependent on the drug...and can't stop taking it without experiencing withdrawal symptoms. People keep taking the drug to avoid the distressing withdrawal symptoms they suffer between doses.

Physical withdrawal symptoms include tremors, sweats, nausea, vomiting and diarrhea. People who are dependent on a drug also may become depressed and anxious, have trouble sleeping or feel withdrawn without the drug. But in the case of dependence alone (not addiction), you're not getting "high" or intoxicated by the painkiller and you don't crave it—you're just searching for continued pain *relief*. While dependence usually takes hold after 10 to 30 days, it can occur in as little as a week's time.

• **Addiction is more serious.** When you are addicted to a drug, in addition to tolerance and physical dependence, you will crave it when it's not being used—sometimes months or years after the drug was last in your system—even when you're not feeling pain. When addiction sets in, you'll use more of the pain medication than intended (a hallmark of addiction known as "loss of control") and/or continue to use it despite the occurrence of serious harm or consequences.

It's a disease involving the brain's reward pathways and a vulnerability to having an enhanced response to mood-altering drugs, including painkillers. Some people will use these medications for their effects on mood (for example, to feel energetic, less depressed and less anxious), while others are genetically or environmentally predisposed to this intensified response.

DO YOU HAVE A PROBLEM?

To be diagnosed with addiction or dependence, you need to be assessed by a professional such as a psychologist, psychiatrist, addiction physician or drug-and-alcohol counselor. But you can begin to consider whether

you might have a problem by answering the questions below. The more questions you answer with "yes," the greater the odds that you've got a potential problem and should see a medical professional.

1. As time passes, do you find yourself needing to increase the frequency or dose of your medication before pain returns?

2. Are you increasingly preoccupied by thoughts of taking the painkiller between doses?

3. Are you experiencing mood changes or changes in your motivation level?

4. Are you noticing problems with your ability to think, concentrate or remember things?

5. Are you experiencing new sleep disturbances, such as the inability to stay asleep?

6. Have you gone to another doctor because the first wouldn't renew your prescription for more medication or increase your dose?

7. Have you ever lied to anyone about how much medication you're actually taking?

8. Have you ever run out of a prescription before you were supposed to because you used more than was prescribed?

HOW TO SEEK HELP

What should you do if you realize that you're in trouble? No one wants to be labeled an "addict," but fear of that diagnosis shouldn't keep you from seeking expert help. Do not attempt to stop taking your medication cold turkey—this approach may actually be physically dangerous because it will precipitate withdrawal, which can lead to changes in blood pressure, pulse and even cardiac function due to hyperactivity of the nervous system.

Depending on your individual situation, outpatient or inpatient care may be necessary to properly supervise your withdrawal process. A specialist can assess your situation and make a treatment referral—self-diagnosis and selection of treatment are rarely enough. Seek professional help. To find an addiction specialist, consult the American Society of Addiction Medicine at ASAM.org.

Possible Opioid Alternative

Tylenol plus Advil can work as well as opioids for pain severe enough to bring people to the emergency room. People reporting moderate-to-severe pain in their arms or legs from sprains, strains or fractures were given *acetaminophen* (Tylenol) with *ibuprofen* (Advil) or with oxycodone, hydrocodone or codeine. Two hours later, people given any of the combinations reported essentially the same reduction in pain. If your doctor prescribes an opioid, ask if Tylenol plus Advil might be an alternative.

Andrew K. Chang, MD, chair of emergency medicine, Albany Medical College, New York, and leader of a study of 416 men and women, published in *JAMA*.

Many Older Adults Leave the Hospital in Worse Shape: Avoid This Fate!

Elizabeth Eckstrom, MD, MPH, professor and chief of geriatrics in the division of general internal medicine & geriatrics at Oregon Health & Science University in Portland. Dr. Eckstrom is coauthor, with Marcy Cottrell Houle, MS, of *The Gift of Caring: Saving Our Parents from the Perils of Modern Healthcare.*

No one loves hospitals. But we need them. If you are over age 70, however, there is a one in three chance that you will leave the hospital in *worse overall shape* than before you got sick or injured. The phenomenon has become so pervasive that health professionals have dubbed such a problem a "hospitalization-associated disability"—caused not by your illness or injury but by your hospitalization.

But it doesn't have to be that way. *Here are eight secrets that can protect you or a loved one from a downward spiral in the hospital…*

SECRET #1: **Start out strong.** As we age, we lose muscle mass and our hearts and lungs work less efficiently. But we are not helpless.

A regular exercise routine—including moves to get your heart pumping, increase strength and improve balance—can help stave off frailty. That will put you in better fighting shape should you ever require hospitalization. So will a nutritious diet. A Mediterranean-style diet, which is rich in fruits, vegetables, nuts, fish and healthy oils, is an ideal choice.

If you know that you are going to have surgery or go into a hospital for some other reason, ask your health-care providers about *prehabilitation* (also known as "prehab")—an exercise-and-nutrition program designed to prepare you for the rigors ahead. Specific therapies are available that will help reduce your chances of functional decline from surgery, cancer treatments or other health issues. Depending on your insurance plan, therapy and counseling prescribed by your doctors related to prehab may be covered.

SECRET #2: **Document your baseline.** Every older adult should (with assistance, if needed) fill out and routinely update a health history sheet, listing health-care providers, medications, major medical problems and, crucially, details about how independently the person handles "activities of daily living," such as walking, dressing, bathing, housework and navigating the community. This is each individual's "baseline"—and you want to make sure that all the doctors seeing you or your loved one in a crisis know what it is. Otherwise, they might not realize when you have suffered a setback.

SECRET #3: **Stay oriented.** When hospitalized, many otherwise sharp older adults can develop delirium, an acute state of confusion brought on by an acute medical illness, in just a few days. If you have dementia or memory problems, you are even more likely to develop delirium in the hospital. So it's important to do everything you can to keep yourself or a loved one oriented to reality.

Wear your hearing aids and glasses. If the hospital asks to send either of these home for safety, a family member or friend should try to bring these items in for at least several hours per day to ensure that the older adult can participate in conversations, health planning and therapy sessions. Stick to as many daily routines as possible, including getting up to dress, wash up and use the toilet, if possible.

Also: Brush and floss your teeth at least twice a day. This will help you feel more like yourself, and some research suggests that it may even help stave off pneumonia by reducing the amount of oral bacteria that can migrate into the lungs.

SECRET #4: **Mind the meds.** Ask the medical staff about the risks and side effects of any new medications prescribed. Watch out especially for any that are on the American Geriatrics Society's Beers Criteria of drugs that are potentially inappropriate for adults over age 65 (known as the Beers list).* Some of these medications can cause confusion and other side effects that raise the risk for hospital-associated declines.

If you or your loved one is prescribed one of these drugs, ask to speak with the physician and/or pharmacist about safer alternatives or lower doses.

SECRET #5: **Get moving.** Within the first week of being in bed, some older adults lose the ability to walk independently. Unused muscles quickly become stiffer and smaller. Lung function declines.

Anyone who can get out of bed should do it—even if it just means shuffling to a nearby chair or the bathroom a few times a day. And don't depend on flimsy hospital slippers. Walking shoes with good tread and a closed heel are best to prevent falls. Some walking-shoe companies (such as ASICS) make a slip-on walking shoe that is easier to get on and off in the hospital.

If a patient must be in bed, a physical therapist should be called in on day one to prescribe bed exercises and make a plan to get the patient up and moving as soon as possible. Nurses should turn immobile patients in bed every two to four hours to prevent bedsores.

SECRET #6: **Speak up for sleep.** Despite widespread calls for change, some hospitals still disturb sleeping patients—at all hours of the night—to check vital signs and perform

*For a copy of the list, go to AmericanGeriatrics.org and search "Beers Criteria." Then click on "Updated AGS Beers Criteria."

INTERESTING FINDING...

Older Surgeons Have Lower Patient Death Rates

Among 892,187 Medicare patients who had one of 20 types of emergency surgery (such as hysterectomy or a heart valve procedure), those performed by surgeons who were age 50 and older had lower death rates during the four-year study period than procedures done by younger surgeons.

Yusuke Tsugawa, MD, PhD, assistant professor, David Geffen School of Medicine, UCLA, Los Angeles.

other care. If that's happening, ask if it's necessary and if you or your loved one might be left to sleep from 10 pm to 6 am. If there is no medical reason to interrupt your sleep during the night, ask the doctor to write an order to not disturb you between those hours.

Also helpful: Open the window blinds during the day, and turn off the lights at night to keep your sleep-wake cycle on track…and stick to mealtimes and other day and night routines. Earplugs can decrease the inevitable hospital noises.

SECRET #7: **Pay attention to fluids.** Dehydration can lead to delirium, urinary infections and constipation, all of which can be major contributors to hospital-associated declines. So make sure that you or your loved one drinks plenty of water (at least 48 ounces daily).

SECRET #8: **Don't go it alone.** It's always a good idea to have a loved one with you at the hospital to watch out for signs of trouble and communicate with the medical staff. Having someone stay overnight is ideal. *Also:* Some hospitals have units, known as Acute Care of the Elderly (ACE) units, staffed by teams of geriatric specialists. Such units have been shown to reduce the risks for functional decline and increase the chances that patients will be discharged back to their homes instead of to nursing homes or other care facilities.

Ask if any hospital near you has an ACE unit. If not, then ask if there's a geriatrician on the hospital staff who could see the patient if needed.

3

Cures for Common Conditions

---

20 Cures for 5 Embarrassing Problems

From dandruff flakes crowning our heads right down to corns on our toes, and other body parts in between, we all experience our share of minor but embarrassing health problems. A stye on the eye? Unsightly wart on the hand? A certain, well, odor that no one wants to claim? It's all part of being human, but you don't have to live with it.

Here, we share some of our favorite remedies from health experts in a range of disciplines including conventional Western medicine, naturopathic medicine, Traditional Chinese medicine, herbalism and homeopathy (see Discipline Key on next page).

Any health problem that could be a sign of something serious should, of course, be checked out by a doctor. But once you've ruled out anything serious and still are left with one of the embarrassing problems here, consult the options and choose the remedy that's right for you—or try several.

DANDRUFF

Many people mistakenly think the cause of their flakes is a too-dry scalp. It's not. Like all skin cells, dead scalp skin naturally sloughs off as new cells form underneath. With dandruff, the shedding is excessive, which can lead not only to visible flakes but also intense itchiness. The condition may be hereditary, and stress and anxiety can contribute.

• **Eat these foods.** Pears, celery, spinach, daikon radishes, carrots, brown rice, fish, oysters and mussels help prevent dandruff. **TCM**

• **Use grapefruit seed extract.** A few drops added to your shampoo can help tame an

---

Bottom Line's 1,000 Cures for 200 Ailments: Integrative Medicine for the Most Common Illnesses with Christine Gustafson, MD, Maura Sughrue, MD, Zhuoling Ren, TCMD, Beth MacEoin, MNCHM, RSHom and Geo Espinosa, ND, LAc, IFMCP, CNS. For more information about the complete book or to order it, go to BottomLineStore.com.

overgrowth of scalp fungus (dandruff may be the inflammatory response to the fungus). Leave shampoo in your hair for three to five minutes before rinsing. Antifungal shampoos with tea tree oil or selenium also can help. **N**

• **Take supplements.** B-complex (100 mg) and biotin (1,000 mcg to 3,000 mcg), taken together with meals, help treat dandruff. **N**

• **Soothe your scalp.** Research has shown that a 30% aloe lotion applied twice daily for four to six weeks improved dandruff. For inflamed patches, rub on a cream made from calendula and chamomile flowers. **HE**

WARTS

These benign tumors are caused by the *human papillomavirus* (HPV). Warts on the hands usually are near the nails or on the fingers and appear either solo or in clusters, shaped like tiny cauliflowers. They may itch and bleed.

• **Wrap in duct tape.** Cover the wart area with duct tape, and leave it on for a week. Remove the tape, soak the wart and debride it with a pumice stone. Wait a day, and repeat the whole process. Repeat as needed until the wart is gone. **CM**

• **Use 17% salicylic acid.** Purchase salicylic acid over the counter, and apply it twice a day to a clean, dry wart, then bandage the area. **CM**

• **Try a raw garlic patch.** Garlic has antiviral properties. Cover the wart and skin around it with a thin layer of castor oil or olive oil, top it with a thin slice of fresh garlic and tape it in place. Leave this on overnight. Repeat nightly for up to three weeks. (The wart will turn black as it dies.) **N**

• **Apply bittersweet nightshade.** The topical application of this plant as an ointment, available in health-food stores, has been shown to be effective in the removal of warts. **HE**

Immune-boosting advice: Avoid alcohol and convenience foods that are packed with chemical additives. Eat foods that are rich in antioxidants such as tomatoes, strawberries, peppers, citrus fruit, blueberries and broccoli.

Discipline Key:

CM = Conventional medicine
TCM = Traditional Chinese medicine
N = Naturopathy
HE = Herbalism
HO = Homeopathy

STYES

A bacterial infection that starts at the root of an eyelash, a stye forms an inflamed bump that looks like a small boil. It reddens and fills with pus and can be both itchy and sore. Usually styes come to a head and burst within seven days, but treatment can help a stye resolve faster. Try not to touch your eyes when you have one, as the infection is easily spread.

• **Apply a compress.** Using a sterile gauze pad soaked in warm water may help in the early stages. Or make an herbal compress—dilute five drops of tincture of eyebright or chamomile (both are infection fighters) or plantain or marigold (both are soothing) in one-quarter cup of water, and soak a gauze pad in the solution. Apply to the stye for 10 minutes three to four times a day. **CM, N**

• **Take Yin Qiao Je Du Pain.** This herbal pill can clear infection and is effective against styes. Find it in Traditional Chinese medicine stores. **TCM**

• **Supplement with zinc.** It's a known immune system strengthener and helps you heal faster. Take 30 mg to 50 mg daily. **N**

• **Use Pulsatilla.** This sublingual remedy may help if your stye is particularly itchy and crusty in the morning when you wake up. **HO**

CORNS

These harmless but often painful and unsightly yellowish bumps are caused by a buildup of hard, dead skin, usually on the toes and other parts of the feet. People with high arches are susceptible because of the increased downward pressure on the toes. Proper-fitting shoes are critical to prevent friction or toe cramping.

• **Find relief with moleskin.** Apply a patch to relieve painful pressure. **N**

• **Soften skin with calendula salve.** Apply this moisturizer/antiseptic two or three times a day. **N, HO**

• **Soak, then rub.** Soak the affected foot daily in a solution of Epsom salts and warm water for 10 minutes to soften the corn, then gently rub it with a pumice stone to remove the dead skin. If you cut the corn or it bleeds, you may need to see a doctor to prevent infection (pus or clear fluid is a sign of this). **N**

•**File, then apply salicylic acid.** Use a file or pumice stone to remove excess skin first. Afterward, apply 40% salicylic acid (available over the counter) to an area a bit larger than the corn and place a corn ring (also over the counter) on top to relieve pressure. Or apply essential oil of wintergreen, which contains salicylates, to the corn at night and wash it off in the morning to prevent irritating surrounding skin. Be sure to use natural, not synthetic, oil of wintergreen. **CM, HE**

Cautionary tip: Anyone with diabetes or circulatory problems in the feet should consult a medical provider before trying to remove a corn.

FLATULENCE

Everyone passes gas over the course of the day, but sometimes it happens too frequently.

Usual culprits: Having too much gas in the large intestine as bacteria act on undigested food, swallowing air while eating or chewing gum, consuming a lot of fiber if your system isn't used to it or a food intolerance. Flatulence also is a symptom of a number of diseases including irritable bowel syndrome, diverticulosis or diverticulitis, celiac disease and thyroid dysfunction. *The remedies below are for the occasional normal bout…*

•**Swallow a probiotic.** Take a combination of *Acidophilus*, *Lactobacillus* and *S. boulardii* daily for 30 days to improve your overall intestinal health. Or take 4 g of glutamine, an over-the-counter amino acid supplement, each day. **N**

•**Try an elimination diet.** There are a surprising number of foods that can upset the stomach and lead to gas. Start with the biggies—stop eating gluten, dairy, soy and processed foods for three weeks, and then reintroduce them one at a time to see if flatulence resumes. **CM**

•**Sip an herbal tea.** Peppermint tea can ease upper gastrointestinal gas and spasms. Ginger tea, brewed with fresh ginger slices, stimulates digestion and reduces gas. Or make fennel tea—pour a cup of boiling water over one to two teaspoons of freshly crushed, dried seeds, let it steep for 10 minutes, strain it and drink before or after meals. **HE, N**

•**Stimulate pressure points.** Try acupressure to move stomach and intestinal energy. While seated, exert pressure with a fingertip for one minute, then repeat.

Where to press: Use the Susanli point on the lower leg, one inch to the outside of and three inches below the kneecap, and the San Yin Jiao point on the inside of the leg, about three inches above the anklebone. Perform on each leg two to three times a day. **TCM**

Eating tip: Prevent flatulence by eating slowly and chewing thoroughly so that your saliva's digestive enzymes can mix with food and begin breaking it down.

Don't Forget Good Old Witch Hazel for Common Ailments

Jamison Starbuck, ND, a naturopathic physician in family practice, Missoula, Montana, and writer and producer of *Dr. Starbuck's Health Tips for Kids*, a weekly program on Montana Public Radio, MTPR.org. She is a past president of the American Association of Naturopathic Physicians and a contributing editor to *The Alternative Advisor: The Complete Guide to Natural Therapies and Alternative Treatments.* DrJamisonStarbuck.com

---

With all the fancy pills and potions that fill most of our medicine cabinets these days, we often forget about the remarkable healing powers of certain "old-fashioned" remedies such as witch hazel. It is still a useful and unique medicine that deserves a place in everyone's home medicine cabinet.

As you probably know, witch hazel is an astringent herb—a plant medicine that makes body tissues contract. Scientists believe that the natural substances known as tannins in astringent plants cause this tightening action. *Conditions that can be effectively treated with one of my favorite go-to natural remedies…*

• **Hemorrhoids.** These swollen and bulging blood vessels in the rectum can be internal or can protrude externally. As any hemorrhoid sufferer knows, they hurt and sometimes bleed. Thankfully, however, witch hazel lessens the throbbing, achy pain of hemorrhoids and reduces their swelling and tendency to bleed. In fact, it works as well as over-the-counter (OTC) hemorrhoid products.

For external hemorrhoids, soak a six-inch by six-inch cloth with witch hazel. I recommend adding one-half teaspoon of witch hazel tincture (a highly concentrated form that's available where botanical medicine is sold) to four ounces of OTC witch hazel. This will make the solution stronger and more effective. Apply the cloth directly to the hemorrhoid and leave it there for 10 minutes. Do this three times a day until the swelling and pain subside.

For internal hemorrhoids, use rectal suppositories made from witch hazel (available at many pharmacies and online). I recommend suppositories that contain witch hazel as well as cocoa butter and other soothing herbs, such as calendula and chamomile. Insert one suppository nightly for at least one week until the pain is diminished.

For both types of hemorrhoids, use witch hazel as soon as symptoms (including pain and swelling) occur.

• **Anal fissures.** These small tears in the anus cause sharp pain and bleed a little with bowel movements. To get relief, soak a cotton ball with liberal amounts of OTC witch hazel and swab the fissure after each bowel movement and at bedtime. Gently blot dry with toilet paper.

• **Acne and razor rash.** Witch hazel helps heal skin inflammation and mild infections. It's great for acne—especially "whiteheads." You also can use witch hazel to treat "barber rash"—or to prevent razor rash, no matter where you shave, by splashing it on your skin immediately after shaving.

• **Allergies and sinusitis.** To soothe irritated nasal passages due to allergies and to reduce the copious mucus that can accompany sinusitis, add one-quarter to one-half teaspoon of witch hazel to four ounces of saline solution to use in a neti pot. The witch hazel will make OTC saline solution more astringent to help dry mucus. Use this solution for nasal irrigation and rinse whenever you have allergy or sinusitis symptoms.

• **Itchy skin and bug bites.** Simply splash witch hazel on your skin as often as needed for relief from bug bites (such as bites from flies and mosquitoes). Some people find witch hazel, which evaporates quickly, more comfortable and effective than the sticky residue of calamine lotion.

Natural Fix for Colds, Sore Throat and More

Jamison Starbuck, ND, a naturopathic physician in family practice, Missoula, Montana, and writer and producer of *Dr. Starbuck's Health Tips for Kids*, a weekly program on Montana Public Radio, MTPR.org. She is a past president of the American Association of Naturopathic Physicians and a contributing editor to *The Alternative Advisor: The Complete Guide to Natural Therapies and Alternative Treatments*. DrJamisonStarbuck.com

It might be hard to believe that something that's been used as medicine for literally thousands of years could be as effective as an over-the-counter (OTC) drug. But it's true. Essential oils—aromatic oils made from the fragrant parts of various plants—were first used by ancient cultures. But they are now popular among consumers of natural medicine—and for good reason.

Unlike OTC decongestants that can spike blood pressure and OTC antihistamines that can cause drowsiness and other unwanted effects, essential oils battle winter ailments safely and without adverse effects. Your best bet is to use essential oils in diluted topical applications that can be inhaled and improve circulation where applied. This form of aromatherapy works particularly well with respiratory complaints.

Caveat: Because essential oils are very concentrated, when used incorrectly they can irritate or burn the skin and mucous membranes (such as the inside of the mouth and nose)

and even the stomach if swallowed. That said, essential oils are high on my list of go-to natural remedies.

Some of my favorites for winter (with instructions for safety)...*

For the common cold: **Spearmint.** Spearmint is less irritating to sensitive, inflamed nasal passages than the more frequently used peppermint or eucalyptus.

What to do: Mix the spearmint essential oil in a carrier oil (such as almond or coconut oil), using a 1:10 ratio. Then put two drops of this mixture above your upper lip—one just below each nostril. This will reduce stuffiness and thin nasal mucus, allowing you to blow your nose effectively and to breathe more easily. Use spearmint oil in this way three times a day.

For sinusitis: **Chamomile.** Because bacteria are common causes of sinusitis, chamomile's antibacterial properties make it good medicine for this annoying and often painful condition.

What to do: Mix the chamomile essential oil with a carrier oil in a 1:10 ratio (as described above). Then put several drops of this mixture on your skin just below your cheekbones, rubbing it into the skin from beside your nose to the outer corners of your eyes near your temples. Be sure not to get this mixture in your eyes! Put another drop or two above each eyebrow—these are sinus points

*To test whether you are sensitive or allergic to essential oils, put one drop of the diluted oil on the inside of your wrist and wait 24 hours. If you see a reaction, do not use the oil elsewhere.

used for acupressure and the application of topical sinus medication.

Lie down with a hot, moist cloth over your face with your eyes closed (leave a little space for breathing through your nose). Cover with a dry towel for five to 10 minutes. You can do this several times a day. The essential oil vapor will reduce congestion and pain and will help you relax and rest.

For sore throat: **Bitter orange.** With its soothing citrus scent, bitter orange has antiseptic properties and promotes circulation of blood and lymph.

What to do: Mix bitter orange oil with a carrier oil in a 1:10 ratio (as described above), and then rub several drops into the lymph glands under your jaw and down your neck for relief of sore throat pain. Wrap a moist, hot towel around your neck, and then cover it with a dry towel. Leave in place for 15 minutes. Then gently stroke downward on your jaw and neck—this promotes lymph drainage. Repeat as often as desired throughout the day.

Better Protection Against the Flu This Winter

Fred Pescatore, MD, a practitioner of natural and integrative medicine in New York City, author of seven books including *The A-List Diet* and former associate medical director of the Atkins Center for Complementary Medicine.

William Schaffner, MD, professor of preventive medicine in the department of health policy and professor of medicine in the division of infectious diseases at Vanderbilt University School of Medicine, Nashville.

The 2017–2018 flu season was the worst in the US since the 1970s—49 million people got sick...960,000 were hospitalized...and nearly 80,000 died. It was a perfect storm—a particularly nasty influenza virus...a vaccine that was less effective than usual...and a growing population of older people, who are most susceptible to the flu and related complications. About 70% of flu hospitalizations and 90% of deaths were among people age 65 and older.

We never know how bad a season will be, but it sure makes sense to protect yourself. So we interviewed an infectious-diseases expert and an integrative physician to bring you a powerful toolkit to help you avoid the flu—and if you do get sick, to help you get better fast.

FLU SHOTS, BOOZE AND SHUT-EYE

Infectious-diseases specialist William Schaffner, MD, advises everyone to…

•**Get an annual flu shot even if you're skeptical.** If you've already gotten one, bravo. But fewer and fewer Americans are doing so. Now new research from the Centers for Disease Control and Prevention (CDC) shows that skipping the shot was a significant contributor to the record-high hospitalizations and deaths in 2017–2018. According to the CDC, only 37% of US adults got vaccinated that season—down significantly from more than 43% the year before. If you're skeptical about the flu shot based on what happened that season—the vaccine was less effective than usual—keep in mind that things would have been even worse without it. If you are vaccinated and still get the flu, you're likely to have a milder infection. It also will be shorter in duration, and you'll be less likely to get pneumonia, to be hospitalized—or to die.

If you're age 65 or older, make sure that you get one of the vaccines licensed for use in older adults. There are two—the high-dose flu vaccine and the adjuvanted flu vaccine. Either one is fine and will give you a bigger immune response than the standard shot. I don't recommend the nasal vaccine for older people.

•**Get extra protection if you think you've been exposed to the flu.** If flu is rampant in your community or a family member brought it home, your doctor can prescribe an antiviral medication (see below). These not only help reduce flu symptoms, especially if taken within 48 hours of the start of symptoms but, according to the FDA, also may help prevent flu if you are exposed. It's still important to get a flu shot, of course, but an antiviral medication can provide additional protection if needed.

Tip: If you're planning a trip during flu season, ask your doctor about prescribing an antiviral for you to have on hand in case you find yourself surrounded by people with the flu. Cruise ships, in particular, are hotbeds for the flu.

•**Cut back on or avoid alcohol during flu season.** Alcohol negatively affects the body's immune response and can increase the likelihood of getting an infection as well as the severity of an infection. Do stay hydrated, though—that helps your immune system function at its best.

•**Stay active.** Regular exercise helps boost immunity, so keep up your fitness routine throughout the winter even when you feel like hibernating.

•**Keep a solid sleep schedule.** Healthy men and women who average less than seven hours of sleep per night are three times more likely to catch a cold, compared with those who get eight hours or more of sleep, and good sleep likely helps ward off the flu, too.

•**Be smarter about hygiene.** Besides frequently washing your hands and using an alcohol-based hand sanitizer, regularly sanitize shared surfaces such as those in bathrooms and kitchens…and doorknobs throughout the house. Don't get too close to sick people if you can help it—viruses can be spread not only by sneezes but also by simply breathing. And stay home if you're sick so that you don't become a dreaded spreader of germs.

NATURAL WAYS TO PREVENT FLU

Integrative medicine practitioner Dr. Fred Pescatore, frequently prescribes dietary supplements for the fall and winter to help his patients prevent colds and flu. *You can use one, two or all three of the following with your doctor's OK…*

•**N-acetyl cysteine (NAC).** This antioxidant can help prevent the flu, and clinical studies have found that it helps ward off flu symptoms even in people who already are infected with the virus. *Typical dose*: 500 milligrams (mg) per day.

•**Olive leaf extract.** This supplement contains a bitter compound called oleuropein that has strong antiviral properties. *Typical dose*: 500 mg per day.

•**Monolaurin.** This antiviral is derived from lauric acid, one of the main fats in coconuts. It destroys viruses by breaking down their outer membranes. *Typical dose*: 300 mg per day.

Other natural preventives…

•**See the light.** Sunlight helps your body produce vitamin D, a potent immune booster. Some scientists think that the lack of sunlight and decreased vitamin-D production in the darker months help explain why flu is so common then. For extra protection, give yourself some full-spectrum light inside your home, too. Light therapy has been shown to enhance the immune system in the winter, and a full-spectrum light box is well worth the investment for this purpose.

IF YOU DO GET THE FLU…

From Dr. Schaffner…

Antiviral drugs can make your illness milder…shorten the duration of the time you are sick…and may prevent serious flu-related complications that can lead to hospitalization. It's best to take an antiviral within 48 hours of symptom onset, so call your doctor the minute you start to feel sick. Classic flu symptoms include sudden onset of fever, aches, chills and tiredness.

Even if you have had the flu for more than a few days, an antiviral drug still may lessen symptoms. That's especially important for people at high risk for flu-related complications, which includes people who are age 65 or older and people with medical conditions such as heart disease, diabetes or asthma.

Oseltamivir (Tamiflu) is the standby, and it's still effective, but now there's a new option—*baloxavir marboxil* (Xofluza), which was approved by the FDA in October 2018. Unlike Tamiflu, which is taken over the course of five days, it's a single dose. It also dramatically cuts "viral shedding," so you're less infectious (Tamiflu hasn't been shown to do this). Overall, Xofluza and Tamiflu are about equally effective, and their costs are very similar.

From Dr. Pescatore…

The following remedies can help reduce the severity and duration of the flu. *You can use one or any combination of these remedies with your doctor's OK…*

•**Oregano oil gargle.** Put two drops of oregano oil in one-quarter cup of water, gargle and spit. It is fine to gargle up to four times a day. Keep in mind—it has an intense flavor, and you'll smell like pizza!

•**Active hexose correlated compound (or AHCC).** This extract from mushrooms has been shown to shorten the duration of flu and ease symptoms. It also improved the immune response in people who took it right after getting a flu shot. *Typical dose*: 500 mg three times a day.

•**Elderberry tea** is an antiviral that's effective for treating flu symptoms and shortening its duration. Drink one cup a day. You also can take it as an extract or a syrup.

•**Robuvit, an antioxidant supplement derived from French oak wood,** helps people recover more fully after flu symptoms have passed. In a study, people who took the supplement daily for three weeks after their flu symptoms subsided had better post-flu strength, sleep quality and attention span, compared with people who didn't take it. *Typical dose*: 200 mg three times a day.

GOOD TO KNOW…

Hand-Washing Myths

Water temperature is irrelevant in hand washing. Cool water is just as good as warmer water to get rid of bacteria. Hotter water does cut through oil more quickly, so hands may feel cleaner—but very hot water can damage skin, which makes it more susceptible to bacteria.

Also: A single pump of foam soap is just as effective for hand washing as four pumps. And 10 to 20 seconds of rubbing hands together, followed by a 10-second rinse, is more effective than five seconds of scrubbing followed by rinsing…but washing for more than 20 seconds gives no additional benefit. Finally, soap marketed as antibacterial is no better at removing bacteria than plain soap.

Study led by researchers at Rutgers University, New Brunswick, New Jersey, published in *Journal of Food Protection*.

Important Reminders for Flu Season

• **Give other people plenty of space during flu season**—people can spread the virus simply by exhaling onto you.

• **Use antibacterial wipes frequently and on just about everything,** including door handles, handrails, buttons on a phone and copy machine, and anything else that other people may have touched.

• **Avoid touching your eyes, nose and mouth**—all are lined with mucous membranes through which the flu virus can get into your body.

• **Set up a humidifier, and use it regularly**—the flu virus appears to thrive in dry air. But clean the humidifier regularly, or it can become a breeding area for bacteria.

Health.com

Stinging Nettle Nixes Allergies, Cough, More

Jamison Starbuck, ND, a naturopathic physician in family practice, Missoula, Montana, and writer and producer of Dr. Starbuck's Health Tips for Kids, *a weekly program on Montana Public Radio, MTPR.org. She is a past president of the American Association of Naturopathic Physicians and a contributing editor to* The Alternative Advisor: The Complete Guide to Natural Therapies and Alternative Treatments. *DrJamisonStarbuck.com*

Stinging nettle, with its odd-sounding name, grows throughout the US and is thought by some to be nothing more than a weed. This deep green, leafy plant can indeed grow to six feet tall or more. And if you're hiking in a damp forest or taking a stroll past a weed-filled, untended lot, you'll likely happen upon nettle. But don't be deceived—stinging nettle is a nutritious spring food and is widely considered to be one of the most useful of botanical medicines. As a food, stinging nettle is often eaten like spinach. It contains calcium, potassium, iron and plant protein. The irritating needles are destroyed by steaming. Some people harvest stinging nettle on their own or buy it at a local farmer's market.

As a medicine, I frequently recommend stinging nettle to treat…

• **Seasonal allergies.** When allergy season begins (or up to a month before, if possible), patients who suffer from annoying seasonal allergy symptoms can start using nettle in tea or tincture form. The typical dose is 16 ounces daily of nettle tea or one-quarter teaspoon of tincture in two ounces of water, twice a day—taken at least 15 minutes before or after eating. The herb helps strengthen the body's immune system to reduce common allergy symptoms such as runny nose, watery eyes, sneezing and fatigue.

For prompt allergy relief: Freeze-dried nettle in capsule form is an effective and convenient way to help fight symptoms. A typical dose is two capsules three or four times a day when you have allergy symptoms. Many of my patients find that they need more nettle at the beginning of allergy season and that they are able to reduce the dose after a few weeks. Once allergy season is over, you can stop taking this herbal medicine.

• **Cough.** Nettle also acts as an expectorant, a medicine that helps push mucus out of your throat and lungs. For patients who have a simple cough or cough due to bronchitis, for example, I often recommend nettle tea or tincture. A typical dose is four ounces of tea, four times a day…or one-quarter teaspoon of tincture in two ounces of water, four times a day.

• **Enlarged prostate.** Men with enlarged prostate experience urinary frequency—especially at night—and difficulty initiating and/or maintaining urination. Nettle root is frequently found in men's prostate formulas, which contain other herbs such as saw palmetto and pygeum africanum.

Scientists aren't entirely sure how stinging nettle works, but because it has multiple medicinal uses, it continues to be studied in North America and Europe. Because the plant is considered generally safe to use as medicine, you can purchase it over-the-counter and follow the manufacturer's instructions.

But if you want to try nettle, it's wise to visit a health-care practitioner who is knowledgeable about botanical medicines. This includes naturopathic physicians. To find one near you, consult The American Association of Naturopathic Physicians, Naturopathic.org.

Caution: If you are allergic to any type of weed, don't use stinging nettle. If you have diabetes, high blood pressure, kidney disease or take a blood thinner, lithium or a sedative, talk to your doctor before taking nettle. This herb can interact with certain medications—especially those listed here and used for the conditions above. Pregnant women should not use nettle.

Food Allergies Not as Common as Most People Think

Food allergies are only about half as common as people think they are. 19% of adults asked whether they had food allergies said they did—but only 10.8% actually had reactions to food that constitute typical allergic responses, such as throat tightening and vomiting. The most common allergy found was to shellfish, affecting 2.9% of adults surveyed...followed by milk, affecting 1.9%...and peanuts, affecting 1.8%.

Among people who did have food allergies, only 48% said that they had been diagnosed with them by a doctor, and only one-quarter said that they had a prescription for the common allergy treatment *epinephrine*.

Study by researchers at Northwestern University, Evanston, Illinois, published in *JAMA Network Open*.

Say Goodbye to Your PPI! This Heartburn Drug Is Riskier Than Once Thought

Jamie A. Koufman, MD, a laryngologist and clinical professor of otolaryngology at New York Eye and Ear Infirmary of Mount Sinai in New York City. She is also founder and director of the Voice Institute of New York and coauthor of several books, including *Dr. Koufman's Acid Reflux Diet* and *Dropping Acid: The Reflux Diet Cookbook & Cure*. VoiceInstituteOfNewYork.com

If you watch TV, you've no doubt heard of the "little purple pill." This medication, sold under the brand name Nexium, is in a class of drugs called proton pump inhibitors (PPIs), which promise to reduce stomach acid and relieve the unpleasant symptoms of heartburn and acid reflux.

Americans spend a whopping $14 billion a year for these products, which also include brand names such as Prilosec, Prevacid, Protonix and Aciphex. Some of these drugs are available only with a doctor's prescription, while others come in over-the-counter (OTC) versions.

Here's what you may not know: While doctors have been liberally prescribing these drugs to their patients for years, there's increasing concern about the harm these drugs can cause, especially when people take them for longer than recommended—just two weeks at a time for the OTC version and up to four weeks for a prescription PPI.

For years, studies have warned that prolonged use of PPIs is linked to serious side effects, including kidney damage, severe diarrhea, bone fractures and low magnesium levels. Recently, a growing body of evidence ties the use of these drugs to even more serious conditions, including heart attack, dementia and esophageal cancer.

Latest blow: A large, six-year study of US military veterans, published in *BMJ Open*, found that those who chronically took a prescription-strength PPI died earlier (of any cause) than the group not taking the medication. The risk for death increased the longer someone took the drug.

Important: Manufacturers continue to stand behind the drugs when used as directed, and many doctors believe these medications do have a place in the long-term treatment of some patients.

Still…if you are taking a PPI and want to stop, you have lots of company. But there's a catch—people who quit PPIs often suffer a big rebound in stomach acid, triggering even worse symptoms than they had before.

For people with *gastroesophageal reflux disease* (GERD), a backflow of stomach contents into the esophagus, the rebound can lead to painful indigestion and heartburn. For people with respiratory reflux, a backflow of stomach acid that can reach the throat, nose, sinuses and lungs, the symptoms can include chronic cough, a burning throat, hoarseness and difficulty swallowing.

Good news: You can likely get your symptoms under control without drugs if you make the right changes to your diet and lifestyle. But first you need to wean yourself off your PPI. *Here's how…*

STEP 1: **Switch your acid-reducing medication.** Stop taking your PPI, and replace it with a histamine H2 antagonist (H2A)—the safer class of acid-reducing drugs that includes Pepcid, Zantac and Tagamet. These drugs are available by prescription and in OTC versions.

At first, you will need to take a dose four times daily, before each meal and at bedtime. If your rebound symptoms are really bad, add a liquid alginate—a product derived from seaweed that is not widely used in the US but can be found online, for sale from the UK, under the brand name Gaviscon Advance Aniseed. Follow label instructions.

Don't despair about taking more doses than you did with a once-a-day PPI—the idea is that after a week or two, you should be able to drop one mealtime pill every few days and gradually go drug-free.

Note: Some people continue to use an H2A medication and Gaviscon, as needed.

STEP 2: **Prop up your sleep.** While you are in reflux detox, you should avoid lying down for the four-hour period prior to your bedtime—and prop yourself up at bedtime to minimize nighttime reflux.

Helpful: Use pillows to get your head at a 45-degree angle and, if needed, put sofa cushions under your arms and legs to create a comfy in-bed throne. Some people sleep in recliners for the first two to four weeks of treatment.

STEP 3: **Eat early and often.** Nighttime eating is a major cause of reflux symptoms. So try to eat 75% of your calories before 5 pm and nothing after 8 pm—or even 7 pm if you can manage that.

Also helpful: Eating five small meals is better than having three big ones.

STEP 4: **Change what you eat.** The heart of your new lifestyle is a diet that is lean, clean, green and alkaline (the opposite of acidic)—low in unhealthy fats and junk foods, high in healthy plants and as low as possible in very acidic foods and beverages, such as citrus and soft drinks.

Dietary acid activates the digestive enzyme pepsin, which is left on the sensitive tissue lining the throat after reflux occurs. Pepsin causes damage and is acid-activated. You will have to be strict at first, while you are getting your symptoms under control.

Over time, however, you may find some foods that are triggers for other people are OK for you…or that you can enjoy your trigger foods in very limited quantities. But make no mistake—keeping your symptoms at bay will mean sticking to a healthy, low-acid diet for life.

So say goodbye to just about all foods and drinks that come in bottles and cans, including store-bought juices, sports drinks, energy drinks and vitamin waters, as well as carbonated sodas. They are all high in acid, which will worsen your condition.

Also, cut way back on red meat, butter, fried foods, chocolate, citrus fruits and condiments and salad dressings (get these on the side so that you can add them in moderation). A salad, for example, that is bathed in too much vinegar is bad for reflux. For condiments, the same is often true. If you add them yourself, you can do so sparingly.

Alcohol—especially late at night —is often problematic. Many people find they need to give up alcohol entirely.

What you can eat: Fish and poultry (baked, broiled, sautéed and grilled are best—not fried), most nuts, grains, tubers (such as potatoes), rice, eggs and many fruits and vegetables—particularly bananas, melons, fennel, parsley and greens.

Bottled or tap water is fine. *Even better:* Alkaline water, which comes in bottles (labeled with a pH of 8.0 or higher)…or it can be made with a filtration device. Good alkaline products are available from Cerra Water. Most people also can tolerate one or two cups daily of caffeinated coffee or tea.

Note: Some people can have more if it's decaf, but for others, all coffee and tea trigger reflux.

OTHER HELPFUL APPROACHES

In addition to the steps above…

• **Try sipping chamomile tea** (other herbal teas will be too acidic).

• **Chew some sugar-free gum**—it can help neutralize acid. Any flavor is fine, except for mint, which can trigger reflux.

• **Suck on manuka honey lozenges.**

• **Once symptoms are under control,** try gradually adding back some foods, such as onions, garlic and tomatoes—all no-no's at first but tasty ingredients in many common dishes. Over time, you may learn that you can't eat sautéed garlic but can tolerate garlic powder. Or maybe you can eat raw tomatoes but not canned sauces or ketchup.

If you are unsure about your triggers, keep a food-and-symptom diary for a month. When you reintroduce possible trigger foods, such as onions, garlic and chocolate, introduce one at a time so that you will know if you get reflux from that particular food. (You will know that day, that evening or the next day when you wake up.)

• **Reserve medications for as-needed use.** You may still need to take a fast-acting H2A medication before an occasional big night out.

6 Surprising Foods That Can Give You Food Poisoning

Robert B. Gravani, PhD, CFS, professor emeritus of food science at Cornell University, Ithaca, New York. He is past president of the Institute of Food Technologists.

Perfected by nature. That's the motto for Live Spring Water. It is "raw" water—unfiltered, untreated spring water—the latest trend in health-conscious circles. *Cost:* $38 for a two-and-a-half-gallon jug…$16 for a refill.

Save your money…and you might be saving yourself something even more valuable—your health. According to the Centers for Disease Control and Prevention, the nation's top health protection agency, drinking "raw" water could increase the risk for serious food-borne illnesses including, potentially, cholera and typhoid. You also could swallow disease-causing parasites including *Giardia, Cryptosporidium* and *Cyclospora*. While no outbreaks have been reported from the bottled variety—and Live Spring, for one, says that it tests its water sources once a year for contamination—public health authorities believe that it's only a matter of time before someone gets sick from bottled raw water.

Unless you like to chase the latest trends, you probably don't have a cooler filled with raw water in your kitchen. *But chances are you do have one or more of the following five other surprising sources of food-borne illnesses…*

• **Melon and other fruits with thick skin.** You might assume that a fruit with a thick, inedible skin—such as cantaloupe, mango, papaya and even avocado—would be perfectly safe. After all, you're not eating the skin. But there have been several food-poisoning outbreaks associated with such fruits.

Risky moment: When you cut into the fruit, you can transfer bacteria from the skin to the flesh. *Protect yourself:* Thoroughly wash fruits that have a thick skin before you cut through them, using water and a produce brush to get at nooks and crannies—soap isn't necessary.

• **Raw flour.** You are probably thinking, *Who eats raw flour?* But if you ever nibble raw cookie dough or lick cake batter off your finger—you do! Recently, dozens of people across the country got sick from eating raw dough made from flour contaminated with the *E. coli* bacterium. A whopping 10 million pounds of flour were recalled because of the outbreak.

Protect yourself: Don't eat raw cookie dough or anything that contains raw flour. And that's a doubly good idea because many recipes containing flour also include another food that is dangerous raw—eggs.

• **Homemade soups and stews.** If you have made a big pot of soup or stew and then left it on the stovetop for hours to cool, you are putting yourself at risk for a lesser known, yet pervasive, bacterium called *Clostridium perfringens*—estimated to cause a million cases of food-borne illness each year in the US. Even though the soup was boiled, the organism forms spores that can survive the cooking process—and then germinate as the food slowly cools.

Protect yourself: Cool soups and stews as quickly as possibly—only *briefly* on a countertop, then in the refrigerator. *Tip:* Transfer hot liquids into large, shallow containers to let the liquid cool down quickly. As soon as it stops steaming, pop it in the fridge. *Alternative:* Buy a nifty gadget called an ice paddle that you fill with water and then freeze—it cools hot liquids quickly with just a little stirring. Then put the now-cool soup or stew into the fridge. Eat within four days, and be sure to reheat to a simmer before serving.

• **Cooked meats—even ones that have been stored properly.** Everyone knows that raw meat can possibly harbor *salmonella* and other bacteria. But even foods that are *cooked* when you buy them, such as deli meats… smoked seafood…store-made deli salads…and precooked hot dogs can harbor Listeria. It's a bacterium that grows in moist, cool temperatures—such as a refrigerator or cooler.

Protect yourself…

Eat meats that you buy cooked soon after purchasing them, and toss anything that remains five days after you opened the pack-

age. With unopened packages, use the "best by" date as a rule of thumb for when to toss. In this way, you won't be eating these foods after the bacterium has had a great deal of time to multiply. *Note*: If you buy frozen hot dogs or freeze the hot dogs when you get them home, you're safer—*Listeria* won't multiply in the freezer.

If there are any spills from deli salads in your refrigerator, clean them up promptly. Once a week, wipe the walls and shelves of the fridge with warm, soapy water, then rinse…and keep the temperature at 40°F or lower.

Listeria is especially dangerous to pregnant women and people with compromised immune systems (from diabetes or cancer, for example). They should be especially cautious and heat not only hot dogs but also lunch meat and smoked seafood until they're steaming.

• **Raw pet food.** This one is a risk both for you and your cat or dog. Raw pet food (meat, bones, organs) is a popular "natural" trend. It's supposed to be closer to the kind of food that a feral dog or cat would eat in the wild. But it's very easy for these foods to get contaminated with *salmonella*, *Listeria* and other pathogens that can make pets and humans sick—the FDA has recalled several brands due to contamination.

As with humans, in pets these food-borne illnesses can lead to vomiting, diarrhea and

Cures for Common Conditions

sometimes fever. Even if your pet doesn't get sick, you can become ill if you contract these bacterial infections after handling pet food.

Protect yourself: It's best to avoid raw food entirely and serve your pet only food that has been cooked, either store-bought or home-made. If you do handle raw pet food, be sure to wash your hands in hot, soapy water for at least 20 seconds.

STAYING SAFE

Now that you know about these frequently ignored dangers, you can protect yourself. But don't ignore the better-known food-safety risks, either. *These include…*

• **Rare or even medium-rare hamburgers.** Make sure burgers reach an internal temperature of 160°F.

• **Raw milk.** It's dangerous. Avoid it.

• **Bagged salad greens.** These have been the cause of many recalls. Better to buy bunches of spinach or heads of lettuce…rinse thoroughly in cold water (no need for soap)…dry thoroughly and refrigerate until use.

• **Sprouts.** Never eat any kind of sprout raw.

Got Nausea? Try a Whiff of This…

If you suffer from nausea, here's a surprisingly simple remedy that really works.

New finding: Among 122 patients who went to an emergency department due to gastroenteritis (stomach flu), those who sniffed isopropyl alcohol (rubbing alcohol) on saturated pads got better relief from nausea than those who took the widely used antinausea drug *ondansetron* (Zofran).

To try this therapy at home: Saturate a few cotton balls with isopropyl alcohol, and then inhale the vapors repeatedly at 10-minute intervals. If you have respiratory issues, check with your doctor first.

Michael D. April, MD, DPhil, emergency medicine physician, San Antonio Uniformed Services Health Education Consortium, Texas.

Quick Posture Fix

Most people have bad posture because they habitually look down. When their gaze drops, their shoulders slump. Keep your eye on the horizon and your posture will improve.

Fitness trainer Joel Harper, author of *Mind Your Body* and the "Your Personal Mind-Body Coach" blog at Bottom LineInc.com.

Dr. Levin's Anti-Migraine Plan

Morris Levin, MD, chief of the Division of Headache Medicine and director of the Headache Center at UCSF Medical Center in San Francisco. He is coauthor of *Understanding Your Migraines: A Guide for Patients and Families*. Dr. Levin is board-certified in neurology, pain medicine and headache medicine.

Medications can help to both prevent and treat migraine, but fortunately there are many lifestyle and other treatment options that can help dramatically—without drugs. *The advice I give the migraineurs I treat…*

KNOW YOUR TRIGGERS

Identifying your migraine triggers and avoiding them is key to preventing an attack. Triggers are highly individual, including particular smells, sounds, lighting, 3-D movies—even weather changes. *Common food triggers include…*

• **Alcohol**—in particular, red wine, perhaps because of its high levels of histamine.

• **Nitrites.** Found in hot dogs, bacon, sausage and processed meats.

• **Monosodium glutamate (MSG).** A flavor enhancer that goes by many names, it is a powerful trigger for many people.

Check the ingredient lists on food package labels for these little-known names for MSG: Autolyzed, hydrolyzed or partially hydrolyzed additives such as yeast, cornstarch, gelatin, milk protein, plant protein, soy and wheat…plant protein extract…textured protein…and yeast extract.

WHEN TROUBLE STARTS

Taking the right steps at the first sign of a migraine coming on can lessen an attack—or avert it. *These natural remedies can help…*

• **Apply a cold pack to the site of the pain.** Cold may reduce blood vessel inflammation. A bag of frozen peas makes a good cold compress. It conforms to the shape of your head, and you can refreeze the bag for reuse. (*Note*: Don't eat thawed and refrozen peas—they can harbor unhealthy bacteria.)

• **Aromatherapy,** a popular migraine treatment in Europe, is not backed by strong scientific evidence, but some patients find it helps them relax and eases their headache pain. Tiger Balm—a mixture of camphor, menthol, cajuput oil and other herbals—is particularly effective and is available in supermarkets and pharmacies. Rub a small amount into your temples at the first sign of migraine. *Other essential oils to try*: Eucalyptus, lavender and peppermint.

• **Drink a caffeinated beverage**—but not more than 100 mg of caffeine (one cup of medium-roast coffee). *Other options*: Strong black tea (50 mg/cup)…green tea (25 mg/cup.)

Warning: Caffeine triggers migraines for some people.

Regular tea and coffee drinkers: To avoid a caffeine-withdrawal headache—another migraine trigger—drink the caffeinated beverage at the same time each day.

VITAMINS AND HERBS THAT HELP

Certain supplements can reduce frequency and/or intensity of migraines. *Try these one at a time for two or three months…*

• **Vitamin B-2 (riboflavin) may reduce migraine frequency.** *Try*: 400 mg/day. Vitamin B-2 usually doesn't have adverse side effects.

• **Magnesium gluconate and magnesium taurate may both prevent migraine.** *Try*: 500 mg to 600 mg/day of either one. Lower the dose if you have loose stools. *Option*: 100 mg of either at the start of a migraine can reduce its intensity.

• **Feverfew has been used for centuries to prevent and relieve migraine.** Studies show that it can reduce migraine frequency and severity. *Try*: A total of 50 mg to 125 mg/day (tablet or capsule) divided into three doses. Feverfew thins blood—don't take it if you are on aspirin therapy or take a blood thinner such as *warfarin* (Coumadin). Also avoid it if you are allergic to ragweed. Other side effects include joint aches and gastrointestinal disturbances.

NERVE STIMULATION

The FDA recently approved Cefaly, a noninvasive nerve stimulator that looks like a headband and is worn across the forehead. It delivers tiny, painless electrical pulses to the upper branch of the trigeminal nerve—the nerve responsible for sensations in your face and head. When inflamed, the trigeminal nerve overresponds to stimuli, possibly causing migraine pain.

Theory: Repeated pinging with electrical pulses might make the trigeminal nerve less sensitive to stimulation. In a recent Italian study, using Cefaly 20 minutes daily for four months reduced migraine frequency by more than 50%.

TAKE NOTE…

What Is a Migraine?

A migraine headache is a cascade of electrical, chemical and inflammation-related blood vessel changes that occur in the brain, typically in distinct stages, but they can overlap…

• **Prodrome.** The warning stage. You may feel "off," irritable or moody…have amplified senses, such as a heightened sense of smell…and crave certain foods, such as sweets.

• **Aura.** Usually occurring from five to 60 minutes before an attack, it involves visual disturbances such as flashing lights, zigzag lines or blind spots.

• **Headache.** Pain, mild to severe, often described as intense pounding or pressure, usually on one side of the head.

• **Postdrome.** The recovery period. You may feel fatigued over the next few hours or days.

The device costs $349, plus $25 for three sets of electrodes (each set lasts about one month), and can be ordered online at Cefaly. us. It requires a prescription from your doctor and may not be covered by insurance. (Cefaly should not be used if you have a cardiac pacemaker, an implanted or wearable defibrillator, an implanted metallic or electronic device in your head or have pain of unknown origin.)

ADDITIONAL NEW TREATMENT

Recent research shows that *calcitonin gene-related peptide* (CGRP), a strong vasodilator produced in neurons involved in the transmission of pain, could trigger and maintain migraines. During a migraine headache, CGRP binds to receptors in the trigeminal nerve. In recent clinical trials, an antibody treatment that blocks the activity of CGRP modestly reduced the number of days per month that patients were disabled by migraine and even eliminated migraines for up to 15% of patients. The FDA recently approved three of these drugs—Aimovig, Ajovy and Emgality—which are all available by injection.

How to Guard Against Dry Eye

Dry eye is more common in winter because humidity outside is low and people keep homes and offices heated as well as dry—so eye moisture evaporates both outdoors and indoors. It helps to use a humidifier in heated environments and avoid directing heat right at your face—for example, direct car vents downward toward your lower body.

Also: Drink lots of fluids so that your whole body remains hydrated...wear eye protection outdoors or use a hat with a visor. If you wear contact lenses, keep them very clean to reduce the risk of itching and infection. See your doctor if dry eye persists.

Marissa K. Locy, OD, instructor, department of ophthalmology, University of Alabama at Birmingham.

To Keep Contact Lenses Bacteria-Free...

Even if you clean your contacts nearly every night, they still might harbor bacteria. Bacteria can form biofilms (layers of microorganisms) that adhere to lenses, making them more resistant against antimicrobial solutions such as lens cleaners. Biofilm formation is a major factor in eye infections related to contact lenses. *To reduce chances of infection...*

•**Wash your hands with soap and water before inserting lenses.** Use the cleaning solution recommended by your doctor or labeled for your type of lenses. Follow the cleaning and storage instructions.

•**Avoid sleeping in contact lenses,** even if you have the "continuous wear" type, since overnight wear is a big risk factor for infection. If you are not careful about cleaning, consider a daily disposable lens. Smokers and those who have diabetes or a weakened immune system are at a greater risk for infection.

Lindsay Ciocco, OD, FAAO, instructor of ophthalmology at The Johns Hopkins Wilmer Eye Institute in Baltimore.

Little-Known Way to Prevent Neck Pain

Clenching your teeth, perhaps you do it unconsciously, can cause neck pain. To prevent it, repeat to yourself throughout the day, "Lips together, teeth apart."

Carol Krucoff, yoga therapist at Duke Integrative Medicine in Durham, North Carolina.

Walking Reduces Varicose Veins

Varicose veins are mostly genetic, but obesity, age and physical inactivity can make them worse. Varicose veins mostly occur in the legs when the vein valves that move blood back to the heart malfunction. Walking contracts the calf muscles, helping circulate blood back to the heart, relieving the blood backup that is characteristic of varicose veins. This can help stop the progression or lessen the effects of varicose veins. Compression socks or stockings can help circulation, too.

If these approaches do not work, several minimally invasive medical procedures are available—ask your doctor for details.

Cheryl Hoffman, MD, interventional radiologist, UCLA.

Leg Cramp Trigger

Adults age 60 and older who consumed alcohol at least once a week were six-and-a-half times more likely to suffer from leg cramps at night, according to a recent study in *Annals of Family Medicine*.

Theory: Chronic alcohol intake worsens the deterioration of muscle fibers that comes with age and contributes to nocturnal leg cramps.

If you suffer from leg cramps: Try cutting back on alcohol—or stopping altogether.

Chloe Delacour, MD, professor of medicine, University of Strasbourg, France.

Treat Your Skin from the "Inside Out"

Alan M. Dattner, MD, a board-certified dermatologist and pioneer in integrating nutrition, holistic medicine and dermatology. He is author of *Radiant Skin from the Inside Out: The Holistic Dermatologist's Guide to Healing Your Skin Naturally*, as well as several professional articles and book chapters relating to holistic dermatology. HolisticDermatology.com

If you have a skin problem and go to a conventional dermatologist, you're likely to get a diagnosis and a prescription for medication that in actuality may only help keep your symptoms in check.

A different approach: In the world of holistic dermatology—where treatment is all about finding the root cause of a problem rather than just controlling the symptoms—the skin serves as a window to what's happening deep inside the body.

A LEAKY GUT

In healthy people, the inside of the small intestine has a cellular barrier that prevents incompletely digested food molecules and toxins from crossing through to the bloodstream. In a condition known as "leaky gut," the cellular bonds holding the intestinal lining together are broken, allowing these materials to slip through, activating the immune system to cause inflammation (see below).

Leaky gut is often caused by an overgrowth of yeast (frequently from a high-sugar diet)… or from specific food components like gluten, a protein found in wheat, barley and rye. In fact, 40% of gluten-sensitive patients analyzed in a study published in 2017 in *World Journal of Gastroenterology* cited eczema or a rash as symptoms.

If you find that you're sensitive to gluten, a gluten-free diet can give a leaky gut time to begin healing. A diet that's low in sugars and simple carbohydrates can reduce the inflammation caused in the gut by yeast and also improve leaky gut. In addition, you should eliminate high-yeast foods such as bread (even gluten-free bread can contain yeast)… cheese…wine…and beer.

Also: Probiotic supplements and probiotic-rich foods like sauerkraut (eaten daily) can replace yeast in the gut with more diverse, healthy bacteria. In addition to the steps described above, try the following holistic strategies to fight…*

ECZEMA

The rough, red, inflamed patches of eczema can cause itching so intense that it's nearly impossible not to scratch. *What to do…*

●**Stop the scratching.** Ice cubes in a wet towel applied to eczema patches for five or 10 minutes provide a satisfying sensation that calms the instinct to itch. *Helpful:* The anti-itch

*To find a holistic practitioner near you, consult the American Holistic Health Association, AHHA.org.

60

supplement Nettle Quercetin from Eclectic Institute.

• **Cure infections.** Cracks, crusting and open scratch marks are vulnerable to infection. To protect yourself, take an antimicrobial herb such as olive leaf. Check with a physician who has experience in prescribing herbal medicine for advice on dosage—it varies depending on the patient. Redness, swelling, tenderness, pus and honey-colored crusting are all signs that an infection should be treated by a doctor. At this point, the organism should be cultured to determine an appropriate antibiotic to use.

• **Ease inflammation.** Try a chamomile or chickweed anti-inflammatory ointment.

• **Try digestive enzymes.** These supplements can improve leaky gut by reducing the size of food molecules to simple building blocks like amino acids that do not trigger a reaction. *What helps*: A digestive enzyme that contains *dipeptidyl peptidase-4* (DPP-4).

ROSACEA

Rosacea is an inflammatory skin condition marked by facial redness, blood vessel enlargement and tiny pimples known as pustules.

• **Avoid problematic foods.** Certain foods dilate facial capillaries. *Common triggers:* Spicy foods...hot liquids such as coffee...and alcohol.

• **Watch out for extreme weather conditions.** Protect the skin from wind, cold and sun whenever possible—all can contribute to redness.

• **Get more vitamin C and the bioflavonoids that accompany it in fruits and vegetables.** Bioflavonoids reduce capillary fragility, which often manifests as broken blood vessels or easy bruising. Eat vitamin C–rich foods such as kale, spinach and broccoli (citrus fruit can aggravate rosacea)...or take a vitamin C supplement (500 mg twice daily).

• **Control your emotions.** Anger, anxiety and embarrassment can cause blood to rush to the face, intensifying rosacea. *What helps*: Deep breathing and meditation.

DANDRUFF

This white and red scaling of the scalp, forehead, eyebrows or chest is caused by an inflammatory immune reaction to a specific type of yeast (called Malassezia) that normally lives on the skin.

Even though antidandruff shampoos containing *ketoconazole* (Nizoral), *selenium sulfide* (Selsun Blue) or *pyrithione zinc* (Head & Shoulders) are designed to kill Malassezia yeast, they won't fix dandruff at its root cause.

• **Reduce yeast.** With dandruff, it's crucial to cut sugar, use probiotics and take an anti-yeast supplement such as caprylic acid.

• **Get the right oils.** Omega-3 fatty acids calm inflammation. Try eating two servings of cold-water fish, such as wild salmon, a week. Use cold-pressed, organic olive oil or safflower oil, and avoid oils heated to a high temperature. *Helpful:* Supplementation with vitamin E as well as vitamin C, B-complex, zinc and magnesium will help the body keep inflammation-fighting oils in their more usable forms.

THE INFLAMMATION FACTOR...

Even though chronic inflammation is widely known to fuel health problems ranging from heart disease and diabetes to cancer and rheumatoid arthritis, it also plays a crucial role in skin conditions.

Here's what happens: When the immune system becomes triggered—due to a variety of causes (see above)—it can attack cells, tissues or organs, as well as the skin, showing up as inflammation. That's why if you have a skin problem such as eczema, rosacea or seborrheic dermatitis (better known as dandruff), it's likely signaling a problem elsewhere in the body.

Look Younger Just by Doing These Face Exercises

Gary Sikorski, creator of Happy Face Yoga and co-author of a study published in *JAMA Dermatology*. You can buy or stream Happy Face Yoga at his website HappyFaceYoga.com.

When age and gravity cause your butt to droop or the backs of your arms to morph into floppy wings, you know what to do—get to the gym and up your squats or add an extra set of triceps moves.

But what about when your cheeks start to sag into jowls and your mouth seems stuck in a frown? Is it possible to exercise a few years off your face?

Well, yes, it may be! We spoke to Gary Sikorski, founder of Happy Face Yoga, to find out how some simple exercises can help you look much younger.

BUH-BYE JOWLS

Face-firming exercise is nothing new. The idea dates back at least as far as the 1960s when fitness guru Jack LaLanne led people through a series of "facenastics." And there have been dozens of face workouts since.

But none of them have been scrutinized by science until researchers at Northwestern University Feinberg School of Medicine decided to take a closer look at my program, Happy Face Yoga. Participants between 40 and 65 years old did two 90-minute training sessions in which I taught them 32 different moves targeting the face and the neck. (Don't worry—you don't need to learn 32 moves to make yourself look younger.) They then did the exercises at home for 20 weeks. For the first eight weeks, they spent a half hour each day flexing their facial muscles. For the next 12 weeks, they cut back to doing 30 minutes of exercises every other day.

Two dermatologists evaluated photographs of each participant taken at the beginning of the study…after eight weeks of facial exercise…and then after 20 weeks.

Results: The photographs showed a roughly three-year decrease in age appearance over the 20-week period. Not bad for just moving your face around at home, right? And it's possible that continuing to do the exercises could erase even more years off your look.

BEFORE YOU START

While changes to the structure of our skin play a large role in how we look as we age, changes to the muscles that underlie all that skin can have their effect, too.

I created 32 facial exercises so people have options, like when you go to a gym and there are so many types of equipment. But even if you do only a few of these exercises each day for 15 minutes, you can help yourself look younger.

Below I'll share three of the most effective facial exercises, but first, here are tips to help you get the most out of the overall program…

• **Because you'll be touching your face,** wash your hands before you do the exercises.

• **Wash your face, too.** You don't want your skin to be slippery with makeup or lotion.

• **Try to avoid touching the skin directly under your eyes,** which is very delicate.

• **Use visualization when you are doing the exercises**—imagine your muscles are moving and strengthening. This visualization tells your brain to send more signals to the muscles to get them working!

• **While you do the exercises, maintain good posture.** Sit up straight. Good posture acts as an anchor and will allow you to focus on the facial muscles you are exercising.

• **Drink lots of water—at least six glasses a day.** Water is the ultimate moisturizer. It helps carry nutrients and oxygen to your skin and muscles and helps flush out toxins.

Three face-firming exercises...

THE CHEEK LIFTER

The idea here is to strengthen the muscles in the cheeks—elevating droopy cheeks to more youthful heights.

1. Form a long/tall "O" shape with your mouth and fold your upper lip over your front teeth.

2. Smile so that your cheek muscles lift. Place your index fingers lightly and directly on the top part of each cheek, directly under your eyes.

3. Relax your cheek muscles, allowing them to return to their original position (keep your mouth in an "O"), and then smile again to lift your cheek muscles. Visualize pushing the muscles up toward your eyes as you smile. You have just completed one "push-up." Repeat nine more times.

4. On the final push-up, hold your cheek muscles up as high as you can. Move your index fingers an inch away from your face, and raise them to scalp level while looking at them to help you visualize your cheek muscles lifting. Continue looking up at your fingers, and hold for 20 seconds. Release and relax.

Do the entire sequence of 10 cheek lifters three times per session.

THE HAPPY FACE LIFTER

This exercise strengthens the entire face and increases blood flow to the muscles of the face, neck and scalp. It's most effective when done standing up.

1. Form a long/tall "O" with your mouth, press your lips against your teeth, then slowly fold them over your teeth. Smile to lift your cheek muscles.

2. Close your eyes, and roll your eyeballs toward your scalp. Adjust your mouth to make the "O" as small as possible. Smile again to further tighten those cheek muscles,

keeping the "O" small. Slowly tilt your head slightly back.

3. Tighten your abdominal muscles and buttocks, lift your chest and contract all your facial muscles. Keeping your eyes closed, slowly raise your hands up and over your head as you visualize lifting every single facial muscle off your body.

4. Hold the lift tightly for 30 seconds while taking long, deep breaths. On an exhale, allow your hands and head to drop toward the floor. Slowly inhale and relax.

Do this exercise one time every morning and every evening.

SCOOPING

This jaw-and-neck exercise firms sagging cheeks and droopy jowls and can diminish wrinkles on the sides of the chin.

1. Open your mouth, and produce an "Ahh" sound. Fold your lower lip over your lower teeth and hold tightly. Extend your lower jaw forward.

2. Using your lower jaw only, scoop up very slowly, as if you're using your jaw to scoop up something very heavy, then repeatedly open it and scoop again. Each time you scoop, tilt your head back so that your chin rises about an inch, incrementally tilting your head farther and farther.

3. Do 10 scoops. By the final one, your face should be about parallel with the ceiling. Keep your chin extended and hold tightly for 20 seconds while visualizing the sides of your face lifting.

Repeat twice for a total of three sets.

Natural Strategies to Knock Out Fungal Infections

Jamison Starbuck, ND, a naturopathic physician in family practice, Missoula, Montana, and writer and producer of *Dr. Starbuck's Health Tips for Kids*, a weekly program on Montana Public Radio, MTPR.org. She is a past president of the American Association of Naturopathic Physicians and a contributing editor to *The Alternative Advisor: The Complete Guide to Natural Therapies and Alternative Treatments*. DrJamisonStarbuck.com

"There's a fungus among us" is a fun rhyming phrase with a bit of truth to it—fungal organisms really do live all around us. But there isn't anything fun about having a fungal skin infection. Fungi like moist, warm environments. That's why they thrive in such places as gyms, swimming pools, locker rooms and public showers.

Among the most common fungal skin infections are athlete's foot, jock itch, ringworm, candida and yeast—all of which can show up as an itchy, red (or white), scaly patch or a simple bright-red wide line in a skin fold, an armpit or the groin. Over-the-counter antifungal creams, including *clotrimazole* (Lotrimin) and *miconazole* (Desenex), can clear up the infection if you catch it early—usually within about a week—before it's created a strong colony of fungal organisms that's harder to kill. But fungal infections can be persistent, and the synthetic ingredients of antifungal medications (such as those described above) should not be used day after day—you may develop a resistance to the drug over time.

My approach is to combine safe topical natural medicine with an internal protocol that improves skin health and boosts resistance to fungi. *What works best...**

• **Use lavender essential oil.** This is my favorite topical antifungal. It can kill fungi, and its scent is pleasant for most people.

What to do: Apply full-strength lavender oil extract to dry, scaly fungal infections and on

*If a fungal infection does not clear up within a week, see your doctor for advice.

nonopen bright-red fungal infections, such as those in the folds of skin, three times a day.

Important: In some people, undiluted oil can cause irritation. Do a skin patch test on a small area before applying to larger areas of skin. Before putting it on any fungal infection where the top layer of skin has been eroded, which is common in athlete's foot, dilute lavender oil with a carrier oil (such as almond or olive oil)—one part lavender essential oil to four parts carrier oil. If your fungal infection is so severe that it is open, cracked and bleeding, see your doctor.

• **Cut out sugar.** Fungi feed on simple sugars, and they thrive on people who eat a lot of sweets. If you've got a fungal infection, avoid sugar, including desserts, candy, honey, maple syrup and even alcohol, as well as "white" carbs, such as bread and pasta.

• **Take a probiotic.** Fungi can live not only on our skin but also in our intestines. Healthy bacteria (aka probiotics) can help—they compete with fungi and eventually crowd it out of the gut. For unknown reasons, an overgrowth of fungi in our intestines makes a fungal infection on the skin more common. Conversely, an abundant gut population of healthy bacteria can reduce fungal skin infections. For those fighting a fungal infection or recovering from one, a typical daily maintenance dose is 10 billion units of a probiotic with acidophilus and bifidus strains.

• **Get more beta-carotene.** This nutrient helps the skin resist injury and invasion by organisms, including fungi. It also helps the skin heal. Eat lots of beta-carotene-rich foods, such as butternut squash, sweet potatoes and carrots, and leafy greens, including spinach and kale. You also can take a beta-carotene supplement. If you have an active fungal infection, I suggest 50,000 international units (IU) of beta-carotene daily for one month.

Note: If you are a current or former smoker, check with your doctor before using a beta-carotene supplement—some research has linked high doses with an increased risk for lung cancer in this population.

Chemical-Free Ways to Avoid Mosquitoes

Since mosquitoes spread diseases, it's important to steer clear of them. Fortunately, there are several nontoxic ways to do that.

Use a small electric fan to create a gentle breeze...pleasant for you, but like a wind tunnel for tiny mosquitoes! Besides making it difficult for them to fly, it disperses the carbon dioxide and human scents that attract them. You can also light your patio with a yellow "bug light" bulb. It won't attract the little bloodsuckers the way that white lights will. It helps to dress in light-colored, loose-fitting clothing, too, since mosquitoes are attracted to darker colors, and it's easier for them to bite through tightly fitted clothing. In addition, eliminate all sources of standing water since mosquitoes need standing water to lay their eggs. Finally, keep the grass cut short and the bushes trimmed so they're less hospitable to mosquitoes.

Joseph M. Conlon, MSc, technical advisor, American Mosquito Control Association, Mount Laurel, New Jersey.

Is Dark or Light Clothing Best for UV Protection?

Color is less important than fabric weave. To protect your skin from ultraviolet (UV) rays, go for tightly woven fabrics such as denim or twill. Sheer fabrics allow more UV rays to reach your skin. Synthetic fabrics are more protective than natural fabrics such as cotton, flax or linen, unless these fabrics have been treated with a chemical sunblock. You can find sun-protective clothing at many outdoor clothing retailers.

Some manufacturers add an ultraviolet protection factor (UPF) label to their clothing, a rating based on the fabric's weight, construction and fiber content. A UPF rating of 50 provides excellent protection.

Barney J. Kenet, MD, dermatologist specializing in skin cancer and cofounder of the American Melanoma Foundation, New York City.

Houseplants That Help You Sleep

Rebecca Shannonhouse, editor in chief, *Bottom Line Health*, BottomLineInc.com.

We know that houseplants, which are a lot cheaper (and less noisy) than air-filtration systems, provide oxygen and help remove some of the harmful "off-gassing" chemicals, such as formaldehyde and benzene, that are often found in the air in our homes.

What you may not realize: Certain plants also can help you get a good night's sleep. For example, neuroscientists have found in lab studies that the scent from the valerian plant increases the activity of the brain's sleep-inducing *gamma-aminobutyric acid* (GABA) system.

Other plants—including lavender, which can slow down your heart rate and reduce anxiety levels—also are known to have sleepytime effects.

Even though some houseplants are notoriously finicky to maintain, many of the air-purifying, sleep-inducing plants are almost impossible to kill. *Good choices...*

• **Spider plant.** Most people sleep better if they turn the thermostat down to the 60°F to 70°F range when they go to bed—luckily, the spider plant thrives in cooler temperatures. Plus, the long tendrils of this undemanding plant are excellent at ridding the air of chemicals.

• **Devil's ivy.** It will thrive in dim rooms and helps scrub formaldehyde, benzene and other chemicals from the air. (The leaves are toxic for pets, so put it in a safe place.)

Also good for the home and bedroom: Areca palm...English ivy...peace lily...and lady palm.

If you have asthma or some other breathing difficulty, just be sure to check with your doctor before putting plants in your bedroom.

Make These Changes in How You Sleep for Relief from Common Aches and Pains

Matthew O'Rourke, PT, DPT, CSCS, OMT, adjunct professor of physical therapy at Simmons University in Boston and a physical therapist in the outpatient clinic at Lahey Hospital & Medical Center in Burlington, Massachusetts.

Whether you like to curl up on your side or sprawl flat out on your stomach, you probably have a favorite sleeping position. But did you know that if you suffer from common aches and pains, this familiar position might be aggravating your pain?

Here's how to adapt your preferred sleeping style for pain relief and better sleep…

NECK PAIN

Back-sleeping is often said to be the best position for neck pain. But back-sleeping can actually increase neck discomfort when using a pillow that's too thick (which causes the head to flex forward) or too thin (which causes the head to flex backward).

For back-sleepers: Be sure to use a pillow that keeps the neck in a neutral position, in line with the spine. When viewed from the side, the ear should be in line with the shoulders or slightly above them.

For side-sleepers: Add a thin pillow or rolled-up bath towel between the neck and the mattress in addition to your regular pillow to provide neck support and prevent the spine from bending to either side.

For stomach-sleepers: This position is the worst for neck pain because you'll need to turn your head to one side or the other, which puts strain on the neck. It's best to try another position, if possible.

LOW-BACK PAIN

Many people say that their backs feel better when they sleep on their backs, particularly if they use a pillow or two to slightly elevate the knees. But side-sleeping often feels more natural.

For side-sleepers: Lie on one side in a "stacked" position, with your shoulders, knees and hips in up-and-down alignment and knees slightly bent. *Helpful*: Place a pillow between your knees. This helps to prevent the top leg from rolling over the bottom, which can twist the spine.

For stomach-sleepers: This position can strain your lower back. However, if you find it difficult to try the positions above, place a pillow under your stomach to reduce excessive spinal extension.

KNEE PAIN

With knee pain, back-sleeping can be painful because the knees are extended all night… but side-sleeping can cause irritation where the knees touch.

For back-sleepers: Try placing a pillow under the knees to prevent them from over-straightening. *Note*: This position can be painful for some people.

For side-sleepers: Sleep with a pillow between your knees or use cloth knee pads (such as those that volleyball players wear), turning them sideways so that the area where the knees touch is well padded.

For stomach-sleepers: This position can put painful pressure on your knees. But if it's tough for you to switch to one of the above positions, put a pillow under your stomach to take some pressure off the knees.

HIP PAIN

For back- or stomach- sleepers: People with arthritis-related hip pain often have more pain when sleeping on their back or stomach. It's best to try side-sleeping (see below). However, a small pillow under the knees (when lying on your back) or under the stomach (when lying on your stomach) may provide some relief.

For side-sleepers: Side-sleeping is usually best for arthritis-related hip pain. *Helpful*: Keep your knees slightly bent and use a pillow (a body pillow works well) between the knees and thighs to keep the hip in a more neutral position. If lying on one side is more painful than the other, switch sides.

YOU CAN CHANGE HOW YOU SLEEP

When you get into bed, start in the position in which you would like to sleep. Then spend about a minute visualizing yourself staying in this position for the night. If you wake up and are out of position, calmly go back to the position you are trying to change to. In most cases, good progress can be made in four to six weeks, but it's something you'll need to keep working on—it's easy to fall back into old habits.

Accident-Prone? 6 Ways to Avoid Mishaps

Steve Casner, PhD, a San Francisco–based research psychologist who studies accidents for NASA's Human Systems Integration Division. He is a certified jet and helicopter pilot and author of *Careful: A User's Guide to Our Injury-Prone Minds.* SteveCasner.com

---

They trip over curbs and walk into glass doors. They lock themselves out of homes. Their cars are covered in dings. They have an orthopedist's number on speed dial.

One of every 29 people is at least 50% more accident-prone than the general population, according to a study published in *Accident Analysis & Prevention.* But what makes someone susceptible to accidents, mishaps and misadventures? The popular perception is that these people are uncoordinated, unintelligent

or unlucky. But researchers have found that these theories don't hold water. With a few exceptions related to specific physical impairments (see below), people are accident-prone not because it's their fate or their inherent nature but because their choices and habits lead them astray. That's good news—choices can be rethought and habits can be unlearned.

Six missteps that can make people prone to misadventures...

• **Placing excessive trust in past experience and learned behavior.** Lessons learned over decades or even generations help protect us. We all know not to stand under a tree during a lightning storm, for example. But people prone to mishaps often put too much faith in learned behavior.

In truth, there are times when relying on past experience is dangerous. Imagine that your town puts in a new sidewalk at an intersection where you often make right turns. For years, you've looked left at this intersection and made your right turn as soon as there's a break in oncoming traffic. The more strongly you trust the past, the more likely you are to forget to look right for pedestrians coming from that new sidewalk.

What to do: When you interact with something relatively new, give the activity your full attention. *Example:* When you buy a new piece of portable technology, stop everything else you're doing and give the tech your undivided attention before fiddling with it on the go.

• **Relying too much on memory.** Is searching for misplaced keys part of your daily routine? Do you chronically leave people waiting because you forgot you were meeting them? If your misadventures often involve forgetting to do things or misplacing things, your problem probably is not that you have a bad memory—it's that you are asking too much of your memory.

Human memory is not designed to recall everything we now expect it to. Our distant ancestors didn't have to remember to make five separate stops while running errands...or remember passwords for 20 online accounts—so modern brains are not especially good at these things either.

What to do: Create systems that take the burden off your memory. *Examples:* You can link things that you forget to things that you never forget. If you often forget to take a pill in the morning, position the pill bottle next to your toothbrush because it's something you never forget to use.

Or write checklists for activities that tend to lead to mishaps, similar to a pilot's preflight checklist. Write a "going out" checklist to ensure that you gather up your keys and phone and zip your purse closed so that nothing falls out. Post these checklists where you'll see them…and get in the habit of reviewing them.

If you are interrupted while completing a checklist, take an extra moment to review it again. Research on airline crashes has found that checklist interruptions are a common cause of skipped steps and accidents.

• **Attributing past mishaps to the fates.** Bad luck plays a role in some misadventures, but the vast majority happen at least in part because of something the sufferer did or didn't do.

What to do: Consciously take personal responsibility for each of your mishaps or accidents. Analyze what happened and what part you played in making it happen even if someone else was primarily to blame. Why were you in a position to have this happen? What could you do to reduce the odds that it will happen again?

• **Doing difficult things while drowsy.** If you do not wake up feeling rested, you are not getting sufficient sleep, and your odds of accidents and other mishaps increase substantially.

What to do: The solution here is obvious, though not always easy to achieve—you need to get more sleep. You could do that by taking naps, getting to bed earlier, improving your sleep habits or consulting a doctor about sleep strategies or medications.

Also, avoid engaging in dangerous or important activities on days when you wake up feeling drowsy. If you cannot rearrange your schedule, make a checklist of what you need to do that day to increase your chance of remembering everything. Minimize distractions during potentially dangerous activities—don't use your radio or phone at all while driving, for example.

• **Operating under the influence of extreme emotions.** Strong feelings—particularly anger, depression and anxiety—can be major distractions that increase the odds of missteps.

What to do: Postpone potentially dangerous activities (and other activities during which you have endured misadventures in the past) until your emotions abate. If postponement isn't possible or the emotions persist, take a few minutes to breathe and calm yourself. At least remind yourself that you are operating with this distraction and make a conscious effort to maintain as much focus on the activity as possible.

• **Behaving impatiently.** Some people run into problems because they are rushing. They fall off ladders because they reach a little too far to the side, rather than take the time to descend and reposition the ladder. They have car accidents because they were speeding, weaving among traffic or tailgating.

What to do: Build extra time into your schedule so that you don't have to rush. Consider how little time rushing really saves. Driving 75 miles per hour (mph) rather than 65 mph on a 20-mile commute saves a mere 2.5 minutes. Rushing is rarely worth the risk.

PHYSICAL REASONS SOME PEOPLE ARE ACCIDENT-PRONE

It's not always mind-set that makes a person prone to have misadventures—there can be physical reasons, too…

• **Hearing loss.** Hearing problems significantly increase accident risk, according to a 2018 study published in *JAMA Otolaryngology—Head & Neck Surgery*. We use our ears to identify nearby potential dangers much more than we tend to realize. This risk is worst for people experiencing the onset of hearing loss—because they have not yet adjusted their behavior to compensate. Hearing aids could reduce accident frequency.

Similar: Loss of other senses, such as declining vision, could increase accident frequency.

• **Aging.** People tend to become slightly more accident-prone as they grow older because age can bring balance problems, muscle weakness and/or memory loss.

• **Multiple sclerosis.** Falls and drops often are among the early symptoms of MS.

4

Focus on Fitness & Diet

The Secret to Eating Healthier: Keep a Food Diary

Every few years, another dietary fad sweeps the country. If you do this one big thing—say, consume fewer carbohydrates or fill up on protein—you'll be healthier and thinner.

But in real life, healthful eating depends on the dozens (if not hundreds) of small decisions that you *make* every day…assuming that you even make decisions. Most people eat without thinking, nibbling at leftovers as you store them after dinner…grabbing a snack when rushing out the door…or taking a few quick swigs of a soft drink.

How many healthy (or unhealthy) foods do you actually consume? You probably don't have a clue. The only way to know for sure is to write down everything you eat.

Compelling research: People who keep a food journal lose weight at twice the rate as those who don't keep track, according to a study published in *American Journal of Preventive Medicine.*

In addition to raising your awareness to what and how much you're eating, a food diary makes you aware of your habits—which can ultimately help you change your behavior and make healthier food choices so that you eat less of the wrong foods and more of the right foods.

FIND YOUR EATING STYLE

It might seem like a hassle to keep a food diary. But you don't have to do it forever…a month is usually long enough. And it's an extremely powerful tool for changing behavior. In fact, it's the best way to identify your eating

Lisa R. Young, PhD, RDN, a nutritionist in private practice and an adjunct professor in the department of nutrition, food studies and public health at New York University in New York City. She is author of *Finally Full, Finally Slim: 30 Days to Permanent Weight Loss One Portion at a Time.*

patterns. Nutritionists have discovered a few main patterns that define an individual's eating style. *For example...*

• **"See food" eaters** might cook healthy, well-balanced meals but still consume hundreds of unnecessary (or unhealthy) calories by eating whatever appears in front of them—doughnuts at the office...sugar next to the coffee maker...soda in the refrigerator, etc.

• **Emotional eaters** turn to food whenever they feel extra-stressed.

• **Mindless eaters** grab food on the run because they're often too busy or harried to enjoy leisurely meals.

You can easily consume 1,000 extra calories a day without even thinking about it. Some people are aware of their eating patterns, but many never realize where the bulk of their calories comes from.

A food diary—including a "cheat" diary (see next page) to account for the dozens of quick, mindless bites that you probably take every day—will help you identify your eating patterns...where your calories are coming from... and the quality of your diet. Are you getting enough antioxidants and fiber? Are you overloading on sugar? Writing it down is the only way to really know.

KEEP IT SIMPLE

One month is the recommended length of time to keep a food diary because that's about how long it takes people to change their habits. One of my clients, a busy hedge-fund manager, soon realized that he would munch mindlessly on junk food. After recording all of these "cheats" for six days, he realized that he needed to think before snacking. (He went on to lose 20 pounds over the next two months.)

The four pillars: A food journal only needs to include four basic pieces of information— what you ate...how much...the food group (fruits...grains...vegetables...meats and alternatives...and dairy)...and how you prepared it. The details are important because people tend to engage in what's known as "perception deception." You may see yourself as an active, healthy person and discount aspects of your behavior that don't align with your self-image.

FREEBIES...
Free Food-Tracking Apps

The best free food-tracking smartphone apps help you pay more attention to what you eat and can make you more mindful about food. *Different apps have different approaches and, therefore, different strengths...*

• **MyFitnessPal** has a built-in social network that makes it easy to interact with others who use the app.

• **Cronometer** has a highly visual interface and lets you customize calorie and nutrient targets.

• **FatSecret** is information-packed and has a search function that lets you add multiple foods at once to the food diary.

• **Nutrition GPA** evaluates food intake with simple yes-or-no questions and does not require attention to lots of numbers.

The New York Times.

Example: You may think that you're eating a healthful diet because you include a whole grain with every meal, but what if you only take a bite or two of brown rice and a double-helping of steak...or the broccoli that you sauté is swimming in butter? Details matter!

JUST A FEW MINUTES A DAY

I advise clients to make diary notes every time they eat, if possible. You'll forget things if you wait until the end of the day...and jotting down an entire day's notes can make it feel like too much work.

If you are comfortable with computers and phone apps (*MyFitnessPal* is a popular app), there are dozens of programs for tracking calories, food groups and portion sizes. But it's just as easy to carry a pen and a notebook...or send yourself a simple text or an e-mail. After you've done it for a few days, it almost becomes automatic.

• **A pre-diary** is good for those who are really committed to improving their diets...and for planners who prefer not to do things on the fly. Every day, write down what you plan to eat—the food groups, the portion sizes, preparation methods, etc. You can use the same diary (using a different-colored pen) to write down what you actually ate.

• **A cheat diary** is one of the most helpful tools. The calories and unhealthful ingredients from foods that you mindlessly pop into your mouth can add up fast. Especially for people who are too busy to keep a more detailed diary, a cheat diary is a good way to become aware of the unhealthy food choices.

• **Focus on portions.** Research has shown that people underestimate how much they eat and drink. They often don't realize that today's supersized portions have far more calories than they imagine.

Example: When I asked students in an introductory nutrition class how many calories were in an eight-ounce serving of a popular soda compared with the calories in a 64-ounce "double gulp," 70% underestimated the proportional increase. (An eight-ounce serving has 100 calories, and a 64-ounce soda contains 800...but most students estimated that the larger beverage only had 300 calories!)

Larger portion sizes may have started in restaurants/packaged foods, but now they're also a problem at home. You need to know how much you're eating—not how much you think you're eating. I advise everyone to buy stackable measuring cups and spoons. You can also buy dishware that marks off serving sizes and even wineglasses with fill lines (the standard serving size is five ounces).

• **Weigh your foods.** A kitchen scale (like the EatSmart Precision Pro Digital Kitchen Scale, among many others) is a great way to know exactly how much, say, a four-ounce serving really is. After using a scale for a while, most people learn to "eyeball" portions with decent accuracy.

Send Your Diet on Vacation

Fifty-one obese men on diets were placed in two groups—one dieted continuously for 16 weeks...the second group took a two-

week break every two weeks (eating just to maintain their weight).

Result: Intermittent dieters lost more weight than continuous dieters (an average of 31 pounds and 20 pounds, respectively) and maintained a greater weight loss (24 pounds versus six-and-a-half pounds) six months later.

Theory: Restricting calories slows down the metabolism. Taking a diet break resets the metabolism.

Nuala Byrne, PhD, head, School of Health Sciences, University of Tasmania, Launceston, Australia.

Easier Than a Diet...and Great for Your Health— Intermittent Fasting

Tina Marinaccio, RDN, integrative registered dietitian nutritionist and adjunct professor in clinical nutrition and food studies at Montclair State University in New Jersey. She leads the nutrition element of Dr. Dean Ornish's Program for Reversing Heart Disease. TinaMarinaccio.com

I am the first to admit that fasting sounds even worse than dieting. But some kinds of fasting can be *easier* than dieting—and have benefits that go well beyond weight loss. In fact, even people who are not overweight can get amazing benefits from fasting, including healthier hearts, stronger muscles and clearer thinking.

The technical term for what I am talking about is "intermittent fasting," which means fasting for short periods—sometimes, just 12 hours—on a regular basis. Most intermittent-fast techniques are not daily, and many allow for some calories even on "fast" days. This is definitely not a hunger strike! Some researchers believe that these intermittent fasts are easier to maintain than daily "caloric restriction"—aka traditional dieting, which basically requires that you eat less than you want every single day forever. Intrigued? *Here's more on the benefits of intermittent fasting and how you could easily try it...*

WHY INTERMITTENT FASTING IS SO HEALTHY

Studies have shown that intermittent fasting can help people lose weight without losing muscle. Maintaining muscle is key to keeping weight off and healthy aging. People on intermittent fasts find it easier to control their appetite even on nonfasting days. *One reason:* They are producing less insulin, a key "hunger hormone."

But there are many more benefits. These kinds of fasts have been shown to reduce blood pressure…reduce blood glucose levels and improve insulin sensitivity…reduce levels of triglycerides (blood fats) and improve the cholesterol profile…reduce inflammation…enhance muscle endurance…and even improve learning and memory. In animal studies, intermittent fasting can reverse type 2 diabetes, slow the progression of cardiovascular disease and prolong life.

Why is this kind of fasting so good for the body? One hypothesis is that our gut biome—the mix of gastrointestinal bacteria that's key to health—needs a rest to function optimally. In addition, fasting has been shown to help the body get rid of damaged cells and regenerate healthy new ones. Humans likely evolved eating this way—food was scarce, and we couldn't spend every day eating and snacking every few hours like we can now. Periodic fasting respects—maybe even resets—our internal body clocks.

CHOOSING A WAY TO FAST

The best fast is the one that fits into your lifestyle. *Here are three options supported by scientific evidence…*

•**Time-restricted eating.** This is the easiest fast to pull off. Every day, you simply restrict eating to a specific stretch of the day. You'll get the most benefits by limiting yourself to eating during just an eight-hour stretch—say, 10 am to 6 pm. But time-restricted eating is something you can ease into—for example, by restricting your eating to 12 hours…and then gradually scaling back to eight hours.

Eating at night, in particular, interferes with the body's natural day-night cycle, disrupting hormones in a way that favors weight gain. And there's psychology—choosing an end-point to the day's eating helps eliminate nighttime eating. *Let's face it:* No one is sitting in front of the TV at night eating carrot sticks. It's more likely to be ice cream or chips.

Tip: Get most of your calories early in the day, meaning you eat a big breakfast and a smaller lunch and dinner. It's fine to eat breakfast several hours after you wake up—that's healthy as long as it's not paired with late-night eating.

•**Periodic fasting.** On two consecutive days, you cut way back on calories—by 75%. The rest of the week, you eat in a normal fashion. The popular 5:2 Diet is an example of this approach.

•**Alternate-day fasting.** In this approach, you alternate days when you restrict calories—to perhaps 500 calories for the day—with days when you eat a normal, healthy diet. This way of fasting is one day on, one day off. It's effective, but some people find that they are too hungry on fasting days to sustain it.

Tip for periodic or alternate-day fasting: To meet your calorie goal and assure good nutrition on partial-fast days, make protein shakes with fruit and some form of healthy fat, such as ground flax or a no-sugar-added nut butter. A low-sugar plant-protein powder serves as the base. Two brands I like are Vega

---

EASY TO DO…

More Sustainable Intermittent Fasting

Intermittent fasting can be sustainable by changing the timing of meals. Eating dinner earlier in the day and significantly extending the overnight fast can make weight loss easier—and can improve metabolism even in people who do not lose weight. Consuming food only between, for example, 10 am and 6 pm, with no bedtime snacks, can improve health without the strains usually associated with intermittent-fasting recommendations.

Caution: People with diabetes or who have a history of eating disorders or who are pregnant or breastfeeding should try intermittent fasting only under medical supervision.

Health.Harvard.edu

and Kashi GoLean (I'm fond of the Vanilla Vinyasa flavor).

Caution: Before you start any fast, discuss it with your health-care provider. That's especially important if you have a medical condition. For example, although fasting may help improve diabetes, people who take blood sugar–lowering agents need to be especially careful about low blood sugar. Plus, some medications need to be taken with food.

**MORE TIPS FOR SUCCESSFUL
INTERMITTENT FASTING...**

• **See a registered dietitian (RD).** An RD can help you determine which of the eating patterns—if any—makes sense for you and help you put a plan into place. He/she can help you choose the most nutritious foods (especially important on days when you don't eat as much as you normally do)...and, if you need them, recommend nutritional supplements.

• **Be extra wary when you eat out on partial-fasting days.** Restaurants use more fat and sugar than you would at home, and portions are huge. It's easier to eat at home so that you know what you're taking in.

• **Consider professional metabolic testing.** How can you know what to eat to cut calories by, say, 75%? You start by calculating the calories you burn at rest—your resting metabolic rate, aka RMR—and then add everyday activities plus physical exercise. Online RMR calculators are notably inaccurate. *Better:* An FDA-approved calorimeter, which measures your RMR when you breathe into it. These instruments are too expensive to make it worth buying one for home use, but many RDs have them in their offices.

• **"Cheat" with nonstarchy vegetables.** If you find yourself extra-hungry on a fasting day, don't suffer too much. The best way to "cheat" is with low-glycemic vegetables, many of which have lots of filling fiber and all of which have very little effect on blood sugar or insulin levels. *Examples:* Salad greens, cruciferous vegetables (broccoli, cabbage, cauliflower, etc.), radishes, zucchini, summer squash, eggplant, tomatoes and mushrooms. *Bonus:* These types of vegetables are especially good at feeding beneficial gut bacteria. *One caution,* *though:* Don't pile on potatoes, winter squashes, corn, peas and the like—these are starchy vegetables that you shouldn't cheat with.

Low-Carb Danger

Low-carb diets are associated with higher mortality.

Recent report: People who consumed less than 30% of their calories from carbohydrates died about four years earlier than those who obtained 50% of their calories from carbs. But this was because most of the low-carb group ate primarily animal-based food or partially hydrogenated fats. Plant-based diets (nuts, plant oils and vegetables), even if low-carb, were not linked to higher increased risk.

Walter Willett, MD, professor of epidemiology and nutrition at Harvard T.H. Chan School of Public Health, Boston, and coauthor of a meta-analysis of 15,428 adults, published in *The Lancet.*

Easy Weight-Control: Eat Slowly

Slow eaters were 42% less likely to be overweight than fast eaters...and normal-speed eaters were 29% less likely to be overweight than fast eaters. Study participants who reduced their eating speed during the six-year study were more likely to lose weight.

Possible reason: It takes 20 minutes after eating for the brain to receive signals of satiety. In that time, faster eaters consume more calories.

Study of nearly 600,000 people with type 2 diabetes by researchers at Kyushu University, Fukuoko, Japan, published in *BMJ Open.*

Great Snack for Weight Loss—Tigernuts

Small, chewy tubers (a bit like tiny potatoes), tigernuts have a mild, nutty vanilla flavor. They are high in resistant starch, which passes through the intestines undigested—stabilizing blood sugar and making you feel full longer. Tigernuts can be eaten raw or in the form of horchata, a drink made from tigernuts and water.

Prevention.com

The Easy Way to Do HIIT

Robert Zembroski, DC, DACNB, a functional medicine physician, board-certified chiropractic neurologist, clinical nutritionist and director of the Darien Center for Functional Medicine in Connecticut. He is author of *Rebuild: Five Proven Steps to Move from Diagnosis to Recovery and Be Healthier Than Before.*

High-intensity interval training (HIIT) is one of the most exciting trends in fitness, but the word "intensity" can scare away all but the most committed. Exercise is *already* hard, you may be thinking, and now experts want to make it harder?

Actually, it's the opposite. Most people find HIIT easier than traditional cardio workouts, such as jogging, swimming or even shoveling snow. Compared with cardio training, HIIT more effectively improves your metabolic rate (for burning calories)…and improves your VO2 max—a parameter associated with cardiovascular health—according to research. In addition, it strengthens the immune system.

What most people don't realize: Even though HIIT alternates periods of all-out exertion with periods of lower-intensity exercise, the intense segments of the workout don't have to be too grueling. *More HIIT facts…*

THE MAGIC OF HIIT

With HIIT, you exercise as hard as you can for 30 seconds to a minute. (The actual exertion level and duration of the "burst" will vary from person to person.) Then you slow down to a lower intensity for a minute or two…then repeat the hard-easy sequence a few more times. The total length of the workout depends on your fitness level and physical abilities.

It's the "explosive" part of the workout that creates what can only be called "magic." People who engage in HIIT have better cardiovascular health—including improved cholesterol profiles and less insulin resistance—than those who do conventional endurance workouts, according to research.

EASE INTO HIIT

HIIT is a safe form of exercise, which poses no more risk for sprain/strain injuries than any other exercise regimen. As with any new workout, however, it's a good idea to get the go-ahead from your doctor before starting HIIT.

I tell people who are elderly or have physical limitations—or are merely new to exercise—to start with a *low-intensity* version of HIIT.

Example: If you're a 65-year-old who has mainly been sedentary, you might start out with a slow walk (the easy part of the exercise at up to 3 mph), then pick up your speed—walking at around 4 mph to 5 mph while swinging your arms for the hard part. After 30 seconds or a minute of fast-walking/arm-swinging, you'd drop back to a stroll for a minute or two, then maintain the cycle for four to five rounds. *To get started…*

• **Choose your sport.** With HIIT, it doesn't matter which activity you choose. You can do the exercise/rest cycles in a swimming pool or on a treadmill or an exercise bike—or using your own two feet. All that matters is that the activity allows you to go all-out for a brief period of time…drop down to a slower level… then go all-out once again. For most people, four of these intervals are enough to get an excellent workout.

• **Don't exercise on an empty stomach.** If you don't have enough blood sugar when you exercise, your body will pull sugar from the muscles first. That's the *opposite* of what you want to happen. To improve body composition, you want to preserve muscle and burn fat. The best way to do this is to exercise within one to three hours after having a small meal.

Good pre-workout meal choices: A couple of scrambled eggs with a few slivers of avocado and a side of veggies. Or a healthful protein bar such as RXBAR, Oatmega or SimplyProtein Whey Bar.

• **Work with your limitations.** Many of my patients have some physical limitations. They might be overweight…out of shape…or deal with arthritis, leg pain or other minor (or not so minor) disabilities. You can still engage in HIIT—you just have to find what works for you. A personal trainer can offer advice.

• **Go low and slow.** To start, I recommend doing an HIIT workout three days a week, for about 10 minutes each time. You'll slowly increase the total time—by increasing the number of intervals and/or the duration of the exertion/rest components—as you get stronger. Aim to work up to 20 to 30 minutes for each session.

• **Don't forget the warm-up and cooldown.** When you start your workout, whether it's biking, jogging or using a StairMaster, slowly go through these movements for the first few minutes…and shift into low intensity of the same exercise for a few minutes of cooldown at the end of the workout.

Each week, you'll find that you can gradually increase the duration and intensity of the workouts.

How to Stay Injury-Free from a Lifelong Triathlete

Tom Holland, an exercise physiologist and certified strength and conditioning specialist located in Darien, Connecticut. He serves as chief fitness adviser for Nautilus, Inc., and is author of *The Five-Minute Exercise Plan.* TeamHolland.com

---

During the past 30 years, exercise physiologist Tom Holland has completed more than 60 marathons, 25 triathlons and several ultramarathons stretching as far as 50 miles. Although the 50-year-old has asked a lot of his body, he has not endured a single significant injury since he separated his shoulder playing football in high school. Avoiding injury is vital to staying active and independent as we age—and even to avoiding physical therapy, which could easily cost $100 per session. *So we asked Holland to share his secrets for remaining injury-free despite being extremely active…*

• **I listen to my body.** I don't subscribe to the saying "No pain, no gain." If I feel an unusual twinge or tweak while I'm exercising, I stop what I'm doing. If I felt something was really wrong in the middle of a marathon, I'd take myself out (thankfully, it has never happened). Pushing through pain is how small issues become major injuries.

That doesn't mean I get to skip my workout whenever something seems off. It just means that I switch my focus to a different part of my body. If the twinge was in my knee, for example, I do upper-body exercises that day instead.

• **I do a little of many things rather than a lot of one thing.** I love running. I could happily run every day. I'm less a fan of swimming and biking, but I took up triathlons anyway—because excessive focus on one activity puts great stress on certain body parts while leaving others underdeveloped, increasing the odds of injury.

A balanced fitness plan includes upper- and lower-body work and addresses all five components of fitness…

Cardiovascular endurance: Activities that get the heart rate up and keep it up for at least several minutes, such as jogging, swimming and biking.

Muscle endurance: Using a muscle continuously over an extended period, such as holding a plank position or ascending long staircases without pausing.

Muscle strength: Such as lifting weights.

Body composition: Making sure, through diet and exercise, that you develop and maintain a healthy balance of fat and muscle.

Flexibility: Such as from stretching, yoga or Pilates.

You can incorporate all of the above without spending hours a day exercising—just don't do the same thing every day!

•**I begin very slowly with unfamiliar exercises and activities.** The risk for injury is greatest when we try new things. We don't yet know the proper forms and techniques...and our bodies aren't yet used to performing the necessary actions.

The first few times I try something, I set aside my ego and keep the reps slow and the difficulty low. There have been times when I've lifted so little weight at the gym that people have asked me if something is wrong. Better that my pride gets hurt than my body.

•**I'm extremely cautious about group fitness classes.** Fitness classes tend to be designed to be challenging for the strongest people in the class—which can leave novices at risk for injury as they struggle to keep up. Many instructors do not closely monitor participants' technique, either—they just shout encouragement from the front of the room. Even yoga can be dangerous for novices. I have a number of friends who sustained injuries in yoga class that could have been avoided with better oversight from the instructor.

Fitness classes can be socially fun and great motivators—I myself take some. But before trying any new class, I confirm that it's appropriate for someone at my level...and I ask the instructor to keep a close eye on my form. If I find that I can't keep up during the class, I don't try to—in fitness classes, ego gets people injured.

•**I'm always working on my balance.** Falls cause injuries. Preventing falls requires maintaining your ability to keep your balance, which naturally declines with age from loss of muscle strength and joint flexibility and changes in the inner ear.

Incorporating balance exercises into your day is as simple as standing on one foot while you brush your teeth, put on your socks or ride an elevator.

For even better balance, add to your workouts an exercise called a *single-leg floor* touch. Stand with your feet hip-width apart. Lift your right foot off the floor, raising the leg behind you, and hinge forward at the waist until your torso is parallel with the floor. As you do so, lightly touch the floor with your right hand. (You should bend your left leg as you do

this—this is *not* a stretching exercise.) Balance for a few seconds in that position, return to start, then repeat for a total of 10 reps. If needed for balance, hold your left arm out to the side or grasp something sturdy. Then switch sides, and do 10 reps with your left leg raised and left hand touching the floor.

•**I don't do exercises that often cause injuries.** I don't do straight-leg lifts—an exercise where you lie flat on your back and lift your fully extended legs. These put too much strain on the lower back. I don't do upright rows, where a barbell (or pair of dumbbells) is lifted repeatedly from waist height to collarbone height with the hands facing inward toward the body in an overhand grip. These put too much stress on the shoulders. And I don't do behind-the-neck lat pull-downs, where a bar attached to weights by a cable is pulled down until it is behind the neck. This also puts excessive stress on the shoulders. (Lat pull-downs are safe when the bar is pulled down to a position *in front* of the head.)

•**I do lateral training.** The most common exercise equipment includes treadmills, ellipticals, stationary bikes and stair climbers. The most common outdoor exercises include jogging and biking. What do all of these have in common? They all feature forward-only or forward-and-back movement, not side to side. That's one reason why seemingly fit people often get hurt when they play basketball, tennis or touch football for the first time in a while—these sports require rapid side-to-side movement, which their exercise routines have not prepared them to do.

I include side-to-side, or "lateral," exercises in my workouts. A lateral elliptical machine, which many gyms now have, is one way to do this. You also can train laterally with simple lateral lunges— stand with your feet shoulder width apart...take a big side step to your right, leaving your left foot where it is...bend your right knee until your right thigh is almost parallel with the floor,

keeping your left leg straight, your right knee approximately above your right foot, and both feet pointed forward. Return to standing without repositioning your left foot, then repeat to the left, and do 10 lunges on each side.

How to Exercise Despite Pain

Marilyn Moffat, PT, DPT, PhD, a practicing physical therapist and professor of physical therapy at New York University, New York City. She is author of two books for the lay audience and four professional books in the field. Steinhardt.nyu.edu/faculty/Marilyn_Moffat

---

Exercise is the magic elixir. It protects the heart, strengthens bones, lifts mood, increases energy, improves memory, boosts metabolism and prevents disease. But how can you get these benefits if your body *hurts?*

That is the problem for millions of Americans with chronic pain, especially knee pain or back pain. You want to exercise, but getting over that "pain hump" while you exercise is just too tough.

The irony is that pain not only makes regular exercise tougher—it also makes it more important. Why? It's a path toward less pain and a greater ability to do everyday tasks.

To learn how to get exercise when jogging or even walking is painful, we spoke with physical therapist Marilyn Moffat, PT, DPT, PhD. She homed in on two of the biggest obstacles that keep most individuals from doing pain-relieving exercise—knee pain and back pain. *Her recommendations…*

FINDING YOUR OWN PATH

I'll provide exercises below that almost everyone can do. But no single exercise is perfect for everybody, and your unique limitations and physical condition will dictate your ideal activity. Many people with chronic joint or back pain benefit from a detailed individual plan developed with a physical therapist. Ask your health-care provider for a recommendation or go to the website of the American Physical Therapy Association (MoveForwardPT.com), and click on "Find a PT" at the top of the page.

It's always a good idea to check with your doctor before beginning a new exercise program.

When trying these exercises, start slowly, be cautious and pay attention to doing them correctly. *Important:* Many people may need to build up to the "hold" times. For example, if an exercise calls for you to hold a pose for 30 seconds and that's too hard, try doing it for 10 seconds. If even that's too hard, just hold it as long as you can. You'll get stronger over time.

Stop immediately if any particular movement causes sharp pain, especially in a joint area. On the other hand, muscle fatigue (even burn) should be expected, especially with strengthening exercises. It's a good thing! *Let's get moving…*

IF YOU HAVE KNEE PAIN

The best way to reduce knee pain is to increase the strength and flexibility in the muscles that support your knee. The key is to find exercises that permit *pain-free range of motion.* That means taking the load off the joint as much as possible. Walking in waist-deep water is a great way to do this—but not everyone has regular access to a pool. *Alternatives…*

• **Seated straight-leg raises** build up the quadriceps, which help support the knees. *What to do:* Sit on the floor with your back against a wall. With one knee bent and the other leg straight out in front of you, wrap

---

EASY TO DO...

Simple Secret to Make Exercise Feel Easier

When volunteers smiled while they ran, their running economy (the volume of oxygen consumed during a workout) improved by a significant amount (2.78%) compared with when they grimaced…relaxed their upper bodies…or ran normally.

For the biggest boost: Grin at 30-second intervals.

Why smiling helps: It reduces the perception of effort…may relax the body…and offers a psychological boost.

Noel E. Brick, PhD, lecturer in sport and exercise psychology, Ulster University, Derry, Northern Ireland.

your hands around your bent leg, then slowly raise the straight leg up, keeping the knee as straight as possible—hold for 30 seconds. Then slowly lower the straight leg back to the floor. Do the exercise two or three times on each side.

• **Bridges** strengthen the hamstrings and quadriceps (key knee muscles), as well as the glutes and both the front and back of your body's core. *What to do:* Lie on your back with your knees bent, and your feet and upper arms on the floor. Bend your elbows to a 90-degree angle, with your fingers pointing to the ceiling. Lift your glutes (butt muscles) off the floor, then straighten one leg out in the air at the level of the opposite knee and hold for 30 seconds. Bend the knee down, put your foot back on the floor and lower your butt. Alternate legs. Do this exercise two or three times per leg.

IF YOU HAVE BACK PAIN

People with spinal stenosis (narrowing of the spaces within the spine) or other degenerative changes in the low back have a hard time with many exercises. Even walking can be difficult with spinal stenosis because each step slightly extends the spine, which narrows the spinal canal, exacerbating the pain.

What helps: Increasing flexibility and core strength. Yoga planks with the spine straight or slightly rounded are especially beneficial—they strengthen the core muscles that support the back as well as the arm and leg muscles. Pay attention to good form.

• **Basic front plank.** Start on your hands and knees with your hands directly under your shoulders and your knees directly under your  hips. Straighten one leg all the way back, then the other leg, and you should be in perfect position. (If weight bearing on straight arms is too difficult, do a plank on your forearms.) Tuck your chin in so that your neck is straight and

you are looking at the floor. Your spine should be in a straight line and not arched. Maintain as straight a line as is comfortable from your head through to your ankles. Hold for 30 seconds. Do two or three times.

• **Side plank also strengthens the core muscles and the arms and legs.** Start by lying on your right side and with your right hand directly under your right shoulder. Ideally your feet should be stacked one on top of the other, but it's fine to start with the bottom knee bent. Lift your hips off the floor, and keep a straight line from your head through your shoulder, hips and feet. As you lift your hips, push your right hand into the floor. (Again, if weight bearing on a straight arm is too difficult, do the side plank on your forearm.) Hold for 30 seconds. Alternate sides. Do two or three times on each side.

AEROBIC FITNESS FOR ANYONE WITH PAIN

Whether you have pain in your knees or back (or hips or somewhere else), getting aerobic activity to improve your circulation and protect your heart can be challenging. But it's vital! *Here are ways to do it…*

• **Recumbent exercise bikes** (the kind where you are seated against a backrest) and seated stepper machines allow you to build your aerobic capacity. Being seated while doing aerobic exercise usually is easier for your back and reduces the forces on your knees that would occur if you were using a treadmill. The seated stepper, which resembles a recumbent elliptical machine, engages your arms as well as your legs. Many gyms have these machines.

What about walking? It's great if you can do it comfortably. *Tip:* To absorb impact, wear sneakers that have good cushioned bottoms, add gel inserts into the sneakers and wear padded socks.

• **When walking on a treadmill,** use the handrails for support and to off-load some of the force of the body weight on your back and knees.

• **When walking outside,** choose school tracks or nature paths if possible—they're a little easier than paved sidewalks and roads—and you might consider walking poles. They help to absorb some impact, engage your upper body, help intensify your workout and improve stability. They are available at sporting-goods stores and online. Be sure to use two poles for the best balance and posture.

A Group Class Can Help You Get More from Your Exercise

Paul A. Estabrooks, PhD, behavioral scientist, professor and Harold M. Maurer Distinguished Chair of the department of health promotions at University of Nebraska Medical Center in Omaha. His research has been published in *Annals of Behavioral Medicine, American Journal of Preventive Medicine* and other professional journals. He is an author of "Group-Based Physical Activity for Older Adults Randomized Controlled Trial," recently published in *Health Psychology*.

We all want to get as many health benefits as possible from the exercise we do. *What most people don't realize:* Group workouts—especially those that have a few special features—offer an array of unexpected health benefits. *What you need to know about this powerful exercise booster…*

If you're skeptical that group workouts could offer more than an intense solitary jog on your treadmill, there's a body of research that gives some convincing reasons why going solo may not be the best approach. *Compared with solo exercise, group workouts are linked to…*

• **Less pain.** When adults exercised for 45 minutes on rowing machines, those who had rowed in groups demonstrated a higher pain tolerance versus solitary rowers, according to research published in *International Journal of Sport and Exercise Psychology*. Researchers theorize that physically syncing up with others stimulates a release of feel-good endorphins.

• **Greater motivation to push harder.** A phenomenon called the Köhler effect motivates people to strive harder when working in a group. Research conducted at Kansas State University found that this phenomenon really kicks into high gear when you exercise with people you perceive as stronger than yourself, inspiring exercisers to work out nearly 200% longer and harder than when working out alone.

Caveat: Simply being in a room with other people isn't enough to reap all of these great benefits. The key is finding what researchers call a "true group class."

THE MAGIC OF A TRUE GROUP CLASS

A true group class is one in which the instructor takes steps to promote bonding among participants and a collective goal. For example, your instructor might start class by saying, "Over the next 45 minutes, we are going to collectively walk the equivalent of three laps around the Parthenon."

Important: Typically, group-based fitness classes are more effective than solo workouts *only* when they use these types of group dynamic strategies. In a meta-analysis published in *Sport & Exercise Psychology Review*, researchers compared the benefits of home workouts, standard exercise classes and true group classes. *Result:* True group classes were deemed the most beneficial—mainly because people stick with exercise longer when they are working out in these groups. Solo exercise at home ranked last.

The special ingredient seems to be the *bonding* that takes place in these classes. Feeling like you belong to a group is a very basic human need…one that research has linked with improved health and longevity—especially as one ages.

WHAT TO LOOK FOR

To find a class with this dynamic…

• **Find an instructor you love.** If you feel inspired and challenged by the instructor, the rest of the class likely feels the same way. This creates a sense of connection among participants and gives everyone something to chat about in the locker room.

• **Exercise with people your age.** A study of 627 adults published in *Health Psychology* found that being in a class with other people your own age improves the chances that you will stick with your exercise plan—more so than being among classmates of the same gender. Look for a class with members who are within about five years of your own age.

• **Look for a class with competition built in.** Boot camps and boutique fitness classes—such as those offered by Orangetheory Fitness, a nationwide fitness franchise, and Flywheel Sports, which offers cycling studios at 42 locations across the US and an app for on-demand cycling workouts you can do at home (with purchase of the Fly bike)—encourage friendly competition by allowing participants to compare their performance results.

• **Experiment with virtual group classes.** No class available? You can still reap the benefits of a collective workout with a virtual group class, such as those offered by Peloton, which provides cycling workouts you can do while streaming live and on-demand fitness classes with instructors and fellow participants.

Note: While on-demand classes offer the benefit of friendly competition, they do not provide the positive effects associated with bonding.

How to Make Yoga Safe for *Every Body*

Carol Krucoff, C-IAYT, E-RYT, a yoga therapist and codirector of the Integrative Yoga for Seniors Professional Training at Duke Integrative Medicine, Durham, North Carolina. She is coauthor of, most recently, *Relax into Yoga for Seniors: A Six-Week Program for Strength, Balance, Flexibility and Pain Relief.* HealingMoves.com

I'd love to try yoga, but… It's a common lament of people with arthritis, osteoporosis or other chronic health problems. But yoga doesn't have to be off-limits if you have one of these conditions.

With a few precautions and a tailored approach, yoga is a wonderfully effective, research-backed method of improving strength, balance and flexibility…easing pain…and relieving the anxiety and depression that are often associated with chronic health complaints.

For anyone with one or more painful and/or limiting chronic conditions, the relaxation

breathing and mindfulness that are central to yoga also can be exceptionally helpful.

Note: Older adults and people with health challenges should look for a class called "Gentle Yoga" or one geared to their needs, such as "Yoga Over 50" or "Yoga for Creaky Bodies." *Follow these steps to ensure that you stay safe if you have…*

ARTHRITIS

Decades ago, people with osteoarthritis and rheumatoid arthritis were advised to rest and "save their joints." Now we know that inactivity can actually cause stiff joints. Yoga relieves pain and stiffness, improves range of motion and sleep, and boosts energy levels and overall mood. *If you have arthritis, be sure to…*

• **Avoid putting excessive pressure on arthritic joints.** Arthritis in your left knee? Keep the toes of your right foot on the ground in single-leg balance poses like Tree Pose. If you have arthritis in both knees, you can relieve the load on your joints by lightly touching a wall or chair.

• **Understand the meaning of different types of pain.** Sharp, immediate pain—especially in a joint—is a sign to ease up. If you have dull pain in your muscles the day after a yoga session, that's likely delayed-onset muscle soreness after using your muscles in new ways—a sign that you're getting stronger! It generally goes away in a few days.

• **Don't overstretch.** This is especially true for people with rheumatoid arthritis, which can render joints loose and unstable. *To tell* *whether it's a good or risky stretch:* Check your breath. If your breath is compromised in any way, back off.

• **Avoid chin-to-chest poses that place pressure on your head.** Poses, such as Plow, place undue pressure on vulnerable cervical spine joints.

• **Turn certain poses around to "take a load" off.** If a pose is bothering an affected joint, try turning it upside down or sideways, taking weight off the joint and letting gravity do the work for you. Child's Pose, for example, can be done while lying on your back in bed.

Caution: Hot, red and/or swollen joints indicate active inflammation. Stick with rest or gentle range-of-motion activities for that joint. Talk with your health-care provider about appropriate treatment.

OSTEOPOROSIS

Yoga is an effective way to improve strength, balance and flexibility in people with osteoporosis. And because yoga improves your balance and strengthens bone, it may help lower your risk of falling and breaking a bone. *If you have osteoporosis, be sure to…*

• **Avoid rounding your spine when sitting or standing,** since this position increases the risk for vertebral fracture. In yoga poses—and in daily life—keep your spine long and hinge forward at your hips, rather than bending at your waist.

• **Don't twist your spine to its end range of rotation.** Instructors may encourage their students to twist as far as possible, using their hands to move even deeper into the twist. This is called end-range rotation and can increase fracture risk in people with osteoporosis. Keep any twists in the midrange, as you would when turning to look over your shoulder while driving. Move slowly, don't round your back and keep your spine elongated.

• **Avoid loading body weight on your neck and/or shoulders** as occurs during such poses as Shoulder Stand and Plow.

• **Keep your head on the ground during supine (face-up) poses.** Lifting your head when lying on the ground creates the forward-flexing, "abdominal crunch" action that can be dangerous because it places excess pressure on vertebral bodies and can lead to compression fractures. Yoga poses that can create this "crunch" are not necessarily supine—they include Standing Forward Bend and Seated Forward Bend. To perform these poses safely, hinge at the hips and keep your spine in neutral (don't round your back).

4 Ways to Build Better Balance

Carol Clements, MA, who has more than 45 years of experience as a personal trainer and teacher of many movemeant arts, techniques and methods. She is also author of *Better Balance for Life* and works privately with clients in New York City. CarolClements.com

When it comes to health risks, most people can rattle off a list that includes being overweight, eating an unhealthy diet and sitting too much. Few people would think to name poor balance as a serious danger…but they should.

Balance is a crucial but under-recognized element of good health. Unfortunately, loss of muscle strength and other factors cause us to become more wobbly as we age. So it's no surprise that one of every four adults age 65 and older in the US reports falling each year.

The good news is, balance is a skill that you can improve. *Here's how…*

GETTING STARTED

Feeling insecure about your balance can lead to a fear of falling, which will inhibit your daily activities—and actually increase your risk of falling. Practicing your balance will help you gain more confidence and overcome any fear you may have.

Important: Balance problems can be caused by a variety of medical conditions. Some of the most common causes are abnormalities in the vestibular system (the inner ear)…weak muscles or unstable joints…less visual acuity…certain medications…alcohol… and various neurological disorders, including peripheral neuropathy—especially involving nerves of the feet. Your doctor can rule out

To Check Your Balance, Start with This Self Test

Balance is a critical element of our overall well-being. But it's not something you can take for granted. It can decline almost imperceptibly, and a dangerous fall can happen in a split second.

A frightening trend: Deaths from falls are on the rise in the US, according to a 2018 report from the Centers for Disease Control and Prevention. The number of people 65 and older who died as a result of a fall jumped from 18,334, in 2007 to 29,668 in 2016. While the reasons for this steep increase are not fully understood, good balance is undoubtedly among the best defenses against this serious danger.

If you're concerned about your balance, be sure to discuss it with your doctor. There can be a variety of underlying causes. If you think your balance is fine, give yourself the following quick self-test to see just how steady you really feel on your feet.

What to do: Stand upright, with your feet together, behind a sturdy chair. Cross your arms over your chest and slowly close your eyes. If necessary, place one hand on the seat back for support. Do you feel stable? Wobbly? Nervous? Notice how you react to this balance challenge. (By excluding sight, you rely on your body's use of sensory nerve endings and other body-orienting input that contributes to achieving balance.)

It's a good idea to tell your doctor about your results—and to repeat the self-test periodically to informally check your balance.

any medical problems that may make balance practice unsafe or give you the go-ahead to begin the regimen described below.

4 BALANCE BOOSTERS

To improve your balance, a good strategy is to fit a few targeted moves into your everyday activities. Within a matter of days, you'll begin to incorporate them into your daily routine—and without even breaking a sweat. *My favorite everyday balance boosters can be done while...*

•**Watching television.** *What to do:* While sitting, take off your shoes and socks, prop one foot up on a coffee table or the couch, and interlace your fingers between your toes.

Use your fingers to spread out all five toes so that they are not touching one another. Maintain this position for one minute. Relax. Repeat on your other foot. Then alternate flexing and pointing each foot 10 times. Finally, try to wiggle each toe one at a time. This may be difficult at first, but remember that you will improve with practice. These relaxed micro-movements of the foot are an important part of standing and balancing.

•**Brushing your teeth.** *What to do:* Lightly place the fourth (ring) finger of your nonbrushing hand on the edge of the sink or vanity, so as you stand, you have that bit of support from your finger on the counter but are not holding on tightly. (Use this finger, since it is capable of only light touch to steady yourself.) Move one foot slightly behind you and off the floor. This exercise will force you to adjust your center of gravity and recruit more hip and core muscles to stabilize yourself. Alternate feet morning and night, optimally for as long as it takes you to brush your teeth. If you lose your balance at first, touch the nonstanding foot to the floor lightly to steady yourself and calmly resume balancing.

To up your game: Stand on one foot without touching the sink...then with your free arm extended overhead.

•**Talking on the phone.** *What to do:* Stand up. With your feet hip-width apart and your knees directly over your ankles, imagine yourself squeezing a balloon between your shins. This squeezing motion, called adduction, will strengthen your adductor muscles of the inner thighs and hips to help keep you stable.

•**Walking down a hallway.** *What to do:* Find a safe, clear hallway and walk down it backward at least once a day.

This exercise requires coordination of reversed foot mechanics and the transfer of weight in the less familiar backward direction. The first time you do this, look over your shoulder and count the number of steps it takes until you reach the end. After that, you can count out that number of steps in your head while keeping your gaze forward. If you feel unsteady, reach out to the wall on either side of you or have someone with you. Gazing forward is easier on the neck, and you can't use sight to orient yourself in the familiar forward direction.

Most important: In addition to these exercises, find an enjoyable activity that keeps you on your feet. Whether it's dancing, playing table tennis, flying a kite or walking your dog, the more you move, the better your balance!

Surefire Ways to Prevent Muscle Loss: Best Foods, Supplements and Exercises

Stuart M. Phillips, PhD, professor in the department of kinesiology and Michael G. DeGroote School of Medicine, McMaster University, Ontario, Canada. He is director of the McMaster Centre for Nutrition, Exercise and Health Research and a fellow of the American College of Sports Medicine and the American College of Nutrition. His scientific papers have been published in *The American Journal of Clinical Nutrition, Medicine & Science in Sports & Exercise* and other leading journals.

Starting in your 30s, your muscles began shrinking, making you imperceptibly but steadily weaker. And now, as each year ticks by, you keep weakening—losing muscle mass at a rate of 0.5% to 1% a year—so that the loss of strength is more obvious. At some point, if it hasn't happened already, you'll be in your kitchen wrestling with a jar of spaghetti sauce and thinking, *Why do they make these lids so much tighter than they used to?*

Loss of muscle mass and strength isn't just an inconvenience. It's one of the most accurate indicators—for seniors and the middle-aged and the young—that disease and death may be in your near future.

Scary findings: Study after study shows that people with less strength are more likely to be hospitalized or to die of any cause, including heart disease, stroke, cancer and pneumonia, within a given period. Scientists haven't figured out all the reasons that strength predicts health and well-being, but it's not only because unhealthy people get weaker—in fact, a reduction in strength is a *better predictor* of dying from cardiovascular disease than is high blood pressure.

If you have told your doctor that you're a bit weaker these days, and he/she said it's a "normal part of aging"—ignore him. You can and should preserve and build muscle mass and strength at *any* age—it's as important to health and longevity as keeping your arteries free of plaque and your cells free of cancer. And you can do it with a surprisingly simple three-pronged strategy—a routine of three simple strengthening exercises (no gym required)...the right diet...and three particular nutritional supplements that are proven muscle protectors. *Here's how to do it...*

BEST EXERCISES

Preserve and build the muscles in your arms, legs, hips and back that you need for everyday strength and activity by doing these three exercises two or three times a week at home or anywhere else (of course, check with your doctor before starting any new exercise routine)...

• **Body-weight squat.** Stand directly in front of a stable, not-too-high chair with no armrest and with your back toward the chair seat and your feet shoulder-width apart. Slowly bend your legs, keeping your back straight and arms at your sides and knees over your toes, and lower yourself onto the chair. Then stand up slowly by reversing the motion. Do this 30 times. If you can't do 30 repetitions at first (and many people can't), start with what you can do, and over a period of days or weeks, work up to 30. (The same goes for the next two exercises.) If you can do even more, all the better—but 30 should be your minimum target.

• **Lunge.** While standing, keep your upper body straight and your shoulders back, and step forward with one leg, lowering your hips until both knees are bent at a 90-degree angle. Return to the standing position. Do 15 times on each side for a total of 30.

• **Push-up or modified push-up.** This oldie but goodie develops the upper back, shoulders, arms, chest and wrists. If you can't yet do "full" push-ups (with only your hands and toes on the ground), start with modified push-ups in which your toes and knees are on the ground...or even with easier "wall push-ups" where you stand facing a wall and place your hands on the wall at shoulder height. Your ultimate goal is at least 30 full push-ups.

Also important: Aerobic exercise to maintain fitness. You don't have to run miles and miles. A 25-minute jog or vigorous cycling just three times a week...or a 30-minute brisk walk five times a week will do the trick.

BEST FOODS

The ideal strategy for staying strong is like a three-level pyramid. The base of the pyramid—the *essential* factor—is exercise as described above, and the most important dietary component for your muscles is protein, the material out of which muscles are made. And believe it or not, despite the prevalence of meat in the typical Western diet, many Americans don't get enough protein for the best possible muscle strength.

The government's Recommended Dietary Allowance (RDA) for protein is 0.36 grams (g) of protein per pound of body weight per day. But that level is the minimum, not the optimum. For preserving and building muscle, we need at least 50% more—0.54 g of protein per pound of body weight per day. And some studies indicate that 0.73 g per pound of body weight is even better. (More than that doesn't build more muscle or strength.)

Problem: Most seniors get only two-thirds of the RDA, or about 0.24 g of protein per pound of body weight per day.

How much protein should you eat? Don't go by the government's RDA. Instead multiply your body weight in pounds by 0.54 to get the *minimum* number of grams per day...and multiply your body weight by 0.73 to get the *maximum* daily grams of protein likely to help your muscles. Then each day, aim to eat an amount in between those two results.

Example: An individual who weighs 150 pounds would multiply 150 by 0.54 to get a minimum daily protein goal of 81 g...and multiply 150 by 0.73 to get a maximum useful daily protein amount of 109 g.

Equally important: Not only do you need enough protein—you need the kind that your muscles can easily use. The best muscle-build-

ing protein has two features. It is *digestible*—the amino acids that are the building blocks of protein are easily absorbed. Protein from meat, poultry, fish and other seafood, eggs and dairy is far more digestible than protein from plants. And the best protein for muscles has a high level of the amino acid *leucine*, which kick-starts muscle-building. The digestible sources of protein mentioned above also have the most leucine.

To optimize muscle-building, you also need to get protein at every meal, because unlike unused carbohydrates and unused fat, unused protein is not stored by the body for later use. *Best strategy:* Eat a highly digestible form of leucine-rich protein, chosen from the above sources, at every meal.

Examples: For breakfast, eat two eggs (12 g protein) and one-half cup of yogurt (6 g). For lunch, cut up four ounces of chicken breast (35 g protein) into a salad. For dinner, eat a six-ounce serving of high-quality (preferably organic) meat or fish (around 40 g protein) along with vegetables and whole grains. For a bedtime snack, have one-half cup of cottage cheese (12 g protein). *Grand total:* 105 g of protein, or just about the perfect amount to help preserve strength for our 150-pounder. *Note:* Some medical conditions, for example kidney disease, can make it dangerous to consume even moderate amounts of protein—check first with your physician.

EASY TO DO...

Bananas Lessen Aches and Pains

Bicyclists had reduced inflammation during recovery if they ate bananas during rides instead of consuming sports drinks or water. They had less evidence of an enzyme that causes pain and inflammation, which usually is treated with drugs such as *ibuprofen*. It may be that antioxidants and other nutrients from bananas are all the body needs to perform better and recover faster.

David C. Nieman, DrPH, professor of health and exercise science at Appalachian State University, Kannapolis, North Carolina.

BEST SUPPLEMENTS

In a recent study by my colleagues and me at McMaster University, we added three nutritional supplements to the diets of older men who also were engaged in an exercise program—and the supplements increased strength and muscle mass more than exercise alone (of course, check with your physician to make sure that any new supplement is safe for you)…

•**Whey protein.** Milk has two main proteins—casein and whey. Whey is separated from casein during cheese-making, and whey protein powder is a supplement containing that by-product. It is unusually rich in leucine.

Suggested amount: If you are meeting your target range of daily protein from food as described above, you don't need a protein supplement. If you fall a bit short, mix enough protein powder into the drink of your choice (many people use milk) to reach the total daily range of protein for your body weight as described above. (Check the label of your whey product to determine how much powder provides that much protein.) Don't get more than 50 g of daily protein from whey powder—it is not a total substitute for protein-rich food. When buying whey powder, look for "NSF" on the label—NSF is a third-party organization that certifies products that have met rigorous manufacturing standards.

Best timing: Take whey protein soon after exercise, which maximizes muscle-building. If you can't consume whey because of an allergy or some other reason, consider a soy protein supplement instead.

•**Creatine.** This amino acid will boost the body's ability to produce energy and help build muscle. *Recent finding:* In a study published in *Nutrients*, just six days of creatine supplementation improved upper-body strength by almost 3%. *Suggested amount:* Two capsules per day, in divided doses, that together total 4 g to 5 g.

•**Fish oil.** The omega-3 fatty acids in fish oil (EPA and DHA) make your muscles more sensitive to protein, encouraging muscle-building. *Suggested amount:* 750 milligrams (mg) of EPA and 500 mg of DHA per day.

4 Best Exercises to Do When You're Stuck in a Chair

Tom Holland, an exercise physiologist and certified strength and conditioning specialist located in Darien, Connecticut. He serves as chief fitness adviser for Nautilus, Inc., and is author of *The Five-Minute Exercise Plan.* TeamHolland.com

If so many of us are always busy, why are our bodies getting weaker and weaker? It's mainly because we spend so much time sitting! The less we move, the more muscle mass we lose, leaving us vulnerable to injury—not to mention increased risk for obesity, diabetes and stroke. But all is not lost.

We recently turned to exercise physiologist Tom Holland, who shared his four favorite exercises for individuals who are stuck in their chairs…*

EXERCISE #1: **No-Hand Get-Ups.** When we sit for prolonged periods, our powerful butt muscles or "glutes" (*gluteus maximus* and *gluteus medius*) begin to atrophy. Weak glutes can affect posture and movement, which can translate into knee injuries and hip problems as other muscles try to compensate for our deconditioned glutes.

What to do: Start from a seated position. Then…

•Stand up from the chair—*without* using your hands to push off or grab hold of anything. That's it.

•Stand up relatively slowly, to a count of about two seconds. Extend your arms straight out in front of you to help your balance.

•Then lower yourself back down even more slowly, to a count of four seconds. This controlled movement—working against gravity—tones your muscles.

•Repeat five to 10 times daily.

EXERCISE #2: **Butt-Pain Stretch.** When people complain of a mysterious pain in their backside, the cause is often due to overuse of the *piriformis*, a muscle deep inside the glute that extends from the pelvis to the outer hip.

*If you are wearing shoes with a heel greater than one inch, take them off before doing these exercises.

Because the piriformis is a major part of our lower-body infrastructure, that "pain in the butt" is a warning that additional pains (including hip pain and low-back pain) are yet to come if this one is ignored.

What to do: *To get a good piriformis stretch and eliminate the pain…*

•Cross your right leg over your left leg so that your right ankle rests on your left knee. You may feel some tension in the upper-back portion of your right thigh.

•*Gently* press your right knee toward the ground, breathing into the stretch. You should feel a stretch in the muscle deep in your buttocks. You should not feel any stress on the knee itself—if you do, try pressing on the inside of the lower thigh just above the knee. Stretch only as far as is comfortable.

•Lean slightly forward, and hold the stretch for 10 to 30 seconds.

•Switch legs and repeat. Do two to three repetitions per side a few times a day.

EXERCISE #3: **Chair Crunches.** This simple exercise works your abdominal core muscles to help prevent low-back pain and other sore muscles and joints.

What to do: To build your core, lean slightly back in your chair. *Then…*

•Lift both knees up so that you are balanced and your feet are six to 10 inches off the ground. (If you are sitting on a couch, scoot toward the front of the cushion, lean back slightly and start from there.)

•Hold that position for 30 seconds…or as long as you can. This exercise is about time, not repetition. Be sure to keep your shoulders down and relaxed, and remember to breathe normally. Perform this exercise once to several times a day.

EXERCISE #4: **Twist Stretch.** This back stretch sounds more complicated than it is… and once you try it, you'll wonder how you ever got through a day without it.

What to do: To get started, sit up straight with both feet flat on the floor. *Then…*

•Place your left hand on the outside of your right knee.

•Place your right hand on the outside of the right armrest of the chair.

•Rotate your upper body to the right. You should feel a stretch in your lower back. Your head should follow along naturally with your upper body. Stretch only as far as is comfortable. Hold the stretch for a count of five, remembering to breathe throughout the stretch. *Note:* If you feel pain, stop—this exercise should not cause any pain.

•Then switch. Place your right hand on the outside of your left knee…with your left hand, hold the outside of the left armrest of the chair… and rotate your upper body to the left.

•Repeat the cycle (turning once on each side) a total of three times. If you sit for long periods (especially in a confined space, such as an airline seat), try to do this stretch at least once every 15 to 30 minutes.

5

Natural Health News

The Ultra-Healthy Foods You're Probably Not Eating

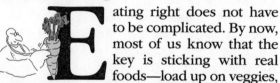

ating right does not have to be complicated. By now, most of us know that the key is sticking with real foods—load up on veggies, along with some healthy fats. We also know that a food can be "low fat," "high fiber" or "gluten free" and still be pure junk.

Yet even the most knowledgeable eaters continue to miss out on plenty of ultra-healthy foods that fly under the radar.

To dispel some of the common myths that prevent so many people from benefiting from these lesser-known foods, we recently spoke with Mark Hyman, MD, a leading expert in nutritional wellness and director of the Cleveland Clinic Center for Functional Medicine.

MYTH #1: **Chicken is always a healthier choice than beef.** *The truth:* There's nothing

particularly healthy about America's most consumed meat—mass-produced chicken.

While the chickens raised in your grandmother's backyard ate a varied diet of grass, weeds, bugs and seeds, chickens raised on most commercial farms today get a steady diet of grains, corn and soy—often topped off with doses of antibiotics and arsenic.

This diet fattens them up quickly, but it produces poultry that is lower in inflammation-fighting omega-3 fatty acids and higher in inflammation-promoting omega-6 fatty acids. Grain-fed chickens also are lower in vitamins and minerals.

What to do: Choose chickens that are certified "100% organic" and pasture-raised (not free range—which only tells you that the birds

Mark Hyman, MD, director of the Cleveland Clinic Center for Functional Medicine in Ohio. Dr. Hyman also is chairman of the board of the Institute for Functional Medicine and founder and director of The UltraWellness Center, based in Lenox, Massachusetts. He is author of several books, including *Food: What the Heck Should I Eat? DrHyman.com*

got outside, not what they ate). If you find that the cost of organic is an issue, "antibiotic-free" chicken is better than conventional but not ideal.

As for that beef: It does have a little more saturated fat than chicken, but 17 large reviews of the scientific literature on saturated fat found no link between saturated fat and heart disease.

That doesn't mean you should go crazy with saturated fat—we're still figuring out how much is healthy. But you should know that a nice grass-fed steak is more nutritious than the typical supermarket chicken breast.

MYTH #2: **Liver is bad for you.** *The truth*: Even people who are comfortable eating steak, pork chops and pot roast may pause before trying that generations-old family recipe for liver and onions.

But liver is much more nutrient-dense than muscle meat—that's why when a lion takes down a zebra, it goes for the liver first. Liver contains ample amounts of vitamins A, B-12 and C, and minerals such as copper, iron, zinc, phosphorus and magnesium. It contains just as much protein as a beef roast or steak—and it's cheaper.

One reason liver fell out of favor is its high level of cholesterol. But research now tells us that eating cholesterol does not significantly raise our blood cholesterol (that's why we now know it's fine to eat eggs, too).

What to do: Whenever possible, choose liver from grass-fed animals. *And don't stop there:* Try other organ meats, such as hearts, kidneys and sweetbreads. Even though they may not sound appealing, they usually taste good!

MYTH #3: **Vegetables are boring.** *The truth*: If you think veggies are dull, you are doing them wrong. The most boring vegetables, such as iceberg lettuce and white potatoes, are the least nutritious.

The best choices are often the "weird" heirloom varieties you find from small farms—everything from purple carrots to knobby kohlrabi to dandelion greens.

As you surely already know, you should fill at least half of your plate with a wide variety of

GOOD TO KNOW...

Foods That Fight Specific Diseases

●**Eggs may help to reduce risk factors associated with diabetes** in overweight and obese people.

●**Eating about 1.5 ounces of pecans daily cuts risk for both heart disease and diabetes** in overweight adults age 45 and older.

●**Yogurt helps protect against colorectal cancer.**

●**Vegetables and berries reduce risk for Parkinsonism** (a group of neurological movement-problem disorders similar to those seen with Parkinson's disease) and slow its progression.

●**Drinking three or more cups of coffee a day reduces the risk for liver disease.**

An overview of multiple research projects recently presented at a meeting of the American Society for Nutrition.

vegetables in a rainbow of colors, and I recommend aiming for seven or eight servings a day as a minimum. Go mostly for locally grown and organic veggies for the best flavor.

A good way to find more variety: Look to the sea. If you have eaten seaweed only as a sushi wrapper, you are missing out. Seaweed is not only rich in vitamin C and iron but also contains hard-to-come-by minerals, such as manganese and iodine, as well as anticancer compounds.

You can find several forms of seaweed, including wakame, kombu and nori, in Asian food markets. And some stores sell roasted, lightly salted seaweed snacks you can munch on like potato chips—without the guilt.

MYTH #4: **Fresh fruit is always the best fruit.** *The truth*: Fruit that is flash frozen at the peak of ripeness can be more nutritious than fruit picked unripe so that it can then be shipped thousands of miles.

A frozen berry loses none of its antioxidants while it waits for you to open up your freezer and toss it into a smoothie or salad. A fresh berry does lose nutrients, and it can go moldy before you have a chance to use it. Frozen fruits are cheaper, too. If you buy frozen fruit, also opt for organic.

What to do: Regardless of the fruit you choose, it's important to not overdo it—especially if you are overweight or have diabetes or prediabetes. While fruit is a lot healthier than candy or juice, it still contains a lot of natural sugar and may raise your blood sugar. Two or three servings a day are plenty for anyone.

MYTH #5: **Peanut butter is a great protein source.** *The truth:* Most commercial peanut butters are loaded with high-fructose corn syrup and industrial hydrogenated oils. Peanuts also can contain the fungus *aflatoxin*, which has been linked to cancer.

An occasional spoonful of peanut butter or handful of peanuts is fine, but this legume (it's not a nut) is not the nutritional powerhouse that tree nuts are.

What to do: If you like nut butters, go for almond, macadamia and cashew butters made without added oils, sugars or other ingredients.

See if you can find a store that grinds nuts into butter on the spot, but buy in small amounts so that the oils do not have a chance to go rancid. Store in the refrigerator.

MYTH #6: **Soy foods are health foods.** *The truth:* Many foods containing soy are among the worst in our diets.

The greatest offender is something you probably do not even know you consume—soybean oil, the oil of choice for most processed, packaged foods. It is the primary source of inflammatory omega-6 fatty acids in the typical American diet.

Processed soy protein is also found in many manufactured foods—for both animals and humans—that are not very healthy. Avoid foods, such as energy and protein bars, fake hot dogs, burgers and shakes, with "soy protein isolate" on the label.

Some fermented tempeh or simple tofu can be fine (if you buy organic to avoid pesticides and the GMO herbicide *glyphosate*) as well as steamed edamame, but there is no good reason to eat a soy hot dog. The soy protein isolate found in such products has been linked in some studies to allergies, cancer and dementia.

Whole-Fat Dairy May Be Good for You

Whole-fat dairy in moderation is not harmful, as once believed, and it may even be healthful. In a large international study, people who consumed, on average, two to three servings per day of full-fat dairy had lower risk for heart disease and stroke when compared with people who ate less than one-half serving of whole-fat dairy per day. One serving could be one cup of yogurt, one slice of cheese or a glass of milk.

Mahshid Dehghan, PhD, a nutritional epidemiologist at Population Health Research Institute at McMaster University, Ontario, Canada, and lead author of the study published in *The Lancet.*

These 4 "Super Spices" Have Hidden Benefits

Joshua Levitt, ND, a naturopathic physician and medical director at Whole Health Natural Family Medicine in Hamden, Connecticut. Dr. Levitt is a clinical preceptor for Yale School of Medicine and collaborates with the Integrative Medicine Center at Yale New Haven Hospital. He is author of *The Honey Phenomenon* and numerous other books and articles. WholeHealthCT.com

When it comes to "superfoods," fruits and veggies aren't the only heavy hitters. A handful of popular spices also have gained a rightful place on this list because of their own research-supported therapeutic effects.

Examples of the best known: Cinnamon for diabetes. Garlic for high cholesterol. Ginger for nausea. Cayenne for pain relief.

What you may not realize: Those same spices have even more benefits—*little-known* but powerful—that are also backed by scientific evidence. *How to use these spices for even greater preventive and curative effect...*

CINNAMON

A small daily dose of cinnamon has been proven in many studies to lower and help regulate blood sugar—crucial for those trying to prevent or manage type 2 diabetes.

Little-known benefit: Cinnamon also can lower high blood pressure.

Scientific evidence: In a recent study published in *Lipids in Health and Disease*, people who ingested 3 g (about two-thirds of a teaspoon) of cinnamon daily had a significant drop in blood pressure after four months—from averages of 136/88 to 122/80.

How to get more: Because cinnamon is so tasty, it's easy to include more in your diet. As a heavy cinnamon user, I buy organic Ceylon cinnamon (the highest quality) by the pound. *Note:* Supermarket cinnamon is usually cassia (or Vietnamese), which contains a compound called coumarin that may damage the liver at high doses in susceptible individuals.

Cinnamon is great on roasted sweet potatoes and squash and adds delightful sweetness to pancakes and waffles. Plus, because it's such a powerful antioxidant, a sprinkle of cinnamon stops apple slices from turning brown—making the treat more delicious and more appetizing.

GARLIC

This potent spice—a rich source of many healing compounds—is proven to lower cholesterol, reducing your risk for heart disease.

Little-known benefit: Eating garlic regularly also may help reduce your risk for colorectal cancer.

Scientific evidence: When Italian researchers analyzed seven case-control studies on garlic consumption and colorectal cancer, they found that people who ate the most garlic reduced their risk for the disease by 37% compared with people who ate the least. These studies measured garlic intake in various ways, so there is no optimal intake. To be fair, there is also research showing *no* correlation between garlic and colorectal cancer risk, but even the potential benefit makes garlic a smart addition to one's diet.

How to get more: Lightly sautéed fresh cloves are likely the healthiest way to consume garlic, but you also can use garlic flakes or powder. I use garlic (usually combined with lemon) in nearly every cooking liquid, sauce and marinade that I make in my kitchen.

GINGER

Dozens of studies have proven ginger's usefulness in easing nausea and vomiting due to everything from chemotherapy to motion sickness to morning sickness.

Little-known benefit: Ginger also inhibits the COX-1 and COX-2 enzymes that play a role in the production of inflammation-causing compounds in the body. This means it works the same way as pain-relieving drugs such as *ibuprofen* (Motrin) and aspirin.

Scientific evidence: A study published in *Phytotherapy Research* found that ginger supplements are comparable to aspirin, *ibuprofen*, *naproxen* (Aleve) and other over-the-counter painkillers in easing muscle pain caused by exercise and other types of strenuous activity.

Research also has shown that ginger is just as effective as the migraine drug *sumatriptan* (Imitrex).

How to get more: For a therapeutic, pain-relieving dose of ginger, take a 1,000-mg supplement, twice daily. For migraine, I recommend up to 1,000 mg at the onset of a migraine. If you want to use ginger to help prevent migraine, add fresh ginger to your daily diet or take a ginger supplement (250 mg to 500 mg daily).*

In the kitchen, add fresh ginger—finely diced or crushed—to sauces and marinades. Used three or more times a week, ginger in doses commonly consumed in the diet can have a mild pain-relieving and anti-inflammatory effect. Ginger is also great in smoothies.

CAYENNE

Cayenne is a powder made from dried, red chili peppers, and it's very hot when used to spice food. But the natural intensity of cayenne and its active ingredient *capsaicin* affect more than your taste buds.

It's the only natural compound that—when applied topically—can degrade *substance P*, a neurotransmitter that tells the brain to transmit pain signals. With less substance P, there's less pain—which is why capsaicin is a common ingredient in many creams, ointments

*If you take blood thinners such as *warfarin* (Coumadin) or if you have gallstone disease, talk to your doctor before using ginger supplements.

and salves for pain problems such as arthritis, nerve pain, foot pain and back pain.

Little-known benefit: Cayenne can also help you lose weight. Capsaicin and other compounds in cayenne work because they have several effects that help you shed pounds—they suppress appetite…increase calorie-burning ("basal metabolic rate")…and burn up ("oxidize") body fat.

In a recent meta-analysis of nine studies on capsaicin and weight loss, published in *Critical Reviews in Food Science and Nutrition*, researchers concluded that the spice "could be a new therapeutic approach in obesity."

How to get more: For patients who want to lose weight, I usually recommend adding cayenne to the diet or using low-dose (2 mg) capsaicin supplements daily. (High-dose supplements can irritate the gastrointestinal tract.)

As a weight-loss aid, I recommend drinking one or more cups a day of warm water with a pinch of cayenne, juice from half a lemon, a teaspoon of honey and ground ginger (using a chunk of fresh ginger the size of half your thumb, from knuckle to tip). Cayenne is also excellent in marinades for fish and poultry and sprinkled on eggs. Plus, it adds a kick to salad dressings.

Best Bread for Digestion

The best bread for digestion is the old-fashioned slow-rising kind—especially for people with irritable bowel syndrome (IBS). When bread dough is allowed to rise twice, for at least four hours total, nearly all the hard-to-digest sugars known as FODMAPs are eliminated. These often are responsible for abdominal pain, diarrhea or constipation that some IBS sufferers experience when they eat bread for better digestion. Bake your own or find artisanal bakers who allow breads to rise for four hours or longer.

William D. Chey, MD, director of the Digestive Disorders Nutrition and Lifestyle Program at Michigan Medicine, Ann Arbor.

The "Natural Flavoring" Myth

Janet Bond Brill, PhD, RDN, FAND, a registered dietitian nutritionist, a fellow of the Academy of Nutrition and Dietetics and a nationally recognized nutrition, health and fitness expert who specializes in cardiovascular disease prevention. Based in Allentown, Pennsylvania, Dr. Brill is author of *Blood Pressure DOWN*, *Cholesterol DOWN* and *Prevent a Second Heart Attack*. DrJanet.com

You pick up umpteen food boxes, bags and cans, and dutifully scan the list of ingredients to ensure that you and your family are eating healthfully. But whether you're peering at a bottle of salad dressing, a can of soup or a container of ice cream, chances are good that you'll encounter that ubiquitous but head-scratching ingredient known as "natural flavoring." *What this buzzword really means…*

• **It's a chemical extract.** According to the FDA, "natural flavoring" or "natural flavor(s)" refers to a chemical flavor extract of either a plant or an animal (considered natural sources) that has been used in the product. Essentially, natural flavorings are by-products of plant and/or animal processing—they provide flavor…but not nutrition, as the label suggests. "Artificial flavorings" are not sourced from nature (from a plant or an animal)—the chemical extract is synthetically processed in a lab. Both natural and artificial flavor molecules are chemically identical…they just come from different sources.

• **Beware if you have food allergies.** Food companies can combine multiple natural flavorings (from different sources) without specifying each ingredient on the label. For a person with allergies to certain plant or animal foods, this could be a problem. While food manufacturers are required to list any of the eight major food allergens (milk, eggs, fish, shellfish, tree nuts, peanuts, wheat and soybeans) on a food label, a plant or an animal extract that's not on that list would show up on the label only as a "natural flavoring."

• **Almost all foods contain natural flavorings.** Natural flavoring is one of the most common ingredients in processed foods (others include *calcium carbonate*, *sodium benzoate* and *xanthan gum*). The FDA definition and regulation of natural flavors has nothing to do with the nutrition of the food product. The sole purpose of natural flavors is to increase the flavor of a processed food product.

My bottom line: To get the biggest nutrition boost, eat a diet of mostly whole foods (not processed), and add your own natural flavorings.

Ketogenic Diet: More Than a Weight-Loss Fad

Tanya J.W. McDonald, MD, PhD, a practicing epileptologist and assistant professor of neurology in the department of neurology at the Johns Hopkins University School of Medicine in Baltimore. Her research interests include dietary therapies for adults with epilepsy, evaluations for seizure surgery and epilepsy in women. She is lead author of "The Expanding Role of Ketogenic Diets in Adult Neurological Disorders," a review article published in *Brain Sciences*.

The ketogenic diet has shaped up as the biggest weight-loss trend of the last few years.

What is not being talked about: Even though there are positive anecdotal reports on using this high-fat, very-low-carbohydrate diet for weight loss—and research is promising (see below)—few people know about its current and potential uses for neurological conditions and other chronic diseases…

NEUROLOGICAL CONDITIONS

• **Epilepsy.** Diet therapy was a common epilepsy treatment until the development of antiseizure drugs in the 1930s. Now researchers are taking a second look at the ketogenic diet because some patients with epilepsy are *drug-resistant*—that is, they have failed to respond to two different medications…and have less than a 5% chance of becoming seizure-free with the use of additional drugs.

Scientific evidence: Research has confirmed that 40% to 50% of adults with epilepsy will improve on the diet with the most benefits seen in patients who stick with it.

Among the many possible mechanisms, the diet is thought to dampen the brain-cell "excitability" that's associated with seizures. It also improves the balance of intestinal bacteria, which appears to provide seizure protection.

The ketogenic diet doesn't replace anti-epilepsy drugs—most patients will continue to take medication, although many will require fewer drugs and/or a lower dose. I advise a variety of epilepsy patients to try the diet for at least three months. If it's effective, they stick with it. If not, they *slowly* resume their consumption of carbohydrates, under the supervision of a medical professional or nutritionist.

• **Brain cancer.** Glioblastoma, a type of malignant glioma, is the most frequently diagnosed primary brain tumor. Early research suggests that a ketogenic diet could help patients with this type of cancer, particularly when combined with radiation and/or other treatments.

In laboratory studies, animals given a ketogenic-like diet showed improved survival times of 20% to 30%. Small studies—many of them case reports (descriptions of individual patients)—have shown improvements in disease progression and survival.

The diet may help because the cells that fuel cancer depend on glucose as an energy source. When you take away glucose with a ketogenic diet, cancer cells may lose the ability to proliferate.

My advice: If you or a loved one has been diagnosed with this type of cancer, ask your doctor if a ketogenic diet might help—and if he/she recommends participating in one of the clinical trials listed at ClinicalTrials.gov. (There are also trials that focus on the use of this diet for other types of cancer.)

• **Alzheimer's disease.** Like the cancer cells described above, the amyloid deposits that are the hallmark of Alzheimer's may depend on high levels of glucose in the blood.

In laboratory studies, animals given extracts that put their bodies into a ketosis-like state (see box on next page) showed improved learning and memory. Studies involving Alzheimer's patients or those with mild cognitive impairment have shown that people given similar extracts had improvements in working memory and visual attention.

How the Ketogenic Diet Works

The term "ketogenic" has become a catchall phrase for any high-fat, low-carbohydrate diet. But in the medical community, the diet calls for a severe restriction of carbohydrates and high amounts of fat. The requirements are so rigorous that the diet should be attempted *only* with the supervision of a doctor, as with any medical therapy.

How it works: Normally, blood sugar (glucose) from carbohydrates is your main source of energy. But when glucose is restricted, your body starts breaking down fat, a process that releases ketone bodies into the bloodstream. Cells use ketone bodies as an alternative fuel source until you start to consume carbohydrates again.

If you stay on the diet long enough, the body enters *ketosis*. (You experience a mild form of ketosis when you have gone all night without eating.) Ketosis mimics a starvation state—it triggers metabolic changes, including those that promote weight loss and improve insulin sensitivity.

The diet emphasizes foods high in fat, moderate in protein and low in carbohydrates (eggs, cheese, avocados, butter, olive oil, cream, bacon, steak, salmon, sardines, nuts, seeds, etc.).

My advice: Because the research is too preliminary to conclude that the diet is—or isn't—effective for this purpose, I wouldn't advise Alzheimer's patients to try the diet without close medical supervision. But if you've been diagnosed with Alzheimer's—or have a high risk of developing it—you might want to discuss it with your doctor.

OTHER USES

•**Weight loss.** The ketogenic diet is a far cry from the plant-rich diets that most experts recommend for weight loss. In its most restrictive form, it limits many vegetables, fruits, beans and grains—all of the foods that can help you lose weight.

Yet people who switch to a ketogenic diet (the plans for weight loss are somewhat less restrictive than those used for some of the conditions described above) do lose weight—and they lose it quickly.

Caveats: Most experts agree that people who follow the diet can lose weight. But it doesn't appear to be any more effective than other, more conventional diets, and the dropout rate is probably much higher.

•**Diabetes.** People with diabetes are usually advised to eat less fat because weight loss and a lower-fat diet have been thought to go hand in hand. But experts are taking another look at the ketogenic diet for diabetes control. *Reasons*: Not only can the diet promote weight loss, but there's some evidence that it improves insulin sensitivity and lowers blood sugar.

Caution: People with diabetes who follow a ketogenic diet have an increased risk for *diabetic ketoacidosis*, a life-threatening condition due to elevated blood sugar and blood acids (ketones).

Keto Rash Becoming More Common

A keto rash is more common as more people follow the keto diet, which strictly limits carbohydrates. It's unclear what causes the uncomfortable rash, but it is similar to eczema. It shows up as red, itchy, raised bumps on the neck, arms, armpits, chest and back and can be very uncomfortable. The bumps can become pigmented or brown over time.

The rash remains rare and, when it does occur, sometimes disappears on its own. But if it develops and does not become better in two weeks, see a dermatologist and explain that you follow the keto diet—otherwise keto rash may not be immediately thought of as a possible diagnosis. In some cases, reintroducing some carbohydrates back into the diet has helped reduce the rash.

Roundup of experts, reported at MensHealth.com.

Better Than Water! How to Stay Properly Hydrated

Dana G. Cohen, MD, an internist who practices integrative medicine in New York City. She serves on the Scientific Advisory Council for the Organic & Natural Health Association and is an adviser to the board of the American College for Advancement in Medicine, ACAM. org. She is author, with Gina Bria, of *Quench: Beat Fatigue, Drop Weight, and Heal Your Body Through the New Science of Optimum Hydration.*

The mantra "Drink more water!" is heard so often that it seems like an obvious truth. *Of course* we should all drink water—preferably eight full glasses a day. Right?

Not so fast. It's true that many Americans don't drink enough water. According to some estimates, dehydration is a problem for up to 75% of adults. But chugging more water from the tap (or from an overpriced plastic bottle) is not the best way to stay hydrated.

New thinking: The water that you get from foods is *more* hydrating than "liquid" water. This gel-like form of water is about 10% more viscous than liquid water. Found inside all living cells, gel water moistens tissues better than liquid water...and contains more electrolytes, which enhance bodily functions.

What does this mean in practical terms? Simply put, *eating* your water is healthier than *drinking* it.

A HEALTHIER "DRINK"

Plant foods typically contain between 80% and 98% water, by volume. The electrolytes mean that gel water isn't merely moisturizing...it's a fuel that improves cognition, judgment and mood.

Of course, you still need liquid water. In fact, if you don't replenish the amount of fluid typically lost through sweating, urination and other bodily functions, it can cause a measurable loss of cognitive abilities...a decrease in the ability of blood vessels to contract/dilate... and an increase in cellular inflammation. But gel water does an even better job at keeping you hydrated.

HOW TO GET MORE

Instead of relying on liquid water alone, I recommend four steps that incorporate diet and exercise for healthful hydration. *To help stay properly hydrated...*

STEP #1: **Drink two green, veggie-based smoothies a day.** Even one smoothie (at least eight ounces) will increase hydration and improve energy, but two are ideal. Why vegetable-based smoothies? Because the gel water facilitates absorption by cell membranes...the fiber clears out toxins and cellular wastes... and the minerals (including natural sodium) improve hydration as well as flavor.

You can make a smoothie with virtually any combination of green vegetables, with a little fruit for flavor.

My favorite hydrating smoothie recipe: Blend at least one leafy green (such as spinach or kale)...a bit of apple, banana or carrot for sweetness...lime juice or apple cider vinegar if you like a little zing...herbs (such as parsley, cilantro or basil)...healthy fats (like avocado oil)...a sprinkling of nuts and/or chia seeds for thickening...and water as needed. Because of the gel water and minerals, a smoothie is much more hydrating than an equal amount of liquid water.

STEP #2: **Be sure to eat hydrating vegetables.** All plant foods contain healthy amounts of gel water, but some veggies are surprisingly good sources.

Examples: Cucumber (96.7%)...romaine lettuce (95.6%)...celery (95.4%)...radish (95.3%) ...and zucchini (95%). Fruit is somewhat less hydrating—watermelon and strawberries are roughly 91% water...grapefruit and cantaloupe about 90%...and kiwi, apples and pears about 84%.

STEP #3: **Use natural salt.** Sodium often gets blamed for dehydration. But the real problem is *processed* salt that's been stripped of beneficial minerals. Natural forms of salt— such as sea salt, Celtic salt and Himalayan salt—contain iron, magnesium, calcium and potassium, in addition to sodium. The minerals improve hydration by increasing the electrical activity within cells.

Are You Dehydrated?

Many people suffer from some degree of dehydration, yet there isn't a reliable test to detect it. You probably know that normal urine should be clear or just slightly yellow. A dark yellow color (or a smaller volume than usual) could mean you're dehydrated.

Other important clues...

•**Your skin "tents" and holds the shape when you pinch it.** Healthy, hydrated skin—particularly on the backs of the hands—should snap back to its normal position.

•**You "fail" the fingernail test.** Press a fingernail for five seconds to flush out the color, then release. It should regain its normal color in one to three seconds. If it doesn't, you're probably dehydrated.

Note: These salts typically contain very small amounts of iodine, so look for versions that are fortified with iodine if you're concerned about your iodine levels.

Also: I suggest avoiding—or at least limiting consumption of—processed foods. They're loaded with unhealthy salt and can be dehydrating because the body has to use water to metabolize them.

Important: Anyone with salt sensitivity can have sharp rises in blood pressure when they consume *any* form of salt, but most people can enjoy moderate amounts (more than the 1,500 mg daily recommended by many health groups) of natural salt without experiencing blood pressure changes. Consult your doctor for advice.

STEP #4: **Move moisture with micromovements.** It's easy to put more water into your body, but how does the water get where it's needed? It travels through *fascia*, the miles of thin, gauzelike tissue that lie beneath the skin and between and around organs and bones. The pulsing of fascia transports water droplets throughout the body. Even the smallest movements increase the pulsing action.

In addition to the standard exercise recommendation (150 minutes of moderate-intensity exercise a week), you can take advantage of *micromovements*—such as foot tapping, head turning and shifting your weight. Twisting motions—such as swiveling your body or moving your head in figure-eight motions—are particularly good because they squeeze moisture through the fascia, just like wringing a wet washcloth releases water.

The great thing about micromovements is that you can do them anywhere, anytime—in the car, at your desk, while watching TV, etc.

How to Make Coffee Even More Healthful

•**Use grass-fed, organic milk,** which contains more nutrients and omega-3 fatty acids than standard milk.

•**Add a spice.** Cinnamon, cloves, ginger or nutmeg will increase the antioxidant content of the coffee.

•**Choose a light roast.** The lighter the roast, the higher the levels of chlorogenic acid, a beneficial antioxidant.

Cynthia Sass, RD, contributing nutrition editor, Health. com.

Are You Eating at the Right Time of Day? Doing So Can Reduce Risk for Disease

Michael F. Roizen, MD, chief wellness officer at Cleveland Clinic and chief of its Wellness Institute. Board-certified in internal medicine and anesthesiology, he has authored 175 peer-reviewed publications and served 16 years on FDA advisory committees. He is coauthor, with Michael Crupain, MD, MPH, of *What to Eat When: A Strategic Plan to Improve Your Health & Life Through Food*.

I n the never-ending diet debates, people focus almost exclusively on what to eat. But *when* you eat may be nearly as important.

Your body's circadian rhythms—the daily cycles that dictate when you awaken, when you're alert, etc.—don't just influence your behaviors like sleepiness. The time-specific, daily release of hormones determines when you get hungry and how much you eat…as well as your body's metabolism—how efficiently you utilize fats, carbohydrates and other nutrients.

What scientists are now discovering: Chrononutrition—the concept that food habits should align with circadian rhythms for optimal health—can have a dramatic impact on your chances of developing a variety of serious conditions. *What you need to know…*

WHY TIMING MATTERS

Suppose that you eat the same carbohydrate-rich meal twice a day—once in the morning and again in the evening. Both meals will trigger a rise in your blood sugar (glucose) levels, but the rise will be higher after the evening meal.

The "master clock" that controls circadian rhythms in humans and other mammals is located in a tiny brain area called the suprachiasmatic nucleus. The clock constantly sends out chemical messages that control key functions in your body. The effects can be profound.

In a study published in *Proceedings of the National Academy of Sciences*, nurses who changed their schedules to night shifts burned about 250 fewer calories a day, even though their jobs were the same. When researchers examined the findings of 17 studies on the effects of shift work, their analysis concluded that night-shift workers were 40% more likely than other workers to develop cardiovascular disease—possibly because their work hours were in opposition to their natural circadian rhythms.

BENEFITS OF EARLY EATING

Most people get hungriest at night. But to realize the health-promoting effects of chrononutrition, the best time to eat most of your daily calories is before 2 pm.

Here's why: The body's cells respond more readily to insulin early in the day—important for food metabolism and healthy weight maintenance, as well as preventing diabetes.

Research has shown that insulin sensitivity is higher during the hours when you're most active. This makes sense because you need energy from your glucose reserve (which depends on insulin) when your muscles are moving. At night, when most people's energy needs are lower, you need less glucose.

THE "THREE-QUARTER" CHALLENGE

What happens when you eat earlier in the day? It's well-established that people who consume most of their calories during the daytime are less likely to be obese. That's why I recommend consuming three-quarters of your daily calories at breakfast and lunch.

Of course, changing your eating schedule isn't easy. People are naturally primed to eat more at night, probably because our ancient ancestors needed to store more calories to survive…and because they didn't live long enough to suffer the effects of harmful conditions such as arthritis, dementia and diabetes.

To get started: Try to get most of your daily calories between about 8 am and 2 pm for at least three days a week—more often if you can. As you become more accustomed to eating mainly during these hours, you can transition into this schedule seven days a week.

If you get hungry at night, have a healthy snack, like raw, crunchy vegetables (or roasted veggies if you prefer).

IMPROVE YOUR BLOOD SUGAR

As mentioned earlier, insulin resistance (the reduced ability of insulin to transport glucose into cells) is higher at night than during the daylight hours. Insulin resistance is a serious health problem because it increases the risk for diabetes, obesity—and even heart disease, cancer and dementia.

Animals given high-fat meals at night are more likely to consume more calories, gain more weight and have more insulin resistance than those that are given the same meals earlier in the day.

Similar changes occur in humans. The weight-management program at Cleveland Clinic encourages not only eating 75% of daily calories before 2 pm but also increased walking and a reduction of simple carbohydrates (such as chips, white bread and other processed foods). People with diabetes who follow the program for as little as two months often improve so much that they're able to discontinue one or two diabetes medications.

BOOST YOUR HEART HEALTH

A consistent finding is that daytime eating lowers high blood pressure, a leading cause of heart disease. The reduction is significant enough, in many cases, that it equals the effects of taking a blood pressure–reducing drug.

When you improve the metabolic state of the body by eating earlier (and healthier) meals, you also reduce the whole-body inflammation that can cause a gradual impairment of kidney function. Reduced kidney function can impair the renin-angiotensin system, a group of hormones that helps regulate blood pressure.

Other benefits: Daytime eating causes a decrease in triglycerides and LDL "bad" cholesterol…an increase in beneficial HDL cholesterol…and a lower risk of developing metabolic syndrome, a life-threatening constellation of symptoms that includes high blood pressure, high blood sugar and elevated triglycerides.

A HEALTHIER EATING PLAN

An optimal eating schedule can't overcome the effects of a poor diet. Everyone should avoid most processed foods and simple sugars (such as white flour) and eat more "whole" foods, including whole grains, beans, veggies, etc. *Also…*

• **Eat your breakfast!** There are surprisingly few randomized trials on the health benefits of eating breakfast, but research has shown that people who skip this meal are more likely to have higher LDL "bad" cholesterol levels. Those with diabetes often have higher blood sugar levels later in the day when they skip breakfast.

Make breakfast either the largest or the second-largest meal of the day. People who aren't normally breakfast eaters should at least practice "less-late" eating and get most of their calories at lunch.

• **Get some protein at breakfast.** A bit of protein reduces food intake later in the day.

Examples: Greek yogurt (with no added sugar), salmon, steel-cut oats and nuts or seeds. Aim to get about 25 g of protein at breakfast each day.

• **Skip the big suppers.** Get no more than about 25% of your total daily calories from snacks/supper combined. If you do eat at the regular supper hour (around 6 pm or 7 pm), have something like a small salad, accompanied by a small portion of a protein-rich food.

Surprising Ways a Top Doctor Uses Nature to Stay Healthy

John La Puma, MD, FACP, board-certified internist and certified California naturalist, who runs an organic teaching farm in Santa Barbara, California. A Lifetime TV and PBS host, he is *The New York Times* best-selling author of *ChefMD's Big Book of Culinary Medicine* and *Refuel*, and coauthor with Michael F. Roizen, MD, of *The RealAge Diet*. DrJohnLaPuma.com

---

Jim, an executive in his 50s, believed that he thrived under pressure. But his blood pressure was too high and so was his blood sugar. He had become overweight. His wife thought Jim was caught up in an overly stressful cycle of working and commuting with no real break. He felt on edge all the time.

Jim knew that he should exercise, eat better, relax more and calm his anxiety. But he was, as his wife saw, essentially stuck. So he came to see me, his doctor. I'm a medical doctor, so I could have given him prescription medication for his blood pressure, anxiety and prediabetes. But instead I prescribed a specific trial of an ancient remedy—nature therapy.

For example, I told Jim to plant four small herb plants in a window box—parsley, sage, rosemary and thyme—and to spend five minutes tending to them daily, with his phone turned off. I instructed him to tell family or friends who thought he was slacking that the time was prescribed by his doctor. And I told Jim to ask his wife for support. He's now following his nature prescription, and he hasn't required any new medications to improve his health.

WHAT NATURE CAN DO FOR YOU

Nature can be *your* medicine, too. Here are some medical conditions that spending time in nature has been shown to improve—acute urinary tract infections...anxiety disorder... ADHD...cancer...cardiovascular disease...depression...diabetes...healing from surgery... musculoskeletal complaints...migraines...upper-respiratory-tract infections...and vertigo.

Example: In a pioneering randomized controlled study by Swedish environmental psychologist Roger S. Ulrich, PhD, post-op patients who had window views of nature from their hospital beds had improved moods, needed less pain medication, had fewer surgical complications and left the hospital sooner compared with similar patients whose rooms had no views. And these patients just *looked* outside.

Even just looking at *pictures* of plants has been shown by researchers at University of Essex in Colchester, UK, to reduce blood pressure, pulse rate and muscle tension after a stressful experience. Putting up beautiful pictures of nature—water, trees, forests or meadows—in your home (or if you are in a hospital, in your room) may sound trivial, but it's not.

Getting outside and into natural environments is even more powerful. People who spend just 30 minutes in a green outdoor space at least once a week are 7% less likely to develop high blood pressure, and 9% less likely to develop depression, than people who spend little or no time, according to a study published in *Scientific Reports*.

There's much more to nature as medicine. *Here are six more powerful ways to use nature to heal what ails you...*

TAKE A FOREST BATH

What *forest bathers* do is walk very slowly in a wooded area for two or three hours. They may cover only a quarter mile doing this. Whenever they feel like it, they sit for a few minutes, just to sense what is around them. A contemplative, sensual immersion, forest bathing has been part of Korean and Japanese disease prevention and treatment for decades. Dozens of peer-reviewed studies show that forest therapy reduces your blood pressure, heart rate and stress hormones... and then reduces the stress you experience for days afterward.

Trees play an important role, releasing essential aromatic oils called *phytoncides* that boost immunity and antiviral natural killer cells. MRI brain scans find that the longer a person is exposed to trees, the less activity there is in the *amygdala*, the part of the brain that controls distress and fear responses, contributing to anxiety disorders and depression.

What to do: Turn off your phone. Find a wooded area and comfortable sitting spot. Don't hurry. *Tune into the sounds first*: Hear the closest sound and then the farthest. *Use your other senses*: Watch the birds, feel the leaves, smell the breeze, appreciate the stillness. Get up and amble a bit. Become aware of your connection with the environment, which strengthens your concentration and focus.

Can't schedule two or three hours? Try meditating for shorter periods in a natural, electronics-free setting. If you already meditate, compare how you feel when you do it in nature versus in your usual spot.

GREEN THE INSIDE OF YOUR HOME

Gardening is excellent medicine for body and mind. Compared with others, gardeners tend to weigh less, are less susceptible to depression and anxiety, have greater self-esteem—and are between 36% and 47% less likely to develop dementia, research finds.

Of course, not all of us have the space to be outdoor gardeners. Plus, we spend up to 90% of our time indoors, often breathing indoor pollutants from household chemicals that can harm our lungs, heart and other organs.

Solution: Garden indoors! Greenery inside is beautifying, a psychological respite—and it literally purifies the air you breathe. Studies show that indoor gardeners get similar benefits to outdoor gardeners.

What to do: Choose houseplants that are especially good at removing toxins from the air. Examples include Dracaena Janet Craig (yes, that's the real name), Boston fern and spider plants.

EXERCISE OUTSIDE IN A GREEN SPACE

A recent Stanford study showed significantly reduced rumination—obsessive worrying—after a 90-minute walk in nature, compared with a 90-minute walk through an urban environment. Any exercise is better than none,

BETTER WAYS...

5 Habits for a Longer Life

Fewer than 2% of people practice habits that can add more than a decade to their lives. Men who adopt the following five healthful habits at age 50 and continue with them from then on may live 12 years longer than men who adopt none of the habits. Women who adopt the habits may extend life by 14 years.

The five habits are eating a healthful diet...not smoking...getting regular physical activity...consuming alcohol only in moderation...and maintaining a normal weight.

Frank B. Hu, MD, PhD, professor, departments of nutrition and epidemiology, Harvard T.H. Chan School of Public Health, Boston, and leader of an analysis of two databases with information on more than 123,000 people, published in *Circulation*.

of course, but "green" exercise appears to be better than indoor exercise at stimulating the release of endorphins, the body's feel-good chemicals, and triggering new brain-cell development.

It takes only five minutes of exercising in nature to boost mood and self-esteem, according to one British study. But like medications, there's a dose-response effect—the more you do, the greater the benefit...without any side effects, of course.

What to do: Exercise outside or in view of nature. Take a lunchtime walk to a park.

BREATHE THIS

Aromatherapy using plant essential oils smells good and is good for you, with proven clinical benefits. *Examples*...

Lavender blossom: Reduces migraine pain and improves sleep quality.

Bergamot orange: Lowers stress and improves fatigue.

Yuzu lemon: Improves premenstrual emotional symptoms and lowers heart rate.

Caution: Whether you inhale, apply or massage essential oils, allergic reactions are possible. To minimize risk, wear gloves and wash your hands. Use a very small amount

and see how you react. And buy certified organic products to make sure that you're not getting any pesticides. If you have a medical condition, talk to your doctor first.

THERE'S AN APP FOR THAT— AND WEBSITES, TOO

Can looking at your phone be "green"? Not if it replaces being in nature. But virtual nature experiences can be beneficial during your life indoors.

What to do: Try the *Calm* app (Apple and Android, $59.99 a year for Calm Premium) to improve mood and Headspace.com (Apple and Android, $12.99 a month) to learn meditation. Find ambient sounds such as waterfalls on YouTube (free) or on an app such as *Rain Rain*, which is great for meditation and sleep (Apple and Android, free). Connect with amateur naturalists on INaturalist.org (free). Find more free resources at my website, DrJohn LaPuma.com/nature-therapy.

TRY PET THERAPY

Most Americans already live with nature inside our homes. About two-thirds of all US households own pets, and dogs especially can provide unconditional love. Ironically, the dirt they bring into our homes may be good for our immune systems—and pets offer connectivity and emotional support to their owners, especially in times of crisis. That is powerful medicine. So, of course, is walking a dog. Dog owners have about one-third lower risk for heart disease than people who don't own dogs—a benefit that's especially strong in people who live alone.

What to do: If you don't have a dog, borrow one! Offer to walk a neighbor's dog, say, once or twice a week. Schedule walks in your calendar as if they were meetings. Your blood pressure will fall. So may your risk for heart disease.

The Real Secret to Lowering Your Blood Pressure

Janet Bond Brill, PhD, RDN, FAND, a registered dietitian nutritionist, a fellow of the Academy of Nutrition and Dietetics and a nationally recognized nutrition, health and fitness expert who specializes in cardiovascular disease prevention. Based in Allentown, Pennsylvania, Dr. Brill is author of *Blood Pressure DOWN, Cholesterol DOWN* and *Prevent a Second Heart Attack.* DrJanet.com

Forget everything that you have read about the latest "superfood" for lowering blood pressure. While it's true that certain foods do provide this remarkable benefit, many people mistakenly assume that there must be one nutritional magic bullet that will do the job on its own.

Is it possible to control high blood pressure (hypertension) with diet alone? Yes, many people can—but only when they take advantage of the additive benefits from *multiple* strategically chosen foods.

Example: Suppose you eat a lot of bananas because you know that this food is high in blood pressure–lowering potassium. That's great, but you'll shave only a point or two off your blood pressure.

To *really* leverage your diet, you need to also regularly consume other foods that help control blood pressure. When combined, the nutrients in these foods work synergistically to give the greatest blood pressure–lowering effects. Then the benefits accrue quickly—for some people, a five-point drop may occur within a week.

What you may not realize: By eating the right foods, losing weight if you're overweight and cutting sodium if you're salt sensitive (see below), some people can achieve blood pressure drops that equal or exceed the effects of drug therapy—with none of the side effects. And if you must take medication, these foods may allow you to use a lower dose.*

*Caution: If you take blood pressure–lowering medication, never change your dose or discontinue it without consulting your doctor.

Some of the best blood pressure–lowering foods are well-known—bananas, leafy green vegetables, etc. *Here are some lesser-known options to add to your hypertension-fighting diet…*

• **Beet juice/beet greens.** As a nutritionist, I usually advise clients to eat whole foods rather than drink juices because of the extra fiber. But beet juice is an exception. It's a concentrated source of nitrates, chemical compounds that quickly lower blood pressure.

When you drink beet juice or eat other high-nitrate foods (such as rhubarb, spinach, beet greens or chard), cells in the linings of blood vessels produce more nitric oxide, a molecule that dilates blood vessels and lowers blood pressure.

Scientific evidence: In a study that was published in *Hypertension* and looked at 64 adults with hypertension (ages 18 to 85), some of the patients drank a daily 8.4-ounce glass of beet juice, while others drank a juice with the active compounds removed (the placebo).

After one month, those given the real juice had average drops in systolic (top number) blood pressure of about eight points, while their diastolic pressure (bottom number) dropped five points. Blood pressure did not drop among those in the placebo group.

You can buy beet juice in health-food stores and juice shops. Or you can make your own by blending/processing cooked beets. To liven

GOOD NEWS...

Yogurt for Heart Health

Eating yogurt may reduce heart disease risk in people with high blood pressure. Men with high blood pressure who ate at least two servings of yogurt each week had 21% lower risk for heart attack or stroke. Risk was cut by 17% for women. The reason is unknown, but probiotics from fermentation in yogurt production may play a role.

Lynn L. Moore, DSc, MPH, director of nutrition and metabolism at Boston University School of Medicine and coauthor of a study published in *American Journal of Hypertension.*

up the flavor, add a little lemon juice, ginger or a sweetener such as stevia.

Caution: If you have kidney disease, consult your nephrologist or a registered dietitian/nutritionist who specializes in kidney disease before regularly consuming beet juice—its high potassium level could worsen this condition.

• **Figs.** These delicious jewels are heart-healthy because they are super-high in potassium, with 232 mg in just two fresh figs. They also have a considerable amount of fiber and polyphenols, compounds that when consumed with additional blood pressure–lowering food can reduce systolic blood pressure by up to 12 points, in some cases.

Fresh figs are scrumptious, but dried figs are easier to find in grocery stores—and many people enjoy their intense sweetness.

What to try: Chop dried figs, and use them as a natural sweetener in oatmeal, pancakes, muffins or even soups.

• **Hibiscus tea.** If you enjoy chamomile and other herbal teas, you might like the delicate floral flavor of hibiscus tea, which is high in flavonoids, plant-based antioxidants with anti-inflammatory effects, and other heart-healthy compounds. One study, which compared hibiscus tea to *captopril* (Capoten), an ACE inhibitor blood pressure drug, found that the tea was just as effective as the medication.

• **Pistachios.** Even though most nuts are good sources of fiber, potassium and magnesium, pistachios are special because they are high in *arginine*, an amino acid that stimulates the production of nitric oxide (discussed earlier).

Important recent finding: A study at Pennsylvania State University found that people who ate 1.5 ounces of pistachios (about 70 nuts, unshelled) daily had drops in stress-related systolic blood pressure of nearly five points compared with those who ate nuts less than once a week.

Not fattening: Nuts are high in calories, but research has shown that people who eat them regularly actually tend to gain less weight than those who don't eat nuts—probably because the fiber and protein in nuts help dieters feel full longer. At roughly 260 calories per 1.5 ounces, you'll need to cut calories elsewhere to prevent weight gain but can likely do so easily because nuts give such a feeling of satiety.

• **Pomegranate juice.** Pomegranate juice contains many different flavonoids. The juice mimics the effects of ACE inhibitor drugs, such as *lisinopril* (Zestril, Prinivil, etc.), which dilate blood vessels and lower blood pressure.

A recent study found that people who drank a little less than two ounces of pomegranate juice daily for a year had average drops in systolic blood pressure of 12%.

The juice is tart, so some people buy sweetened versions.

My advice: Avoid the added sugar. Instead, add a little stevia or other natural sweetener. One pomegranate yields about half a cup of juice.

• **White beans.** Like many of the other foods described earlier, white beans are chock-full of potassium. One cup contains more than 1,000 mg of potassium. (A cup of black beans has about 800 mg.)

Potassium acts like a natural diuretic and removes sodium from the body. Many people are sensitive to sodium, which means that their blood pressure will rise if they consume too much (the standard recommendation is no more than 2,300 mg daily). Research has shown that one of the best ways to lower blood pressure is to increase your potassium–sodium ratio.

Diets Good for the Heart Help Hearing

People who ate a Mediterranean-style diet or the antihypertension DASH diet were about 30% less likely to develop moderate or severe hearing loss over a 22-year period than people whose eating habits were less healthful.

Analysis of 71,000 women in the Nurses' Health Study II by researchers at Brigham and Women's Hospital, Boston, published in *Journal of Nutrition*.

Best Oils to Lower Cholesterol

In a recent meta-analysis that ranked fats, including oils, for their effectiveness at controlling blood lipids, sunflower, rapeseed, safflower and flaxseed oils did the best job at controlling LDL "bad" cholesterol. Olive oil, a staple of the heart-healthy Mediterranean diet, came in at the middle of the pack.

Lukas Schwingshackl, PhD, postdoctoral researcher, department of epidemiology, German Institute of Human Nutrition, Potsdam-Rehbruecke, Nuthetal, Germany.

Fiber Fix Extends Life

In a new finding, healthy adults who ate the most fiber (25 g to 29 g per day) had a 15% to 30% lower risk for heart disease, colorectal cancer, type 2 diabetes—and even death from any cause—compared with those who ate the least fiber, according to a review of 240 studies over 40 years. Americans eat, on average, only 15 g of fiber daily.

Good options: Whole grains (such as oatmeal and brown rice), lentils, beans, artichokes, raspberries and pears.

Jim Mann, PhD, professor in human nutrition and medicine, University of Otago, Dunedin, New Zealand.

EASY TO DO...

Squeeze Away High Blood Pressure

Squeeze a handgrip at one-third your strength in your nondominant hand for two minutes... rest three minutes...repeat three more times. Do this three times per week to drop your systolic blood pressure.

Based on a study by researchers at University of New England, New South Wales, Australia, published in Medicine.

Weight Loss Can Reverse AF

Atrial fibrillation (AF) is a dangerous heart rhythm condition that usually progresses from periodic short episodes to more persistent forms. But more than half of overweight or obese people who lost at least 10% of their body weight reversed this persistent form or rid themselves of AF entirely.

Melissa E. Middeldorp, PhD, arrhythmia researcher at University of Adelaide, Australia, and coauthor of a study published in Eurospace.

This Supplement Fights Diabetes and Protects Your Heart

Michael Murray, ND, a leading authority on natural medicine. He serves on the Board of Regents of Bastyr University in Seattle and has authored or coauthored more than 30 books featuring natural approaches to health, including Bottom Line's Encyclopedia of Healing Foods and The Encyclopedia of Natural Medicine. DoctorMurray.com

Expensive drugs are not the only option for people with type 2 diabetes to control blood sugar and protect cardiovascular health. A natural supplement called *berberine* can provide both of these benefits as well.

The supplement, derived from goldenseal root and other plants, activates an enzyme that makes the body more sensitive to insulin, thus helping to control blood sugar. A 2015 statistical review of 27 clinical trials concluded that berberine can control blood sugar as effectively as the go-to diabetes drug *metformin*.

Bonus: Like the diabetes drugs called *GLP-1 agonists* and *SGLT2 inhibitors*, berberine is good for the heart. It reduces high blood pressure, improves the ability of blood vessels to dilate and helps prevent heart failure. Side effects—uncommon and usually mild—can include nausea and stomach upset.

What to do: Before you take any supplement, discuss it with your medical doctor or naturopathic physician to rule out any possible interactions with another medication. *Example*: Berberine can interfere with the effectiveness of certain antibiotics and other drugs. A typical dose is 500 mg two to three times daily before meals, but discuss the right dosing for you with your doctor. If berberine works, your doctor might be able to reduce the dose of one or more of your diabetes drugs.

Pump Iron for Heart Health

Weight training improved cardiovascular risk factors, including high blood pressure, diabetes and elevated cholesterol, more than walking or biking, according to a study of more than 4,000 men and women.

Best: Combine weight training—often done at a higher (more heart-protective) intensity—with aerobic activity, which is also beneficial for heart health.

Maia P. Smith, PhD, MS, statistical epidemiologist and assistant professor, department of public health and preventive medicine, St. George's University School of Medicine, Grenada.

Vinegar Can Do Wonders for Your Blood Sugar

Carol Johnston, RD, PhD, professor and assistant director of the School of Nutrition and Health Promotion at Arizona State University, Phoenix. Dr. Johnston has published nine papers on the medical use of vinegar in leading medical journals.

Apple cider vinegar is a classic home remedy with traditional uses ranging from reducing age spots to easing arthritis. Only one use is scientifically proven—a specific effect on blood sugar that is beneficial for anyone with diabetes or prediabetes. *Here's what you need to know…*

•**The scientific evidence of vinegar's blood sugar benefits is strong and consistent.** A recent statistical analysis of the 11 best studies concluded that consuming vinegar with a meal, compared with having the same meal without vinegar, reduced postmeal blood sugar spikes by an average of 40%.

Why this matters: Much of the metabolic damage caused by diabetes—and prediabetes—is caused by these spikes.

•**Any vinegar works.** Sorry, apple cider vinegar enthusiasts. It's the acetic acid—in every vinegar—that blocks absorption of carbohydrates and helps clear blood sugar from the bloodstream.

•**Raw vinegar is best.** Cooking can break down acetic acid.

•**You don't need much.** Studies suggest that two tablespoons of vinegar is a good "dose." Less isn't as effective—and more doesn't add any benefit.

•**Timing matters.** For the best effect on blood sugar, consume vinegar at or near the start of a meal.

•**Consider a premeal drink.** For the most reliable effect, dilute two tablespoons of vinegar in a glass of water and drink it with the first bites of the meal. You can sweeten it with a non-nutritive sweetener such as stevia. Or try a commercial flavored apple-cider-vinegar drink made by Bragg.

•**Make your own vinaigrette** if you'd rather incorporate vinegar into a salad or vegetable dish (after the vegetables are cooked). Why? Store-bought vinaigrettes often have more oil than vinegar. Mix your own using two parts vinegar to one part oil. Try red wine vinegar—it delivers acetic acid plus a healthy dose of cell-protecting polyphenols. Mustard counts, too—most mustards are rich in vinegar.

•**Start your next meal with a dish dressed with vinegar.** And while you don't want to be eating a lot of bread, if you do have a slice, instead of slathering it in butter, dip it in vinaigrette.

Got Diabetes? Here's How to Save Your Feet

David G. Armstrong, DPM, MD, PhD, a podiatric surgeon and professor of surgery at Keck School of Medicine of University of Southern California in Los Angeles. Dr. Armstrong is coeditor of the American Diabetes Association's *Clinical Care of the Diabetic Foot.* Dr. Armstrong is also founder of the Diabetic Foot Global Conference (DFCon.com), an international symposium, and lead author of "Diabetic Foot Ulcers and Their Recurrence," published in *The New England Journal of Medicine.*

Feet are easy to ignore...unless they hurt. That's one big reason many people with diabetes are at risk for losing their feet—their disease has robbed them, to a large extent, of what doctors call "the gift of pain."

Here's what happens: Diabetes damages nerves, which can lead to a loss of feeling. This means that an ill-fitting shoe or an ingrown toenail can start a silent cascade of injury, leading to a foot ulcer (open sore or wound) and infection.

Many people with diabetes also have poor blood flow, and that can allow an infection to fester—raising the risk that an unnoticed cut or blister could lead to the loss of toes, a foot or even an entire lower leg. Such amputations happen nearly 75,000 times each year in the US.

Even worse danger: Once a person with diabetes has a foot ulcer, his/her chance of dying in the next 10 years *doubles.* If the foot ulcer leads to amputation, the five-year risk for death is 70%.

But those tragic complications don't have to happen to you. *Here are five simple steps to help prevent foot ulcers and limb loss...*

STEP #1: **Watch your blood sugar—and more.** If you maintain good control of your blood sugar, your heart and kidneys will thank you—and so will your feet. Of course, you need to take your medications, watch your diet, and if your feet are still healthy, use them to stay active—walking is good preventive medicine for your whole body.

Warning: If you already have nerve damage in your feet, talk to your primary care doctor or foot doctor (podiatrist) about the right dose of walking for you. There may be

---

INTERESTING FINDING...

Take a Bath for Better Health

Hot baths can reduce blood sugar and chronic inflammation in a similar way that exercise can. Study subjects sat up to their necks for an hour in 102°F water each day for two weeks.

Implication: People not able or unwilling to exercise might be able to reduce the risk for diabetes and other inflammation-related ills. Ask your doctor whether hot baths are safe for you.

Christof Leicht, PhD, a lecturer in exercise physiology at Loughborough University in the UK and leader of a study of overweight, sedentary men published in *Journal of Applied Physiology.*

---

times when you have to stay off your feet to save them.

STEP #2: **Be smart about your shoes and socks.** You need to wear *both*—whether you're inside or outside your house. (If you've lost sensation in your feet, don't walk around the house barefoot! At least wear house slippers.)

In choosing your socks, start with a clean, lightly padded pair with no irritating seams. Choose well-fitted, supportive shoes with plenty of room for your toes (no pointy-toed shoes!)—and get in the habit of checking inside for foreign objects before slipping them on. Even though high heels aren't recommended, women with diabetes may want to wear moderate heels (no more than two inches) for special occasions.

Buying tip: It's widely known that you should shop for shoes late in the day, when your feet may have swelled a bit, but this is *vital* for people with diabetes so that they don't buy shoes that are too tight. And stay away from cheap plastic and vinyl shoes—they may be less expensive, but they don't breathe enough, which causes your feet to perspire, increasing the chance for a blister to develop.

If diabetes has already caused changes, such as neuropathy and especially a previous blister or wound on your feet, talk with a podiatrist about the best shoes and inserts for you. These supportive shoes can be pricey (more than $100), but insurers often cover at least one pair per year—though you may want more so that you can allow your shoes to air out for a day between wearings.

Also: See your podiatrist at least once a year to make sure your feet are healthy and you're wearing the right shoes.

STEP #3: **Knock your socks off!** You need to do this *every day* to get a good look at your feet. Carefully examine the tops, the soles, the heels—and between your toes, where moisture and friction can lead to trouble. Use a mirror (or ask a family member to help if needed).

Goal: Get to know your feet so well that you will notice changes from day to day. Any new redness could signal trouble. Look for swelling, calluses, sores, blisters or ingrown toenails, and let your primary care physician or podiatrist know about these warning signs.

Important: There's one other time to strip off your shoes and socks—each and every time that you see your primary care doctor (not just your podiatrist). Take off your socks as soon as you reach the exam table. That way, both of you will remember to look at and talk about your feet.

STEP #4: **Watch out for hot spots.** If areas of your skin heat up, that can be a sign of inflammation. If you detect that heat early enough, you may be able to head off an ulcer.

Helpful: Consider doing your foot check in the morning before you've been walking on your feet all day. But if that doesn't work for your schedule, just be sure you do your foot check regularly.

Do not be surprised if your doctor asks you to take the temperature of your feet in several spots each day—looking for areas of one foot that are a few degrees warmer than the same areas of the other foot. This can be done with an inexpensive thermometer that can be purchased online, such as Advocate's Non-Contact Infrared Thermometer or Equinox Digital Non-Contact Infrared Thermometer.

Also: If you and your podiatrist are game, you can try out newer heat-sensing socks. These can be paired with your smartphone or other devices to send alerts to you. One such product, Siren Smart Socks for Diabetics, can

be found at RoyalPlazas.com or by calling Siren at 888-459-5470.

STEP #5: **Pamper those puppies.** Dry skin is more easily damaged, so after washing your feet in warm (not hot) water, apply a rich moisturizing cream. Keep toenails trimmed, straight across—and if that becomes difficult for you, ask your health-care providers for nail-trimming help. Make sure to ask your podiatrist before going to a nail salon. *Also, avoid these missteps…*

•**Do *not* put moisturizer between your toes**—excess moisture there can promote infection. Use talcum powder or cornstarch in those areas.

•**Do *not* warm your feet with hot-water bottles or heating pads**—you might not feel when it's too hot. Wear warm socks instead.

•**Do *not* use acids or chemical corn removers,** which could damage the skin and lead to foot ulcers. See a podiatrist for help.

•**Do *not* attempt "bathroom surgery" on corns, calluses or ingrown toenails.** Consult a podiatrist.

•**Do *not* smoke.** Quitting is one of the best things you can do to improve blood flow—to your feet and everywhere else. Do not give up trying if you have not quit yet.

Get an Extra Edge Against Cancer with This Integrated Plan

Mark A. Stengler, NMD, a naturopathic physician and founder of The Stengler Center for Integrative Medicine in Encinitas, California (MarkStengler.com). He has served on a medical advisory committee for the Yale University Complementary Medicine Outcomes Research Project and is author of *Outside the Box Cancer Therapies* and coauthor of *Prescription for Natural Cures* and *Prescription for Drug Alternatives* (both from Bottom Line Books, BottomLineStore.com).

More than one-third of American adults reach for vitamins, herbs or other natural medicines when they have colds or other routine (and hopefully mild) health problems. Similar remedies can help when you have cancer.

To learn more about the best and safest ways to use natural therapies—also known as complementary and alternative medicine (CAM)—to fight cancer and its complications, we spoke with Mark A. Stengler, NMD, a naturopathic physician who treats cancer patients.

HOW CAM CAN WORK

Research has shown that many so-called "alternative" treatments can enhance the effects of conventional cancer care such as surgery, radiation or chemotherapy…reduce treatment side effects…and possibly improve survival.

This type of integrative care doesn't *replace* conventional cancer treatments. Rather, with the guidance of a doctor, complementary therapies are added to a patient's treatment plan.

Important: To ensure that the therapies described below would be appropriate for you, consult the Society for Integrative Oncology (IntegrativeOnc.org) to find an integrative oncologist near you…or check with The American Association of Naturopathic Physicians (Naturopathic.org) to locate a naturopathic doctor who also treats cancer patients.

Also: Be sure to ask the doctor you choose to be in touch with your oncologist. *Here's how CAM can help with problems that plague most cancer patients…*

• **Get relief from "chemo brain."** It's estimated that three-quarters of cancer patients will experience some degree of mental cloudiness. Known as "chemo brain," it can include mood swings, memory loss and mental fatigue. It eventually improves, but some patients will feel like they're in a mental fog years after their treatments have ended.

What helps: The omega-3 fatty acids in fish oil supplements—a typical daily dose is 1,000 mg total of *eicosapentaenoic acid* (EPA) and *docosahexaenoic acid* (DHA) combined—help regulate acetylcholine, a neurotransmitter that increases nerve growth factor and improves memory as well as energy levels.

The omega-3s also increase the effectiveness of *5-fluorouracil* and other chemotherapy drugs, according to a study published in *Clinical Nutrition Research*. In research published in *Cancer*, lung cancer patients who took fish oil along with chemotherapy had a greater one-year survival rate than those who didn't take the supplements.

Note: Fish oil may cause stomach upset in some patients, along with bleeding in those who are taking anticoagulant medications such as *warfarin* (Coumadin), *apixaban* (Eliquis) and *rivaroxaban* (Xarelto).

• **Boost energy levels.** Ginseng is one of the more effective supplements for cancer patients. A number of studies have shown that it reduces treatment-related side effects, including weakness and fatigue. A double-blind study in *Journal of the National Cancer Institute* found that patients who took ginseng had less fatigue than those given placebos.

My advice: The American form of ginseng (*Panax quinquefolius*) is more effective than the Asian form. *Typical dose*: 1,300 mg to 2,000 mg daily. It rarely causes side effects, although it may lower blood sugar in those with diabetes.

Also helpful: Glutathione, a "super antioxidant" that can be combined with chemotherapy to reduce toxin-related fatigue and other side effects. It's usually given in an IV solution. Side effects are unlikely, but it may interfere with some chemotherapy drugs. Be sure to consult an integrative oncologist to see whether you will/won't benefit from glutathione.

• **Improve immune response.** Turkey tail is one of the best-studied medicinal mushrooms. Available in capsule form, the supplement has chemical compounds (beta-glucans) that stimulate many aspects of the immune response, including antibody activity—important for inducing the death of cancer cells.

Impressive research: A study published in *Cancer Immunology and Immunotherapy* found that postsurgical remissions in colorectal cancer patients were twice as common in those who were given turkey tail. *Typical dose*: 3,000 mg daily. Side effects are unlikely.

A NUTRITIONAL BOOST

Conventional oncologists receive little training in nutrition, but it's a critical issue for cancer patients. One study found that 91% of cancer patients had nutritional impairments, and 9%

were seriously malnourished. Research shows that malnutrition contributes directly or indirectly to a significant number of cancer deaths due to poor appetite and the disease process of advanced cancer.

Loss of appetite is a major cause of malnutrition and muscle loss (*cachexia*). I advise patients who are losing weight to address these problems by getting more calories.

With every meal you eat, include high-fat foods such as olive oil, coconut oil, avocado, nuts and seeds. A 10-year study, published in *Archives of Internal Medicine,* looked at more than 380,000 adults and found that a Mediterranean-style diet, which is high in olive oil and other healthy fats, reduced cancer deaths in men by 17% and 12% in women.

Also helpful: Protein shakes. They can provide the extra protein that's critical for cancer patients. Up to 80% of those with advanced cancer experience muscle loss. Protein shakes can help reverse it.

Best option: Ready-made whey protein or pea protein shakes—both are nutritious, have 5 g of sugar or less per serving and are readily available in health-food stores.

My advice: Get 1 g to 1.2 g of protein per kilogram (2.2 pounds) of body weight every day. This means that someone who weighs 150 pounds will need about 68 g to 82 g of protein daily. You can get that much from two or three servings of a typical whey protein beverage, which comes ready-mixed or in a powdered form.

Caution: If you have moderate or severe kidney disease, check with your doctor for advice on your protein intake.

Massage for Cancer Patients

Susan G. Salvo, EdD, LMT, instructor, Louisiana Institute of Massage Therapy, Lake Charles. SusanSalvo.com

There's a widely held misconception that massage causes cancer to spread. In fact, the American Cancer Society and National Comprehensive Cancer Network recommend massage, as long as precautions are observed.

Research has shown that massage can improve sleep and reduce pain, anxiety, depression and fatigue in cancer patients. It also can decrease side effects related to chemotherapy, radiation and surgery. In research, participants received a 30-minute massage once daily, biweekly or weekly.

Precautions: Your massage practitioner should have training in oncology massage. For a referral, ask your doctor or check the Society for Oncology Massage at S4OM.org.

Also, tell your therapist your goals for therapy...the type of cancer you have (as well as tumor sites and metastases)...the treatments you've received, including side effects...locations of any implanted devices, such as a port for chemo...and any restrictions made by your doctor.

Insurance may cover the cost of massage for cancer patients.

Exercise Fights Glaucoma

The most physically active people (those who exercised moderately to vigorously 30 minutes a day, five days a week) were 73% less likely to develop glaucoma than the least physically active, according to a study that tracked 5,000 adults over several decades.

Theory: Exercise may change the blood flow to the optic nerve or affect intraocular pressure. More study is needed.

Victoria Tseng, MD, PhD, ophthalmologist, UCLA Jules Stein Eye Institute, California.

An Orange a Day May Keep Macular Degeneration Away

People who consumed at least one orange daily were 60% less likely to have age-related macular degeneration 15 years later than people who did not eat oranges. The protective effect may be due to the flavonoids in oranges—but no benefit was found from consuming other flavonoid-rich foods, such as apples, or from flavonoid supplements.

Bamini Gopinath, PhD, principal research fellow at Westmead Institute for Medical Research, Westmead, Australia, and lead author of a study published in *The American Journal of Clinical Nutrition.*

Vitamin D Curbs Lung Attacks

Flare-ups of chronic obstructive pulmonary disease (COPD), called lung attacks, cause shortness of breath, coughing and increased mucus production. Nearly all COPD deaths are due to lung attacks.

New finding: COPD patients deficient in vitamin D who took supplements had a 45% decrease in the rate of these attacks.

If you have COPD and suffer lung attacks: Get your blood levels of vitamin D tested. If it's below 10 ng/ml, ask your doctor about taking 2,000 IU of vitamin D daily. (For general health, a recommended level is typically 20 ng/ml to 50 ng/ml.)

Adrian R. Martineau, PhD, MRCP, clinical professor of respiratory infection and immunity, The London School of Medicine, and Dentistry, Queen Mary University of London, UK.

The Science of Knee Health

• **Increased fiber intake can reduce the chance of developing symptomatic knee osteoarthritis.** People who have the highest intake—21 grams daily from grains, legumes, nuts, fruits and vegetables—had a 30% lower chance of developing the condition over a four-year period, compared with those with lowest fiber intake.

• **Weight loss may slow cartilage loss in the knee.** Patients who lost 5% to 10% of body weight over four years had slower degeneration of their knee cartilage than those who stayed at a stable weight.

• **Noisy knees, known as crepitus, may indicate development of arthritis pain in the near future.** People with the most crepitus were most likely to develop symptomatic knee osteoarthritis within one to four years.

• **A Mediterranean-style diet for people with knee osteoarthritis** can reduce knee pain and bring a better overall quality of life. The diet focuses on olive oil, fruits, nuts, vegetables and whole grains.

Roundup of multiple research studies reported in *University of California, Berkeley Wellness Letter.*

Self-Massage for Pain Relief and Other Benefits

Tiffany M. Field, PhD, director of the Touch Research Institute at University of Miami Miller School of Medicine, which focuses on the effects of massage therapy. She is author of *Touch*.

You may not be able to give yourself the giggles by tickling yourself, but you can tap into the proven health benefits of massage by letting your own fingers do the kneading. There are plenty of reasons to enjoy the oohs and aahs—massage can improve symptoms of health conditions ranging from chronic pain to depression to anxiety, high blood pressure and even painful autoimmune diseases.

With moderate-pressure massage, pressure receptors located directly under the skin are activated, starting a chain reaction that, among other benefits, decreases levels of the "stress hormone" cortisol. That's the source of many of the benefits. *How to tap into these benefits on your own…*

• **Grab a tennis ball.** If you're unsure of how much pressure to apply or if your fingers are stiff, a tennis ball is a perfect (and inexpensive) massage tool. Just hold the ball in one hand, and roll it up and down your legs, across your arms or over any place that needs some kneading. The movements can be circular or back-and-forth. As long as you are moving the skin in front of the ball as it rolls, you're getting benefit.

For a back massage, stand against a wall and put the tennis ball between the area you want to massage and the wall. Shift your weight from one leg to the other, or slide your back up and down along the wall to roll the ball.

For a foot massage, use your hands or place the ball on the floor and roll one foot over it at a time. Hold on to a table or counter for balance or try it sitting down.

• **Give yourself an extra hand.** Massage tools, available in fitness stores and online, are great for hard-to-reach areas.

Examples: Lie down on a cylinder-shaped foam roller, and roll back and forth over it to massage your entire upper body. If you prefer to sit up, try a curved massage stick or wooden massage-beads-on-a-rope.

• **Enhance the experience with an oil or lotion.** You might find this more comfortable than a "dry" massage. Consider a lavender-scented product—lavender is scientifically proven to have a relaxing effect.

• **Get pro advice.** While you certainly don't need formal training to give yourself a massage, an instructional session with a certified massage therapist will be helpful. You'll learn new movements to keep the massages interesting and even prevent soreness. To find a massage therapist, contact your state's licensing board or go to the website of the American Massage Therapy Association (AMTAMassage.org) and click "find a massage therapist."

New Diet for Chronic Pain

Some people with a gluten sensitivity (confirmed by a blood test) suffer from "gluten neuropathy," which can cause nerve pain or numbness that generally affects the hands and feet. In a study of 60 adults (average age 70) with gluten neuropathy, researchers found that those following a strict gluten-free diet (no wheat, barley or rye) were 89% less likely to have pain than those who consumed gluten.

Panagiotis Zis, MD, PhD, honorary senior lecturer, University of Sheffield, UK.

Tai Chi for Fibromyalgia

When 226 adults with the chronic pain condition fibromyalgia were randomly assigned to twice-weekly aerobic classes or tai chi classes, those in the tai chi group reported significantly more improvement in pain intensity, fatigue, depression and overall well-being after 24 weeks.

Theory: The gentle movements and emotion-regulating effects of tai chi are especially effective for fibromyalgia.

Chenchen Wang, MD, director, Center for Complementary and Integrative Medicine, Tufts Medical Center, Boston.

High-Intensity Exercise Delays Parkinson's Progression

People with early-stage Parkinson's who exercised three times weekly at high intensity—80% to 85% of maximum heart rate—for six months had no worsening of their symptoms. The study showed that using a treadmill is effective, and other studies have shown that weight training also is beneficial.

Daniel M. Corcos, PhD, professor of physical therapy and human movement sciences at Feinberg School of Medicine, Northwestern University, Chicago, led a study published in *JAMA Neurology*.

Natural Help for Epilepsy

About one-third of people with epilepsy still have seizures despite taking medications. But a daily program of progressive muscle relaxation—deep breathing while tensing and then relaxing muscles—reduced seizures in these patients by 29%. A similar mindfulness-related "focused attention" program cut seizures by 25%.

Other behavioral interventions that may reduce stress are likely helpful as well.

Sheryl Haut, MD, a neurologist at Montefiore Medical Center, The Bronx, New York, and lead author of a study of 66 medication-resistant epilepsy patients, published in *Neurology*.

Curcumin Fights Dementia

Bill Gottlieb, CHC, a natural health coach in Middletown, California, certified by the American Association of Drugless Practitioners. He is author of 16 books that have sold three million copies including *Speed Healing*. His Bottom Line videos can be found at BottomLineInc.com/author/bill-gottlieb. BillGottliebHealth.com

Specially formulated supplements of curcumin—the active ingredient in the spice turmeric—improve memory and focus in people who don't have dementia. They also may reduce the risk of developing Alzheimer's disease.

Scientific evidence: Researchers at UCLA Longevity Center recruited 40 healthy middle-aged and elderly people. For 18 months, 21 of them took a curcumin supplement twice daily, while 19 took a placebo. At the beginning and again at the end of the study, their short-term verbal and visual memory abilities—such as recalling memorized words and images—were tested. And their brains were scanned for toxic amyloid plaques and tau tangles, two signs of Alzheimer's.

Key findings: After 18 months, participants taking curcumin had significantly improved results on the memory tests. (*Bonus*: They also had improved mood.) Participants taking the placebo had little or no improvement in memory. What's more, the follow-up brain scans showed that the curcumin group, compared with the placebo group, had lower levels of amyloid and tau deposits.

THE RIGHT KIND OF CURCUMIN SUPPLEMENT

While curcumin in its natural state—in the spice turmeric and in many supplements—is poorly absorbed by the body, there are five formulations that research has shown are well-absorbed. The UCLA researchers used one of them, Theracurmin, at a dose of 90 mg twice daily. (A one-month supply costs about $53.) The other four are Meriva, Curcumin C3 Complex, BCM-95 and CurcuWIN. All are available online.

More research is needed before we know whether curcumin supplements actually prevent Alzheimer's disease. Curcumin supplements have a strong safety record, but they can cause stomach upset in some people. And they act as blood thinners, so doctors generally say that curcumin should not be taken by people using blood-thinning drugs. To determine whether curcumin is safe for you—and what a proper dose might be—it's best to work with a doctor who has studied this supplement.

If you take curcumin, though, you may find that you experience more benefits. It's a powerful anti-inflammatory and antioxidant that has been found to help relieve arthritis pain, ease muscle soreness after exercise and relieve allergy symptoms.

High Physical Fitness = Lower Dementia Risk

Women who had the highest level of physical fitness in middle age were nearly 90% less likely to develop dementia in later life than women with a moderate fitness level. And when highly fit women did develop dementia, its onset was an average of 11 years later—at age 90 rather than 79.

The study, published in *Neurology*, used a bicycle exercise test to measure cardiovascular capacity of women at an average age of 50. It then followed the women for 44 years, testing for dementia six times. Among women judged highly fit, 5% developed dementia...compared with 25% of those judged moderately fit, 32% of those with low fitness and 45% of those who had to stop the test because of cardiovascular problems.

The study involved a relatively small number of women, all of them from Sweden, and their fitness levels were measured only once. Changes over time were not considered.

Helena Hörder, PhD, researcher, University of Gothenburg, Sweden, and leader of a study of 191 women, published in *Neurology*.

Gentle Exercise for Cognitive Health

Gentle exercise may reverse cognitive decline in as little as six months. Among people with cardiovascular disease risks who never exercised and had verified cognitive concerns but not dementia, those who exercised three times a week for six months—while following the heart-healthy DASH diet—averaged 47 points on a scale testing executive-thinking skills at the end of the study. Those who exercised but did not follow the diet averaged 42 points...those who did not exercise or follow the diet averaged 38. Exercise included a 10-minute warm-up followed by 35 minutes of continuous walking or stationary cycling.

James Blumenthal, PhD, professor of psychiatry and behavioral sciences, Duke University School of Medicine, Durham, North Carolina, and leader of a study of 160 adults, published in *Neurology*.

Boogie for a Better Brain

Rebecca Shannonhouse, editor in chief, *Bottom Line Health*, BottomLineInc.com.

If you're not a fan of treadmills or stationary bikes, here's some good news—dancing offers certain benefits you can't get from a sweaty gym workout. We have known for some time now that aerobic exercise helps guard against age-related cognitive declines, but there was not much research on dancing. To learn more, researchers asked adults, average age 68, to do traditional endurance workouts (such as cycling)...or to go dancing (doing, for example, the mambo or cha-cha).

Study results: After 18 months of weekly exercise, people in both groups had increased volume of the hippocampus, the part of the brain that plays a key role in memory and learning. But the dancers had an edge—they showed more improvement in balance than those in the workout group.

Why is dancing so great?

Part of the benefit comes from the mental workout—memorizing arm movements, step patterns and rhythms, the researchers explained. In the study, dance routines were also changed every two weeks, which challenged the dancers' balance systems and required mental effort to learn the choreographies.

Bonus: For many people, dancing is more fun than going to a gym.

To get started: Look for dance classes in your community—ideally a type of dance that involves aerobic conditioning and endurance to promote blood flow to the brain…coordinated movements that require memory and balance…and social interaction. In addition to the dance styles used in the study, Latin-style Zumba is a good choice. Mix it up every so often to keep it mentally challenging…and fun!

Volunteering Stops Brain Shrinkage

Brain shrinkage is a normal part of aging and causes a decrease in memory and mental sharpness. When retired people served as mentors to young children in public schools in a two-year program—helping students learn to read—the gray matter and a key memory region in their brains stayed the same size and, in some cases, grew slightly. This may be associated with a reduced risk for Alzheimer's disease. Any type of sustained purposeful activity that involves leaving your house and interacting socially with others may have similar benefits.

Michelle C. Carlson, PhD, professor, department of mental health, Johns Hopkins Bloomberg School of Public Health, Baltimore.

GOOD TO KNOW…

The Magic of Music!

Music activates parts of the brain that are unaffected by Alzheimer's disease—helping patients who listen to familiar tunes experience less anxiety and feel more grounded in reality.

The Journal of Prevention of Alzheimer's Disease.

This "Outside the Box" Therapy Helps with Depression and More

Steven C. Hayes, PhD, codeveloper of acceptance and commitment therapy (ACT) and professor of psychology at University of Nevada, Reno. He is author of 44 books, including *Get Out of Your Mind and Into Your Life: The New Acceptance and Commitment Therapy.* His more than 600 scientific research articles have been published in a number of professional journals, including *British Journal of Psychiatry, Journal of Consulting and Clinical Psychology* and *Psychology of Addictive Behaviors.*

You want to change. You want to escape painful feelings, such as sadness, anxiety or shame…and rid yourself of any troubling thoughts you might be having, such as *No one likes me.* Or you want to change ineffective or dangerous behavior, whether it's drinking too much, arguing with your loved ones or being a couch potato.

Psychotherapy is an option. But will it work for you?

An approach you may not be aware of: An increasing body of scientific evidence shows that an action-based therapy known as *acceptance and commitment therapy* (ACT) can be highly effective in treating a range of mental health problems, including depression, anxiety disorders, chronic pain syndrome and drug and alcohol abuse. *Here's how ACT could help you—or a loved one…*

AN "OUTSIDE THE BOX" THERAPY

A number of other types of therapies guide you through your past to understand where "wrong" feelings come from. Sometimes, however, you can end up mired more deeply in the very thoughts you're trying to dispel. With these therapies, negative thoughts and feelings are the enemy. Not so with ACT. With this "outside-the-box" therapy, you become aware of your thoughts and feelings *without* treating them as "good" or "bad." This means that you don't argue with your thoughts. And above all, you don't try to subtract, suppress or eliminate them…you *accept* them.

Acceptance doesn't mean that you put up with feelings like hopelessness or anxiety. Because they aren't battling their thoughts and feelings, people who use ACT become more able to behave in healthier, more fulfilling ways—to do things they want to do and feel are worthwhile.

ACT helps you learn how to step back from thoughts by recognizing that they're yours… but they're not you. (ACT therapists call this *defusion*.) With this approach, you're not exhausted and frustrated by constantly trying to control or change your thoughts and feelings.

HOW ACT WORKS

The key to ACT's main principle—paying attention to your thoughts and feelings and accepting them—is "defused mindfulness." This might mean observing your emotions as they grow stronger…noting where you feel them in your body or how they begin and end…and how they combine with other experiences. Defusion is the process of looking at thoughts with an attitude of dispassionate curiosity.

ACT offers many defusion techniques to blunt the power your thoughts have over you—sometimes in a matter of minutes.

***TECHNIQUE #1*: If you have a persistently troublesome or unpleasant thought,** such as, *I'm a failure* or *I always feel like an outsider,* distill it into a single word, such as *failure.* Say the word out loud, rapidly, once a second for 30 seconds (research shows that is the sweet spot in terms of rate and length). At the end of this time, see whether the thought has the same powerful hold over you. This simple technique has been shown to work even with very painful thoughts.

***TECHNIQUE #2*: Give your mind a name, like Casey, and as you focus on a distressing thought,** preface it with, *Casey says…* This technique creates a gap between you and your thought so that you can look at your thinking rather than automatically believing your thinking.

The *commitment* part of ACT means transforming your acceptance of your thoughts and feelings into positive, meaningful action. If you're no longer overwhelmed by your feelings, you can turn the energy you once spent trying to change or control them toward discovering what you truly care about and linking your actions to that choice.

Treatment with ACT can yield significant improvement in as few as four to five sessions. Eight to 12 weekly sessions are a more common course. However long the therapy takes, homework is *always* an important part of ACT. People typically spend 45 minutes a week with the therapist, leaving a lot of time in between sessions.

For homework, you may practice the skills learned in the session and try out new techniques to observe thoughts and feelings dispassionately in real life, gradually turning this new approach into a habit.

Important: No particular therapy works for everyone. If mindfulness is unappealing to you or you aren't ready to look deeply into your own pain, values and sense of self, you may do better with a different type of therapy. But if you're intrigued by the ACT principles—especially if you've tried other therapies without satisfactory results—this approach could be worth a try.

To find an ACT therapist: Visit the website of the Association for Contextual Behavioral Science (ACBS) at ContextualScience.org. While ACBS doesn't certify therapists, each listing includes the therapist's background and training in the technique.

THE SCIENTIFIC EVIDENCE…

There are approximately 250 randomized trials of acceptance and commitment therapy (ACT). In clinical trials, it has been shown to improve not just various emotional and psychiatric problems but also help individuals become more effective in addressing health issues, such as diet and exercise, and dealing with physical disease.

For example, just four sessions of ACT were associated with substantial improvements in depression. More impressively, when participants were contacted five years later, 40% of those treated still reported minimal or no depressive symptoms.

Saffron Relieves Depression

Hyla Cass, MD, integrative psychiatrist in private practice in Los Angeles. She was an assistant clinical professor of psychiatry at UCLA School of Medicine for more than 20 years and is author of several best-selling books. CassMD.com

For years, researchers have been nibbling around the idea that saffron, the prized culinary spice that can be taken as a supplement, is a remedy for depression. But now the evidence is big. In a review of seven randomized controlled trials published in *Neuropsychiatric Disease and Treatment*, researchers concluded that saffron supplements are just as effective as antidepressant drugs for treating mild-to-moderate depression.

Why that matters: Prescription antidepressants can cause side effects including weight gain, digestive upset, low libido, insomnia and anxiety, while saffron is associated only with occasional mild symptoms such as dizziness or nausea. It's very safe at recommended doses (see below), although pregnant women should check with their doctors first.

Saffron works in several ways. Its active ingredients *safranal* and *crocin* boost the neurotransmitter *serotonin*, as do most antidepressants. But saffron also reduces neuro-inflammation, the chronic, low-grade brain inflammation that underlies many cases of depression and reduces levels of stress hormones. *Best practices…*

• **Use the right kind of saffron supplement.** Look for a product standardized to at least 2% safranal (it also will contain crocin), such as Saffron Extract from Swanson Superior Herbs (about $20 for a two-month supply). Most studies used 30 milligrams (mg) daily—the dosage that I typically prescribe.

Note: Saffron can be toxic, but only at doses of 1,500 mg or more. (Include saffron in your diet, too—it might help and tastes great.)

• **Combine saffron with other natural remedies.** In my view, saffron should be part of a natural, nondrug protocol. I often prescribe omega-3 fatty acids and 5-HTP. (Check

BETTER WAY...

Lift Weights to Lift Your Mood

Add weights to your workout to improve your mental health.

Recent finding: In addition to improving muscle tone and bone health, regular strength training may help fight depression. An analysis of 33 studies found resistance training closely associated with reduced depressive symptoms—and the result was seen even when there was no increase in physical strength.

Study led by researchers at University of Limerick, Ireland, published in *JAMA Psychiatry.*

with your doctor first, especially if you are taking other medications.) Saffron often starts to work in a week or two on its own, but it is especially effective when combined with these other remedies.

• **If you already take an antidepressant, don't stop on your own.** What you might try is to gradually reduce your drug dose under a physician's supervision while taking saffron and other natural remedies mentioned above. This process can take several months.

• **Adopt an antidepression lifestyle.** That includes regular exercise…a non-inflammatory diet that eliminates sugar, white flour, wheat and gluten, and maximizes fresh foods from the perimeter of the supermarket…seven to eight hours of sleep a night…spending quality time with family and friends.

Giddyup for PTSD

Therapeutic horseback riding could help military veterans with *post-traumatic stress disorder* (PTSD).

Report: Vets who participated in a riding program had 87% declines in PTSD scores after just six weeks.

University of Missouri College of Veterinary Medicine.

6

Private & Personal

Natural Ways to Reverse Erectile Dysfunction

If you're a man reading this article, there's a reasonable chance that you have erectile dysfunction (ED)—you have not been able to achieve and maintain an erection that is satisfactory for you and your partner. While it happens to some younger men, by age 40 22% of men have ED in some form, ranging from moderate/intermittent to severe, and by age 70, about 50% do. It's often progressive—it'll get worse if you don't do something about it.

But isn't the solution easy? After all, Viagra, Levitra and Cialis—prescription drugs that increase blood flow to the penis—are popular. They certainly help. But side effects can be severe, including headache, facial flushing, blurred vision, temporary hearing loss and back pain. Worse yet, these drugs actually can interfere with enjoyable sexual intercourse,

says integrative urologist Geo Espinosa, ND, because another possible effect is penile desensitization—you get an erection but then can't enjoy intercourse. Yet another is difficulty reaching orgasm.

The good news is that in most cases ED can be prevented—or treated—without these drugs, Dr. Espinosa told us. He rarely prescribes them, generally only when impotence is caused by medical care such as treatment for prostate cancer. *That's because the more natural interventions discussed below almost always work to restore erections...*

THESE SUPPLEMENTS MAKE A DIFFERENCE

There are four nutrients and herbs that I prescribe to prevent or reverse ED.

Geo Espinosa, ND, LAc, IFMCP, CNS, a naturopathic doctor, licensed acupuncturist, certified functional medicine practitioner and authority on holistic urology and men's health. He is clinical assistant professor in urology at New York University Langone Medical Center in New York City and author of *Thrive, Don't Only Survive,* coeditor of *Integrative Sexual Health* and coauthor of *Bottom Line's 1,000 Cures for 200 Ailments: Integrative Medicine for the Most Common Illnesses.* DrGeo.com

Important: Don't start taking these on your own. Do so under medical supervision (more on that below). You'll also need a little patience. These supplements work gradually, so they're best used on a daily basis, not right before sex. *Here they are…*

• **L-citrulline.** This amino acid converts in the body to L-arginine, which in turn boosts levels of nitric oxide, a gaseous chemical that relaxes the "smooth muscle" in the penis, opening up penile arteries and improving blood flow. These changes also are good for your cardiovascular system—L-citrulline can reduce high blood pressure, for example.

Scientific research: L-citrulline has been shown in clinical studies to improve erectile function in men with ED. In research at David Geffen School of Medicine at UCLA, it also has been shown to be effective when combined with other supplements. My typical prescription is to take L-citrulline twice a day on an empty stomach for a daily total of 750 milligrams (mg) to 1,500 mg.

Warning: If your blood pressure is low, either naturally or through treatment, L-citrulline can bring it down too low.

• **Horny goat weed (Epimedium grandiflorum).** This herb is rich in icariin, which, like the L-citrulline described above, boosts nitric oxide. It also helps normalize enzymes that control penile blood flow. My typical prescription is to take horny goat weed twice a day on an empty stomach for a daily total of 200 mg to 400 mg. Like L-citrulline, it may reduce blood pressure too low in people with low pressure.

• **Ashwagandha.** This herb from India boosts testosterone. Testosterone deficiency is a common cause of low libido and ED. Ashwagandha also is an adaptogen, an herb that helps the body deal with stress, a major factor in ED. It reduces the stress hormone adrenaline, which in excess tightens arteries, decreasing blood supply to the penis. My typical prescription is to take ashwagandha twice a day on an empty stomach for a daily total of 500 mg to 1,500 mg. It may cause stomach upset in some people.

Important: Don't take this supplement unless you have a testosterone deficiency—only a test done by your doctor can tell you that.

• **Rhodiola rosea.** This is another herbal adaptogen that helps restore physical and mental energy. Exhaustion, particularly at the end of a difficult day, is a common cause of ED.

Scientific research: Salidroside, one of the active ingredients in rhodiola, helps maintain the flow of oxygen to the corpora cavernosa, the spongy penile tissue that fills with blood to create an erection, according to a study published in *Evidence-Based Complementary and Alternative Medicine.*

Disclosure: Dr. Espinosa is cofounder of XY Wellness, LLC, a company that sells a combination ED supplement product called XYVGGR.

HOW TO USE THESE SUPPLEMENTS

Seek out a complementary/integrative health professional, such as a naturopathic doctor, who can guide you. These supplements often work best in some combination depending on the patient's overall health profile. It's especially important to work with a complementary health-care professional if you already are being treated for ED—and even more so if you have another condition such as diabetes or heart disease and already take prescription medications or other supplements. A good integrative physician also will help you make essential lifestyle changes that are part of your journey back to sexual health.

THE GOOD-IN-BED DIET

Men with ED often have cardiovascular disease and/or diabetes, both of which impair blood flow. A diet proven to control and reverse those two deadly diseases also is effective for ED—the Mediterranean diet, rich in vegetables, fruits, beans, whole grains, fish, nuts and seeds, and olive oil, with a minimum of red meat, processed meat and refined carbohydrates.

Scientific evidence: In research published in *The Journal of Sexual Medicine,* Italian doctors studied more than 600 men with diabetes. Compared with men who ate the fewest foods in the Mediterranean diet, those who ate the most were 17% less likely to have any level of ED and 38% less likely to have severe ED (having erections infrequently or not at all). In another study, men newly diagnosed with type 2 diabetes ate either a Mediterranean diet or a low-fat diet. After eight years, those eating the Mediterranean diet were much less likely to have developed ED.

THE EXERCISE PRESCRIPTION

Exercise is a must in any approach to preventing and reversing ED. It improves circulation, boosts testosterone and reduces stress.

New scientific finding: In a scientific paper published in *Sexual Medicine*, researchers analyzed data from 10 studies on exercise and ED and found that six months of regular exercise helped reverse ED in men who were sedentary, overweight, had high blood pressure or had cardiovascular disease. *My recommendations...*

● **Interval training.** Compared with moderate aerobics, high-intensity interval training will help you shed more weight, get fitter faster and add more testosterone-triggering muscle.

What to do: Whether your aerobic activity is walking, running, biking or swimming, do it at a moderately easy pace for 60 sec-

onds—and then as fast as you can for 15 to 20 seconds.

Caution: Men who haven't regularly physically stressed their bodies should consider getting a cardiovascular evaluation that includes a stress test to confirm that their heart can handle the workout.

● **Dead lifts.** A circuit of strength-training exercises for all your muscles is great for you. One particular exercise should be part of your training, though—the dead lift. You lift a weighted bar off the ground to the level of your hips, then lower it slowly back. Dead lifts use the large muscles of the legs, buttocks and back, and the more muscle, the more testosterone.

Safe, correct form is very important, so learn from a trainer at a gym or by watching one of the many YouTube videos on dead lifts. Do the exercise as part of your strength-training program at least two to three days a week. A set is lifting the weight six times in a row. Work up to six sets, resting two minutes between sets. If you are able to do more than six repetitions without resting, the weight is too light.

REDUCING PERFORMANCE ANXIETY

If you're not confident before sex—if you're anxious about achieving or keeping an erection, an anxiety common in men who have experienced ED—it's more likely you will have erectile difficulties.

Smart idea: Just as professional athletes visualize their desired outcomes before performing, creating mental images of a successful performance such as getting a hit, making a basket or sinking a putt, you can visualize successful sexual performance. Take a few minutes to visualize yourself getting erect and enjoying intercourse. And then start sex with more confidence.

It's important to realize that no one thing alone reverses ED. But the right diet, exercise regimen, supplement combination and mental attitude can indeed reverse ED—close to 100% of the time.

Natural Ways to Boost Testosterone

Geo Espinosa, ND, LAc, IFMCP, CNS, a naturopathic doctor, licensed acupuncturist, certified functional medicine practitioner and authority on holistic urology and men's health. He is clinical assistant professor in urology at New York University Langone Medical Center in New York City and author of *Thrive, Don't Only Survive*, coeditor of *Integrative Sexual Health* and coauthor of *Bottom Line's 1,000 Cures for 200 Ailments: Integrative Medicine for the Most Common Illnesses*. DrGeo.com

You know that testosterone—often referred to simply as "T"—is the main male sex hormone, responsible for a man's sex drive and performance. What you may not realize is that T does more than power his libido and penis.

Throughout the adult male body—in muscles (including the heart muscle)…bones…brain…and the immune system—there are receptors for vitality-giving testosterone. This means that low T doesn't only hurt a man's sexual wellness…it can hurt his overall health as well.

Good news: If you've been diagnosed with low T (see box at right), you can stimulate your own production of testosterone—achieving optimal, disease-preventing levels—just by making a few lifestyle modifications…

T-BOOSTER #1: **Lose the belly fat.** Extra abdominal fat generates the enzyme aromatase, which turns testosterone into estrogen.

What to do: The best way to shed extra pounds (especially harmful belly fat) is to stop eating refined carbohydrates such as sugar and white flour. And one of the best ways to do that is to eliminate all processed foods, most of which contain sugar and/or refined carbs. Another common source of excess carbohydrates is alcohol. If your T is low, you're better off saying no to beer, wine and spirits.

T-BOOSTER #2: **Get your shut-eye**—particularly from 4 am to 7 am. The male body produces the most testosterone during these three hours, when rapid eye movement (REM) sleep usually occurs. Deep, restful sleep is essential for optimal T.

What to do: Difficulty falling asleep or getting back to sleep after waking up is often caused by worry—your mind is racing as you anxiously think about your health, your finances, your work or your relationship. To stop this unhealthy habit, keep a notebook on your night table and write down your thoughts before bed and/or if you wake up and can't get back to sleep—make a list of what you're worried about or what you think you need to do. Doing so will calm your mind, ease your worries—and let you fall asleep.

T-BOOSTER #3: **Lift a weight.** Regular exercise is a must for boosting testosterone—but it has to be the right kind of exercise. For T production, research strongly supports the use of weight-training.

Here's why: Using the biggest muscles of the body sends signals to the brain that the muscles need more testosterone—and the body starts producing more.

More from Dr. Geo Espinosa...

Do You Have Low T?

A clinical diagnosis of low testosterone is made when the level of a man's total testosterone, as measured by a blood test, is 299 nanograms per deciliter (ng/dL) or lower. But an optimal level of total testosterone is 600 ng/dL to 800 ng/dL. Anything below 600 ng/dL puts you at risk for health problems and a lower quality of life. If you answer "yes" to one or more of these questions, ask your doctor for a blood test to measure your "total testosterone" level to see if you have low T…

1. Do you have extra belly fat? Abdominal fat is linked to low T.

2. Do you feel tired all the time? Daytime fatigue is a common symptom of low T.

3. Do you feel a lack of motivation—at work, in relationships and in your personal interests? Low T can make you apathetic and indecisive.

4. Are you a man in your 60s or 70s who feels that you just don't have the vitality and positivity you once had? If so, you may have low T.

5. Do you have little desire for sex—and when you try to have sex, do you have trouble achieving an erection? Those are each signs of very low T.

What to do: Deadlift a barbell or kettlebell. In this exercise, you bend over at your hips and bend your knees to lift the weight off the floor. Return to standing, hold the weight, and then put it back on the floor. Repeat this lift until your muscles are fatigued. A dead lift uniquely targets your hamstrings, glutes, core, upper back and arms.

Learn the safe, correct way to do a dead lift (including the amount of weight that's right for you) from a trainer, exercise book or video, and then do dead lifts every other day, at least three times a week.

T-BOOSTER #4: Take targeted supplements. Some nutritional and herbal supplements are uniquely effective at helping your body produce more testosterone, preserving the testosterone your body is producing or making sure that your testosterone gets to its receptors. *Men with low T should consider taking the following supplements…**

• Zinc, a mineral that stimulates the Leydig cells in the testicles that produce testosterone. Take 30 mg daily. *Caution:* More is not better. Taking more than 30 mg of zinc a day lowers copper levels, which can be harmful.

• Vitamin D, which aids in the production of testosterone. The amount of vitamin D you take should be guided by a vitamin D test.

• Rhodiola and ashwagandha. Stress generates the hormone cortisol, which inhibits the production of testosterone. These herbs are adaptogens, which balance the body when it is under stress. Take 250 mg of rhodiola, twice daily…and 250 mg of ashwagandha, twice daily.

T-BOOSTER #5: Make love, make T. Sex stimulates the production of testosterone and is good for the health of your prostate.

What to do: Although many factors affect sexual frequency—including the desires of your sexual partner—I recommend sex at least twice per week to optimize testosterone. Many of my patients consider this my best advice!

*When considering the use of herbs and supplements, consult a naturopathic or functional medicine doctor for advice on dosage and potential interactions with medications. To find such a doctor near you, consult The American Association of Naturopathic Physicians, Naturopathic. org, or The Institute for Functional Medicine, IFM.org.

Important: I recommend testosterone replacement therapy only as a last resort—for men whose T is so low that lifestyle changes don't adequately improve their levels and whose low testosterone is causing or complicating a chronic condition. In 99% of my patients, the right lifestyle changes do the trick.

Women: Let's Talk About Orgasms

Lauren Streicher, MD, clinical professor of obstetrics and gynecology at Northwestern University Feinberg School of Medicine and medical director of Northwestern Medicine Center for Sexual Health and Menopause, both in Chicago. She is author of *Sex Rx: Hormones, Health, and Your Best Sex Ever.* DrStreicher.com

Has your doctor ever asked you how often you use your vibrator? Or if you even have a vibrator?

If the answer is "Certainly not!" you're not alone. Almost no doctors ask women about vibrators—or orgasms—at all. Most women won't bring up or even think about this topic on their own. Yet for many women whose sex lives decline after menopause, as often is the case, the use of a vibrator is a safe and effective way to restore the joyful (and healthful) sex that they miss. It's good for relationships, too.

Gynecologist Lauren Streicher, MD, often recommends vibrators as a health device. She is on a mission to get women to talk about sexuality, including the inability to have an orgasm, with their doctors. *We talked with her about what that could accomplish…*

• **Why should women talk about sexual problems, including a lack of .orgasms, with their doctors?** Because sexual pleasure is important for most women's physical and emotional health and, if a woman has a partner, for her romantic relationship. Vibrators can help—and doctors should feel comfortable recommending them. More than half of American women ages 18 to 60 have used them at some point in their lives, but that means nearly half never have.

That is a missed opportunity because vibrators can help many women, both before and after menopause, with desire, arousal, lubrication and, yes, orgasm.

•**Is not being able to have an orgasm really a health condition?** It is if it's negatively affecting a woman's life. Many women enjoy sex without orgasms, and in fact, most women don't have orgasms during intercourse and they still consider it a pleasurable experience.

But when a woman—or a man, for that matter—has an orgasm, it not only feels good, it also can be profoundly relaxing for him/her. Often, it decreases stress and helps a woman sleep better.

Plus, levels of the hormone prolactin go up after orgasm—and that's true for both men and women—which increases bonding with your partner. Men also really like their partners to be orgasmic and to enjoy themselves, and it can strengthen a relationship.

Many women, particularly as they get older, are distressed that they can no longer achieve orgasms. Some are not able to have an orgasm at all, while others find that their orgasms are not as strong as they once were and/or take a very long time to happen. Most women I see with these issues used to have orgasms just fine, and then something changed.

The medical term for this is "female orgasmic dysfunction." Often, it's related to menopause. That said, if a woman doesn't have orgasms but it doesn't bother her, she does not have a dysfunction.

•**How does menopause affect sexual pleasure and orgasms?** There are several ways. One is a decline in libido that is related to the decline in estrogen that starts around perimenopause and continues for the many years that follow. That estrogen drop also reduces genital blood flow—and the ability to have an orgasm is tied to good blood flow.

It's similar to erectile dysfunction in men. Also, medical conditions such as cardiovascular disease, diabetes or pelvic surgery can reduce blood flow. For a woman, good blood flow to the clitoris allows the tissue to become engorged, aroused and stimulated and keeps nerve endings healthy and responsive.

•**How exactly does a vibrator address all that?** Most women need direct clitoral stimulation to have an orgasm. For younger women, manual or oral stimulation, or even just the contact during intercourse, can be sufficient. But as women age, they may need something to increase the intensity of the sensation. Even women who are not able to have an orgasm with other kinds of stimulation very often can have them with vibrators.

The clitoris actually has receptors that specifically respond to vibration. That vibrating stimulation also increases blood flow, which in turn increases lubrication. If it is a dildo-type vibrator, regular use also can help maintain elasticity of vaginal tissues.

•**If it doesn't seem like a comfortable topic, how can a woman bring up to her partner the idea of using a vibrator?** She might say something like, "I love when we have sex, but I think it would be fun to try something different, and I hear that using a vibrator can make sex more pleasurable." She might mention that she read a health article—such as this one—reporting that vibrators can help women her age and that many women use them.

•**Aren't many men put off by the idea of their partners using vibrators because it implies that the men aren't "enough"?** That's sometimes true, but not as often as you might think. In one national survey, published in *Journal of Sex & Marital Therapy*, 70% of men said that vibrators are not intimidating. In fact, a man can take the lead on this and say to his female partner, "I've heard it's much more pleasurable for many women with a vibrator, and I'd love for you to have that kind of pleasure, so I bought you one." How any particular couple handles this topic is very individual—in some, the woman takes the lead, in some the man, and some couples like to shop for vibrators together.

Of course, vibrators also can enhance same-sex relationships. Nor does anyone's sexuality have to stop when the person's not having sex with a partner. By discovering more about your own body and how to sexually satisfy yourself, you'll facilitate your ability to achieve orgasm in an intimate relationship, too.

• **Can older women who have never had orgasms start to have them?** Absolutely. A typical woman who has never experienced an orgasm—and who is likely to be quite reticent about all these matters that we've been discussing—just needs "permission" from a health professional to use a vibrator...and in some cases, a little help finding her clitoris. And then, she usually is just fine.

• **Do you hereby give all our readers permission?** I do!

THE DOCTOR'S GUIDE TO SEXUAL AIDS

One type of vibrator that I recommend is a small, external bullet-style clitoral vibrator that you can hold on the right spot—either on your own or while you're having intercourse with your partner. There also are couples' vibrators that are U-shaped. They slide in the vagina so that the man can put his penis in at the same time as the woman is getting direct clitoral stimulation.

Many women also benefit greatly from lubricants after menopause. For intercourse, I recommend silicone-based lubricants—they're very slippery and won't damage vaginal tissue. Water-based lubricants are good, too, and are the best choice if you are using a vibrator or other sex toy, because silicone lubricants do not mix with silicone toys.

If you are using a water-based lubricant, however, be sure to choose one that has low osmolality—a measure of dissolved particles. Many popular lubricants have high osmolality, but that can dry out tissue (the opposite of what you are trying to accomplish!) and increase the chance of irritation and infection.

Note: Water-based low-osmolality lubes include Pulse H2Oh!, Good Clean Love, Sylk, System JO and Slippery Stuff. When using a vibrator, use a water-based lube only because silicone-based lubes can damage the silicone used in many vibrators.

Steer clear of lubes with chemicals in them for flavor or warming—these can damage delicate vaginal tissue. But warming your lube is a really nice option. Pulse is a lubricant-warming dispenser sold with low-osmolality water- or silicone-based lubricant pods.

Many women are nervous about shopping for vibrators.

Tip: Look for women-friendly erotic shops near where you live. There's also a big selection of products available online, of course. That can be overwhelming, but if you shop for my recommendations above, it should be less daunting. I don't have any financial connections to any of these companies.

What Matters Most When It Comes to Breast Cancer Risk

Kristi Funk, MD, board-certified breast surgeon and cofounder of Pink Lotus Breast Center in Los Angeles. She is author of *Breasts: The Owner's Manual*. PinkLotus.com

You probably know the odds—one in eight women will be diagnosed with breast cancer at some point in her life. *What you may not realize:* In spite of all the focus on genetic testing and BRCA genes, most cases of breast cancer are not genetic. There's a lot of emphasis on family history when it comes to all forms of cancer, but 87% of women diagnosed with breast cancer do not have a single first-degree relative (mother, sister, daughter) with breast cancer. The older you are, the more likely it is that breast cancer is caused by things you eat or do, not your genes. This means there's a lot that's within your control! *An ever-growing body of*

121

research has shown what the myths are and what matters...

THE MYTHS

The following have zero to do with breast cancer...

Bras: Myths abound about underwires, cup size and how old you were when you started wearing a bra, but there is no research to support any increase in breast cancer risk due to bra usage.

Antiperspirant: Multiple studies have failed to find any conclusive links between the aluminum chlorohydrate in antiperspirants and breast cancer.

Hair relaxers: No association has been found between breast cancer and how often relaxers or straighteners are used, the number of burns experienced or the type of relaxer. Still it's always a good idea to choose products without parabens and phthalates, which have been linked to cancer.

Mobile phones and power lines: While much debate surrounds mobile phones and brain health, they do not emit the right type of energy—or a high enough amount—to damage breast cell DNA. The same goes for living near power lines. Multiple studies have debunked the idea that the electromagnetic fields (EMFs) generated by high-voltage power lines increase breast cancer risk.

Breast surgery: If you have had breast-reduction surgery, numerous studies support the finding that your risk for breast cancer actually decreases. On the flip side, research shows that most implants—no matter what type, the positioning or how long you've had them—do not cause breast cancer. They do make cancer harder to detect, however, so you should have more rigorous screening—such as an ultrasound along with your mammogram. *Note:* Some new concerns have been raised about textured implants possibly causing a form of lymphoma, but not breast cancer. Additional research is ongoing.

Coffee: No link between coffee consumption and breast cancer has ever been found, and there even is some evidence that drinking coffee may have a protective effect.

Note: Artificial sweeteners have not been linked to breast cancer, but they have been associated with obesity and insulin-resistance (so have no more than two servings a day).

HERE'S WHAT DOES MATTER

The good news is that there are many positive steps you can take to lower your risk for breast cancer. *Not surprisingly, they involve diet, exercise and other lifestyle choices, such as...*

• **Watching your weight.** Being overweight or obese is the single most preventable cause of breast cancer worldwide. Having more fat tissue raises your estrogen and insulin levels. Extra weight increases your risk by anywhere from 50% to 250%. The research is very clear that the risk for breast cancer is much higher if you are overweight postmenopause, although the exact reason for that is not known.

• **Lowering the amount of alcohol you drink.** Alcohol is the other big enemy of healthy breast tissue. All types of alcohol increase estrogen levels, and estrogen is a potent fuel for cancer cells. One drink a day increases your breast cancer risk by 10%...two drinks, by 30%...three drinks, by 40%—you can see where this is going. However, one drink a day does ostensibly provide heart-health benefits. To keep the heart-health benefits and minimize breast cancer risk, stick to no more than one drink a day (or seven over a week) and make it red wine with its breast-friendly resveratrol and anti-estrogen effect.

• **Colorizing your plate.** Aim for a meal that's 70% fresh fruits, vegetables and leafy greens. Fruits and vegetables are loaded with phytonutrients, as well as anticancer and anti-inflammatory properties that directly target cell mutations and put the brakes on cancer development. They prevent and repair DNA damage, destroy harmful cells, inhibit blood supply to tumors and protect against cell damage from environmental toxins.

•**Going meatless more often.** Animal protein, including fish, can increase your risk for breast cancer. Think of it as a side dish, not the main star of your plate. Even egg consumption should be limited to two a week.

In one large-scale UK study, a high intake of meat (red meat, white meat, processed meat, poultry) showed increases in breast cancer risk when compared with vegetarians. Red meat was particularly flagged—the study found a 41% increased risk. But even poultry increased participants' risk by 22%.

Yes, fish contains omega-3s that generally are beneficial, but fish—like meat and poultry—causes the body to produce *insulin-like growth factor-1* (IGF-1), which has the primary job of promoting cell growth. That's great when you are a child. Once you're an adult, you need some IGF-1 to repair cells after exercise, for example, but an excess is going to send cell production into overdrive, including production of cancer cells.

To make matters worse, conventional meat in the US and Canada contains a growth hormone (zeranol) that has been banned in Europe for decades because of its link to early puberty, which increases breast cancer risk. In fact, zeranol has been shown in labs to turn healthy breast cells to cancer in only 21 days.

Note: Even if you choose organic or grass-fed meat, be careful how you prepare it. When meats are well-done or char-grilled, cancer-causing compounds can form on the surface. Women who consistently eat well-done hamburgers, bacon and steak have a 362% higher risk for breast cancer than women who consume meat cooked rare or medium.

•**Moving your body more.** Women who get just three to four hours a week of moderate-to-vigorous physical activity have 30% to 40% lower risk for breast cancer than women who are inactive. Work out more than four hours a week, and you'll enjoy a 58% decrease in risk. Activity reduces estrogen levels, improves insulin sensitivity and maintains weight loss.

•**Finding alternatives to hormone replacement therapy.** Decades of evidence show that hormone replacement therapy (HRT) can increase risk for breast cancer. According to the Women's Health Initiative, there are 25% more breast cancers in HRT users than nonusers. To relieve the symptoms of menopause, try topical vaginal estrogen and laser treatments for vaginal dryness. For hot flashes, try herbal remedies such as black cohosh, evening primrose oil and soy. Acupuncture, biofeedback and yoga also may be beneficial. If you do decide to try HRT or bioidentical hormone replacement therapy (BHRT), take the lowest possible dose for the shortest amount of time necessary.

•**Avoiding environmental toxins.** Minimizing your exposure to *endocrine disrupting compounds* (EDCs) such as BPA, phthalates and parabens, which lurk in many household products, can help lessen your breast cancer risk. Choose organic and locally grown foods when possible, filter all water sources, fill your home with houseplants that act as potted air purifiers and pass on personal-care products that list EDCs on the label.

•**Finding time for daily stress relief.** Acute or chronic stress impairs the immune system, which gives diseases the opportunity to flourish, so take 20 minutes a day to do something that centers you such as yoga or meditation.

New Breast Cancer Risk

Women within a normal weight range but who had excess visceral fat had nearly twice the risk for invasive breast cancer as those with the lowest body-fat mass, according to a 16-year study of 3,460 postmenopausal women.

To check your body fat: Methods such as bioimpedance analysis, which uses an electric current to determine fat/muscle ratio, may be available in your doctor's office or gym.

Neil Iyengar, MD, medical oncologist, Memorial Sloan Kettering Cancer Center, New York City.

BETTER SCREENING...

Mammogram Alternative Coming?

Traditional mammograms are not only uncomfortable but can be unreliable in distinguishing between benign and aggressive tumors.

Now in development: A dye-infused pill that travels through the digestive system and into the bloodstream, where it "lights up" tumors so they can be easily identified.

Molecular Pharmaceutics.

Too Many Women Are Skipping Breast MRIs

Among more than 422,000 women who got mammography at a screening facility that also offered magnetic resonance imaging (MRI), only 6.6% of those with a high lifetime risk for breast cancer got the additional MRI screening. A woman is considered at high lifetime risk if she has risk factors such as a strong family history of breast cancer or inherited mutations to certain genes, such as BRCA1 or BRCA2.

Takeaway: Discuss your breast cancer risk level with your doctor and ask whether MRI is appropriate.

Christoph I. Lee, MD, associate professor of radiology and health sciences (adjunct), University of Washington School of Medicine, Seattle.

To Reduce Painful Side Effect from Breast Cancer Treatment...

A new noninvasive test known as *bioimpedance spectroscopy* (or BIS) detects *lymphedema*—arm swelling that often results from standard treatment for breast cancer such as lymph node surgery or radiation. Early detection with BIS enables the use of home therapy, including compression sleeves and massage. In a study with 146 women, BIS identified 49 women with lymphedema—and home therapy greatly reduced symptoms in 40 of them.

Lyndsey Kilgore, MD, a researcher and resident, department of surgery, University of Kansas Cancer Center, Kansas City, and leader of a study presented at the annual meeting of the American Society of Breast Surgeons.

HPV Testing to Replace Pap Smears?

HPV testing is better than the usual Pap smear at detecting early signs of cervical cancer risk. Virtually all cervical cancer is caused by the *human papillomavirus* (HPV), and unlike a Pap, an HPV-based screening can detect precancerous lesions before cell abnormalities become evident. In the future, HPV testing may replace Pap smears.

Gina Ogilvie, MD, DrPH, professor of medicine at University of British Columbia in Vancouver, Canada, and lead author of a study of 19,009 women published in *JAMA.*

New Hope for Bladder Cancer

Brant Allen Inman, MD, MS, a urologist, associate professor of surgery at Duke University School of Medicine and a member of the Duke Cancer Institute, all in Durham, North Carolina. He specializes in diagnostic tests/therapies for bladder cancer and other genitourinary malignancies.

After years without any significant treatment advances or new prevention strategies, bladder cancer is finally getting its due.

Recent developments: The FDA approved five new drugs in 2016–2017 for the treatment of metastatic bladder cancer. It's an important development because these cancers are often deadly, with a five-year survival rate as low as 15% when the cancer is advanced.

Even though the prognosis for people diagnosed with early-stage bladder cancer has been good for quite some time—up to 95% are alive after five years when the cancer is confined to the inner layer of the bladder wall—a late-stage diagnosis now has more treatment options than ever before. In some cases, a new treatment option can double survival time.

What's more, research is uncovering additional steps that can help prevent bladder cancer from recurring after it's been treated—strategies that also will help protect people from developing this malignancy in the first place.

PREVENTION IS BEST

Even though bladder cancer does not get as much public attention as certain other types, it is the sixth most common cancer in the US (and the fourth most common among men), with about 81,000 new cases diagnosed every year.

The good news is that most bladder cancers (about 75%) are non-muscle invasive—that is, they're limited to the lining of the bladder…are usually diagnosed early…and respond well to treatment.

One distinguishing characteristic of bladder cancer is its recurrence rate. More than half of all people treated for this malignancy will have a recurrence. For this reason, it's crucial for anyone with bladder cancer to do everything possible to prevent a recurrence.

Smokers are four to seven times more likely to develop bladder cancer than nonsmokers. The toxins from cigarette smoke are excreted from the body in the urine—and spend many hours concentrated in the bladder, where they can trigger cancer-causing changes. *Other ways to help prevent a bladder cancer diagnosis or recurrence…*

• **Eat more kale.** Cruciferous veggies (such as kale, broccoli, cauliflower and cabbage) are high in isothiocyanates, chemical compounds that inhibit the ability of cancer cells, including bladder cancer cells, to proliferate. Men who consumed cruciferous vegetables more than five times a week were 51% less likely to develop bladder cancer than those who ate them less than once a week, according to the Health Professionals Follow-Up Study.

• **Stay hydrated.** People who drink more water urinate more frequently, which reduces chemical concentrations and exposure times from cigarette smoke (including secondhand smoke), workplace chemicals (such as poly-aromatic hydrocarbons and dyes), air pollution, etc.

Important exception: Research has shown that people who drink water from private wells that may be contaminated with arsenic are at increased risk for bladder cancer. Water that contains high levels of nitrate, a by-product of fertilizers and animal feedlots, has been linked to higher rates of bladder cancer in postmenopausal women.

Take note: If you drink well water, get it checked!

CATCH IT EARLY

After prevention, early detection is, of course, the best way to avoid bladder cancer deaths.

An annual urine test may be worthwhile if you're at high risk—for example, you're already having symptoms (discussed below)…you are exposed to workplace toxins that increase your risk…you're a smoker…and/or you have a personal or family history of bladder cancer.

Important: About 80% to 90% of patients who are diagnosed with bladder cancer will have visible traces of blood in the urine. Blood can appear for many reasons, including urinary tract infections (UTIs) or prostate problems. However, if you see blood in your urine, I advise that you assume it might be cancer and see a physician or possibly a urologist.

Other red flags: Frequent trouble urinating…feeling pain or burning while urinating…and feeling that you need to urinate right away, even when the bladder isn't full. Particularly in women, bladder cancer may be misdiagnosed as a recurrent UTI. A urine culture (not just an in-office urinalysis) is needed to diagnose UTI correctly.

DRUG BREAKTHROUGHS

The checkpoint inhibitors that were recently approved by the FDA target proteins that weaken the immune system. In doing so, the drugs—*pembrolizumab* (Keytruda), *avelumab* (Bavencio), *durvalumab* (Imfinzi), *nivolumab* (Opdivo) and *atezolizumab* (Tecentriq)—intensify immune activity against tumor cells.

An older form of immunotherapy, called *intravesical therapy*, uses a bacterium (BCG) that's instilled into the bladder. This approach inhibits cancer progression and can reduce the risk for recurrences by about 40%. BCG causes an inflammatory reaction that leads to the recruitment of other immune cells to the bladder, which helps eradicate bladder tumors and helps prevent them from recurring.

Depending on the stage of the cancer, checkpoint inhibitors are an important advancement

125

because they can help patients who didn't do well with BCG or other treatments—or who improved initially but later suffered a cancer recurrence.

The drugs aren't a cure, but they can double the survival time in some cases of metastatic cancer that has not responded to chemotherapy. This means the average survival time of six months is increased to 10 to 12 months.

Another potential benefit: It's hoped that checkpoint inhibitors will control cancer well enough that removal of the bladder, which has been required in those who haven't responded well to other treatments, can be delayed or avoided altogether—but this is still being studied.

Downside: Immunotherapy drugs can increase levels of inflammation throughout the body. Many of these inflammatory reactions are minor and can be managed with topical creams or by stopping the drug temporarily for a couple of weeks. However, in some cases, the reactions can be severe and, in very rare cases, even fatal. When the reaction is more severe, the drug is stopped and the overactive immune system is suppressed by giving steroids and other immunosuppressive drugs.

If You See Blood in Your Urine...

Christopher Kelly, MD, a physician at Columbia University Medical Center in New York City, and coauthor of *Am I Dying?! A Complete Guide to Your Symptoms—and What to Do Next.*

I t can be scary to see blood in the toilet bowl, but stay calm and consider these points...

• **Relax if you have recently eaten beets.** Some people have a genetic tendency to absorb beet pigment from the intestine. Even a small amount of beet salad or borscht can give urine a pinkish tint.

Caution: If you've eaten beets your whole life and only recently noticed urine-color changes, see your doctor.

• **Make an appointment if you see blood in the urine after intense exercise.** This is relatively common among serious athletes (such as marathon runners) but is unlikely to occur in casual exercisers. Dark urine (brown rather than red) that's accompanied by muscle pain could indicate rhabdomyolysis, the breakdown of muscle tissue. Blood in the urine also can be a sign of a urinary tract infection.

• **Get to an ER** (or see your doctor immediately) if you notice blood in the urine in any other situation, particularly if you're age 50 or older. It's the earliest symptom of bladder cancer. The vast majority of patients with bladder cancer will have visible blood—it might appear bright red, coffee-colored or yellowish—in the urine. Doctors assume that bloody urine in an older patient means cancer until they can prove otherwise.

Natural Cures for a Leaky Bladder

Jamison Starbuck, ND, a naturopathic physician in family practice, Missoula, Montana, and writer and producer of *Dr. Starbuck's Health Tips for Kids*, a weekly program on Montana Public Radio, MTPR.org. She is a past president of the American Association of Naturopathic Physicians and a contributing editor to *The Alternative Advisor: The Complete Guide to Natural Therapies and Alternative Treatments.* DrJamisonStarbuck.com

M ost women (and many men) have had that "oh, no!" feeling of leaking urine when lifting a heavy object or laughing a little harder than usual. The occasional incontinent moment isn't a big deal. But when it happens daily, it's a problem. Prescription drugs such as *oxybutynin* (Oxytrol) and *tolterodine* (Detrol) can relieve symptoms of this condition but often cause side effects, including dry mouth and constipation. Natural medicine is safer and can offer long-term relief. *The main types of incontinence...*

• **Stress incontinence and urge incontinence.** If you lose urine when the bladder is stressed—as with a big sneeze—that's stress incontinence. If you have a sudden urge to urinate and lose urine if you can't get to the toilet almost immediately, that's called urge incontinence. With both of these types of incontinence, weak pelvic-floor muscles are often to blame. *My advice...*

Urinate on a schedule: I suggest urinating every two hours while you are awake, whether you feel the urge or not. If your bladder is emptied more regularly, you're less likely to leak. If nighttime incontinence is a problem, stop liquids four hours before bed. Instead, have a piece of fruit—it's watery and refreshing but won't fill your bladder the way a beverage will.

Tone up: If your pelvic muscles are weak, Kegel exercises are the go-to solution...for both women and men.

What to do: While you're sitting or even standing, contract the muscles you would use if you suddenly wanted to stop the flow of urine. Do 10 contractions in a row, three times daily. You should notice a benefit within 10 days. If you hold a lot of tension in your lower abdomen or hip muscles—which often occurs in those who are sedentary—focus on gentle stretching, abdominal massage and deep breathing to help reduce incontinence.

Check for food allergies: Food allergies cause irritation and inflammation. When the bladder wall is irritated, it's more sensitive and reactive, and this can lead to incontinence. Dairy, wheat and eggs are common triggers. If you suspect that you have a food allergy, ask your doctor about IgG blood testing to check.

•**Temporary incontinence.** Excess caffeine, alcohol, smoking, a diet high in salt and even acidic and spicy foods can irritate the bladder and cause incontinence, along with such symptoms as urinary frequency and urgency. Avoid the potential irritants above one at a time until you find the culprit(s).

Try botanicals: Corn silk and gravel root soothe bladder tissue and calm the urge to urinate. A typical dose is one-quarter teaspoon (in tincture form) of an equal blend of these herbs, added to two ounces of water and taken three times daily (15 minutes before or after meals) until your incontinence improves. These herbs can be used for a long time, but it's best to talk to your doctor if you plan to take any herb for more than a month or so.*

Drink enough water: It may seem odd to drink more water if you're running to the bathroom all the time, but if you don't drink enough, your urine becomes concentrated, which aggravates the bladder and leads to incontinence. Drinking too much water can do the same. Use this formula—one-half ounce of water per pound of body weight daily. Your bladder will thank you!

*Consult your doctor before using corn silk if you take medication for diabetes, blood pressure or inflammation, or if you take *warfarin* (Coumadin) or diuretics...and before taking gravel root if you have liver disease or take a seizure drug or the antibiotic *rifampin* (Rifadin).

Feminine Products Linked to Infections

In a recent finding, women who used vaginal deodorizers or feminine washes were three and a half times more likely to report having a vaginal infection and two and a half times more likely to have a urinary tract infection than women who did not use these products.

Theory: These products may prevent the growth of healthy bacteria needed to fight off infection.

To play it safe: A woman's cleansing routine should involve washing daily with water and perhaps a mild, unscented soap.

Kieran O'Doherty, PhD, associate professor of psychology and researcher who focuses on the human microbiome, University of Guelph, Ontario, Canada.

Colonoscopy Isn't the Only Test That Helps Prevent Colon Cancer...

Andrew M.D. Wolf, MD, an internist and associate professor of medicine at University of Virginia School of Medicine in Charlottesville. He is a member of the American Cancer Society's (ACS) Guideline Development Group and chair of the ACS's Colorectal Cancer Screening Work Group.

Colonoscopy has generally been considered the gold standard for detecting and preventing colorectal cancer. But it's not the only option.

What you may not realize: A handful of other tests—which are easier, cheaper and quicker—are now available and may encourage more people to actually get tested. *What you need to know...*

THE INCONVENIENCE FACTOR

The American Cancer Society (ACS) and other major health groups have urged Americans to regularly undergo colonoscopy. And with good reason. Colonoscopy can detect more than 90% of cancers and precancerous polyps that are larger than about one-half inch.

The problem is, more than one-third of Americans who should be screened for colorectal cancer haven't had screening—in part due to the onerous "prep" that includes fasting and drinking quarts of a foul-tasting liquid and often means spending hours on the toilet as your insides empty out.

EASIER TESTS

New guidelines from the ACS advise patients with average risk for colon cancer (that is, no family history, genetic syndrome, inflammatory bowel disease or personal history of radiation to the abdomen or pelvic area to treat

a prior cancer) to undergo regular screenings starting at age 45. Previously, screening started at age 50, but the age has been dropped to 45 because in recent years the percentage of colorectal cancer cases involving younger adults has risen. The recommended tests include colonoscopy, CT colonography and sigmoidoscopy (discussed later)—along with a number of high-sensitivity stool tests.

Colonoscopy is most effective at detecting precancerous polyps, but for people who won't go for the procedure, stool-based tests (when performed regularly) can be almost as accurate as colonoscopy at detecting colorectal cancer.

Caveats: If you test positive on one of these tests, you'll still need to follow up with colonoscopy. And the tests must be repeated every one to five years, depending on the test. Colonoscopy is typically undergone every 10 years (more frequently if polyps are detected). *Other tests to discuss with your doctor...*

• **Guaiac fecal occult blood test (gFOBT).** This test uses a chemical (guaiac) to detect a blood component in stools. The presence of blood is a common sign of cancer. The test can detect 60% to 80% of colon cancers, though it is even more accurate if done every year, as recommended.

However, all stool tests, including gFOBT, are more likely than colonoscopy to miss precancerous polyps, which are less likely to bleed than cancer. This is why gFOBT should be repeated yearly—to catch the polyps that have turned into early-stage cancer and begun to bleed.

What it involves: You use an applicator stick to smear a bit of stool on a test card. You repeat this on two or three consecutive days, then return the cards to your doctor (or mail to a testing laboratory).

Pros: gFOBT only requires a stool "smear." The test usually costs $25 or less and is covered by insurance.

Cons: You must collect several smears... give up red meat for several days because the test can't differentiate dietary animal blood from human blood...and temporarily quit taking medications, such as aspirin or *ibuprofen* (Motrin), that can cause intestinal bleeding.

•**Fecal immunochemical test (FIT).** A more recent variation of the gFOBT, FIT uses an antibody to detect blood hemoglobin in a stool sample. It's about 80% effective at detecting cancers, though is even more accurate when repeated yearly, as recommended.

What it involves: Test kits vary by manufacturer, so read directions carefully. Typically, you stick a long-handled brush into a stool sample…transfer the sample to a special collection card…and mail it to a testing laboratory. The cost is about the same or slightly more than the gFOBT, and it's covered by insurance.

Pros: You only need a single stool sample… there are no dietary restrictions…and the test only detects human hemoglobin from the lower digestive tract, which reduces false readings from dietary sources and noncancerous causes of stomach/upper-intestinal bleeding.

Cons: Like gFOBT, the test usually misses precancerous polyps. Still, due to FIT's improved accuracy and convenience, most experts consider it to be a better test than gFOBT, but the latter remains available based on its low cost and track record of detecting cancers.

•**Cologuard.** This is the newest screening test. It combines blood-stool detection with the ability to detect DNA mutations often associated with colorectal cancers. Overall, Cologuard can detect about 92% of cancers—better than gFOBT and FIT. It also can detect more than 40% of "advanced" polyps (larger or with more precancerous features) compared with about 25% for FIT. The test is expensive—about $650, though it is covered by Medicare and most insurers.

What it involves: A small container is placed under the toilet seat to collect a complete stool, which is then sent to a testing laboratory.

Pros: Cologuard is done at three-year intervals rather than every year. It doesn't require preparation or dietary restrictions.

Cons: It has more false positives (about 13%) than other tests, which lead to more unnecessary follow-up colonoscopies.

THE OTHER OPTIONS

•**Flexible sigmoidoscopy.** Like colonoscopy, it utilizes a flexible, camera-tipped tube to examine the lower part of the colon (the sigmoid colon) and the rectum. Repeated every five years, it provides some of the same benefits as colonoscopy but doesn't require sedation. Most insurers cover it.

The downsides: Sigmoidoscopy won't detect polyps/cancers in the upper half of the colon. Also, the lack of sedation, while considered safer, means the procedure is more uncomfortable than colonoscopy.

•**CT colonography,** also known as virtual colonoscopy, is an imaging test that is comparable to colonoscopy at detecting advanced adenomas and cancers. It is noninvasive, and sedation isn't required.

However, CT colonography requires a bowel prep, and you must drink a contrast dye. Medicare and many private insurers do not cover CT colonography. CT scans produce radiation exposure, but newer technology has lowered the amount of radiation considerably.

INTERESTING FINDING…

Nuts May Improve Colon Cancer Survival

People with stage 3 colon cancer who ate two or more one-ounce servings of tree nuts (such as almonds, walnuts, pecans) weekly had 46% less cancer recurrence and were 53% less likely to die over six-and-a-half years than people who rarely ate nuts. The equivalent of seven almonds a day is enough. Tree nuts have cancer-protective properties that benefit healthy people, too.

Charles S. Fuchs, MD, MPH, director of Yale Cancer Center, New Haven, Connecticut, and leader of a study published in *Journal of Clinical Oncology*.

Hypnosis for IBS

Hypnosis improves irritable bowel syndrome (IBS) and other stomach issues. The brain and gut exchange chemical messages with each other, so when people are under hypnosis, targeted suggestions about abdominal and bowel discomfort help them develop coping mechanisms that reduce pain and improve quality of life. Cognitive behavioral therapy also helps, and both methods are recommended by the American Gastroenterological Association.

Megan Riehl, PsyD, a gastrointestinal health psychologist and assistant professor of medicine at University of Michigan, Ann Arbor.

A Stool Can Help You "Go"

In a recent study, 52 healthy adults—nearly half of whom reported straining and one-third who said they had trouble completely emptying their bowels—propped their feet on a stool when using the bathroom for four weeks.

Results: More than 70% of participants reported faster bowel movements, and 90% reported less straining.

Reason: Propping your feet on a stool straightens the bend in the rectum, which increases the sensation of bowel emptying and reduces straining.

If you suffer from constipation: Try using a seven-inch stool.

Rohan Modi, MD, gastroenterology fellow, University of Virginia, Charlottesville.

Biofeedback Helps Serious Constipation

Dyssynergic defecation affects one-third of constipated patients and is the result of pelvic floor nerves and muscles not working properly. In research, instrument-guided biofeedback therapy was effective treatment. It usually is done in a medical office, but it may be available at home in the future.

Satish S.C. Rao, MD, PhD, professor in the department of gastroenterology at Augusta University, Georgia, and lead author of a study published in *The Lancet*.

New Prostate Cancer Test

A new blood test (known as Oncotype DX AR-V7 Nucleus Detect Test) reveals whether a patient's circulating tumor cells contain the protein AR-V7 and determines the most effective treatment for patients with advanced prostate cancer. Participants who tested positive for AR-V7 survived twice as long when they were treated with a specific chemotherapy than with hormone-targeting therapy, the two standard treatments. Those who tested negative for the protein lived seven months longer when they took the hormone-targeting drugs, compared with chemotherapy.

Alison L. Allan, PhD, associate professor of oncology, Schulich School of Medicine and Dentistry, Western University, London, Ontario, Canada.

Post Prostate Surgery Mistake

A mistake most men make after prostate surgery is delaying anti-incontinence surgery. Up to 42% of men develop incontinence after removal of their prostates. Surgery for the incontinence improves quality of life in more than 73% of those who opt for it. Ask your doctor about it if you have urinary leakage more than one year after prostatectomy. By then, men will have recovered as much as they could without surgery.

Allen F. Morey, MD, professor of urology and Paul C. Peters, MD, Chair in Urology at UT Southwestern Medical Center, Dallas, and senior author of a study of 572 patients, published in *Urology*.

7

Money Manager

5 Money Mavens Reveal Their Most Memorable Mistakes

Everyone has made big errors with money that he/she would rather forget—even some of the country's shrewdest financial pros. We recently asked five money mavens to recount their most memorable blunders...and what lessons they learned that could be useful to investors and consumers of all ages. *Here are their answers...*

Terri Spath, CFA, CFP

MISTAKE: **I was so reluctant to sell a stock that I turned what should have been a minor loss into an enormous one.** In the late 1990s, I invested $50,000 in Bibb Manufacturing Company, a century-old textile maker that produced bedding and towels for Walmart and other retailers. I had studied the company for months and thought it was a bargain at $12 per share. But something unforeseen happened. The price of cotton soared, driving up costs for textile makers. The stock dipped below my purchase price, but I wasn't going to be deterred by a little volatility. At every leg down, I didn't want to admit that I was wrong or turn a loss on paper into a real one, so I came up with sophisticated rationalizations to hang on. By the time I dumped the stock at $6, half my investment was gone. The company never recovered, went bankrupt and was taken over by a competitor.

Lesson learned: Don't make exceptions to a valuable rule. *The rule that I violated:* When a stock falls 10% below my purchase price, I sell it. No exceptions. Why 10%? That's the point at which you must start gaining noticeably more (12% in this case) than you lost just to get back to even. My rule doesn't always work out. Sometimes stocks do bounce back strongly. But it guarantees that I never take a big loss, which

131

is what really ruins investors' long-term returns because it can take so long to recover.

Terri Spath CFA, CFP, chief investment officer at Sierra Investment Management, a financial advisory firm that manages over $3.5 billion in assets, Santa Monica, California. SierraInvestment.com

Natalie Choate, JD

MISTAKE: I wasn't careful enough when I took the required minimum distribution (RMD) from my IRA—and I had to deal with a 50% penalty. A few years ago, I decided to use the money from my RMD, which I've been taking since age 70½ (as required by IRS rules), to contribute to my favorite charities. I was careful to follow the rules, requesting that my IRA provider send me nine checks payable to nine different charities.

I mailed the checks to the charities well before the deadline of December 31, but I didn't notice that one charity never sent me back a receipt.

In February of the following year, I received a surprise notice from the IRA provider. It turns out that one of the charities had never received (and therefore never cashed) its check, and my IRA provider had added the amount of the check back to my account. That meant I had a shortfall of $500 in my RMD for the year just ended. I quickly got a new check and resent it to the charity, but by the time I did that, I owed the IRS a $250 penalty.

Lesson learned: You can't rely on your financial adviser or brokerage to make sure that you take the correct RMDs from your IRAs and other retirement accounts—or even to tell you if a requested distribution somehow fails. You should always do a final review in late December to make sure you are in compliance.

Good news: The IRS gives seniors a break if an RMD mistake is deemed to be legitimately beyond their control. (For directions on challenging an RMD compliance penalty, go to IRS.gov and search for "IRA Required Minimum Distributions FAQs.") I appealed my penalty on the notion that a check sent through the US mail should not have failed to arrive. The IRS agreed, and I did not have to pay the penalty, although it cost me months of letter writing, documentation and aggravation.

Natalie Choate, JD, an attorney specializing in estate planning for retirement benefits at the law firm of Nutter McClennen & Fish, Boston. Nutter.com

Mark Germain, CFP

MISTAKE: When I gave a close family member a large loan, I thought I was being smart by drawing up a promissory note—but I never considered what I would do if the family member couldn't pay me back. A relative approached me for a six-figure loan he wanted to use to buy some property. I'm well aware that big loans should be made "official" even among family members, so we went to an attorney and signed a formal loan agreement that said he would pay me back over three years at 6% interest.

Unfortunately, my relative got sick and wound up in and out of the hospital for two years, unable to make even minimum payments to me. Even worse, he couldn't afford to pay the municipal taxes on the property and was at risk of having it confiscated by the city. I had to shell out another $20,000 just to cover his taxes. With the interest and principal payments, plus the additional property-tax loan, what he owed me ballooned. But I wasn't about to ruin relationships in the family by taking him to court and winning a judgment. My three-year loan has now turned into a 12-year loan that may never be fully paid back.

Lesson learned: No matter how business-like you are, it's not smart to loan money to family and friends unless you will be OK both financially and emotionally if you are not paid back. A study by Lending Tree found that people who lend money to their relatives get back an average of just 57% of the amount loaned.

Mark Germain, CFP, founder and CEO of Beacon Wealth Management, a financial advisory firm with more than $250 million in assets under management, Hackensack, New Jersey. BeaconWealthManagement.com

Amy J. Schmitz, JD

MISTAKE: **I bought a house for the wrong reasons.** When I took a new job in Missouri in 2016, I wanted to take advantage of low mortgage interest rates before they might rise. I also wanted to avoid the expense and bother of putting my possessions in storage and having to do a major move twice. Under time pressure before starting the new job, I chose a home after only two days of looking. The professional inspection turned up problems, but my real estate agent convinced me that the issues were minor. I convinced myself that they were manageable because I wanted to feel settled and secure. The house turned out to be a money pit requiring tens of thousands of dollars in repairs.

Lesson learned: For much of the past decade, buying instead of renting seemed like a no-brainer. But renting can be more financially efficient in the long run if it gives you the time to do a thorough search and evaluate the realistic costs of owning a home. Uncertainty over mortgage rates and high home prices in many areas have made the decision to buy an even more complicated one. For instance, in 2018 the monthly costs of buying and owning a home were up 14% over the previous year,

more than three times the annual increase in rent rates nationally.

Amy J. Schmitz, JD, the Elwood L. Thomas Missouri Endowed Professor of Law at University of Missouri School of Law in Columbia. Law.Missouri.edu/about/people/schmitz

Dana Anspach, CFP

MISTAKE: **I got an exciting stock tip from a trusted friend and invested without doing my own research.** Back in 2010, I invested in a Toronto company called Element 21 that dealt in rare-earth metals. These little-known industrial metals are essential components in electric cars and missile-guidance systems. My friend, who was a very successful businessman, told me that rare-earth metals stocks were about to soar. I was so intrigued that I bought nearly $12,000 worth of shares.

But it turns out that Element 21 was a sports-equipment company focused on developing golf clubs using alloys of a rare-earth metal called scandium. Scandium never did revolutionize the golfing industry...and I lost 95% of my investment.

Lesson learned: Do your own research about a stock before you invest—even if someone you trust says that it's a good bet. At the very least, do an online search on the company, read some professional analysis of the stock and understand what could go wrong if you invest. This lets you judge the risk you are taking and whether that risk aligns with your personal goals and needs, something that well-meaning people who feed you stock tips may not be considering.

Dana Anspach, CFP, founder of Sensible Money, an investment advisory firm with $170 million in total assets under management, Scottsdale, Arizona. She is author of *Control Your Retirement Destiny*. Sensible Money.com

Online Banks Beat Brick-and-Mortar Banks

Online banks outperform brick-and-mortar banks on every factor evaluated by JD Power. Overall consumer satisfaction with online-only banks is 860 out of a possible 1,000—compared with 807 for traditional banks. The largest performance gaps are in the areas of products, fees, communication and problem resolution.

The highest-performing online bank, which is Charles Schwab, scored 865. It got especially high marks for website satisfaction. Number two, Ally Bank, scored 864 and got very high ratings for interest rate competitiveness. Third-ranked Discover Bank scored 860 and had the biggest year-over-year improvement of any bank studied.

US Direct Banking Satisfaction Study at JDPower.com.

Beware CD Rates That Are Too Good to Be True

Gerri Walsh, JD, senior vice president for investor education, Financial Industry Regulatory Authority (Finra), Washington, DC. Finra.org

A 4% annual yield on a five-year certificate of deposit sounds tempting, doesn't it? Especially since most five-year CDs pay less than 3% at press time.

Don't be tempted. These high-yield CDs often are just marketing ploys to lure you into buying high-commission financial products, according to the Financial Industry Regulatory Authority (Finra), which has fielded dozens of inquiries and complaints about these bait-and-switch tactics in the past year.

How the ploy works: Ads in local newspapers promote CDs with yields as much as one-third higher than the best-prevailing rates. To qualify for the high-yield CD, however, you're required to go in person to a designated office, where a salesperson aggressively pitches different—and often less liquid and potentially more risky—investments such as equity-indexed annuities, which link your returns in part to stock market performance. These are riskier than CDs, hard to understand and often have costly fees. And in fact, the firms that take out the ads don't even offer high-yield CDs.

If you insist on getting the CD that was advertised, the firm claims that it was offered for a short promotional period that has already expired. Or in some cases, the firm will send you to a local bank to buy a lower-yielding CD, then pay you a cash bonus that covers the difference between what you were promised and what the bank CD yields.

What to do: If you want a CD, be sure to get it from a reputable bank or credit union where it is insured by the FDIC or NCUA. You can compare rates at DepositAccounts.com or Bankrate.com.

Credit Card Tricks

B eware of these five tricks from credit card issuers…

•**Low interest rates may not be as low as advertised**—ads often say "as low as" and charge many customers higher rates.

•**Cards labeled as gold or platinum don't necessarily have more value** than any others—compare card benefits, not their names.

•**Business-card hype overpromises the benefits of cards in a business's name** and may put your personal credit on the line despite what is printed on the card.

•**Big bonuses may require very big purchases** within a set amount of time, such as $2,000 in one month to earn 25,000 airline miles.

•**Preapprovals do not mean the advertised card is yours**—you still must apply for the card and go through the entire approval process before it will be issued.

Roundup of credit card experts, reported at the website, MoneyTalksNews.com.

Popular Credit Card Perks Are Changing

A mong the perks being eliminated by various card issuers is price protection, which helps you get the lowest price on any purchase, and purchase protection, which replaces lost or stolen merchandise.

Perk being added by some issuers: Cellphone protection, which pays to replace or fix cell phones lost to damage or theft if the phone bills are being paid with the card.

Check whether your cards' perks have changed and whether they still meet your needs.

Matt Schulz, senior industry analyst at CreditCards. com.

Credit Smarts

People who repeatedly try to open new card accounts to get sign-up bonuses generate ongoing inquiries, which reduce their credit scores. At some point, this causes card issuers to refuse to allow new card accounts to be opened.

What to do: Try calling the issuer that denied the card—ask whether you can change some existing lines of credit in a way that will lead to approval. Or give yourself a cooling-off period—waiting six to 12 months to apply for new cards may be enough to get you approvals again...and hard inquiries—which occur when you apply for a credit card or a loan—stay on your credit report for only 24 months, so if you wait that long, they will disappear.

WiseBread.com

To Reduce Fees, Don't Be Shy...

To get out of credit card fees, just ask. Holders of major credit cards who asked for a late-fee waiver got it 84% of the time...70% got an annual fee lowered or waived...85% got a higher credit limit...and 56% who asked for a lower interest rate got one. In all, 60% of credit card holders have asked for one or more of these items. Younger baby boomers (ages 53 to 62) are most likely to ask for a fee waiver—97% of them had either a fee reduced or waived be-

cause they asked. Younger millennials (ages 18 to 26) were the least likely to ask, and 68% had never asked for a fee waiver.

Study by CreditCards.com.

How to Improve Your Credit Score Even If You Have No Cards

• **Become an authorized user of someone else's card**—even if you never use the card, its activity will be associated with your name.

• **Get a credit-builder loan**—banks and credit unions occasionally offer small loans specifically designed to build credit.

• **Passbook and CD loans also are offered at times** and help build credit as you pay them down.

• **Federal student loans build credit** if you pay them consistently on time.

• **Peer-to-peer loans set up through a P2P service can build credit** as you repay them.

• **If you have or are considering a mortgage, paying on time each month will help** improve your score over the long term. Auto loans do the same thing.

• **Personal loans,** when a bank offers them, also are effective.

• **Rent payments help as well,** but credit bureaus count them only if landlords report them, and many landlords do not bother—you can ask whether your landlord will do this.

Roundup of experts on building credit, reported at MarketWatch.com.

Why You Need to Check Your Child's Credit History

A federal law that went into effect in September 2018 makes it easier to do this—and it can be important, because thieves are increasingly stealing children's Social Security numbers and using them to create phony identities under which they take out loans or credit cards. In 2017, the Federal Trade Commission received 14,000 complaints of identity theft targeting people age 19 and younger (latest data available). The fraud can go unnoticed for years unless parents check their children's credit histories—which few parents do.

For information on what to do under the new law, be sure to log on to the special FTC webpage, Consumer.FTC.gov/articles/0040-child-identity-theft.

The Wall Street Journal.

Financial Aggregation Services Are Too Risky

These online services, such as Mint.com, let you track your credit card and bank accounts, investment portfolios, loan information and monthly bills. But keeping so much financial information with one company exposes you to potentially catastrophic data-theft fraud if the company is hacked.

Steven J.J. Weisman, Esq., an attorney, author of *Identity Theft Alert* and founder of the scam-information website Scamicide.com.

How a Social-Media Professor Protects His Privacy Online... and You Can, Too

Andrew Selepak, PhD, director of the master of arts in mass communication program with a specialization in social media at University of Florida College of Journalism and Communications, Gainesville. Jou.UFL.edu

When news broke that the political data firm Cambridge Analytica harvested personal data from nearly 90 million Facebook users, many people rushed to abandon Facebook.

But before you delete your Facebook account, make sure you're not jumping into a swimming pool to get out of the rain. We spoke to Andrew Selepak, PhD, director of the social-media master's program at University of Florida, to learn how to reduce the amount of personal data that Facebook and other services can get their digital mitts on.

•**Look before you leap.** Facebook, Google and all the other wonderful "free" services that we use every day are not free. Your personal information is how you "pay" to use these platforms—it says so in the multipage, tiny-font user agreement that we all agree to without reading. In the wake of Cambridge Analytica, significant numbers of Facebook users are considering moving their photos, videos, conversations and political rants to alternative sites such as Instagram and WhatsApp. Although that's understandable, it's important to understand that Facebook's practices aren't unique.

Instagram is owned by Facebook. So is WhatsApp. Google, which pioneered the data-harvesting business model when Mark Zuckerberg was still in grammar school, is the world's biggest search engine. Close behind is YouTube, which is owned by Google. Your Internet service provider monitors your browsing...your browser monitors the websites you visit...and the websites you visit monitor how long you stay and what you do while you're there.

•**Focus on search as much as social.** If you're currently using Google to find a new social-media platform, you are already surrendering data in a quest to stop surrendering data. Consider a switch to DuckDuckGo.com. Although this Google-alternative search engine has a silly name, its mission is serious. DuckDuckGo does not collect or share any personal information. Unlike Facebook alternatives—which can't compete with Facebook's functionality, familiarity, user base or reach—you can ditch Google today in favor of DuckDuckGo without suffering through any learning curve or diminished user experience. DuckDuckGo will serve up ads based on your search terms, but it doesn't sell any personal information.

• **Switch to a private e-mail service.** Nearly every free e-mail program collects keyword data and shares that with third parties. Consider using FastMail. FastMail lets you migrate your Gmail or Yahoo account—and most other popular e-mail programs—so that you don't have to start from scratch. Much of the functionality is the same, including e-mail search and calendar/contact syncing from your phone or tablet. But unlike mainstream e-mail, it doesn't mine personal data or sell your information. The trade-off is that instead of paying with your data as you do on "free" services such as Gmail, you pay with actual money. A basic plan costs $3 a month or $30 a year.

If you are looking to take your privacy a step further, consider ProtonMail. With servers based in Switzerland, all user data is fully protected by strict Swiss privacy laws. ProtonMail encrypts all user information and only the account holder can decrypt it. So even if ProtonMail wanted to sell your information, that information would be worthless to information brokers. ProtonMail is free, but donations are accepted. It's also worth noting that some e-mail services have started allowing users to opt out of data collection, however. To see if yours does, search online for your e-mail provider and "opt out data collection."

• **Use a virtual private network.** Virtual private networks (VPNs) give you secure, private web browsing. These services charge around $35 to $80 per year. You can turn them on and off with the click of a button. VPNs make it nearly impossible for anyone to monitor your activity by making it appear that your activity is taking place through a distant server, not at your computer or phone. The drawback is that VPNs—like TunnelBear or SaferVPN—also thwart benign personal data collection that exists for convenience and to enhance user experience.

Example: If you're using a VPN in Los Angeles and open Yelp or Google to search for Indian restaurants near you, you might get a list of great places to eat in Leipzig instead of LA.

• **Throw away your reward cards.** Just as Google and Facebook aren't actually free, rewards cards take your information in ex-

---

GOOD TO KNOW...

Warning Signs of ID Theft

Don't miss these important identity-theft warning signs...

• **Bills stop arriving**—the thief could have changed the address on your account.

• **You are rejected unexpectedly,** for example, by receiving a health insurance claim denial for a procedure that you did not have.

• **You get intrusive phone calls** that seem legitimate and try to get personally identifiable information from you.

• **You get strange texts or e-mails,** such as one confirming a new PIN that you did not request.

• **You do not get your tax refund**—or if the IRS sends a letter that tells you that you have submitted two tax returns.

WiseBread.com

---

change for a few pennies saved on deodorant. Rewards programs track the time of day you shop, the amount of money you spend and the things you buy. That information, of course, is for sale—and much of it winds up in Facebook and Google server farms, as well as in the data warehouses maintained by the companies that make almost any product you buy.

• **Stick with a dumb home.** The porch light comes on when your phone says the sun has set. Your deadbolt locks automatically if your phone moves away from your home. Smart homes, connected homes and the Internet of Things are amazing technological advances that represent the wave of the future. They're also data factories that churn out huge amounts of personal information, all of which is then collected and sold by the companies that give these devices life. Many smart home devices feature digital assistants such as Amazon's Alexa, Google Assistant and Apple's Siri. These voice-directed devices are always listening—they have to in order to function.

Example: When you say your "wake word," Amazon Alexa begins streaming audio to the cloud. You can set privacy settings to turn off the microphone and prevent these devices from waking or taking instructions, but then, what's the point of owning one?

•**Find a new digital meeting place.** For those determined to leave Facebook, there are promising but underdeveloped social networks such as Ello, Vero and Mastodon. The benefit is that they're not Facebook. The drawback, however, is that they're not Facebook. That means the people you know likely aren't using them and they're comparatively primitive in terms of user-friendliness and functionality. If you're alone on a sparsely populated second-tier social network, it defeats the entire point, which is social interaction. If you're fed up with social media but still want a secure way to communicate and share with family and friends, consider establishing a simple text-message thread or joining a free workflow collaboration app such as Trello, which you and your pals can turn into a private—although limited—social network just for you.

PROTECT YOUR PERSONAL DATA ON FACEBOOK

After the Cambridge Analytica scandal, Facebook updated its privacy settings and made them easier to find and navigate. Here are easy ways you can make your Facebook experience safer and more private now. The Settings menu can be accessed by clicking on the triangle in the upper-right corner of your Facebook page. (The following instructions are for Facebook on a desktop computer. The instructions are a bit different for the Facebook app on your smartphone or tablet. But if you start by tapping on the "hamburger menu"—the icon that looks like three stacked dashes—you should be able to find the Settings menu.)

•**Shut out third-party apps.** The problem isn't just that Facebook has your data. It's that all the associated third-party apps you use have access to it, too.

Go to: Settings>Apps and Websites. From there, just check off all the apps you'd like to remove. Of course, if there's an app you can't live without, feel free to keep it. Just remember that it's likely selling your data.

•**Don't let your likes become ads.** If you like a post about a company or product, for example, Facebook's default settings allow that

like to be used as a promotion designed to get your friends to like it or share it as well.

Go to: Settings>Ads>Ad Settings>Ads that include your social actions. From there, switch visibility to "No One."

•**Don't let Facebook sell your browsing data.** Also by default, Facebook shares information from the websites you visit with its advertisers, which is why if you're a cyclist, you'll see ads for bikes when you're on Facebook. So many sites have integrated Facebook Like buttons and other options connected to Facebook that it's easy for the social-media giant to see most of what you do online. Go to Settings>Ads>Ad Settings>Ads based on data from partners and ads based on your activity, and set both to "Not allowed."

Facebook Folly

Logging on to websites through Facebook is very convenient, but it can give hackers access not only to your Facebook account but also to any account that you reach through Facebook. That means a single hacking incident at Facebook can jeopardize your security at a huge number of sites—which is exactly what happened in the recent Facebook breach affecting at least 50 million users. Facebook says it has no evidence that the hackers got into accounts at other sites through Facebook, but this is uncertain—and the risk of having it happen outweighs the small convenience of using Facebook as a sign-on service.

Roundup of experts on computer security, reported in The New York Times.

Keep Hackers Out of Your Home

Keep hackers out of your home by protecting all of your connected appliances. TVs, refrigerators, baby monitors and other objects now may be connected to the Internet for remote operation—and therefore may be vulnerable.

Self-defense: Use multifactor authentication for each appliance, such as a password plus a security key or onetime code sent to your phone. Pay attention to all notices of security updates and download and install all of them. Install malware protection on every device. Change default user names and passwords on each device as soon as you set it up.

Roundup of experts on Internet of Things security, reported at MarketWatch.com.

Two Easy Ways to Improve Your Online Security

You can enhance your online security with two simple steps...

• **Secure your home Wi-Fi network.** Turn on your router's network encryption and the firewall, and change the router's default network name and password. The default user-names and passwords are easy to look up online, so anyone can hack yours if you didn't change it. Check the router's user manual or go to the manufacturer's website for information about keeping the network secure.

• **Get rid of online accounts that you do not use.** You may never even know that someone has hacked into an account you never use, so it is best to get rid of them. Sign in and delete them directly if possible. Go to AccountKiller.com and Backgroundchecks.org/justdeleteme for instructions on removing accounts from sites such as AOL and Facebook.

Kiplinger's Personal Finance.

Scammers Using Smartphones to Steal Account Info

Scammers have been adapting an old e-mail trick to text messages. Cybercriminals are sending fraudulent text messages to users claiming they are from trusted sources such as Apple, Facebook and Comcast. Once you click the link, you are taken to a fake website. If you log in to this spoofed website, your personal information may be compromised.

Self-defense: Be wary of text messages, not only e-mails. If in doubt, confirm the legitimacy of a message by contacting the company by another means before inputting account information.

Komando.com

Beware Roku-Activation Scams

New, potentially confused owners of Roku streaming-video devices search the Internet for help activating an account and find websites that charge fees ranging from $30 to $150. In some cases, the sites do help with setup. In others, they just steal your credit card information.

Self-defense: Setting up your account and activating your Roku is free. If you have trouble with the instructions that come with the device, go to Support.Roku.com.

Luke Bouma, editor of the website CordCutterNews.com.

Apple Touch ID Scam

Beware this scam involving Apple Touch ID on iPhones.

How the scam works: Certain apps downloaded from the Apple App Store ask for fingerprint ID to grant you access to some features. But when you touch the fingerprint reader, you automatically authorize an unexpected payment that you likely don't notice. Some victims were charged as much as $120. Apple has removed the rogue apps Calories Tracker, Fitness Balance and Heart Rate Measurement, but others could show up.

Self-defense: Use Touch ID only with familiar apps you trust…and watch the screen for an unexpected payment.

Steven J.J. Weisman, Esq., an attorney, author of *Identity Theft Alert* and founder of the scam-information website Scamicide.com.

Are Your Apps Stalking You?

James Goepel, JD, professor of cybersecurity law and strategy at Drexel University, Philadelphia, and founder of Fathom Cyber, a consulting company that assists companies with privacy and cybersecurity. FathomCyber.com

Apps on your smartphone are tracking your location—even many apps that don't need your location or ones that you seldom or never use. Knowing which ones track you and why can help preserve your privacy and keep your information out of the hands of criminals.

• **Location tracking is the rule, not the exception.** Whatever the app category—social media, weather, news, travel, entertainment, educational, utilities, games and more—an app might routinely track your location and might not make it clear that it is doing so.

• **App companies and others make money on your location data.** Apps can use location information to build profiles of your daily movements, the shops you frequent, where you park and even how fast you drive. They use this information for their own purposes and share or sell it to advertisers. And the more your data is shared, the more places it is stored and the easier it becomes for criminals to also acquire.

• **Not all location tracking is bad.** Certain apps use location information for obvious and needed reasons, such as when you "check in" to a restaurant on social media or get directions from a navigational app.

• **Don't throw the baby out with the bathwater.** Disabling all location tracking is rarely the right solution. You can't get directions, local coupons or weather alerts if the apps don't

know where you are. When opening an app for the first time, if it asks for permission to see your location and you feel that there is no benefit to you, say no.

• **Find out which apps are monitoring your location data.** With just a few clicks, you can unmask the apps that are tracking you. For iOS (Apple devices)…

To disable location services, go to Settings > Privacy > Location Services and toggle the "Location Services" switch. If you want some apps to access your location, leave Location Services enabled and grant permission app by app.

Android phones often have custom menus. A common way to disable location services on Android devices…

Go to Settings > Security & Location (you may have to click on "Advanced" first) > Location. Switch "Use Location" on or off or tap on App Level Permissions to grant permission to individual apps.

Beware the "Grandparent" Scam

This scam steals an average of $9,000 in cash from people age 70 and older. Scammers call a victim and claim to be a grandchild in trouble—or to be law-enforcement personnel holding a grandchild. Callers say that the grandparent is getting the one and only phone call about this…must keep it confidential…and must deliver cash to help the grandchild. Scammers give explicit instructions on how much cash to send and how to deliver it—often they ask the victim to send money by UPS, FedEx or the postal service.

Self-defense: Never act right away even if a story seems very dramatic. Call the family member or a friend even if the voice on the phone warns not to do that. Use a phone number that you know is legitimate, not one the caller provides.

Also helpful: Be very careful about posting personal information on social media—that is where thieves often get the family information they use to create a convincing scam.

Federal Trade Commission, FTC.gov.

---

8 Clever Ways to Boost Your Home's Value Before Selling

Will Johnson, a Murfreesboro, Tennessee–based real estate agent who leads the Will Johnson Group, a team that includes both home-selling and home-staging professionals. He previously led The Sell and Stage Team with RE/MAX International. WillJohnson.exprealty.com

---

You may already know the basics about prepping a home for sale to make the most profit possible—apply fresh paint…clear out clutter…let in lots of light…and, budget permitting, update antiquated bathrooms and kitchens.

But other powerful strategies for prepping a home for sale often are overlooked…and new value-adding strategies have emerged in recent years, in part because of changing buyer preferences. These modifications also make the home more enjoyable for you until you do move out.

Make the right changes and you might boost your home's price by 3% to 7%—maybe more if you invest wisely in some bigger-ticket modifications.

Eight new and little-used strategies for prepping a home for sale in today's real estate market…

•**Install some basic home-automation tech.** In the past, home owners who invested in technology that let them control elements of their homes via remote control or a smartphone tended to get little or none of this investment back when they sold.

Today, however, this kind of home tech might return its cost many times over. In part, that's because the cost of these devices has dropped…but it's also because installing these items can subtly shift buyers' perceptions of your entire home.

Homes that have this tech are more likely to be viewed as up to date…while those that lack it are more likely to seem out of date. And it's more important than ever for homes to seem up to date when they go on the market because an increasing percentage of home buyers belong to younger generations who put great value on technology and modernity.

Some examples of home-automation tech: The Nest Learning Thermostat ($249) and "smart" door locks such as Schlage Sense (available for $199) and Kwikset Kevo (available for $168).

•**Paint every interior wall that can be seen from your home's main entrance the same color.** Decorators often recommend using different paint in different rooms or even on different walls in the same room. That can make a home more visually compelling…but more difficult to sell. When every wall within eyeshot of the home's entryway is painted the same color, it creates visual "flow"—each room seems to draw visitors into the next. It creates a warm, welcoming first impression for buyers entering the house for the first time. When each room feels connected to the next, it makes the entire space feel larger, too.

•**Use off-white or beige paint for these entryway-visible rooms.** Certainly, other paint options are more stylish and compelling, but they can be divisive and alienating. If you plan to sell soon, it is best to make the safe paint choice. Create visual interest in these rooms with brightly colored area rugs…throw pillows…furniture…and/or lamp shades.

•**Display positive words as wall art.** You know you should take down your family photos before potential buyers see your home—pictures of your family make it psychologically challenging for buyers to imagine their families living there. But what should you hang instead? Artsy signs or sculptures that feature upbeat words or phrases are an effective option. *Examples*: "Happiness"…"Family"…or "Welcome Home."

You can find these signs for $10 to $15 apiece in home stores, hobby stores and online.

Tip: Search online for "positive word art" to find a multitude of inexpensive options. It might sound silly, but putting positive words on display does seem to make some buyers feel more positive about a property. Word signs are so inexpensive that there's no reason not to give this a try.

•**Remove window screens.** You probably know to open blinds and curtains to let as much light as possible into your home when it's shown to buyers. But there's another way to increase the amount of natural light in your home that many home sellers and even real estate pros miss—take out window screens. Mesh screens block about one-third of sunlight. They also obscure the view through the windows…and many screens have frayed wires or small holes that can subtly create a sense that the entire property is old and worn. Store the screens neatly in a closet, basement or garage where potential buyers will see them—that way, they won't worry that they would have to buy new screens for the house if they happen to notice that the screens are not in the windows.

•**Provide a virtual-reality tour online.** Just a year or two ago, it would have been fair to dismiss interactive video "tours" of homes in real estate listings (in which viewers can "move around" inside and outside a home on their computer screens) as gimmicky. But these "3-D" tours have been catching on with buyers rapidly, in part because the technology

is improving. The cost of having these video tours made is dropping, too. Some real estate photographers now offer packages for home sellers that include virtual-reality tours for only around $100 more than they charge for still-photography packages.

Tip: Choose a photographer who uses Matterport 3D scanning technology if possible. It's the state of the art for virtual-reality video tours.

PRICIER UPGRADES

The following home upgrades usually have price tags in the thousands of dollars—but they often more than pay for themselves when a home is sold. They're particularly worth considering if they're in a part of the home that needs to be renovated anyway.

•**Add showerheads in the master bathroom.** When home buyers see showers with multiple showerheads—two or more directional showerheads plus a "rainfall" showerhead that drops water from directly above—they imagine themselves surrounded by warm, soothing water every morning. A shower with three or more showerheads conveys a sense of peace and relaxation, and buyers are drawn to homes that make them feel these things. Expect to pay at least $1,000 to have a plumber install extra showerheads.

Note: An oversized master-bath bathtub can be a selling point…but if budget or bathroom-size limitations force you to choose between an upgraded shower or tub, opt for the shower. A relatively small percentage of home buyers take frequent baths, so even a very impressive tub will have fairly narrow appeal.

•**Install a big, rectangular sink.** If you're redoing your kitchen or master bath anyway and space permits, spend a little extra and install a trough sink—an oversized sink that's several feet in length. It's an element that catches the eye of many buyers these days, especially when it's made of concrete or stone. You'll probably pay $1,000 or more for the sink and installation, but this amount might be more than recouped in buyers' additional perceived value of the kitchen or bathroom. Choose a trough sink with a bottom that

---

TAKE NOTE...

Best Day to List Your Home for Sale

The best day to list your home for sale is a Saturday in the first half of May. Homes listed for sale in this time period sold two weeks faster than average at a price $2,500 higher than the average for listings at other times of year.

In general, spring is the best time to sell a home, since the weather is good for moving, people are looking forward to summer, and many have tax refunds to spend.

Zillow.com

slopes toward the drain because trough sinks with level basins don't drain well.

AFFORDABLE WAYS TO CREATE AN OUTDOOR "ROOM"

Home buyers increasingly want homes that connect them with the outdoors. A good way to do this is to transform a simple patio or deck into an outdoor "room"—not with actual walls, but with many of the comforts and amenities of a room. *This room might feature...*

- **Fireplace or cooking area**
- **Comfortable-looking outdoor furniture**
- **Patio heaters**
- **Stone wall or some other attractive border to define the edge of the space**
- **Awning or some other covering.**

Include an attractive sink and countertop in your outdoor room, too, if possible—outdoor sinks are an uncommon but attractive amenity, so this can help your outdoor room stand out from those that buyers have seen at other homes.

An outdoor room can make your home feel larger, too—it adds additional living space beyond the home's footprint.

Similar: If your home is in a tight, urban space, it might be possible to transform a roof deck into an outdoor room. Include plants in planters...and walls or screens for privacy from neighboring buildings.

Cities That Reward You to Live There

Ollolai, Italy, will sell you a home for one euro if you refurbish it within three years at a cost of about $25,000...and Albinen, Switzerland, is giving grants of about $25,000 per adult plus about $10,000 per child for families with parents younger than age 45 who move there full-time to a home valued at about $200,000 or more, and who stay in the home for at least 10 years.

In the US, Curtis, Nebraska, will give free land to families that build certain types of single-family homes on it within a specified time period...Harmony, Minnesota, offers cash rebates of $5,000 to $12,000 to people who build approved single-family homes with market value of at least $125,000...and Niagara Falls, New York, offers student-loan reimbursements up to $7,000 over two years to recent graduates who live in specific areas for at least two years.

Roundup of experts on city residency incentives, reported at GoBankingRates.com.

Buying a Home? Beware These Fees

RealEstate.com

- **Lender fees** include appraisal, credit report and processing charges.
- **You also may be charged flood certification, tax service and other fees**—ask what each actually pays for and if any can be eliminated or reduced.
- **Escrow fees** pay the agent who takes in money, disburses it and records paperwork.
- **Title fees** pay to make sure that your home has no undisclosed restrictions or ownership issues—but other fees also may be included, and those can possibly be reduced or eliminated.
- **Government fees** are transfer taxes that are charged by counties and some cities and can vary widely—check in advance to avoid being surprised.
- **Real estate fees** may include pest inspection, home inspection, well and septic inspections, soil reports and other specific services and may be paid by the buyer or the seller.
- **Transaction coordination fee** pays for someone to handle all the real estate paperwork and usually is not negotiable, but you can ask your real estate agent to pay it.

Sneaky Mortgage Claims

- **No points or fees**—lenders who say this typically charge higher interest rates instead.

- **No-cost mortgage insurance**—mortgage insurance is required if you put less than 20% down, but some lenders claim not to charge for it…and increase the interest rate instead.

- **Trick to pay off your mortgage faster**—this means refinancing a 30-year loan to a 15-year, but monthly payments will be much higher.

- **Call now for a low, low rate of X%**—find out the Annual Percentage Rate (APR)…if the APR is significantly higher than the quoted rate, that means you must pay points and fees to get the low rate.

RealEstate.com

Lower Your Mortgage Rate with a Phone Call

The easiest way to lower your mortgage rate is to simply call your mortgage lender, and ask for a reduced interest rate. (This is called a "mortgage loan modification" and typically is offered because of hardship in paying the loan.) Some lenders will agree, especially if your rate is much higher than current rates—which averaged 3.75% for a 30-year fixed-rate mortgage as of August 2019. This works best if your mortgage lender and mortgage servicer are the same company—and if the lender understands that you are not asking to refinance but only to get a lower interest rate on your current mortgage.

If the lender says no and your rate is high enough to make refinancing attractive, consider pursuing that option. You also can reduce your interest costs by making extra payments on your existing mortgage—just be sure to designate that the payments are to be applied to the principal, which will reduce the total amount on which interest is charged.

MoneyTalksNews.com

When Renting a Home Beats Owning

Renters build more wealth than home owners if they take the savings from not owning a home and invest all the money at a sufficiently high rate of return, according to a recent study.

Although there are some parts of the US where home prices have skyrocketed, there are many more parts where prices have stayed relatively stagnant. In those areas, renting, calculating the savings compared with owning, and investing all of those savings in stocks and bonds result in a better return than buying a home and relying on its appreciation for wealth building.

Ken Johnson, PhD, associate dean and professor, department of finance, Florida Atlantic University College of Business, Boca Raton, and coauthor of a study published in *Journal of Housing Research*.

7 Big Secrets About Divorce That Could Cost You Big

Charles D. Jamieson, Esq., an attorney based in West Palm Beach, Florida, who has been practicing marital and family law for nearly three decades. He is author of the free e-book *Planning Your Divorce—7 Important Considerations for Going Your Separate Ways*. CJamieson Law.com

What you don't know about divorce could cost you big if your marriage ends. *Here are seven things that experienced divorce attorneys know that many people nearing or enduring the divorce process do not…*

- **Using social media during your divorce could prove pricey.** If you bad-mouth your spouse on social media, your spouse's attorney might use these posts in court to make you look like a bad person. If you post pictures of fun things you do or fun places you go, your spouse's attorney might use these to make it appear that you spend recklessly or don't take proper care of your children.

What to do: Stop using social media until your divorce is final. Delete any existing posts that are critical of your spouse…or that show you spending money or enjoying yourself without your spouse—but remember that your spouse's attorney still can subpoena deleted pictures and comments. Do not assume that your spouse cannot access your social-media posts—even if you "unfriend" your spouse from your account, he/she might remain close with one of your acquaintances who still has access.

• **Taking your divorce to court will benefit only the attorneys.** Some spouses insist on contesting divorces in court "out of principle." That's a bad idea unless one of your principles is paying attorneys roughly 10% of the value of everything you own. Other spouses refuse to settle because they "want their day in court." But divorce court does not offer the fair hearing and sympathetic ear you might expect. The judge who handles your divorce probably will have dozens or hundreds of cases on his docket. He isn't going to be able to dig deep to discover the truth about you and your spouse or carefully weigh who should receive each possession…he's going to get a thumbnail sketch of the relationship and take his best shot. Whether the result is to your liking is an expensive gamble.

What to do: If you are offered a settlement that you can live with, take it. Do this even if the settlement doesn't seem "fair." No one thinks his divorce settlement is fair. The system isn't designed to produce fairness…it's designed to end the marriage according to the laws of your state.

• **Your spouse's lawyer will love it if you find new love.** If your spouse's attorney learns that you have a new romantic partner before the divorce is final, the attorney likely will try to use this against you. He might try to make you appear unfaithful even if the relationship did not begin until after you separated from your spouse. He might make a big deal about the fact that you're spending marital assets wooing or cavorting with this new lover. And

if you have minor children, he might question whether it is safe and responsible for the court to allow you to have or share custody now that this partner is in the picture.

What to do: Don't date until your divorce is final. If you already are dating, end the relationship…or at least put the relationship on hold until the divorce is final.

• **Your jewelry and other small valuables might mysteriously disappear.** Jewelry, collectibles and other small valuables sometimes go missing immediately before or during the divorce process. Both spouses inevitably deny knowing where these items have gone and claim that the other must be hiding them. It can be impossible to prove who is lying.

What to do: Move all of your jewelry and other small valuables out of your home if you suspect that divorce proceedings could be imminent. Store them in a bank safe-deposit box that your spouse does not have access to…or in the home of a trusted friend or relative.

• **Your spouse's "gambling losses" actually might be hidden assets.** Say that in the months before your spouse files for divorce, he makes a confession—he lost a small fortune gambling in a casino. Maybe your spouse really did lose this money…or maybe he has thousands of dollars in casino chips stashed somewhere in hopes of keeping them out of the pool of assets divided in the divorce.

What to do: Tell your divorce attorney about any recent gambling trips or gambling losses by your spouse. Divorce attorneys and divorce courts are familiar with the casino-chip ploy. There are ways in which to obtain the records for casino-chip purchases and other ways to get your share of these assets.

• **You will grieve—and it could cost you.** Maybe you think that you won't grieve over the end of your marriage because the relationship was troubled for some time and you're happy to see it end. Maybe you think that you won't grieve because you're not very emotional. Don't bet on it.

Virtually everyone who is going through a divorce endures considerable grief. That grief can cause them to make emotional decisions when it's crucial that they make rational ones—perhaps accepting an unfavorable settlement just to end the pain of the divorce process...or battling it out with a spouse over every last detail as the attorney's fees pile up.

What to do: See a therapist who specializes in marital issues or in dealing with grief. Not only should this help you avoid making bad grief-driven decisions, it also makes it less likely that you will discuss your emotions at length with your divorce attorney. Divorce attorneys often become sympathetic ears for their clients, but they are not trained to help clients with emotional matters...and they typically charge much more per hour than therapists.

•**Venting your anger at your spouse likely will hurt you and your kids much more than it hurts your spouse.** It might feel good to behave angrily toward your spouse during your divorce—but your spouse's divorce attorney will use your angry calls, voice mails and texts to make you appear immature and unstable. And the more spouses snipe at each other during a divorce, the greater the emotional fallout for their kids—even when those kids are already grown.

What to do: If you and your spouse cannot speak civilly with each other during the divorce process, do not cut off communication entirely—that would force you to communicate exclusively through your attorneys, which would inflate legal bills—but do communicate only via e-mail. With e-mail, you can wait until you have cooled down to respond to a message that makes you angry.

A therapist can provide tips for keeping your anger in check, too. *Warning:* Do not spitefully sell off, give away or destroy your spouse's possessions. If you do this, you likely will be required to compensate your spouse for the losses as part of the divorce terms.

Saving for College Is Trickier Than Ever: Traps and Opportunities

Mark Kantrowitz, a financial-aid expert who has been involved in the college-savings sector for more than 25 years and adviser to SavingForCollege.com. He serves on the editorial board of *Journal of Student Financial Aid* and has testified before the US Congress about student aid. PrivateStudentLoans.Guru

If you're saving money to pay for a child or grandchild's education, the federal tax law includes some tricky rules and opportunities that you need to know about. *But proceed with caution—the rules can be difficult to interpret and contain some potentially costly gotchas...*

529s FOR ELEMENTARY TUITION

Money invested in a 529 college savings plan, a form of tax-advantaged account, now can be spent on kindergarten through high school (K–12) tuition without triggering federal income taxes or penalties upon withdrawal. Previously, withdrawals from a 529 were tax- and penalty-free only when used for college expenses. Of course, using money saved for college to pay for precollege education means a shorter period of tax-free investment growth and a smaller college fund. *But if you still want to use 529-plan money for K–12 education, be aware of these three less obvious traps...*

•**There could be *state* taxes and penalties.** Many states have adjusted their tax codes to permit tax-free withdrawals from 529 plans now that the federal government has done so...however, not all have done this. Contact your state's 529-plan administrators to confirm that there won't be state-tax consequences before using 529 money for K–12 tuition.

•**Not all K–12 costs qualify.** You can spend 529 savings on a wide range of college costs, including tuition, room and board, textbooks and activity fees. But when it comes to K–12 costs, only tuition qualifies. Also, K–12 tuition withdrawals are capped at $10,000 per year per student.

• **Some kids could lose their K–12 scholarships.** If you have significant assets in a 529 plan and your child receives (or hopes to receive) a need-based scholarship from a K–12 school, that scholarship might soon shrink or disappear. Most K–12 private schools have historically not factored 529 savings into their calculations when they decide which students and prospective students qualify for need-based aid. But many of these schools likely will start doing so now.

Helpful: Private K–12 schools are unlikely to consider 529 savings in accounts owned by grandparents even if those 529s name the grandchild as beneficiary. To this end, grandparents who want to help save for college could open a 529 account themselves, rather than contribute money to a 529 account opened by the parents. To maximize long-term investment gains, this account could be opened before a grandchild is born, naming a grandparent or other family member as beneficiary. Then change the beneficiary to the child once he/she is born and has a Social Security number. (Grandparent-owned 529s can have implications for college financial aid, but there's a way to avoid this—see below.) While you can have one 529 account and use it for multiple grandkids, it's almost always easier to set up a separate account for each student—a 529 plan can have only one beneficiary at a time, so it can get complicated if there are two grandkids in college at the same time. Plus, the annual contribution limit is per beneficiary, so having separate 529 plans lets you save much more.

NEW "KIDDIE TAX" RATES COULD AFFECT COLLEGE SAVERS

The accounts known as UGMAs (Uniform Gifts to Minors Accounts) or UTMAs (Uniform Transfers to Minors Accounts) are alternatives to 529 plans. UGMAs/UTMAs do not provide tax-free investment growth as 529s do, but there are no penalties if UGMA/UTMA savings are used for something other than education. And investment profits from an UGMA/UTMA are considered income for the child, not the parent—a distinction that can lead to low tax rates, thanks in part to the new tax law.

Here's why: Prior to 2018, children's investment income above $2,100 was taxed at their parents' top marginal tax rate—this prevented parents from avoiding taxes by stashing their own investments in the names of their kids. For most families, that top marginal rate was between 15% and 28%, but it could have been as high as 39.6% for high earners. But under the revised "kiddie tax" rules that took effect in 2018, investment income above $2,200 (for 2019) in a child's name is taxed at the rates that apply to trusts and estates—the parent's tax bracket is no longer a factor. (These rules apply to children younger than age 19…or younger than age 24 in the case of full-time students with limited earned income.)

That change will result in very low taxes on UGMAs/UTMAs as long as the child has no more than $4,800 in unearned income each year. After the $2,200 threshold is met, the child's next $2,600 in unearned income now is taxed at a modest 10% rate. Rates climb quickly after that (first to 24%, then to 35% and finally 37%), limiting the appeal of larger UGMAs/UTMAs, but the low tax on up to $4,800 in annual unearned income does hold some appeal. *Despite this, there are three things worth knowing before you put money in an UGMA/UTMA…*

• **529 plans still offer the superior tax deal—usually.** Modest annual income from an UGMA/UTMA might now trigger only minimal taxes, but 529 investment profits generally are not taxed at all. UGMAs/UTMAs come out ahead from a tax perspective only if the money is not spent on qualifying educational expenses.

• **UGMA/UTMA savings are out of your control.** Money you put in a 529 account still is legally yours. You could even change the account's beneficiary if you like. When you put money in an UGMA/UTMA, it belongs to the child. When that child turns age 18 or 21 (this varies by state), he can spend it however he likes.

• **UGMAs/UTMAs can cost you financial aid.** UGMAs/UTMAs are legally owned by the student—and the more assets a student owns, the less financial aid he is likely to receive. A 529 account has a much smaller effect on financial aid because it is legally owned by the parent.

Helpful: Assets in a 529 account owned by a grandparent are not included in college financial-aid calculations. But when those grandparent-owned 529-plan assets are withdrawn and used to pay a student's educational expenses, that counts as income for the student—which could reduce aid. To avoid this, do not tap grandparent-owned 529s until after January 1 of the student's sophomore year, if possible. Financial-aid decisions are based on a family's finances during the "prior prior year."

WHEN A COVERDELL EDUCATION ACCOUNT IS BETTER THAN A 529

Until 2018, a tax-advantaged savings vehicle known as a Coverdell Education Savings Account had two notable advantages over a 529 account. One was that Coverdell money could be spent on K–12 costs, not just college costs, without triggering taxes or penalties—but now 529 accounts can do that, too.

The Coverdell's second advantage was that it does not restrict savers to a limited menu of investments as 529s do—Coverdell accounts typically offer a broad range of investments and let owners change their investment choices as often as they'd like. That advantage remains, although investment choice usually is not a problem for 529 account holders because most 529 plans have a good selection of investment options. But if you want greater control over your investment choices, that could be a reason to invest in a Coverdell. And Coverdell funds can be used for a wide array of education costs for K–12, with no annual dollar limit on disbursements (not just tuition). *When considering a Coverdell, here are three limitations worth knowing about...*

• **Coverdells have low contribution limits.** You cannot contribute more than $2,000 per year per beneficiary. In contrast, annual contributions to 529 accounts are virtually uncapped. (Total 529 contributions are capped in some states, but rarely below $235,000 or $300,000 per student.) Note that you can contribute to both a Coverdell and a 529.

• **Coverdells have income limits.** For 2019, you're not allowed to make the full contribution if your modified adjusted gross income is above $95,000 ($190,000 if married and filing jointly)...and you cannot make any contribution if it is above $110,000 ($220,000 if married and filing jointly). There are no income caps with 529s.

• **Coverdells have age limits.** Contributions are not allowed after the beneficiary turns age 18...and the money generally must be withdrawn within 30 days of the beneficiary's thirtieth birthday. There are no age restrictions with 529 accounts.

---

4 Best 529 College Savings Plans

All four of the following 529 college savings plans have low costs, strong management and exceptional investment options...

• **Bright Start College Savings, Illinois.**

• **Invest529, Virginia.**

• **Vanguard 529 College Savings, Nevada.**

• **my529/Utah Educational Savings, Utah.**

Caution: Five plans were given negative ratings because they have no compelling advantages and have at least one significant disadvantage, such as high fees. They are College SAVE, North Dakota...Florida 529 Savings Plan, Florida...Franklin Templeton 529 College Savings, New Jersey...GIFT College Investing Plan, Arkansas...and TD Ameritrade 529 College Savings, Nebraska.

For more information, go to 529.Morningstar.com/state-map.action.

Morningstar Inc.

Loopholes in 529 College Savings Accounts

The beneficiary of a tax-advantaged 529 account can be switched without penalty to any direct relative of the original beneficiary. Switching beneficiaries helps avoid the IRS rule that allows account holders to change fund choices only twice per calendar year. Parent-owned 529s may reduce a child's financial-aid package by up to 5.64% of the value of the account when applying for financial aid, but 529s owned by grandparents do not count at all until withdrawals to pay for college start. Then the money is considered income to the student. Some states, but not all, allow 529 funds to be used for K–12 education—for instance, for private high school. But other states tax the gains portions of withdrawals for K–12 use, although those gains are not federally taxed. Rules can be quite complex—consult your financial adviser.

The Wall Street Journal.

Common Student-Loan Scams and How to Avoid Them

Student-loan-debt-consolidation scam: Companies say that they can put all your loans from various lenders together for a fee—typically called a processing, consolidation or administrative fee—so that you have only one monthly payment. But you never have to pay for this—just log on to StudentLoans.gov, and you can consolidate on your own.

Advance-fee-for-better-loans scam: Scammers say that they can get you a better deal on loans if you pay them in advance. They normally ask for 1% to 5% of the loan amount or just a payment of $1,000 up-front. This is a pure scam—you should never pay up-front for claims such as this and should apply for all student loans directly and on your own. Student loans may have fees, such as a 1% default fee, but these fees are never paid in advance.

Roundup of experts on student-loan scams, reported at Credit.com.

Alternative to College Loans

More than two dozen colleges are offering, or developing, "income-sharing" programs.

The colleges pay students' tuition and possibly other expenses. In exchange, students pay a percentage of their eventual salaries, ranging from less than 3% to as much as 15% based on their majors, for up to 10 years. Colleges offering the programs include Clarkson University, Lackawanna College, Messiah College, Purdue University and Norwich University.

Clare McCann, deputy director for education policy at New America Foundation, a nonprofit think tank, Washington, DC. NewAmerica.org

College Aid for Students Already in College

There is no rule requiring students to apply for aid and scholarships only while in high school. In fact, some scholarships and grants are specifically directed at students already in college—often ones from local businesses and civic organizations. And students who transfer from two-year community colleges to four-year institutions may have the ability to receive special scholarships.

Important for all students: Fill out the Free Application for Federal Student Aid (FAFSA). It determines aid eligibility and is used by many states, colleges and private organizations in their decision-making on allocating funds.

Roundup of experts on college aid, reported in *The Wall Street Journal.*

College Discounts Are Negotiable

Beth V. Walker, a financial planner and founder of Center for College Solutions in Colorado Springs. Walker is also author of *Never Pay Retail for College.* CenterForCollegeSolutions.com

Tuition tops $50,000 a year at lots of private colleges, but that's not what many students actually pay. These days, college tuition is like hotel room rates. There's a

149

steep official price, but people often get big breaks—if they know how. When students are accepted by colleges, many are informed that they qualify for discounts of a few hundred to tens of thousands of dollars per year, with the largest discounts coming from private colleges. Discounts typically are called "academic" or "merit" scholarships even if the student is not a classroom star. (This is separate from need-based financial aid.)

To obtain and increase discounts…

• **Apply to several schools where you would be in the top 25% of the class based on SAT scores and GPA.** Colleges use big discounts to lure these students away from more prestigious schools. CollegeData.com lists "average" and "high" SAT scores and GPAs for each college's most recent class—the midpoint between these offers a rough sense of what's required to be in the top 25%.

• **Don't apply "early decision."** Students who are accepted in early decisions are locked into attending that college, so they can't leverage offers from competing schools. (Applying "early action" is fine—that doesn't lock the student into attending.)

• **When you receive discount offers from colleges, wait a few weeks.** When a college notifies a student that he/she has been accepted (along with discount offers), it may not have offered all of the discounts it can afford, leaving room to revise offers.

• **Request a match.** If one college has offered you a better discount or lower tuition than another college, call your preferred school's financial-aid department a few weeks before the May 1 deadline. Ask whether it can match the competing school's offer. Say that you want to avoid taking on excessive debt, and ask the preferred school whether it can get closer to the competing school's offer. There's no downside to trying this, and it often leads to increased discounts. (Even if there is no competing offer, it's worth asking whether a bigger discount is available.)

Note: The competing offer that you cite must be from a school that is equal or close to your preferred school's ranking.

Smarter Charitable Giving

Make sure your donation is used the right way by choosing a charity that scored a perfect 100 for fiscal responsibility plus good governance. *Examples…*

Education: Seeds of Hope Charitable Trust.

Human and civil rights: Congressional Medal of Honor Foundation…Equal Justice Initiative.

Environment: Appalachian Voices…Acadia Center.

Health: Community Volunteers in Medicine …Cystic Fibrosis Research Inc.

Community development: Habitat for Humanity chapters in Collier County, Florida, Ventura County, California, and San Gabriel County, California.

Human services: Kostopoulos Dream Foundation…Navy SEAL Foundation.

International: Books for Africa…Kids Alive International.

Animals: WildAid…Big Cat Rescue.

CharityNavigator.org

7 Awful Mistakes People Make When Creating Their Own Wills

Gregory S. DuPont, CFP, JD, managing partner of DuPont & Blumenstiel, an estate-planning, business and taxation law firm in Dublin, Ohio. He regularly reviews do-it-yourself wills for clients. DAndBLaw.com

Drafting a will does not necessarily have to rise to the complexity of rocket science, so using a low-priced online "do it yourself" service such as Rocket Lawyer, LegalZoom or Quicken WillMaker Plus can be a reasonable option for simple estates. Although hiring an experienced estate-planning attorney certainly is a safer choice, if you're not willing to pay the hundreds of dollars that an attorney would charge for a straightforward will, these digital services are better than having no will at all. They generate perfectly acceptable state-specific documents by providing fill-in-the-blank forms or questionnaires that generate completed forms. With their assistance, you might be able to write your own will in less than an hour for just $40 to $100. *But if you do take this route, beware of the following mistakes people commonly make when preparing their own wills…*

MISTAKE: **Attempting to disinherit a descendant by omitting any mention of him/ her in the will.** This sounds reasonable—if you don't want to leave money to someone, why mention the person in your will? But when descendants are not mentioned at all, they often contest those wills on the grounds that they were left out accidentally.

Better: Mention the disinherited heir by name, and expressly state that you are not leaving this person a portion of your estate. *Example:* "I acknowledge that John Smith is one of my children, for whom I make no provision."

MISTAKE: **Including end-of-life or funerary preferences.** Would you want to be removed from life support if you were in an irreversible coma? Would you rather be buried or cremated after you die? It's important that your heirs know these things—but your will is not the place to tell them. Wills often are not consulted until several days after the death, at which point it's too late for your heirs to follow these directions.

Moreover, your will has no legal standing until you die, so your health-care providers and heirs would not be bound to follow end-of-life medical guidance in your will even if they did know about it.

Better: The proper estate-planning document for detailing end-of-life medical care and funerary preferences is a living will. (Rocket Lawyer and LegalZoom offer DIY living-will creation tools.)

MISTAKE: **Setting conditions for inheritances.** Maybe you want one of your children or grandchildren to receive a portion of your estate only if he/she stays off drugs or gets married or graduates college. These are not uncommon desires. But who will monitor the situation and decide whether your conditions have been met? This often becomes more complex than people anticipate, creating uncertainty for your will's executor and potentially leading to estate-draining lawsuits. *Examples:* If the condition you set is no drug use, is drug testing required or just a lack of drug-related arrests? Is marijuana use allowed in states where it's legal? If the condition is a college degree, does an online or community college qualify? You can try to cover all the possible bases in a self-written will—but you won't succeed.

Better: Conditional inheritances usually are more trouble than they're worth, but if you feel that you must include one, it's worth paying an estate-planning attorney to help you consider the potential complications and contingencies and draft a will that truly will do what you want.

MISTAKE: **Leaving assets to pets.** As far as the law is concerned, your pet cannot be an heir—it is (however much you may love it) simply personal property. If you do try to leave money or any other asset to a pet, the courts likely will allocate it to another of your beneficiaries instead.

Better: Leave your pet and money for its care to someone who will take good care of the animal and who has agreed to do so. If you want to formalize this arrangement to ensure that there are no misunderstandings, you could add a "pet protection agreement" or "pet trust" to your estate plan. (Rocket Lawyer and LegalZoom offer DIY documents for this.)

MISTAKE: **Leaving significant assets directly to minors.** If you do this, the court will appoint a guardian to look after the assets—and perhaps claim a fee from your estate—until the child turns 18 (or slightly older in some states). And upon that birthday, all of the assets instantly will fall under this heir's control even if he/she is still too immature to handle the inheritance responsibly.

Better: Following instructions in a DIY will-creation tool, you could specify in your will that assets left to a minor should be placed in a Uniform Transfers to Minors Act (UTMA) account when you die. The assets would then be administered by a custodian of your choice whom you name in the will, such as a trusted family member, and the beneficiary would gain full control over them at or around age 21 (depending on your state).

Note: UTMAs are not accepted in South Carolina or Vermont, which follow a similar but older law, the Uniform Gift to Minors Act (UGMA).

If even age 21 is younger than you'd like for an heir to take control of an inheritance, you could instead leave the money to a trust that names the minor as a beneficiary. With a trust, you can grant control over the assets whenever you choose—but unlike with an UTMA, it's generally worth hiring an attorney to set up a trust.

MISTAKE: **Assuming that all of your assets will be distributed as dictated by your will.** The beneficiary designations on certain accounts and assets, including 401(k)s, IRAs and life insurance policies, take precedence over the beneficiaries you name in your will. *Example:* A man removes his gambling-addict son from his will but fails to remove him from the beneficiary designation on his 401(k), accidentally handing over much of his savings to someone who is likely to lose it.

Better: Confirm that the beneficiary designations on your accounts and insurance policies distribute your assets according to your current wishes. There is no need to include these accounts and policies in your will.

MISTAKE: **Failing to follow rules about required witnesses.** Sometimes people who draft their own wills do a great job crafting the documents—then blow it when it comes to signing their names at the end. Depending on your state, either two or three people must witness you signing your will. In some states, your witnesses must witness each other signing as well and/or signing an affidavit in the presence of a notary. There are some crucial rules about who these witnesses can and can't be, too—in most states they must be at least 18 years old and must be "disinterested," meaning that they can't be people who are named as beneficiaries in the will. If you fail to follow witnessing rules to the letter, your will could be ruled invalid.

Better: Read the witnessing rules provided with your DIY will carefully, and follow them precisely.

WHERE TO STORE YOUR WILL

If you pay a lawyer to draft a will, it likely will be stored in the lawyer's office. But when people draft their own wills, they often store them either in bank deposit boxes or in their own homes—and both of those locations can cause problems. It might be difficult and time-consuming for your executor to gain access to your bank deposit box after you die. If you store the will in your home, he/she might struggle to find the document there...or one of your descendants could find your will before the executor, dislike how you divided up your assets and hide or destroy the document.

Better: If you store your will in your home, be sure to inform the will's executor and several other trusted family members or friends where to find it, and don't divulge the location to family members you do not completely trust.

Or for even greater security, file your will with your county's probate court if this is allowed prior to death where you live, and let your heirs know that you have done so. If you do file your will with the court, you will have to refile if you later modify the will or move to a different county. Filing a will with the court makes it public record, so this is not the best option if keeping the will private is a priority.

8

Insurance Insider

Fight Unfair Medical Bills...and Win!

ew things are quite as frustrating, time-consuming or financially and emotionally fraught as dealing with large, incomprehensible medical bills. Before you give in, read on to find out how other consumers have fought back—and won. (Names and certain identifying characteristics have been changed to protect patients' identities.)

•**Get your insurer to pay up** when you've opted for an out-of-network provider. The key here is to arm yourself with information about what any out-of-network service you will be having *should* cost.

Example: Jim chose an out-of-network surgeon for an outpatient procedure knowing full well that his out-of-pocket costs would be higher than if he had gone with a doctor in his health insurance plan's network. But after-

ward, when the surgeon's bill arrived, he was shocked to discover that his insurance was covering only $500 of the $3,000 total.

When he called his insurance company to ask why the reimbursement was so low, a representative said that the insurer had used what's known as the "usual, customary and reasonable" (UCR) formula to determine what other providers charge for the same service in the area where Jim lives. But Jim sent the bill to a patient advocate, and her examination of the insurance company's explanation of benefits (EOB) revealed that the UCR was way off. Upon further investigation, the insurer realized that it had used an incorrect pricing formula. After it reprocessed the claim, Jim's share of the bill was only $50.

Fight-back strategy: First check your insurance plan for its policy on out-of-network

Maureen Lamb, founder and CEO of Medical Bill Support, LLC, a medical-billing advocacy group, Holderness, New Hampshire, and a member of the Alliance of Professional Health Advocates. MedicalBillSupport. com

153

coverage. If you think that the reimbursement you are getting for an out-of-network provider's bill is too low, call your insurer and ask for an explanation. You also can ask your provider to check whether the procedure was coded properly—coding mistakes can lead to under-reimbursement or even a rejected claim.

To check whether you are getting the correct information from the insurance company, search the database at Healthcare Bluebook (HealthcareBluebook.com) or at FAIR Health (FairHealthConsumer.org) to locate the UCR rates for hospital procedures, lab tests and more by zip code. If you find a higher UCR than the one your insurer is applying, request that it use that higher amount, which should increase your reimbursement.

•**Don't pay for someone else's oversight.** As the executor of his father's estate, Michael tried to resolve an outstanding $10,000 hospital bill that his dad had incurred before he died. According to the paperwork, Medicare had paid its share, and his father's secondary insurance should have covered the balance but had not.

When Michael called the secondary insurer, he was told that it was too late for the insurer to pay the bill. The hospital billing office, it turned out, had not submitted the claim to the secondary insurer within its required time frame. The hospital admitted its error and, upon request, wrote off the $10,000 balance.

Fight-back strategy: Never pay a health-care bill until a private insurer or Medicare and your secondary insurance have paid their share. Also, be aware that every insurance company has a "timely filing limit." Generally, in-network claims must be submitted by the provider's billing office within 90 days of the date of service, and for out-of-network claims, the submission limit generally is 180 days, but this time frame varies. Check your insurance statements to make sure that your bills have been submitted to your insurer, and if they haven't, follow up with the provider's billing office to request that this be done.

Tip: If you are on Medicare, set up your own account on Medicare.gov so that you can review the payments for your bills there. If you have secondary insurance, make sure that the provider's billing office has your information and that it's correct—if it isn't, you will never be billed correctly.

•**Get help for an unavoidable out-of-network bill.** When three-month-old Tyler experienced severe breathing problems, his parents rushed him to the closest emergency room. Tyler was admitted to the hospital for several days, resulting in a bill of $25,000. But because the hospital was not considered in-network, the parents' insurance company paid the bill at the out-of-network rate, which resulted in a balance of $20,000 billed to the parents.

They asked their insurance company to pay the bill at the in-network rate because it was an emergency and they had had no choice but to use the closest hospital for their son and keep him there until he was well enough to be discharged. But neither the insurance company nor the hospital billing office would budge despite the parents' multiple calls. Finally, the parents appealed to their state's insurance commissioner, and then the insurance company agreed to pay the entire outstanding balance of $20,000.

Fight-back strategy: Even when you think you've done everything right, you may be hit with a surprise medical bill—and find no relief from your insurance carrier or service provider. If you are covered by employer-sponsored insurance, you then can contact your employer's human resources department to ask for help—an HR staff member might be able to go to bat for you with the insurer. Or you may be able to appeal your case to the state insurance commissioner (search at NAIC.org) or attorney general. (To find your attorney general, go to NAAG.org.) Provided you have a legitimate extenuating circumstance, their intervention might induce the insurer to pay an additional amount.

•**Don't let a simple mistake derail you.** John and Sally's son Peter had a chronic medical condition that they managed with medications costing $600 a month. With insurance, the parents' share of the bill was reduced to $30 a month. But things changed when Sally and John divorced and Peter had to be transferred from his father's insurance plan to his mother's new plan. In the tumult around the divorce, both parents forgot to update the pharmacy about the change of insurance and the new billing address. As a result, the monthly $600 invoices accumulated at an old address, unprocessed by the new insurance plan. Eventually the bills were in danger of being sent to a collection agency.

Fight-back strategy: Always make sure that your insurer has your correct home address so that you can review your EOB statements along with your bills to make sure that they are correct. If you spot any outdated information, contact your insurer immediately. Even better, instead of relying only on snail mail, set up an online account with your insurance company—then you can proactively check to make sure that your medical bills are being received and paid properly.

Is That Checkup Really Free?

Charles B. Inlander, a consumer advocate and healthcare consultant based in Fogelsville, Pennsylvania. He was founding president of the nonprofit People's Medical Society, a consumer-advocacy organization credited with key improvements in the quality of US health care, and is author or coauthor of more than 20 consumer-health books.

Both the Affordable Care Act (ACA)—commonly called "Obamacare"—and Medicare make a big deal about preventive services that are covered without requiring beneficiaries or policyholders to pay a deductible, use coinsurance or make a co-payment. Depending on your age, such services as a regular preventive mammogram or a routine colonoscopy (for adults over age 50) require no additional out-of-pocket cost to you even if you haven't met your annual deductible. You are also entitled to an annual wellness visit with your doctor to review your current health status and lay out a plan to improve it (if necessary).

Sounds great, doesn't it? And it is. But like most things involving health insurance coverage, there are a lot of strings attached. For

WHAT TO DO...

When a Claim Is Denied...

If a health-insurance claim is denied, document everything involved in the claim when you ask for reconsideration. Include test results, doctors' notes, even evidence from clinical research and peer-reviewed journals if relevant. *Also...*

● **Be sure to stick to facts and avoid emotion**—for example, show that you need a specific medicine or treatment so that you can work.

● **Get the name of a doctor within the insurance company to connect directly with your own physician**—this can make a big difference in consultations about treatment.

● **Double-check every detail involved in your submission for accuracy**—a minor billing-code error can cause a rejection.

Eliot Fishman, senior director of health policy, Families USA, a nonprofit consumer-advocacy organization, Washington, DC, quoted at MarketWatch.com.

many people, what they thought was a free service ends up costing them a good deal of money. *How to know when a preventive or wellness service is really free—or not...*

● **Know the terminology.** A friend of mine complained that he was billed by his doctor for an annual physical when his insurance policy stated he was entitled to a free annual wellness visit. He assumed that an annual physical is a wellness visit—a logical assumption to make. But under both Medicare and the ACA, they are *not* the same. A similar situation applies to certain mammograms, colonoscopies and other screening tests. These are free only for preventive screening (that is, when you have no symptoms). If a test is ordered because of a symptom or because the doctor suspects something may be amiss, it is not free—and you can be charged. To add to the confusion, even if you were symptom free, if something is discovered from the test, you still might be charged!

● **Know what's covered.** It's important that you check out what preventive and wellness services you are entitled to under your health plan. If you are on Medicare, I recommend checking the list of covered services on the Medicare.gov website (put "Your Medical Coverage" into the search box). You also can call 800-MEDICARE to ask about covered services and terms of coverage. If you are insured on a plan governed by the ACA, go to HHS.gov and search for "preventive care." You also should contact the insurance company that issues your policy to find out the full terms. And if you are covered through your employer, confirm what the free preventive services are directly with the insurer.

• **Watch what you say.** As noted above, an annual physical is not the same as a wellness visit. In fact, other than taking your blood pressure or reviewing tests that you've already had, the purpose of the wellness visit is to discuss what you should be doing to maintain your health. If you even say something like "I've had a ringing in my ears lately, can you check it out?" the visit is no longer considered a wellness or preventive visit—it becomes a physical or checkup, for which you will be charged... plus you will also be charged for treating your condition (effectively paying for *two visits*). So be very clear with your doctor that you are there for a free wellness visit...and that you will make another appointment to discuss a symptom or treatment of a chronic condition.

• **Don't become overwhelmed.** As confusing as all this can be, remember that preventive health services really can help you live a longer, more active life. Make sure your doctor knows that you want all the free preventive services you are entitled to and that are appropriate for your age and condition.

Get Your Insurer to Cover the Right Back-Pain Treatment

Heather Tick, MD, who holds the Gunn-Loke Endowed Professorship of Integrative Pain Medicine at University of Washington, Seattle. She is author of *Holistic Pain Relief: Dr. Tick's Breakthrough Strategies to Manage and Eliminate Pain.* HeatherTickMD.com

If you have chronic back pain, the best treatment that medical science has to offer may have nothing to do with drugs (including dangerous opioid pain relievers), and yet your insurance company might be willing to pay only for drugs! That twisted situation is a result of insurance companies not having caught up with the latest evidence that nondrug back-pain treatments can work.

Example: In a recent *JAMA Network Open* study of health insurance plans, only 11% covered acupuncture and 20% covered psychological counseling. Even physical therapy, covered by all, was inconsistently covered—some plans allowed only two visits.

Don't accept this situation! If your doctor recommends trying an evidence-based nondrug treatment for back pain such as physical therapy, chiropractic, acupuncture, therapeutic massage and/or psychological counseling to relieve stress, it's a positive sign about the doctor. Major medical organizations including the American College of Physicians now advise that these nondrug approaches should be the first thing you try. *To get nondrug back-pain treatment covered...*

• **Ask your doctor to avoid using the word "alternative" or "complementary" in any communication** with insurers or in your medical chart. These are outmoded ways to describe proven approaches and may dissuade insurers. Instead, your provider can use a term such as "evidence-based nonpharmacologic therapy."

• **If your claim is denied, ask your health-care provider to help you appeal.** Your physician, physician's assistant or nurse practitioner should send a letter to your carrier outlining the evidence for the opioid-sparing treatment.

It's extremely helpful if she/he cites specific supporting research.

• **If your health insurance appeals fail, use your HSA or FSA if you have these accounts.** The tax-free dollars in a health savings account (HSA) or flexible spending account (FSA) can be used for most nonmedication therapies. To decrease the odds that your use of the account will be challenged, ask your practitioner to write a prescription or note calling for the therapy and submit a copy of it when applying for reimbursement from the account.

Insurance May Not Pay for This Screening

Insurance may not pay for colorectal screening to start at age 45—despite a new recommendation from the American Cancer Society that people at average risk get a colonoscopy or a less invasive test at this age. (Colonoscopy is preferred for people with a family history of colorectal cancer.)

Why there's an insurance gap: Other organizations still call for screening to start at age 50.

Heather Hampel, MS, LGC, licensed genetic counselor and associate director and professor, division of human genetics at The Ohio State University Comprehensive Cancer Center, Columbus.

Medicare Now Covers Diabetes Prevention

Angela Forfia, senior manager of prevention with the American Association of Diabetes Educators, Chicago. DiabetesEducator.org

Did you know that Medicare has started covering the cost of certain diabetes-prevention programs for participants diagnosed with prediabetes? Nearly half of Americans age 65 or older have prediabetes, meaning that they are at significant risk for type 2 diabetes. Unfortunately, most people who have prediabetes do not realize they have it.

Diabetes-prevention programs provide education…personal counseling on lifestyle changes that can prevent or delay type 2 diabetes…and access to support groups with the goals of increasing physical activity, improving eating habits and achieving modest weight loss—weight loss of just 5% to 7% often can dramatically reduce type 2 diabetes risk.

According to the Centers for Disease Control and Prevention (CDC), these programs can reduce the odds of developing type 2 diabetes by 71% among people over age 60 who have prediabetes.

Medicare's coverage is provided for free to Medicare enrollees who qualify. (Many private health plans also cover diabetes-prevention programs.)

What to do: Use an online screening tool to determine whether you are at risk for prediabetes. *Example:* "Risk Test Hedgehogs (Hedgehogs on Vacation)" is a 60-second prediabetes screening video available on YouTube.

If you could be at risk, ask your health-care provider for a prediabetes blood test. If your doctor tells you that your blood test results meet the criteria for prediabetes, ask whether he/she knows of a Medicare Diabetes Prevention Program (MDPP) in your area. If not, locate diabetes-prevention programs in your area through the CDC's database (NCCD.CDC.gov/ddt_dprp) and contact one to ask whether it is a Medicare program. Even if no program in your area is covered by Medicare, consider paying out of pocket—it is better than getting diabetes.

HSA Myths That Can Cost You Big

Roy J. Ramthun, president, HSA Consulting Services, LLC, a health-care consulting practice specializing in HSAs, located in Houston. Previously, Ramthun was a senior adviser to the Secretary of the US Treasury. AskMrHSA.com

You may know that a health savings account (HSA) lets you set aside pretax earnings to pay health-care expenses.

But HSA rules are complex, and if you don't understand exactly what they say, you might leave a lot of money on the table—and you might even get hit with monetary penalties. *Here are seven costly HSA myths you must protect yourself from…*

OPENING AND CONTRIBUTING TO AN HSA

MYTH: **I'm automatically eligible to fund an HSA if I have a qualifying high-deductible health insurance plan.**

Reality: You might not be eligible if you or your spouse has a flexible spending account (FSA), which similarly lets you contribute pretax money to be used for health care—but only until a specified deadline. Even a spouse's FSA typically will disqualify you because money from one spouse's FSA can be used to pay the other spouse's medical expenses.

Exceptions: You can have an FSA and still fund an HSA if the FSA is a "dependent care" FSA that covers expenses such as child care or elder care, not medical bills…a "limited purpose" FSA that covers only dental and/or vision expenses…or a "postdeductible" FSA that covers most medical costs but only after a deductible of at least $1,350 ($2,700 for a family) in 2019 has been paid with non-FSA dollars. (Figures for 2020 are $1,400 and $2,800, respectively.)

MYTH: **The deadline for contributions to an HSA is the end of the year.**

Reality: If you fund your HSA by having your employer deduct pretax money from your paychecks, that withholding likely will end at the end of the calendar year—but you also can make contributions on your own up to the income tax filing deadline for that tax year, which is typically April 15 of the next year. (You cannot get an extension on this deadline even if you file for an extension on your tax return.) This is especially helpful if you want to maximize your contributions, but in the second year, you no longer have a high-deductible health insurance plan that qualifies you to contribute to an HSA.

Your total HSA contributions for a particular tax year, including both payroll deductions and your own contributions, are subject to an annual limit, however—in 2019, that limit is $3,500 for an individual or $7,000 for a family, plus an extra $1,000 allowed for people age 55 or older. (Figures for 2020 are $3,550 and $7,100, respectively.) This limit includes contributions that you make by April 15 of the following year. Contributions you make on your own rather than through payroll deductions will be subject to Social Security and Medicare taxes, though not income taxes.

SPENDING HSA MONEY

MYTH: **There's a deadline for when you can reimburse yourself from an HSA after you use non-HSA money to pay for a medical expense.**

Reality: There is no deadline on taking reimbursements from an HSA. As long as the HSA was open when the health-care expense was incurred, you can use it to pay that expense with pretax dollars from the HSA—even years later. *Example:* You have just $100 in your HSA when you require surgery that leads to $10,000 in out-of-pocket costs. You can initially pay these medical bills from your nontax advantaged savings…then make pretax contributions to the HSA for months or even years… and reimburse yourself from the HSA in stages or all at once depending on your preference.

MYTH: **Money in an HSA account can be used to pay medical expenses only for someone with a qualifying high-deductible health plan.**

Reality: You must have a high-deductible health plan to make contributions to *your* HSA, but once money is in the account, you can use it to pay not only your own medical expenses but also medical expenses of your spouse and dependents—even if they do not have a qualifying insurance plan.

MYTH: **I can use my HSA to pay health insurance premiums.**

Reality: Usually this is not allowed, but there are exceptions. HSA dollars can be used to pay health insurance premiums for yourself, your spouse and/or dependents if the premiums are for someone receiving federal or state unemployment benefits…or continuation coverage such as COBRA (which allows the person to purchase health insurance temporarily through a former employer after losing a job).

If you are age 65 or older, HSA money also can cover premiums for Medicare and for long-term-care insurance up to certain limits.

MYTH: **Money I put in an HSA will earn almost no interest.**

Reality: That's up to you. Most HSA accounts are indeed at banks or credit unions earning little or no interest—but you could instead set up an HSA with a provider that lets you invest the money in stocks, bonds and/or mutual funds. *Examples:* Health Savings Administrators…HSA Bank…Optum Bank…HealthEquity.

Investing HSA dollars in stocks or stock mutual funds can be risky if you expect to need the money to pay health-care costs soon because the value of the investments could fall. But if you don't expect to need it soon, HSAs can be a wonderful way to invest because you don't have to pay taxes on the money when you earn it or when you withdraw it, assuming the withdrawals are for qualified health-care expenses. That's a better tax break than you'll get even from a conventional or Roth IRA or 401(k). (If you're worried that you'll never need this money for health-care costs, stop worrying—the typical couple has $280,000 in out-of-pocket health-care costs after age 65, according to Fidelity Investments.)

If your employer does not offer an HSA provider that includes investment options, open an HSA with a provider that does, and periodically transfer money from the employer-selected HSA to this HSA. There should not be any tax consequences as long as this is done via a direct transfer from one financial company to the other. Check with both HSA providers about potential transfer fees, and transfer money only a few times per year if there are transfer fees. Do not close the employer-selected HSA account even if you don't like it—many employers will deposit payroll deductions only to the HSAs that they selected.

MYTH: **It's illegal to spend money from an HSA on non–health-related expenses.**

Reality: It's not illegal—it just means that you will have to pay income tax on this money and potentially a 20% penalty. You won't face that penalty if you spend the money after you reach age 65.

How Safe Is Your Drug Plan?

Charles B. Inlander, a consumer advocate and health-care consultant based in Fogelsville, Pennsylvania. He was founding president of the nonprofit People's Medical Society, a consumer-advocacy organization credited with key improvements in the quality of US health care, and is author or coauthor of more than 20 consumer-health books.

A controversial health insurance program is growing by leaps and bounds throughout the country. With "step therapy," your insurer requires your doctor to prescribe the cheapest effective prescription drug for your condition (lowest step) before allowing you to use more expensive drugs (higher step). It's not only being required by private insurance companies, it is also being used in Medicare prescription drug plans (Part D).

Latest development: As of January 2019, Medicare Advantage plans have the option of using step therapy for Part B drugs—those directly paid for by Medicare to practitioners (including oncologists and dermatologists) for treatment of such conditions as cancer or psoriasis.

Insurers argue that just because a drug is new or more expensive, that does not mean it is better or more effective than an older brand-name medication or its generic equivalent. In fact, for most people, the older drug probably does work just fine. However, while step therapy programs grow, research has uncovered many unintended consequences, such as patients getting sicker or not improving when forced to take a cheaper drug that is less effective than a more expensive one. Some insurance plans won't even cover newer, more expensive drugs.

The good news is, you can still get the benefits of the step therapy philosophy—without losing out if there's a drug you really need. *Here's how…*

• **Check with your insurer.** If your employer's health plan covers your medications, ask the insurer if your doctors are required to use step therapy programs. The same applies if you have a Medicare prescription drug plan (Part D) or are a member of a Medicare Advantage plan. Terms of coverage may change from year to year, so carefully review all information about meds that the insurer provides. *Insider tip*: Make sure you check your insurer's formulary (list of drugs covered) at least annually—and ask the insurer whether any drug you're taking is part of a step protocol. In addition to requiring step therapy, the insurer can add or drop drugs from the formulary at any time.

• **Don't hesitate to file an appeal.** Several states have passed legislation, or have pending legislation, allowing you to appeal an insurer's decision to deny coverage via a step therapy program. Your appeal will be considered within three days, but your doctor will need to make the case for a higher-step drug based on your response to a lower-step drug and/or other factors. *Insider tip*: Even if your state has no specific laws regarding step therapy appeals, you can still appeal a negative decision through your state's insurance department or directly through Medicare (if you are in traditional Medicare or a Medicare Advantage plan).

• **Use caution if you're switching plans.** If you plan to—or must—switch your health plans and are already taking a high-step-level, expensive drug, make sure that your new plan both covers that drug and will allow you to stay on it. Even if you stay in a plan only to find that your insurer is dropping that expensive drug you are on, don't be afraid to file an appeal.

Step therapy has an upside, too: Even if you are not in a required step therapy program, ask your doctor whether you can be prescribed the lowest-cost drug that is effective for your condition. In most cases, it will do the job.

Watch Out for This Sneaky "Gotcha" Fee

Charles B. Inlander, a consumer advocate and health-care consultant based in Fogelsville, Pennsylvania. He was founding president of the nonprofit People's Medical Society, a consumer-advocacy organization credited with key improvements in the quality of US health care, and is author or coauthor of more than 20 consumer-health books.

A friend of mine recently went to an urgent-care center with a bad sore throat. She had been there many times in the past, and the facility always accepted her insurance plan. After handing over a co-pay of $15 for urgent care, she left with a prescription. To my friend's surprise, she received a bill two weeks later from a nearby hospital demanding a $100 "facility fee" for using the urgent-care facility. It turns out that the hospital had recently purchased the urgent-care center and was adding this fee to all bills at the center. None of this was disclosed to my friend when she was at the center. To make matters worse, her insurer would not pay the extra fee. More on this later.

Facility fees are one of the biggest rip-offs the hospital industry has ever come up with. Across the country, consumers who go to "off-site" urgent-care centers or medical practices (they are not located on a hospital's campus but are owned by the hospital entity) are being charged facility fees that in some cases are higher than the cost of care that was provided. Sadly, the fees themselves are perfectly legal despite complaints to federal and state regulators and legislators from consumers and even some doctors.

The hospital industry defends these "gotcha" charges by saying the patient is receiving better care because the facility has all the hospital's resources behind it. But in most cases, nothing from the patient's perspective changed at the urgent-care center or doctor's office after being bought by the hospital. Now, with off-campus, hospital-owned urgent-care centers and medical practices growing in huge numbers (nearly 50% of all doctors are now hospital employed), these facility fees are becoming much more common. But you can protect yourself from paying up. *Here's my advice to help you avoid these costly bills…*

• **Pick up the phone.** Plan ahead and find out if any urgent-care facility in your area that you may want to use in the future is owned by a hospital. If it is, ask if it charges facility fees. If so, ask what that fee is. Also, call your insurance carrier and ask if your plan covers facility fees at noncampus, hospital-owned urgent-care centers and/or medical practices (this includes hospital-owned, off-campus clinics that might perform colonoscopies, mammograms and other diagnostic tests).

Insider tip: Be aware that nonhospital-owned facilities or medical practices cannot add these charges. So if you want to be sure to avoid facility fees, use nonhospital-owned urgent-care centers and medical practices.

• **Fight back.** My friend disputed her charge directly with the hospital's billing office, saying that she was never notified of this policy. The hospital still wouldn't budge. But she fought on, taking it to her state's consumer-protection bureau. This agency intervened, and the hospital dropped the charge for her. If you believe that you were *not* notified about a facility fee, either verbally or in writing (it's often in the fine print of paperwork you receive), before getting treatment, dispute it. You should first challenge the charge directly with the hospital. If turned down, ask if your insurer will help you fight the charge. And if that fails, try your state's consumer-protection agency (get contact information at USA.gov/state-consumer).

Insider tip: Also contact your congressional representatives. Both your state and federal representatives can often help in these situations. Hospitals do not want to get on their bad side. And the more that political leaders

hear about this practice from their constituents, the more likely the hospitals are to limit or ban these fees.

Don't Count on Low Mileage for an Insurance Break

Douglas Heller, insurance consultant for the Washington, DC–based Consumer Federation of America. He conducted the low-mileage study, which can be found at ConsumerFed.org (search for "low-mileage driver").

Many people assume that they get a discount on their auto insurance if they drive just a few thousand miles a year. But depending on which insurance company you use, that's not necessarily true.

A study conducted by the Consumer Federation of America obtained multiple quotes in a dozen cities from the websites of five major auto insurance companies. Quotes were based on identical criteria except for one variable—the number of miles driven annually, which ranged from 2,500 to 22,500.

Results: Outside of California, where state law requires all insurers to heavily weigh mileage in setting premiums, quotes from Progressive and Farmers typically did not vary at all based on miles driven, while very-low-mileage discounts from other insurers averaged 6%, or $102. Geico's discount averaged 8%… Allstate's, 11%…and State Farm's, 13%. Some insurers say that they don't use mileage driven as a factor because drivers often provide incorrect estimates. Because of the California State requirement, very-low-mileage drivers in Los Angeles saw an average discount of 30%, or $346, across all insurers.

What to do: If you currently drive very little or expect a major drop-off, possibly because of a change in jobs or retirement, ask your insurer whether it will offer you a significant discount. If it won't, shop around to see whether your low mileage helps get you a better deal elsewhere.

INTERESTING FINDING…

Drowsy Driver Alert

Drivers who shave as little as one to two hours off their recommended sleep times are nearly twice as likely to have accidents.

University of Surrey.

Best Auto Insurers

The best auto insurers in each US region based on customer-satisfaction scores on a 1,000-point scale...

- **Southeast**—Farm Bureau Insurance, Tennessee, scoring 888.
- **New York**—New York Central Mutual, 869.
- **Central**—Shelter, 858.
- **Texas**—Texas Farm Bureau, 857.
- **North Central**—Westfield, 855.
- **New England**—Amica Mutual, 852.
- **Mid-Atlantic**—Erie Insurance, 852.
- **Northwest**—PEMCO Insurance, 850.
- **California**—Esurance, 847.
- **Florida**—Allstate, 847.
- **Southwest**—The Hartford, 832.

J.D. Power 2019 US Auto Insurance Study.

Safer Driving for Elderly Parents

Don't wait until after an accident to talk about safe driving with elderly parents and relatives. About 83% of older drivers never speak to a doctor or family member about their driving ability, so the issue does not come up until there is an accident or other problem.

To make the discussion productive, focus on safety rather than age or ability, and use "I" statements instead of "you" statements—"I am concerned about your safety when you drive," rather than, "You are no longer driving safely." That keeps the talk nonthreatening and prevents it from sounding as if they are about to lose their freedom. Be sure to research, plan for and discuss alternatives to car use so that your relative knows he/she will not be isolated when the time comes to stop driving.

Recommendations from AAA Foundation for Traffic Safety, reported in *USA Today.*

Where to Get Home Insurance Discounts

Groups to join for price breaks on home insurance...

- **AAA**—check the website for your region to find out about offers.
- **AARP**—it offers a program in association with The Hartford.
- **Wholesale clubs**—Costco has a partnership with Ameriprise in most states, and BJ's has one with Geico.
- **Other types of organizations,** including alumni associations, professional groups and unions, may have arrangements with specific insurers.

Always shop around to make sure that you are getting the lowest rate available.

Roundup of experts on home-insurance discounts, reported at MoneyTalksNews.com.

College Tuition Insurance

College tuition reimbursement insurance protects you from total loss if your child is unable to finish a semester due to mental or physical health problems. Without the insurance, many colleges don't provide refunds after the first six weeks of a semester.

About 200 schools now offer the policies through insurers that typically charge about 1% of tuition, fees and room and board...and reimburse 75% to 100% of those costs. You also can get a policy directly from an insurer, such as Allianz Tuition Insurance.

Katharine Ruby, a finance expert at College Coach LLC, a college admissions and finance consulting firm headquartered in Watertown, Massachusetts. GetInto College.com

9

Tax Talk

Avoid These Red Flags That Can Cause Audits

ome red flags that trigger IRS audits may not be ones that you can, or want to, avoid—for instance, making a lot of money. The odds of an audit increase as your income goes up. IRS statistics for 2017 (latest data available) show that individuals with incomes between $200,000 and $1,000,000 and no Schedule C had an audit rate about double that for all other taxpayers. But there are ways to deal with many of the red flags—in part by taking a little extra care in preparing tax returns and being aware of the proper filing requirements, which are pretty clear in the instructions for each reporting form. For instance, if there is a Schedule C, which is used to report income or losses from a business that you operated or a profession that you practiced as a sole proprietor, the odds double again that you will face an audit, but there are ways to reduce those odds.

Here are potential red flags and ways you could deal with them...

1. Being self-employed. If you are self-employed, you cannot avoid having expenses that are red flags, but disclosing those expenses on your Schedule C and answering all the related questions can reduce the questions the IRS might have. An example of what to do is to show that for items whose allowable amounts are limited, such as certain entertainment costs or business gifts, you are deducting the right amount. Where the form asks questions—such as what is your inventory method, basis of accounting or home usage for business purposes—you must respond.

Edward Mendlowitz, CPA, partner, WithumSmith+Brown in East Brunswick, New Jersey, Withum.com. Mendlowitz is admitted to practice before the US Tax Court, is author of 25 books and hundreds of articles for business and professional journals and writes "The Pay-Less Tax Man" blog at BottomLineInc.com...with Peter Weitsen, CPA, partner, WithumSmith+Brown.

2. Taking deductions for large charitable contributions and not filing Form 8283. There are strict rules for charitable deductions requiring disclosure for noncash amounts over $500 and over $5,000 (which also has appraisal requirements). Overlooking these will cause an inquiry. Further, very large deductible amounts in relation to your gross income, including low interest and dividends and high mortgage interest, will pique an agent's interest. Many times the relative amounts do not seem logical. Provide an explanation of what may seem like illogical amounts.

3. Deductions for rental losses. These always raise an alarm. They are limited in amount for a given year but can be carried forward. Make sure the Schedule E reporting rental income is fully and properly completed. Form 8582 (Passive Activity Loss Limitation) might also be required to be filed, and this also raises the audit potential.

4. Alimony deductions. This requires the Social Security number of the recipient, so do not omit this. If you have multiple former spouses receiving alimony, attach a schedule with the required names, Social Security numbers and amounts. Receiving alimony and neglecting to report it will generate a notice and possibly an audit.

Note: Under the new tax laws, for written divorce and separation agreements executed after December 31, 2018, alimony will no longer be deductible by the payer or be deemed income to the recipient.

5. Writing off a hobby loss. This raises the issue of whether the transaction was engaged in for a profit or is just a hobby and therefore should not be deductible. You may not be able to stop an IRS notice about this, but you can prevail with the proper records and proof of your business intent, such as advertisements, sales and recognition within the industry.

6. Deducting business meals, travel and entertainment. These deductions are no longer allowed in many instances. Where they are not, make sure you identify the clearly deductible purpose when listing these expenses. Instead of showing one amount on the line provided on the form, write in the item with a brief description in the miscellaneous section where items are listed for which there are no lines on the form.

7. Failing to report a foreign bank account. This disclosure is a big deal. Failing to check the yes/no box on the bottom of Schedule B is a cause for an inquiry or an audit. Further, if you have income from the foreign account, make sure you report it on Schedule B even if no Form 1099 was provided to you from the payer. And if required, file the properly prepared disclosure form.

8. Claiming 100% business use of a vehicle. Unless the auto sits in a garage or in front of the place of business and is solely used for business purposes, it is not possible to have the auto used 100% for business. Be smart and allocate between the actual business and personal portions.

9. Incorrectly reporting the health premium tax credit. These are confusing and not always handled properly. Read the instructions, and carefully report the credit properly.

10. Taking an early payout from an IRA or 401(k) account. Early distributions need to be reported and, if applicable, you need to self-report the early distribution penalty. This is done on IRS Form 5329. If you believe the penalty should not be assessed, include an explanation of the reason. Further, if you receive a distribution that is rolled over and is tax-

SCAM ALERT...

Tax Refund Scam Can Outwit IRS Safeguards

In the latest tax refund scam, a scammer files a return in someone else's name, with a refund due. After the IRS sends the taxpayer the refund, the scammer calls that person, claims to work for the IRS, says an inaccurate refund was sent and asks that person to "return" the money—but it goes to the scammer. It can take months to clear this up with the IRS. The IRS will never call about returning money.

If you receive such a call, contact the IRS (800-829-1040).

Steven J.J. Weisman, Esq., founder, scam-information website Scamicide.com.

free, make sure you report this properly on the right line of your Form 1040.

11. Claiming day-trading losses improperly on Schedule C. Day trading is a type of "business" that is eligible for special tax treatment if a mark-to-market election is made under IRC Section 475. This permits reporting capital losses as ordinary losses, disregarding wash sales and deducting as business expenses margin interest and trading costs on Schedule C, while the trading transactions would be reported on Form 4797 as ordinary income or loss. Note that this election converts capital gains into ordinary income. None of this income is considered as earned income, so it is not eligible for retirement account deductions or self-employed medical expense deductions. Without the election, the trades are considered capital transactions, with losses limited and expenses treated as investment costs that are no longer deductible on Schedule A. Not treating the transactions properly will likely generate a notice from the IRS and possibly result in an audit.

12. Operating a marijuana business. Federal statute bars tax deductions for sellers of controlled substances that are illegal under federal law, such as marijuana. The only deductions permitted are for the cost of the product. Rent, sales and other operating costs are not permitted to be deducted. Those in this business need to know the full tax treatment when reporting their operations. Again, not doing it properly can result in a notice from the IRS.

13. Failing to report gambling winnings or claiming big gambling losses. Winnings over $600 and up to $5,000 may generate a Form 1099G, depending on the nature of the activity. You need to be familiar with the rules, which can be found on the instructions for Form 1099G. Failure to receive the 1099G does not negate the need to report the proper amount of winnings. Also, losses are deductible against the winnings, but not in excess of the winnings, nor are any expenses deductible unless you are in the business of gambling (not covered here). Omitting any income or not reporting the losses properly can result in an audit.

14. Engaging in currency transactions. Cash received in a commercial transaction of over $10,000 must be reported on Form 8300. Omitting this can cause an audit and create serious consequences.

15. Claiming the foreign earned income exclusion. If you lived and worked abroad, you may qualify for an earned income exclusion. This must be reported on Form 2555 and included with your individual tax return. This is something the IRS usually looks at, so it must be properly claimed and reported.

There are other areas where the IRS sends a notice or a bill indicating an adjustment to your return. These are not audits, and the additional tax can be accepted and the bill paid or questioned by writing promptly with your explanation or by providing the correct or corrected information. These notices head off many audits and are working quite effectively for the IRS. But, if you disagree, promptly responding is important. These notices also correct math errors, question incorrect Social Security numbers and add items to your return that you did not report but for which the IRS has a Form 1099, K-1 or other income reporting document that had been filed with them by the payer.

Dealing with Tax Return Filing Extensions, Delinquent Returns and Amended Returns

Edward Mendlowitz, CPA, partner, WithumSmith+ Brown in East Brunswick, New Jersey, Withum.com. Mendlowitz is admitted to practice before the US Tax Court, is author of 25 books and hundreds of articles for business and professional journals and writes "The Pay-Less Tax Man" blog at BottomLineInc.com...with Peter Weitsen, CPA, partner, WithumSmith+Brown.

Tax-compliance issues may be raised by extensions for filing income tax returns, delinquent filing of returns or amended returns. To taxpayers, these usually cause special concern about the risk for being singled out for an audit, but as far as the IRS is concerned, these are handled routinely. *However, here are some things to be aware of…*

INCOME TAX FILING EXTENSIONS

If you won't be able to file your return on time, you must use Form 4868 to request an extension by the tax return due date. However, you cannot extend the payment, so if you believe you will owe tax, you must pay it by the due date. If you miss the due date for the payment, then pay it as soon afterward as you can to minimize the interest and penalties.

The extension will give you six additional months to file, and the form, which is relatively easy to complete, can be e-filed. Many tax programs include this with their software. If you do not file for an extension and submit your return late, there will be a penalty of 5% per month up to 25% based on the balance owed. If you will be getting a refund, there will be no penalty. Filing for an extension will not trigger an audit. However, if you file late without an extension and are audited and then you owe tax, the late-filing penalty will be assessed on that entire balance due.

There are various reasons that taxpayers may not be able to complete a return on time. These include not yet receiving some Schedule K-1s from so-called pass-through entities or 1099s from various sources of income… charitable contribution confirmation letters… certified appraisals for property contributions over $5,000…data you need from a spouse you are divorcing…or other documents with information that you need to report on your tax return.

Other reasons…

• **You are involved in pending litigation or a tax audit.** Reporting certain transactions might prejudice your position, or you might be awaiting a resolution that could affect an item on this year's return.

• **A medical emergency precluded you from assembling your information or searching for a tax basis** for securities or other assets that have been sold.

• **A tax preparer was unable to devote the necessary time to get the return ready to file on time** or faced a complicated situation that required more time to analyze.

• **Some people with self-employed businesses might want to delay opening and/or funding a SEP pension plan** or delay making the payments to a 401(k) or SIMPLE plan they had already established.

Some people that did not file a prior year's return feel that filing this year's return before the return for the prior year would draw extra IRS attention. However, irrespective of what you did not file, you should file this year's return by the due date or extended due date.

Also, do not forget to file for state and local extensions if applicable, and pay the tax you anticipate owing. Note that some states might disallow the extension if you did not pay at least 90% of the tax due by the due date.

DELINQUENT RETURNS

Chances are that if you missed filing a return recently, the IRS hasn't yet notified you. It could take a few years, but at some point you likely will be sent a delinquency filing notice unless no record exists anywhere of you receiving any sort of income. When you get that notice, it would be helpful for you to send in your return immediately. If you cannot do this, get it prepared as quickly as you can and file it.

If you owe money, there will be penalties. If you are due a refund, it will be sent routinely about two months after you file. No interest will be paid on any refunds due you. Be aware that refunds will not be paid on returns filed more than three years late. So, if there was excess tax withholding and/or estimated payments, you will forfeit the refund of these amounts. However, there will be no late-filing penalties.

If you have a complicated financial situation and if you contact a professional tax preparer before the IRS contacts you, you have a very good chance that the IRS will not go any further than assessing late-filing penalties. I know from dealing with many clients that have not filed for multiple years that any show of a good-faith attempt to rectify the situation likely will not have the IRS going further to initiate criminal actions.

An easy way to become compliant is to have a return prepared using whatever information you have and to use estimated amounts for what you don't have. You should state somewhere on the return, "Taxpayer did not have all of the necessary information but made good-faith reasonable estimates to report correct amounts." You can also contact the IRS requesting copies of all income statements for you that have been filed with the IRS. Use those when you prepare your return.

Alternatively, the IRS sometimes prepares a "substitute" tax return based on information it received from sources such as your employer(s) and investment firms. The resulting tax may be higher than if you had filed a return because it would not include itemized deductions or exemptions. If so, you should file your own return and pay the lower tax you calculate.

AMENDED RETURNS

Occasionally, mistakes occur on a return that you filed and you want to correct them. It is really quite easy. You just file an amended return using Form 1040X. On that form you indicate the change, explain it if necessary, recalculate your tax and either mail a check or request a refund. You also can calculate the interest and penalty...or wait for the IRS to bill you. If you have a complicated change and are requesting a refund, be sure to attach the documentation.

Amended returns cannot be filed before the due date or more than three years after the later of the date when you filed or the original due date including extensions. If you noticed the error after you filed but before the due date, you can wait until after the due date to file an amended return or can immediately file a "superseding return."

It may not make sense to file an amended return just because you discover an arithmetic error or you omitted information provided on a 1099 sent to the IRS. The IRS computers will make the corrections and will send a bill for any balance due or the extra refund you

are entitled to get. Interest and penalties will be assessed on balances due. However, if the omission is quite large and you want to keep the interest and penalty as low as possible, then file as quickly as you can.

Unless the refund would be extremely large, the filing of an amended return would not increase the chances of an audit.

All forms mentioned here can be downloaded at IRS.gov.

Lessons from Taxpayer Victories and Defeats

Edward Mendlowitz, CPA, partner, WithumSmith+ Brown in East Brunswick, New Jersey, Withum.com. Mendlowitz is admitted to practice before the US Tax Court, is author of 25 books and hundreds of articles for business and professional journals and writes "The Pay-Less Tax Man" blog at BottomLineInc.com.

Taxpayers were already frustrated with the old rules. And now with the new tax law, they must learn to deal with a slew of additional rules that may befuddle them and accidentally get them into trouble, often in ways that result in IRS penalties or extra payments. But smart taxpayers can save money by learning lessons from past challenges to IRS rulings—whether those challenges resulted in taxpayer victories, defeats or mixed outcomes.

Here are some notable cases from recent years that went to the US Tax Court and the lessons they provide on how to avoid tax problems while saving money in the future...

FILE AND FILE AGAIN

When arguing cases with the IRS, it's important to refile all pertinent financial information and documents at every step of the process. After losing their home in foreclosure and facing serious medical expenses, a retired couple stopped paying taxes, which eventually totaled $60,000. They claimed hardship and offered to settle. But when it came time to review their case, the IRS officer did not have access to papers the pair had already submitted at the outset of the case, and they were turned down.

The facts: The IRS issued a notice to James and Tina Loveland that it intended to seize their assets because of unpaid taxes. The Lovelands provided all of the financial information requested by the agency and proposed a compromise settlement, but the IRS officer rejected the offer. Then, instead of asking for an appeals hearing, the Lovelands offered to negotiate a multiyear installment plan to satisfy the IRS, but that effort failed, too. The IRS then filed a tax lien against the Lovelands' property. At that point, the couple asked for a hearing and requested that the IRS reconsider its rejection of their most recent offer.

Critically, never along the way did the Lovelands resubmit the financial information that they had submitted when they had originally proposed a settlement.

IRS Position: The agency refused to review the Lovelands' second offer because the couple had previously decided not to appeal.

In addition, the IRS declined to consider their proposed installment agreement or their claim of economic hardship because the Lovelands had not resubmitted the necessary financial information along with the proposal.

Tax Court Ruling: Although they chose not to appeal, the Lovelands had not in fact engaged in a hearing or an administrative proceeding in a meaningful way, so the IRS had no right to deny their offer for a compromise on that count.

Moreover, the court ruled that the IRS had abused its discretion by declining to consider the compromise offer, the proposed installment plan and the claim of economic hardship. It remanded the case to an appeals office for consideration "consistent" with its opinion. The case is pending, but because it has been sent to an appeals office with implicit criticism of the IRS ruling, the Lovelands are undeclared victors—at least so far.

Lesson: Despite the apparent victory, the couple should have submitted full and complete information the second time, depriving the agency of an excuse to rule against them for lack of proper paperwork.

Loveland and Loveland v. Commissioner, 151 Tax Court No. 7 (2018)

ACT IN GOOD FAITH

Changes in tax laws have muddled the rules surrounding many real estate transactions and deductions, largely as a result of the 2008–2009 financial crisis. Relying on tax software is not a fail-proof fallback in complicated real estate situations, as one California couple found. The court took that into consideration when dismissing some penalties—a taxpayer victory.

The facts: Karl and Christina Simonsen bought their Northern California townhouse in 2005 for nearly $695,000 with the help of a mortgage. Five years later, under financial stress, they moved out to convert it into a rental property. Subsequently, the couple sold the property to a third party for less than the outstanding balance on the mortgage. In such a "short sale," the bank takes the proceeds, agrees to forgive the debt on the property and frees the seller from future payment obligations.

The Simonsens, relying in part on popular but possibly outdated tax software, said that the short sale and the bank's subsequent debt forgiveness were separate transactions. First, they reported the steep loss on the sale as a deduction. Second, they excluded from their calculations the money they received from the sale under a 2007 law addressing cancellation of debt income. Such income, used to pay off part of the mortgage, was not taxable, the Simonsens reasoned.

IRS Position: The short sale and debt cancellation were one transaction. So there was no loss and no cancellation of debt income to exclude from their tax bill. Accordingly, the Simonsens were liable for nearly $70,000 in income tax on the debt cancellation based on what they would have owed if they hadn't deducted a loss on the sale and accounting for the income they received on the sale. In addition, they faced a penalty of nearly $14,000.

Tax Court Ruling: The short sale and debt cancellation were in fact one transaction—the latter was dependent on the former. And the cancellation of debt income was not excludable. In short, the court agreed with the IRS position that there was neither a gain nor a loss on the sale of the property for tax purposes, and they owed the $70,000.

However, the court also ruled that the Simonsens were not liable for a $14,000 penalty. That was in part because they had acted with reasonable cause and in good faith—especially given the murkiness of the rules and the confusion generated by the tax software.

Lesson: First and foremost, taxpayers should be alert to the tax consequences of short sales and foreclosures. In particular, changes made in the run-up to and after the 2008–2009 financial crisis can trip up any number of calculations, including the cancellation of debt income. Also be aware that information from tax software may not be definitive, especially if you are not using updated online versions.

Opportunity: Penalties do stand a decent chance of being dismissed, especially if petitioners can show that they are acting in good faith.

Simonsen and Simonsen v. Commissioner, 150 Tax Court No. 8 (2018)

HEALTH-CARE CONFUSION

With ongoing changes in health-care insurance, one of the easiest ways to run afoul of IRS regulations is by tripping over Affordable Care Act (ACA) rules. One key point—and this applies to all kinds of tax-related cases—is that even if you lose on the main argument, there's a decent chance that the court will throw out often-steep additional penalties that the IRS frequently seeks. And that's definitely a taxpayer victory.

The facts: In 2014, Californians Steven and Robin McGuire received a $7,092 health-care insurance tax credit under the ACA, based on their combined income level. Robin was not working when they got the credit but soon started a job that raised their combined income, making them ineligible for the credit. The pair quickly alerted the California health-care insurance exchange, which for unknown reasons never responded.

The McGuires made multiple attempts to notify and otherwise engage with the exchange. However, with no response, they did not switch to what they later argued would have been a much lower-cost policy than the one that was being subsidized. Critically, the couple made no mention of that $7,092 subsidy on their tax return.

IRS Position: The IRS demanded that the McGuires repay the $7,092 credit in full, even though the state exchange had failed to respond to the couple's inquiries. Moreover, the IRS levied an "accuracy-related penalty"—generally 20% of the underpayment, or an estimated $1,418 in this case—because they didn't report the credit on their return.

Tax Court Ruling: The court ruled mostly in favor of the IRS, acknowledging that despite the California exchange's lack of response, the court was not meant to address issues of fairness and forced the McGuires to pay back the $7,092 credit in full.

However, the tax court—without explaining precisely why—ruled against the accuracy-related penalty that the IRS sought. So the McGuires were off the hook for that amount.

Lesson: Navigating the tax consequences of the ACA is tricky, and the bureaucracies running the system may not be efficient. Lack of response does not negate a consumer's obligation to communicate change of status. Nor will bureaucratic glitches prevent you from facing hefty payments if things go awry.

However, appealing IRS rulings in such complicated cases may result in the elimination of what often are substantial and onerous penalties.

McGuire and McGuire v. Commissioner, 149 T.C. No. 9 (2017)

Don't Be Ruled by Taxes

Vinay Nair, PhD, visiting financial economics professor, The Wharton School, University of Pennsylvania, Philadelphia, and founder of 55ip, a financial technology company that helps money managers, reported by Harry Berkowitz, personal finance editor, *Bottom Line Personal*, BottomLineInc.com.

Some of my biggest regrets as an investor have involved bad decisions I made when I was trying to minimize my taxes.

In early 2018, for example, I considered selling some of my stock funds because the funds, and the overall market, had become so pricey. However, I held off because I was afraid that realizing my long-term profits would result in a big capital gains tax bite. The market took a dive later in the year, making me regret my tax-focused hesitation.

Overall lesson: "You should judge investments mainly on their current valuations and potential," says Vinay Nair, PhD, visiting financial economics professor at The Wharton School at University of Pennsylvania and founder of 55ip, a financial technology company that helps money managers. "If you're paying taxes, it means you are making profits, which is the point of investing."

To be honest, I already knew that—but I dislike taxes so much that I let my emotions get the best of me. *So here's what I am going to will myself to do from now on…*

• **Don't assume the tax bite is bigger than it really is.** For tax year 2019, the most you will pay on capital gains from investments held more than one year is 15% or 20% (depending on your income)…and if your income is $78,750 or less ($39,375 or less for single filers), you'll pay zero.

• **Don't delay.** Don't wait until December to decide on whether and how to adjust your investments. If you do wait, you may miss out on opportunities. That may include an opportunity to rebalance your portfolio before the markets rebalance it for you—in a negative way.

able income is up to $39,375 for single filers or up to $78,750 for couples filing jointly. If your income exceeds those amounts, you still can take advantage, but you'll pay a higher tax rate of 15% or 20% on the overage.

Important: Any gains that you realize will be included in your gross income for the year. So if your goal is to maximize use of the 0% long-term gains tax rate, you want to cash out just enough of your investments in a given year to still qualify for it.

Example: A retired married couple receives $45,000 in part-time earnings, $5,000 in interest and $20,000 in pension payments for 2019—a total of $70,000. After taking the standard deduction of $24,400, their taxable income is $45,600. They could realize long-term capital gains of up to $33,150 and qualify for the 0% rate on those gains.

What if you want to continue to hold a particular appreciated stock but take advantage of the 0% rate? You can sell shares to lock in your profits (which results in a realized capital gain on those shares) and then immediately buy back shares in that stock. The IRS "wash rule," which requires you to wait 30 days to repurchase a security on which you are taking a tax deduction, applies only to investments that you sell at a loss, not at a gain.

Pay 0% Cap-Gains Tax

Jean Fullerton, CFP, principal at Milestone Financial Planning, which oversees $146 million in assets, Bedford, New Hampshire. MilestoneFinancialPlanning.com

The record-long bull market has given many investors big gains. But that comes with the potential for whopping capital-gains taxes when they sell stocks or funds. Fortunately, because of a higher standard deduction in the new federal tax law, it is easier for many Americans to pay no long-term capital-gains tax at all.

For 2019, you qualify for the 0% rate on all of your long-term capital gains if your tax-

Property-Tax Loophole for Older Americans

Abigail Walters, a researcher at the Center for Retirement Research at Boston College, Chestnut Hill, lead staffer for the Governor's Council to Address Aging in Massachusetts and one of the coauthors of a recent paper about property-tax deferrals. CRR.bc.edu

Many people can't resist a program that lets them defer payment of property taxes. And it might be a great deal that preserves money for other spending needs. But there's a catch.

Two dozen states let some seniors defer the payments until they sell their homes or die. Property-tax deferments have particular appeal now because under the new federal tax law that took effect in 2018, fewer people

HELPFUL INFO...

Are Bank Rewards Taxable?

Bank rewards are taxable if you do not have to spend anything to earn them. *Example:* If you get a $200 reward for opening an account and arranging direct deposit, the reward is taxable—you will receive a form 1099-INT from the bank and must report the amount when doing your taxes. But credit card and travel rewards, including ones earned by using bank-issued cards, are not taxable—even if they can be redeemed for cash back. The reason is that you have to spend money to receive the rewards, which are considered a nontaxable rebate on your purchase.

Caution: There are some gray areas. If you get a credit card bonus just for signing up, without any purchase required, it is taxable. And if you get airline miles directly from a bank, perhaps for opening a new account, their value, as determined by the bank, is taxable, since you did not have to make a purchase to receive them.

WiseBread.com

will see any advantage in deducting property-tax payments. But the deferments are rarely free—interest is almost always charged, meaning that when you eventually sell or die, you (or your estate) very likely will have to pay more than the total of the deferred taxes.

The states that offer property-tax deferrals are Arizona, California, Colorado, Florida, Georgia, Idaho, Illinois, Maine, Maryland, Massachusetts, Michigan, Minnesota, New Hampshire, North Carolina, Oregon, Rhode Island, South Dakota, Tennessee, Texas, Utah, Virginia, Washington, Wisconsin and Wyoming.

Note: In some states, the program is not offered in every municipality in the state. While these programs tend to be created by states, property taxes are paid to municipalities, so many states offer those particular municipalities the right to modify programs or not participate at all.

Rules and terms vary from state to state and even from town to town, but typically the of-fers are available to home owners who are at least 62 to 70 years old...and who have household incomes below a cap that often is set between $20,000 and $60,000. In a small number of states, including Colorado and New Hampshire, there are no income caps in some or all municipalities...or the caps are set at higher levels in certain municipalities such as the $75,000 cap in Howard County, Maryland.

Usually deferrals are available only on primary residences, and often the home owner must have lived there for at least five years. Additional restrictions might apply. Property-tax deferrals are flexible—home owners can choose each year whether to defer.

If a property-tax deferral is available to you, is it something you should take advantage of? As with many financial opportunities, it depends. *What you should do...*

• **Contact your municipality's assessor's office to confirm whether there's a program in your area** and to see whether you qualify for it.

• **If you choose to defer, ask what interest rate is imposed on property-tax deferments.** This varies from 0% in Marshfield, Massachusetts, to 8% per year in Texas. (When interest rates are set statewide, and not by municipality, they almost always are between 5% and 8%—but in South Dakota, the rate is a more attractive 4%.) The rates usually are fixed, but it is worth confirming this before signing up.

• **If the interest rate is higher than the rates available to you on a home-equity loan, deferring your property tax might not be a great idea for you.** You likely would be better off paying your taxes and taking out a home-equity loan instead—as long as you can afford to pay back the loan according to its terms. With tax-deferral programs, the bill comes due when you sell the home or die. If a couple owns the home, you typically can delay paying until the second person dies. But monthly repayments on home-equity loans typically begin immediately.

Tax Help for First-Time Home Buyers

Tax advantages for first-time home buyers are being offered in several states. The accounts give would-be home owners a boost in saving for a down payment. Account details vary, and the list of states offering the accounts has been changing as more legislatures consider them.

Montana offered one of these accounts as early as 1998...accounts also are available in Iowa, Mississippi, Colorado and Minnesota... and Oregon and Alabama recently started them. Some states also make the accounts available to people who are reentering the home-purchase market after not owning for a number of years.

Details and qualifications vary widely—consult a real estate professional or accountant for details.

Roundup of experts on tax-advantaged home-buying accounts, reported at CNBC.com.

Commuting Tax Benefits Lost

The Tax Cuts and Jobs Act eliminates companies' right to deduct transportation costs from their taxes, so many firms will no longer offer the benefits unless they do so as part of an employee's taxable wages instead of as tax-free fringe benefits. Some companies may offer a salary-reduction arrangement that lets you put aside up to $265/month (the 2019 limit under the law) to pay for mass transit and/or another $265 per month for parking (in pretax dollars). Also, companies that want to hire you still may pay your moving expenses—but now must treat the added expense as part of your taxable salary at the new job. Ask if the firm will "gross up" moving expenses to cover the additional tax you will owe on them—some firms will.

Roundup of tax experts, reported at MarketWatch.com.

10

Investment Insight

5 Simple Ways to Reduce Your Stock Risk but Stay in the Market

The robust US economy has convinced many investors that they can keep riding the 10-year bull market in stocks even higher. But overconfidence—or neglect—could be dangerous, possibly leaving you vulnerable to losing years of accumulated gains. That's because there are plenty of factors that could trigger a recession and bear market by late 2019 or 2020, including deepening foreign economic weakness and continuing trade disputes.

That doesn't mean it's wise to try to "time the market" by dumping stocks entirely. Instead, many advisers say, it's a good time to reduce risk by scaling back the stock portion of your portfolio to more moderate levels. But how do you accomplish that?

Answer: Baby steps.

Adopt simple strategies that ease your portfolio back to a mix of stocks, bonds and cash that you feel comfortable holding even in rough times. *Important:* If you haven't established long-term target allocations for different types of assets, a reasonable starting point is 60% stocks and 40% bonds and cash. (The amount of cash will depend on your risk tolerance and your possible need to draw on your portfolio for income, perhaps in an emergency.) Your optimal mix may be more conservative or aggressive depending on how long it will be before you need the money, your income needs and risk tolerance.

To help you, we spoke with five leading financial advisers about the strategies they use to reduce their clients' stock exposure so that they'll be better protected when bad times do roll around…

Peter Lazaroff, CFA, CFP

Stop making new purchases of stocks (including stock funds). If you regularly contribute to your portfolio and your current asset mix isn't very far out of balance, you can bring it in line by simply redirecting new money. Instead of buying more stocks, put the money into bonds—preferably in the form of a relatively short-term, investment-grade bond fund that is not badly hurt by rising interest rates—or leave it in cash. You also can stop automatic reinvestment of dividends thrown off by stocks you own. This incremental strategy is particularly useful for taxable accounts in which selling stocks too aggressively could generate big capital gains taxes.

Peter Lazaroff, CFA, CFP, co-chief investment officer at Plancorp, an investment-advisory firm that manages $4 billion, St. Louis. PeterLazaroff.com

Scott B. Tiras, CPA, CFP

Dollar-cost average away from stocks. Many people are used to "dollar-cost averaging" their way into stocks—that is, adding to a position with a fixed amount of money every month so that they are buying more shares when prices are low and buying fewer shares when prices are high. Over time, this can result in a lower average buying price—a good thing. But when you are already too heavily invested in stocks, you can choose to do the reverse—sell a fixed value of the stocks each month. That way you are still taking advantage of the market's remaining gains and possibly locking in more and more of your profits—but reducing your exposure in case the market starts retreating. This is a more aggressive approach than the one above, and you can choose to mix the two approaches to achieve your target allocations more quickly.

What to do: Determine the dollar amount of stock that you need to sell to reduce your stock holdings back to your long-term target allocations. Divide the amount by 12. Over the following year, each month on a given day, sell that dollar value of stock regardless of market conditions.

Caveat: If selling from a taxable account, you might generate taxable capital gains, so take this into account and weigh it against the value of reducing your portfolio's risk.

Scott B. Tiras, CPA, CFP, president of Tiras Wealth Management, a financial-advisory practice with $2.2 billion in assets under management, Houston. TirasWealth.com

Mark Germain, CFP

Sell your "highest-risk" assets first. This approach is for investors who have built up a relatively aggressive portfolio but who want to reduce risk now. Paring back your riskiest stocks leads to a stronger emphasis on stocks of high-quality companies with strong balance sheets. These tend to be less damaged by a market downturn.

Three criteria to identify the "highest-risk" assets in your portfolio...

•Pinpoint your most overvalued stocks. Look at the current price-to-earnings ratio (P/E) of all your stocks compared with their long-term historical P/Es, which you can find at Morningstar.com, and jettison those that are most out of whack.

•Determine which stocks are in historically volatile sectors, such as biotech and small-cap growth stocks.

•Zero in on speculative investments that no longer fit into your long-term plan...or that just keep you up at night, such as the social-networking service Twitter or electric-car maker Tesla.

Mark Germain, CFP, founder and CEO of Beacon Wealth Management, a financial advisory firm with more than $250 million in assets under management, Hackensack, New Jersey. BeaconWealthManagement.com

Jonathan D. Pond

Once you reach your target asset allocation, rebalance your portfolio using the method that institutional investors use. Various financial institutions and pension funds typically use "thresholds" as signals of when to rebalance rather than limiting the practice to once a year. A typical threshold is whenever assets in a given class move away from their target allocations by five percentage points or more. Threshold rebalancing requires more portfolio oversight and can increase your trading costs and capital gains taxes, but it has two advantages. In rising stock markets, it locks in and protects your profits. In falling markets, it forces you to accumulate more shares of stocks at lower prices so that you don't have to guess when a bear market has bottomed to get back in.

Jonathan D. Pond, president of Jonathan D. Pond, LLC, an investment-advisory firm with $280 million in assets under management, Newton, Massachusetts. JonathanPond.com

Rick Miller, PhD, CFP

Play with "house money." Investors often become so enamored of a particular stock that they have a hard time trimming back that holding even if the stock seems grossly overvalued and at risk for big losses. This can be problematic because even if you reduce the overall stock exposure in your portfolio, you're still courting outsized risk with this holding. *Wise solution*: Sell enough shares in this stock to generate the amount of cash that you originally invested in the stock. That way, even if the stock plunges, you can't end up losing more than you invested, and you could achieve further gains with the money still invested. For example, say you invested $10,000 in Amazon three years ago. Your shares are worth about $24,000 today. You take out the original principal ($10,000) but keep the rest ($14,000) invested.

Rick Miller, PhD, CFP, CEO of Sensible Financial, a financial-planning and investment-advisory firm with more than $450 million under management, Waltham, Massachusetts. SensibleFinancial.com

---

Don't Let Fear Drive You Away from Stock Bargains

Mark Tobak, MD, a psychiatrist in private practice in Mamaroneck, New York, and former chief of inpatient geriatric psychiatry at St. Vincent's Hospital in Harrison, New York. He is author of *Anyone Can Be Rich!: A Psychiatrist Provides the Mental Tools to Build Your Wealth*. MarkTobakMD.org

---

For more than 10 years, the stock market has mostly risen, but memories linger of when it went down, down, down. Those memories were reignited recently when the Dow Jones Industrial Average plunged more than 1,300 points, or 5.3%, over two days in October 2018, as rising interest rates and trade tensions between the US and China scared investors…and then again plunged in December of that year.

It can be hard to tell when a market pullback is just a blip…part of a healthy correction of 10% or more…or the start of a bear market that could last months or even years.

Either way, be on guard against falling into the costly traps that often are triggered by plunging asset values. *Here are two ways that human psychology fools us into making bad decisions in times of financial loss, and what we can do about it…*

•**Our brains liken investment losses to being robbed.** Money that once was ours has been taken from us (even if our investments overall have net gains). It feels like a violation, and being violated is so unpleasant that we might flee from stocks and stock mutual funds, greatly diminishing our long-term investment returns.

What to do: If feelings such as these gnaw at you when your investments decline in value, check how many shares you have of particular stocks and funds. Assuming that you haven't already sold any shares, it will be the same number that you had before the pullback hit (maybe even more, if dividends were reinvested). Use this share count to reassure your mind that in this sense, nothing has been taken from you. Instead, the market decline has temporarily affected what other people would pay you for your shares.

•**Our brains warn us to run in fear when share prices are falling.** The primitive part of the brain encourages us to flee from danger, and a tumbling market seems dangerous. But in the long run, we're better off buying than selling while share prices are depressed.

What to do: When stock prices drop and your panicky mind screams, "Sell—this is dangerous," respond with the thought that "stocks are on sale for a short time only, and I'm shopping for bargains." That doesn't mean you should load up indiscriminately, but it does mean that you should have a plan for finding bargains. Keep in mind that by April 2012, stocks overall had recovered from the bear market of 2007–2009, and since then the S&P 500 has quadrupled from its 2009 low.

If bargains don't excite you, reframe yourself in your mind as a hero who takes wounded, bleeding stocks under your care until they recover. You're less likely to be scared out of the market if you cast the stocks as the victims and yourself as the rescuer.

Invest Like a Nobel Prize–Winning Economist

Raife Giovinazzo, PhD, CFA, manager of the Fuller & Thaler Behavioral Small-Cap Equity Fund (FTHNX), which had five-year annualized returns of 9.12% vs. 5.94% for the Russell 2000 Index and ranked in the top 2% of its category. Nobel Prize winner Richard Thaler is a founder and principal of the firm. FullerThalerFunds.com

Most investors get hurt from time to time by their own big mistakes, often driven by self-defeating emotions rather than analysis. Fund manager Raife Giovinazzo, PhD, CFA, benefits by spotting investment opportunities among those mistakes made by other investors—and you can, too.

Example of how investors hurt themselves: In December 2018, when the stock market plunged, many investors panicked and sold, then failed to get back in as stocks rallied in the new year. Emotional decisions like that are why investors overall earned annualized returns of just 5.3% over the past two decades versus 7.2% for the S&P 500 stock index.

To benefit from investor mistakes, Giovinazzo puts into action the principles of his colleague—and PhD adviser—Professor Richard Thaler, who won the 2017 Nobel Prize for Economics. He is hailed as the father of behavioral finance, which applies psychological insights to explain why our brains seem hardwired to make wrong investment moves.

Here's how you can use those principles to find attractive stocks…

FAVOR RATIONAL ANALYSIS

Long-term investors are most successful when they base their decisions on hard, rational analysis rather than psychological biases such as the desire to feel good or smart or even to be entertained by financial commentators on TV. To that end, I try to inoculate myself from making irrational mistakes.

I never watch channels such as CNBC for investment ideas because the financial media's goal is to make the stock market as vivid, sexy and urgent as possible. I also avoid reading interviews or profiles with celebrity or "visionary" CEOs. Their charisma can cloud your judgment and make you fall in love with their companies. Better to let actions speak louder than words—are executives buying their own stock…and are they delivering profits?

I concentrate on small and mid-sized companies because they provide more opportunities to benefit from behavioral analysis. There is a lot less information and professional analysis of these companies versus large ones, which means that many investors tend to rely on their feelings and instincts in assessing them as investments. These investors wind up making more frequent mistakes, such as the ones described below. Instead of falling victim to these mistakes yourself, take advantage of them. I screen small- and mid-cap stocks specifically for moments when it looks like investors are acting irrationally. That's when the best buying opportunities present themselves.

The two major types of mistakes that I focus on…

• **Stocks where investors are overreacting to bad news.** *There are two psychological behaviors that kick in when bad news hits a company…*

• Loss aversion, the fear of losing money, even just on paper, which leads investors to abandon a stock at the worst possible time.

• Availability bias, the tendency to make decisions based on information and events that are most recent, most memorable, personally observed and/or traumatic, rather than considering the complete picture.

The clue that investors may be getting emotionally caught up and overreacting is a stock's share price falling at the same time that *insiders*—such as the CEO, CFO and/or other executives—are buying shares, either with their own money or on behalf of the company through stock buybacks. Such insiders typically have the best understanding of a company's inner workings and long-term prospects. They know whether a company's poor performance is not as dire as the market believes, so they aren't so likely to panic over losses. *Example:* In the second half of 2018, when many small banks suffered stock price drops, insiders at those banks swooped in to buy shares at bargain prices.

It's generally legal for corporate insiders to buy stocks as long as they notify the SEC of their trades within two business days and their purchases are not based on specific information unavailable to the general public.

Editor's note: You can find recent insider activity for specific stocks free at the investment research firm website InsiderInsights.com.

• **Stocks where investors are underreacting to good news.** If a company becomes significantly more profitable, you would think it would attract investors and its stock price would rise. But that's often not the case. One reason is what behavioral finance calls anchoring. When investors have a strong, preconceived notion about a stock and new information is introduced, they tend to be slow to change their expectations. I look for underreaction when the company announces a big quarterly earnings surprise, which means it performed much better than a consensus of Wall Street analysts tracking the company thought it would.

Most important: I use events such as insider buying and earnings surprises just as initial screens. Before I actually invest in a stock, I dig into the fundamentals of the business to make sure that its balance sheet and future prospects are strong. I like to see strong positive cash flow, especially relative to the company's debt levels…a high return on investment…and a powerful position in a market niche.

Editor's note: To gather data on fundamentals for a stock, check investment research firm website Morningstar.com.

3 Stocks for Good Times and Bad

Douglas Gerlach, editor in chief of the Investor Advisory Service newsletter and author of six books, including *The Armchair Millionaire*. Madison Heights, Michigan. InvestorAdvisoryService.com

Douglas Gerlach is well-known for his "all-weather" investing—his newsletter urges investors not to try to time the market but to keep their stock allocations fully invested even if the market or economy

is in trouble. To make that work, he aims to pick stocks that do well, relative to the market, in good times and bad. According to Mark Hulbert, a longtime tracker of investment newsletter performance, Gerlach and his team had the top-performing stock newsletter model portfolio in 2018, with a 1.7% loss versus a 6.8% loss for the broad Wilshire 5000 index. Over the past 20 years, Gerlach's portfolio has returned 12.5% annualized versus 7.8% for the index.

Gerlach's secret? Finding "high-quality" companies that exhibit *consistent annual earnings growth* (at least 15% annualized over the past five years for small companies and 7% for large companies)…*stable profit margins*…and *clear long-term advantages over competitors. Some of his favorite stocks…*

• **Dollar General (DG)** is a deep-discount retailer with 15,472 stores in 44 states. It has grown rapidly in recent years by adding new stores in small-town locations. During economic downturns, it attracts additional customers looking to save money.

• **Fiserv (FISV)** provides essential backroom services such as electronic fund transfers and payment processing for more than 12,000 banks and credit unions. The business should continue to grow steadily as consumers use new services online and through their smartphones.

• **O'Reilly Automotive (ORLY)** is an aftermarket auto-parts retailer with about 5,200 US stores. As more consumers hang on to aging vehicles, there's more demand for replacement parts.

10 Great Stocks for the 2020s

Michael Lippert, CFA, JD, manager of the Baron Opportunity Retail Fund (BIOPX), New York City. Over the past 15 years, the fund ranks in the top 11% of its category, returning an annualized 12.31% vs. 9.01% for the S&P 500 Index. BaronFunds.com

Most investors are too focused on day-to-day events that drive the market in the short term, whether it's quarterly earnings reports, political pronouncements or unemployment statistics. *Better:* Investors should also look ahead over the next several years to the kinds of growing trends that are likely to propel industries over the long term.

Here are some of the most powerful trends that could dominate the stock market in the 2020s and the 10 best stocks to take advantage of them...

TREND: **Hundreds of prestigious colleges will offer degrees entirely online.** A few dozen, including Harvard, Yale, Georgetown and UC Berkeley, already let you earn a master's degree by taking online classes. As more students who have grown up with the Internet seek less expensive alternatives to on-campus education, the undergraduate and graduate online-learning market is likely to grow about 7% annually and reach $325 billion by 2025. *Favorite stock...*

• **2U (TWOU)** has carved out a niche as the leading online software platform for higher education. The company has established online graduate degree programs for more than two dozen leading universities (including the ones listed earlier). *Recent share price*: $14.18.*

TREND: **Businesses around the world will turn personal data into gold mines.** Only recently has powerful software technology emerged that allows any business—no matter what size—to scrutinize the mountains of daily data it collects on customers. That enables the businesses to gather insights that can save them money or suggest new ways to profit. The global market for analytic software that sorts through all this raw data is growing 30% a year and will be a $40 billion market by 2023. *Favorite stocks...*

• **Splunk (SPLK)** provides more than 15,000 companies including Coca-Cola, Hyatt and Nasdaq with analytic software to spot trends, anomalies and cyber-security threats in their own data and systems. *Recent share price*: $122.72.

• **Guidewire Software (GWRE)** sells core systems, analytics and digital-marketing software and services to property and casualty

*Prices as of August 7, 2019.

insurers in 30 countries. Such a narrow focus might seem like a drawback, but Guidewire has a near monopoly on a sector of the insurance industry that needs to update its antiquated technology and that will grow steadily for decades. *Recent share price*: $95.69.

TREND: **At least two million self-driving vehicles will hit the road by the middle of the next decade, mostly with ride-hailing services.** The proliferation of these vehicles is inevitable because they will have a dramatic impact on improving safety and reducing congestion. Prototypes now are being tested by nearly 50 major automakers and technology companies. Some are likely to start selling self-driving models in 2020, and the market is expected to grow to $65 billion globally by 2027. *Favorite stock...*

• **Aquantia (AQ)** produces ultrahigh-speed semiconductor chips for the auto industry. The chips allow the thousands of bits of data from sensors, cameras and radar systems in vehicles to be continuously collected and analyzed in milliseconds to safely maneuver vehicles. Because Aquantia is a supplier to a large share of the industry, it's a less risky bet than investing in any particular car manufacturer. *Recent share price*: $13.15.

TREND: **One-third of all US corporate bonds will be traded electronically.** That will allow investors to buy and sell bonds cheaply and efficiently like stocks. Remarkably, most trading in the $40 trillion US bond market still is done over the phone. New electronic marketplaces will allow investors to trade more quickly, find the best prices and minimize transaction costs. *Favorite stock...*

• **MarketAxess Holdings (MKTX)** is the dominant bond e-trading platform in the US. It controls 85% of the daily volume of US corporate bonds that have started to trade electronically in the US, about $4.4 billion worth. *Recent share price*: $348.67.

TREND: **More than 75 billion "smart" products will send and receive data via the Internet by the end of the next decade.** That's up from about 20 billion today. Competition among smart-product manufacturers and suppliers will be fierce, making it difficult for investors to pick winners. But there is a completely overlooked area. It is focused on the needs of engineering firms and manufacturers' research divisions that create new smart products in which tiny electronic parts, mechanical systems and communication technology all must work together seamlessly. *Favorite stock…*

•**Ansys (ANSS)** is a global leader in simulation-design software, which allows engineers to test out multiple concepts when designing products, reducing the need for physical prototypes and resulting in faster, shorter development time. *Recent share price*: $201.89.

TREND: **Hundreds of new data centers will be needed to physically store, maintain and interconnect the "cloud."** These warehouses, equipped with state-of-the-art computer servers, networking gear and security, are needed to handle the ever-increasing amount of data we upload to the Internet. The global data center market is likely to grow 13% annually and reach $12 billion by 2023. *Favorite stock…*

•**Equinix (EQIX)** is one of the world's largest data-center operators, with more than 200 properties in 24 countries and nearly 10,000 clients locked into recurring contracts, including the mega cloud vendors Amazon, Google and Microsoft. *Recent share price*: $533.09.

TREND: **Scores of deadly cancers will become survivable, even manageable, with the help of sophisticated DNA analysis.** The analysis is used to screen for diseases and identify the best treatment options. The market for genome-sequencing equipment that is used to analyze the structure of DNA is likely to grow 19% a year and reach $25 billion in 2025. In addition, the market for diagnostic tests for detection of cancer and other diseases should grow 12% annually and reach $22 billion by 2024. *Favorite stocks…*

•**Guardant Health (GH)** makes "liquid biopsy" kits for hospitals and oncologists that test for dozens of types of cancer. The kits are sophisticated blood tests that detect DNA fragments shed by cancerous tumors. *Recent share price*: $109.70.

TAKE NOTE…

Weather-Related Investment Opportunities

Investment opportunities from wet weather and rising sea levels…

•**Home-improvement companies,** such as The Home Depot (HD) and Lowe's (LOW), should do well as people look for ways to protect basements and property near shorelines.

•**Water-pump manufacturers** that help people cope with flooding also may get more business—firms include Gorman-Rupp (GRC) and Roper Technologies (ROP).

•**The need to upgrade infrastructure can help some companies in the construction industry—**and also be good for **auto manufacturers** that specialize in high-margin pickup trucks, which will be increasingly in demand. That could benefit Ford (F), General Motors (GM), Toyota (TM) and Nissan (NSANY).

Barrons.com

•**Illumina (ILMN)** controls about 70% of the world market for the high-tech tools and equipment that are essential for gene sequencing. *Recent share price*: $292.87.

TREND: **Two-thirds of all money spent on advertising will be spent online.** This year, for the first time, more money will be spent on digital advertising—$129 billion—than on the total combination of television, print and radio ad spending, according to the eMarketer research firm. Online ad spending in the US is projected to represent two-thirds of all ad spending by 2023. *Favorite stock…*

•**The Trade Desk (TTD)** makes software that helps ad agencies and companies buy and optimize advertising for desktop and mobile devices. It's one of the few US technology companies that has had success bringing foreign advertising to online shoppers in China. *Recent share price*: $257.23.

4 Big Trends in Health Care and How to Profit

Jason Kritzer, CFA, and Samantha Pandolfi, comanagers of Eaton Vance Worldwide Health Sciences Fund (ETHSX), Boston. Over the past 15 years, the fund has returned 10.04% annualized vs. 9.01% for the S&P 500. EatonVance.com

One of the best ways to keep your investment portfolio healthy this year and beyond may be to focus on health care. In 2018, as the S&P 500 stock index lost 4.4%, the health-care sector gained 6.5%. And that wasn't a fluke—it's because health-care companies have unique traits that allow them to thrive late in economic expansions.

On one hand, these companies are growing strongly, thanks to demand from an aging population and the introduction of many innovative new drugs, other treatments and medical devices. On the other hand, if the economy stumbles, consumers still resist cutting way back on medical care. A recent CNBC study found that over the past three decades, when the stock market dropped more than 10% in a six-month period, the S&P 500 lost an average of 14% but health-care stocks lost an average of just 5%.

We asked health-care stock fund managers Jason Kritzer, CFA, and Samantha Pandolfi how to find the most attractive growth prospects in health care that also offer downside protection…

FOUR BIG TRENDS

We're cautiously optimistic about the health-care sector. We are emphasizing companies and industries that should remain strong in the face of various political, social and technological trends…and avoiding those that pose too much risk. For example, in 2018 we added to our drug stock holdings because valuations were compelling, but we cut our exposure to overvalued biotechnology stocks. Also, a slowdown in price increases for drugs is hurting drug distributors. And we're avoiding hospital stocks, partly because of continued uncertainty over the fate of the Affordable Care Act (Obamacare), which has provided hospitals with extra money from insured patients.

Here are four trends that are likely to propel health care in 2019 and beyond—and the stocks most likely to benefit from these trends…

1. *TREND*: Political gridlock in Washington, DC, which means little action on reducing drug prices. Pharmaceuticals have been under pressure since the 2016 presidential election, when both candidates promised to give the federal government's Medicare Part D program the authority and tools to negotiate lower prescription drug prices. But Congress, which is conducting extensive hearings on prescription-drug pricing at time of press, is unlikely to pass legislation to authorize price controls. When that becomes clear to more people, drug stocks should rally.

Stock likely to benefit: Novartis (NVS). The Swiss pharmaceutical giant has remade itself in recent years. It has been divesting its consumer health-care businesses and plans to spin off its eye-care business so that it can focus on developing blockbuster drugs—and it has the wherewithal to do so. Novartis also has completed a deal with Tilray, the high-profile Canadian marijuana company, to distribute its medical marijuana products in dozens of countries.

2. *TREND*: The prospering business of health care for animals and pets. Globally, the animal health-care market is expected to grow nearly 6% a year and reach $64 billion by 2025. Rising standards of living in emerging markets mean a wider adoption of protein-based diets, driving greater demand for livestock vaccines and supplements. In the US, consumer spending on pet health care is driven by enormous innovations in medications and other treatments. Compared with makers of drugs for humans, pet-pharmaceutical companies have a much faster route to FDA approval, and once on the market, their products are largely paid for in cash without facing insurance reimbursement issues.

Stock likely to benefit: Zoetis (ZTS). Although it's not a household name, Zoetis was a division of pharmaceutical giant Pfizer for more than 60 years until it was spun off in 2013. Since then, its stock performance has crushed the returns of the S&P 500. The company has become the largest pet-pharmaceutical firm in the world, selling more than 300 product lines ranging from livestock vaccines to new medications such as the recently launched Simparica, a chewable flea-and-tick drug for dogs. Zoetis is counting on recent acquisitions to fuel growth, including the veterinary technology firm Abaxis, which specializes in diagnostic instruments that let veterinarians analyze blood samples immediately and provide more cost-effective diagnoses and treatments.

3. *TREND*: The big expansion of Medicare. This government-sponsored health-care program is projected to grow at an annual rate of 7.4% through 2026 as more than three million baby boomers hit age 65 each year. Medicare beneficiaries typically have a choice of several plans, but enrollment for years has been dominated by for-profit insurers that offer Medicare Advantage. These government-funded private health-care plans are a popular alternative to "original Medicare" because they often offer additional perks such as reimbursements for gym memberships, coverage for dentists and eye doctors and capped out-of-pocket expenditures at reasonable costs. In addition, Medicaid, the government-sponsored health coverage for low-income Americans provided through private insurers, is expected to grow 5.8% annually through 2026.

Stock likely to benefit: UnitedHealth Group (UNH) is the largest health insurer in the US, with about 50 million members—20% more than its nearest competitor, Anthem. A big piece of the company's business is focused on Medicare Advantage and Medicaid. Analysts expect UnitedHealth earnings to grow 15% annually over the next five years, thanks in part to its highly profitable but lesser known divisions. Its OptumRx division manages pharmacy benefits for health plans and processes more than one billion prescriptions per year. Its Optum division is a leader in data-analytics consulting, analyzing patient health-care data and claims to find ways to reduce costs and improve patient treatment.

4. *TREND*: Innovations in medical equipment. Many investors assume that medical breakthroughs are focused on new drugs. But some of the most exciting and profitable areas of health care are in high-margin, patent-protected devices inserted in the body to treat disease and manage pain. The medical-device industry is getting a boost from the two-year suspension of the federal excise tax on medical devices sold domestically, which began last year. Globally, the medical-device market is expected to grow 4.5% annually from 2019 to 2023.

Stock likely to benefit: Boston Scientific (BSX) is a medical-equipment powerhouse with more than 13,000 products that offers very strong growth prospects. Its stents and balloon systems are among the best-selling devices used by doctors to deter or clear blood clots. Boston Scientific also is a major player in the field of pacemakers and has 30% of the market for equipment used to perform endoscopies. Strength in these niches and others generates strong cash flow that the company is using to acquire fast-growing businesses, mostly companies focused on interventional treatment, which involves implanting tiny devices in the body to diagnose and/or treat diseases. The company's recent acquisition deals include BTG, which makes a tiny coil inserted into the lung's airways to treat emphysema, and Vision Medical, which makes a scope that collects cells from fallopian tubes to provide early diagnosis of ovarian cancer.

Investors Gain New Protections Against Fraud

Gerri Walsh, JD, senior vice president for investor education at Finra, Washington, DC. Finra.org

Investors who are the most vulnerable to financial exploitation are getting a new layer of protection. The added protection comes in the form of two new rules created by the Financial Industry Regulatory Authority (Finra), which is authorized by Congress to oversee the brokerage industry.

Under the first rule, when a customer opens an account or updates information in an account, a brokerage must ask whether the customer wants to designate someone who is at least 18 years old as a "trusted contact" and provide contact information for that person. Of course, the decision of whether to provide this information, which is optional, will be based in part on whether the investor feels comfortable choosing someone to fill this role. (Existing customers can choose to add the information to an account even before the brokerage asks for it.)

Under the second rule, if you are 65 or older, your broker is permitted to put an initial hold of up to 15 business days on any questionable disbursements of funds or securities from your account if he/she reasonably suspects that you are being financially exploited. *Reason for the 65-or-over rule:* Seniors lose about $3 billion annually to fraud and scams, often because diminishing physical and mental abilities make them less attentive and easier targets for con artists. Once assets leave a brokerage because a customer has been conned by an outside fraudster, it's very difficult to recover them.

A 15-day hold gives the firm time to investigate the suspicion, contact you and (if necessary) your trusted contact...or even reach out to law enforcement or adult protective services. Your trusted contact could provide information about your health, your whereabouts and/or other information to help the firm decide whether there is a problem and how to deal with it. In the past, even if a broker knew how to contact, say, a customer's family members, privacy restrictions made it difficult to do so.

Avoid This Extra Fee on Funds

Pam Krueger, CEO of Wealthramp.com, an online service that matches investors with registered financial advisers, and executive producer of *MoneyTrack: Money for Life* on PBS stations.

The costs of investing through financial advisers or brokerages continue to plummet. But there's one sneaky fee that just won't disappear—and it could cost you tens of thousands of dollars in returns over your lifetime. When you invest in a mutual fund, you could be sold a share class that tacks on an extra fee in addition to the annual expense ratio. It's known as a "12b-1" fee. It can range from 0.25% to 1%, which means it could cost you as much as an extra $1,000 annually on a $100,000 investment.

Fund companies say that 12b-1 fees are charged to cover their marketing costs. But the majority of the fee goes right back to the person who sold you the fund shares as a recurring commission. That provides a powerful incentive for your adviser or broker to push you into these high-fee shares even if cheaper shares of the same fund, without the 12b-1 fee, are available.

The practice is not illegal for brokers, but investment advisers registered with the Securities and Exchange Commission are held to a higher "fiduciary" standard. They are required to put clients' interests above their own. That includes disclosing whether they will receive any revenue-sharing payments when selling you mutual fund shares and suggesting cheaper alternatives.

Self-defense: Check whether the fund shares you own or are considering buying charge 12b-1 fees. To do so, look up a fund at Morningstar.com and click on the "Purchase" tab near the top of the page. It will show the different share classes and which, if any, charge 12b-1 fees. Tell your adviser or broker that you want the cheapest share class available. More expensive share classes provide no additional rights or advantages. If you own the shares in a tax-deferred account, you can sell them and buy the cheaper share class or shares of a similar fund without 12b-1 fees. In a taxable account, you'll need to weigh the potential immediate capital-gains tax bite of selling versus the recurring costs of the 12b-1 fee if you hang onto the shares.

11

Consumer Confidential

Secrets of Getting What You Want When You Complain to Customer Service

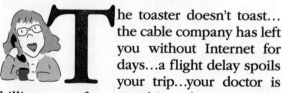

The toaster doesn't toast... the cable company has left you without Internet for days...a flight delay spoils your trip...your doctor is billing you for something that insurance should have covered.

Such things happen to consumers *frequently*. And if you dread the thought of having to deal with customer service to resolve such problems, that's exactly the feeling many companies want to inspire. I've spent my career studying how businesses handle customer complaints. If companies make it a hassle to get actual service from customer service, many consumers just let it go. That's why you're forced to interact with cumbersome au-

tomated phone systems, wait on hold again and again, and then reach employees who have little power to help you. Many banks and credit card companies have even created databases that rate how valuable a customer you are. After you enter your account number, your call is routed to either a higher-level service agent who actually might help you...or an "overflow" call center that probably won't.

Even though the cards are purposely stacked against you, there are things you can do to vastly improve the odds that you will get the resolution you deserve as a consumer. *Here are the big mistakes many consumers make when trying to get problems resolved and what to do instead...*

***MISTAKE:* Giving up quickly.** I have found that most consumers with a complaint make

Amy J. Schmitz, JD, the Elwood L. Thomas Missouri Endowed Professor of Law at University of Missouri School of Law, Columbia, where she teaches courses in consumer-dispute resolution. She is coauthor of *The New Handshake: Online Dispute Resolution and the Future of Consumer Protection.* Law.Missouri.edu/about/people/schmitz

183

only a single phone call and then give up if the problem isn't resolved—even if they are in the right and have a good case. That's because they have learned from experience that a first unsuccessful call often leads to a time-sucking series of similar frustrations.

What to do instead: Based on how important the complaint is to you and how much money is involved, decide *up front* on the amount of time and effort you are willing to put into getting the problem resolved. At least that way, you'll feel more in control of the situation because you know that your efforts won't be out of proportion to the amount of harm caused to you. *Example:* I took a flight in which both the in-flight entertainment and Wi-Fi systems weren't functioning. So I decided I would spend just a few minutes writing a brief e-mail to the airline customer service department describing the problem and asking for 10,000 frequent-flier miles. I would wait a week, follow up with a quick phone call if necessary, and then stop pursuing it no matter what the outcome. Within a few days, I received an e-mail back from the company awarding me 5,000 frequent-flier miles. It was not as much as I had asked for but worth it for a quick e-mail.

MISTAKE: **Not specifying the compensation you seek.** Many consumers are vague about what they want, either because they haven't thought it through or they don't want to ask for too much or too little. But I've found that if you wait for the company to suggest compensation, the offer likely will be worth less than what you deserve—and even might require you to spend more money if, for instance, the company sends you a coupon for a certain amount off your next purchase.

What to do instead: Decide what compensation/resolution to request before you contact customer service. *Example:* "I'd like a full refund" or "Please send me a replacement." Be reasonable, but don't be apologetic. If the agent you speak to declines your request or tries to negotiate it downward, ask what's the maximum amount the agent is authorized to give you. You might need to speak to a supervisor or even a higher-level employee to get what you want.

If you reach an impasse over what the resolution/compensation should be, try to think of a creative solution. *Example:* I bought a blender that arrived with a damaged electrical cord. The merchant's customer service department agreed to replace the machine but insisted that I pay to ship it back so that the company could verify that the blender really didn't work. Shipping was going to cost me nearly as much as the blender, but the company wouldn't budge. So I suggested an alternative that was accepted—I took photos of the blender and the dangerous, damaged cord as proof and e-mailed the photos to customer service.

MISTAKE: **Not getting customer service on your side.** Most consumers understand that swearing or being otherwise rude is detrimental to resolving their problems. But it's not enough just to be civil. For the best chance of success, you need to make the customer service agent an ally and motivate him/her to help you.

How to do that: Before you ever speak to an agent, if a recorded message asks whether you will agree to take a short survey about your upcoming service experience after the phone call, agree to it. The agent most likely will be aware that you opted to take the survey and will be looking to earn a positive review even before he hears your problem.

In every conversation, try to build rapport. Launch the conversation not with a complaint but on a positive note by mentioning your loyalty in specific terms. *Example:* "I've been a satisfied customer for 22 years." After you calmly explain your issue and what you want, say, "I'm struggling here and would so appreciate it if you would take this on for me." If you start to get angry or notice yourself starting to rant, tell the agent, "I want to let you know that this situation has upset me, and it has nothing to do with you personally."

Don't interrupt when the agent is speaking...and avoid using certain trigger words. A study of transcripts from customer service call centers found that agents were most resistant to helping customers who used aggressive words such as *angry*, *hassle* and *nightmare*... when customers used the second-person pronoun when complaining (as in, "Your product

The Social-Media Mistake

Bad-mouthing companies in online venues such as Facebook and Yelp is risky. A scathing comment can harm a company, it's true—and that's why numerous businesses have filed defamation lawsuits in reaction to social-media posts.

What to do instead: If you feel compelled to publicly voice your discontent with the company or to warn others, do it in a way that protects you from legal problems. Certainly do not make any false statements, which can be the basis of defamation. Instead, focus on the facts of your experience.

Example: Writing online that you got food poisoning after you ate at a restaurant is fine (if it's true). Writing that the restaurant has made everyone you know sick or that the restaurant staff purposely gave you food poisoning—both claims that I've seen made online that were not true—is potentially defamatory.

If your conversation with an initial customer service agent isn't getting you anywhere, use the "e" word. Say, "I need to escalate my case. Please let me speak to your supervisor." If the supervisor isn't helpful, you may need to escalate again and talk to someone in the customer-retention or customer-loyalty department.

Discounts That Actually Cost You Money

Akshay Rao, PhD, professor of marketing at University of Minnesota Carlson School of Management in Minneapolis. He has coauthored two papers on consumers' misinterpretations of percentage discounts. CarlsonSchool.umn.edu

Retailers have latched onto a way to offer giant percentages off that are mesmerizing to shoppers—but that are not what they seem. *The pitch:* You get a gigantic discount—typically 50%, 60% or even 70% off—but the fine print notes that you get that discount only on a second or third of multiple similar items. Signs in store windows and on store shelves (and online) shout out the percentage...and shoppers often don't do the math to see just how unimpressive these offers typically are.

Example: Based on an offer of "Buy two, get the third 50% off," you happily tote three items to checkout, where you then receive a total discount of 17% (because you pay full price for the first two items).

Marketing professor Akshay Rao, PhD, has identified additional ways shoppers often get percentages wrong in potentially costly ways...

•**Get-more vs. save-more mistake.** A store offers your favorite ground coffee for 50% off the usual $10 a pound some weeks...and it offers 50% more coffee for free when you buy a pound for $10 during other weeks. When should you stock up?

Many shoppers would view these deals as interchangeable because the special offer is 50% with each. But with 50% off, you're paying $5 per pound...and with 50% more cof-

was no good," rather than, "This product was no good")...and when customers repeatedly interrupted the agents.

The time at which you call can make a difference. If you can help it, don't call on Monday morning or during lunch hours anywhere in the country. That's when customer service typically is deluged with complaints and when agents will have the least time (and patience) to focus on you.

MISTAKE: **Going straight to the CEO with your complaint.** Some consumer advocates have told consumers in recent years to skip customer service altogether and go right to the top—generally with an e-mail to the CEO—because the head of a company has the ultimate power to resolve problems. E-mails are so easy to send that this option can sound appealing. But in my experience, writing to (or calling) bigwigs isn't effective unless you can show that you've already worked your way through the company's customer-grievance process and didn't get a satisfactory resolution.

What to do instead: As unpleasant as it may be, work your way up the food chain.

fee, you're paying $10 for 1.5 pounds, which is $6.67 per pound and 33% more costly.

• **Double-discount mistake.** A clothing store is selling the sweater you want for 50% off its list price...but when you take it to the register, the sales person confides that next week the sweater will be on sale for 30% off list price, plus there will be a storewide 25%-off coupon that can be "stacked" onto the sale price. Would you save money by putting off the purchase?

Most people mentally add up the 30% and 25% discounts in the second offer and conclude that a combined 55% off beats the 50% off. But when there are two discounts applied to one item, the second inevitably applies to the already-discounted price, not the initial price. If that sweater's original price is $100, it's marked down 30% to $70...then the 25% discount is applied to that $70, for a final price of $52.50—which is more than the $50 you would pay with the simple 50%-off sale. Returning next week wouldn't just be an inconvenience...it would cost you money.

How to Buy Appliances That Will Last Much Longer

Chris Zeisler, master service technician who is with RepairClinic.com, a Canton, Michigan–based website that sells appliance parts and offers free appliance-repair videos and advice. Zeisler has nearly 30 years of experience in appliance repair.

Your major appliances don't have long to live. While today's cars last longer than ever, the phrase, "They just don't make 'em like they used to," is nearly 100% accurate when it comes to refrigerators, dishwashers, clothes washers and dryers—even as these major appliances creep upward in price.

Why? Appliance makers are continuing to cut production costs by replacing durable metal parts with cheaper plastic ones. They're also stuffing their appliances with more and more electronics and advanced features. Those latest, greatest features attract shoppers

in showrooms—but packing more features into an appliance means there are more systems that can fail...and many of those electronic components are absurdly expensive to replace, so you end up replacing the entire appliance instead.

Here's how consumers can identify the appliances that are likely to last as long as possible—and avoid those likely to fail fastest...

THREE GENERAL STRATEGIES

• **Pick appliances that have only the features you truly value.** New features might seem neat, but as noted above, each extra system or feature is one more thing that could fail. That doesn't mean we must buy stripped-down, nothing-but-the-basics appliances, but it does mean that it's prudent to choose appliances that have only the features that really matter to us. *Example:* Some refrigerators include two ice makers—one in the freezer and another in the fridge. One ice maker is great...but how badly do we really need the second one?

• **Favor the brands that have easily available and relatively inexpensive replacement parts.** These include Amana, JennAir, KitchenAid, Maytag and Whirlpool (all made by Whirlpool Corp.) and Electrolux and Frigidaire (both owned by Electrolux of Sweden). Having readily available, affordable parts makes it more likely you will keep an appliance longer. *Example:* If the part you need for your eight-year-old washing machine will cost $50 and arrive in two days, it makes sense to fix it...but if it will cost $150 and arrive in three weeks, you might reasonably decide that it's time for a new washer.

• **Whatever appliances you purchase, buy surge protectors, too.** Most people are savvy enough to plug their computers or televisions into surge protectors...but very few think to do the same with their appliances. That's unfortunate because most of today's appliances are loaded with electronic components that are just as vulnerable to power surges as consumer electronics. *Helpful:* Many electric dryers and some other appliances have special plugs that do not plug into standard outlets—or standard surge protectors. Either obtain a surge protector designed for this outlet from an appliance store or protect this and all of your other appliances and electronics by paying an electrician $500 to $1,000, depending on your area, to install a whole-home surge-protection system.

APPLIANCE-SPECIFIC TIPS

• **Refrigerators.** For a longer life, avoid fridges that have multiple separate compartments, each with its own access and temperature settings, such as fridge drawers that can be opened without opening the main doors. These can be convenient, but each separate compartment might have its own fan and fan motor, among other parts, greatly increasing the number of parts that could fail.

Also consider the positioning of a refrigerator's condenser coils before buying. You probably already know that regularly clearing dust and pet hair off a refrigerator's coils can reduce the strain on its motor and compressor, extending the refrigerator's life (and reducing its electricity consumption). Home owners are much more likely to do this if they can get to the coils relatively easily. If getting to the back of a fridge would mean pulling the heavy appliance away from the wall, lean toward one that has coils on the bottom (with a removable "toe kick plate or grill" at the base of the front for access). If your kitchen layout allows relatively easy access to the back of the fridge, coils located there might be easier to get to.

Note: Refrigerator buyers often wonder which fridge configuration lasts longest—top freezer...bottom freezer...or side by side. It turns out that none of these configurations has a notably longer life span than the others. Buy whichever you prefer.

Brands: Whirlpool and its higher-end sister brand KitchenAid tend to make more reliable refrigerators.

• **Dishwashers.** For a longer life, avoid units that boast of multiple moving spray arms and "wash zones." The added complexity and extra moving parts increase the odds of problems—and many dishwashers without these features do a fine job washing dishes.

Also, check how well a dishwasher's warranty covers its dish racks before buying—you want at least five years of coverage. Dish racks might seem like a very simple part not worth worrying about, but dish-rack failure often is the problem that dooms a dishwasher. When the vinyl coating on a dish rack wears through, the metal beneath soon rusts and breaks apart. Replacement racks tend to be so expensive—often $200 to $300—that it can make more sense to replace the entire dishwasher. (Continuing to use a rusty dish rack is unlikely to be a long-term solution, either—bits of rusty metal are likely to damage the inner workings.) If the dishwasher comes with at least five years of dish-rack coverage, that's a sign that the manufacturer has confidence its racks will last.

If dishwasher noise doesn't bother you, perhaps because you usually run your dishwasher when no one is in the kitchen, consider skipping units that trumpet their exceptionally quiet operation. Quiet dishwashers are no more likely to fail than other units, but when they do break down, their added sound insulation can make it time-consuming to access and replace failed parts, increasing repair cost and the odds that it will make sense to replace rather than repair the machine.

Brand: KitchenAid is the most reliable dishwasher brand (and its warranties typically include five years of dish-rack coverage).

• **Clothes washers and dryers.** For a longer life, avoid washers and dryers that have especially elaborate digital display screens and control panels with large numbers of buttons, lights and LED readouts. Electronic control systems tend to be expensive and failure-prone. The more elaborate these are, the more cost-prohibitive it tends to be to replace them—some cost more than $300 for the screen alone.

Front-load washers tend to last slightly longer than top loaders, on average. Why? Front loaders use less water on average—although there are some low-water-use top loaders on the market, too—reducing the stress on their pumps. They also have sturdy metal bearings holding their tubs in place, whereas many, though not all, manufacturers use less durable plastic bearings in top loaders.

Brands: Whirlpool and its sister brand Maytag tend to be dependable choices. These brands offer an extremely wide range of washers and dryers, they have a record of reliability at reasonable price points, and parts for them are readily available. It's not clear that spending more for a prestige-brand washer/dryer will result in longer product life.

9 Cool Products That Will Make Your Life Easier—Most Under $25

Jon Jesse, vice president for industry development at the International Housewares Association (IHA), Rosemont, Illinois. He is a former senior vice president of Kohl's and, prior to that, was a housewares buyer for Marshall Field's in Chicago. Housewares.org

Sometimes it's the little things that make the biggest difference when it comes to enjoying a day—whether you're making dinner, taking a shower, relaxing in bed or hanging out at the beach. So we asked veteran gadget guru Jon Jesse of the International Housewares Association to pick his favorites from the 2,200 companies from 45 countries that exhibited at the latest International Home and Housewares Show in Chicago. Here's what he likes. *All are available online and in major home stores, and some directly from the manufacturer…*

IN YOUR KITCHEN

Longer-lasting fruits and vegetables: **FreshPaper.** Double, triple, even quadruple the life of your spinach, berries and other produce by laying down a sheet of this paper in your refrigerator's produce bin. It contains organic spices that inhibit bacterial and fungal growth. Each sheet lasts about a month (until its maple syrup–like scent, from fenugreek, fades). An eight-sheet pack costs about $10*— and saves up to $50 a month on produce that didn't spoil. Fenugreen.com/freshpaper

Bonus item: This product wasn't at the show, but it's a cool one…

No more hunting for the oregano: **Spice-Bands.** To easily find the spice you want

*Prices in this article are recent prices at online retailers.

among the sea of lookalikes in your cabinet, wrap one of these brightly colored bands around the top of each jar. A set of 20 bands in nine colors includes 16 preprinted with the names of popular spices and four you can label with a dry-erase marker. *Bonus:* The silicon bands also provide a better grip for easier opening. About $10. EBase4.com/spicebands

IN YOUR DINING ROOM

Elegant table linens you don't have to clean: **Sassafras Paper Table Linens.** Now that your salad greens are staying fresher and you can find the herbs de Provence, why not throw a fancy dinner party? These disposable linens let you set a classy spread without having to wash and iron (or dry-clean) them the next day. That's especially convenient for away-from-home meals such as picnics and tailgating parties. The Italian-made tablecloths and napkins look, feel and drape like cloth with an attractive slight sheen. The damask pattern (*damascato*), in burgundy or champagne, would pair well with a Thanksgiving tablescape, while the contemporary *bollicine* (Italian for bubbles) pattern would be a nice fit for a baby shower…or cocktail soiree. Two tablecloths 39 inches square or one tablecloth 55 inches square cost about $10. Larger sizes also available. Napkins are about $8 for a set of 20. SassafrasStore.com/paper-table-linens

IN YOUR BATHROOM

No more clogged showers: **Shower-Shroom.** This clever gadget keeps hair from ever clogging your drain. The small, cylindrical silicone device fits inside standard stall-shower drain openings (you place it underneath the drain cover) and catches hair with minimal disruption to the flow of water. Pop it out every few weeks, swipe the hair off with a paper towel and put it back. There's also a TubShroom and SinkShroom for bathtubs and sinks, respectively. About $12. TubShroom.com

IN YOUR BEDROOM

Make romance hot and live to tell about it: **Candle Impressions flameless candle.** Candles in your bedroom (or living room) set a romantic mood—but so do these easy-to-use and surprisingly realistic battery-powered LED "candles." They're made of wax and feature a "burnt" wick at the top to support a flickering "flame." (And all with no fire risk.) A timer lets you program the candle. Two AA batteries provide up to 1,000 hours of romantic light. About $30 for a set of five. CandleImpressions.com

ON THE GO

***Carry your lunch in style:* Iceware Insulated Lunch Purse.** These faux-leather totes, with insulated reflective lining to keep foods hot or cold, are dead ringers for fashion-forward women's purses. They come in a variety of styles and colors. About $50 and up, depending on the size.

***Drink the H2O you need:* Hidrate Spark 3.0.** It's easy to forget to drink water when you're out and about. This smart bottle lights up to remind you to sip more. An internal sensor tracks how many ounces you've gulped. You can customize your "hydration goal"—and, if you want, use the free Hidrate app to sync the bottle to your smartphone, Fitbit or other selected fitness trackers. About $55. HidrateSpark.com

***Best new beach tote:* Bogg Bag.** This roomy rubberlike tote is dotted with ventilation holes and has a unique treaded, flat bottom so it resists tipping. Made of a durable, antimicrobial material, it's great for the beach or farmers' market—rinse away any sand or dirt with a hose. It also works well for grocery shopping, the gym or pool, sporting events, camping, boating, picnics and gardening. Available in 18 colors. The Bogg Bag (19 x 15 x 9.5 inches) is about $65. BoggBag.com

***Better umbrella:* Revers-A-Brella.** The clever mechanics of this product mean that when you come in from the rain and close your umbrella, it doesn't drip all over you—because the umbrella folds upward like a bowl rather than downward, trapping water inside it—you then can just shake out the water. The upward folding also keeps you drier getting in and out of your car. There are automatic- and manual-opening models of various sizes and designs. About $20.

Great New Assistive Devices

Chris Cusack, partnership manager of *Disability Horizons* magazine, a UK-based online lifestyle publication for the disabled. He was a judge for the Accessible Tech in Employment Hackathon event held on Google's London campus in 2017. DisabilityHorizons.com

Clever new "assistive technologies" now reaching the market can help you or a loved one better use a computer if it is difficult…enjoy the outdoors if you need extra support to walk…navigate better if you have low vision or blindness…and much more. Also, some of these devices are useful for people who are not disabled but would just like to make things easier.

MOBILITY

Wheelchairs and conventional walkers are not the only devices that can help you get around…

***More comfortable crutch:* Ergobaum** distributes users' body weight over the length of their forearms instead of in the armpits. Many people find this less stressful for the arms, particularly when crutches are needed for more than a few days. ($189 for a pair,* ErgoActives.com)

***"Walker" you can use for jogging:* Afari Mobility Aid** has three large wheels plus bicycle-like steering controls and brakes. It lets people who need extra stability when walking move at faster speeds than with a traditional walker. It also works on unpaved surfaces. It is currently being produced in small quantities,

*Prices are from online retailers and may be below the manufacturers' retail prices.

so availability is limited. (Starting at $1,875, Mobility-Tech.com)

Alternative: Trionic Veloped is another walker capable of traveling off-road. There are versions for golfing...hiking...and hunting—the golfing model can carry golf clubs, for example. ($1,300 to $1,400, Trionic.us/en)

Strong, portable lift: **Molift Smart 150** is a hoist capable of picking up a person who weighs as much as 330 pounds to transfer him/her from a bed to a wheelchair or vice versa. Yet this hoist folds down into two sections weighing less than 30 pounds apiece (including rechargeable battery) that can easily fit into the trunk of a car. It gives you the freedom to travel even if you can't get yourself up out of bed and your partner can't lift you. ($3,955.50, Etac.com/en-us/products)

Clothing tailored for wheelchair users: **Chairmelotte** designs mostly women's garments specifically for wheelchair users. (The company also has a small selection for men.) The clothing is cut to be comfortable, stylish and flattering while seated, not while standing...there are extra zippers where people who use wheelchairs are likely to need them, such as up the side seam of skirts and pants... and the sleeves are cut to allow the full arm motions needed to propel a hand-operated wheelchair. (Chairmelotte.com)

HAND USE

Many conditions can lead to hand tremors or hand-strength problems. *Among the tech that can help...*

Gadget that controls tech with head movements: **GlassOuse** lets you control the cursor on a PC or Mac computer screen using small movements of your head rather than with a traditional computer mouse. It can control Bluetooth-enabled Android phones, tablets and smart TVs, too. GlassOuse is worn on the face like eyeglasses, only with no lenses. (If you wear actual eyeglasses, it can sit just above them.) Users can operate its "mouse button" by tapping a finger pad...biting a specially designed switch...or blowing a puff of air—these button units are sold separately. ($499 for GlassOuse plus $29 to $129 for the attachments, GlassOuse.com)

Software that takes dictation: **Dragon Home** is not the only software program that converts spoken words into typed text on a screen, but it is the most accurate. While most apps and programs that attempt this are prone to misunderstandings, Naturally Speaking learns your accent and speech patterns so that the more you use it, the more accurate it becomes. The company that makes this software has been improving its speech-recognition software for decades, so its products are some of the most sophisticated. ($150, Nuance.com/dragon)

Spill-avoiding spoon: **S'up Spoon** has an easy-to-grip handle and a very deep head (almost like a pipe) to cut down on spills. ($15.74, with shipping from the UK, Sup-Products.com)

Alternative: Liftware Steady is a high-tech spoon that has sensors and motors hidden in its handle to counteract hand tremors. The head of the spoon remains largely steady even if your hand does not. Fork and spork attachments also are available. ($195, Liftware.com/steady)

Pour hot liquids without spills: **"Kettle tippers"** such as MaxiAids' The Tipper are not new or high-tech, but they are quite useful. They support the weight of a kettle as you pour, reducing the odds of spills and burns. ($37.95, MaxiAids.com/the-tipper)

LIMITED EYESIGHT OR BLINDNESS

Useful items for people who have vision problems...

Glasses that use sound to paint a picture of your surroundings: **Eyesynth smartglasses** scan the area in front of the wearer and convert the visual environment into a tonal soundscape. With practice, users can learn to interpret its sounds so that they can navigate indoor and outdoor areas—it's a little like having sonar. Eyesynth creates its soundscape using only tones, not words, and it does so through small vibrations in the user's facial bones rather than with an earpiece, so it is not overly distracting. The company is getting ready to release the product, but you can reserve one for a deposit of about $600. (Final price expected to be about $2,800. Eyesynth.com/?lang=en)

Cane that warns of obstacles: **UltraCane** uses ultrasonic waves (people can't hear them) to identify upcoming obstacles. It then silently warns its user about these obstacles via vibrations in its handle. Unlike conventional canes, it identifies obstacles at head or chest height, such as low tree branches, in addition to those at or near ground level. (About $800, UltraCane.com)

Easy way to access the Internet via voice: **Amazon Echo speakers** weren't designed for the blind, but devices such as this that offer access to a "virtual assistant" can be tremendously useful for people who cannot see (and for people who have limited use of their hands, too). You can ask Echo's virtual assistant, Alexa, to check your messages, place a phone call, look up information online, play music and more—all with your voice. ($99.99, Amazon.com)

Alternative: The Amazon Echo Plus does everything that the Echo does and serves as a smarthome hub. Together with compatible smarthome devices, you could tell Alexa to lock or unlock your doors…adjust your thermostat …or turn on or off any device that plugs into a power outlet. ($149.99 plus chosen smarthome devices)

HEARING/SPEAKING

A pair of products for people who suffer from hearing loss or who communicate via sign language…

Headphones that let you hear even if your eardrums cannot: **AfterShokz headphones** convey sound through small vibrations in the cheekbones, bypassing the eardrums.

They're a way for people who have eardrum damage or certain other ear problems to hear again. These headphones can be used to listen to music or podcasts, but if you combine AfterShokz with a smartphone and the Petralex sound-amplification app (Petralex.pro, free for iOS or Android), it could improve your ability to hear ambient sounds around you, too. Note that although AfterShokz headphones bypass the eardrums, a functioning inner ear still is needed for them to successfully convey

sound. ($49.95 to $150 depending on model selected—higher-end models are lighter and offer wireless Bluetooth connectivity, among other advantages, AfterShokz.com)

Wake Up! Alarm Clocks That Will Really Get You Out of Bed

Ashley Timms, editor in chief of *Gadget Flow*, an e-commerce marketplace that features new products each day, most of them tech products. GadgetFlow.com

D o you tend to oversleep? Do you hate the heinous blare of your bedside clock…or does the music it plays just lull you back to sleep? *The following alarm clocks and other devices can get you out of bed more reliably and/or more pleasantly—some even can improve your sleep…*

• **Rug that forces you out of bed.** Ruggie is a soft mat that's placed on the floor beside your bed. It has a digital-time readout and settable alarm functions for different days of the week. When Ruggie's alarm sounds, you must put both of your feet on it for three seconds to 30 seconds (you choose the duration) to turn it off—ensuring that you're no longer under the covers. $99 list, but recently available online for $74. Ruggie.co

• **Clock that wakes you by simulating the sunrise.** The Beddi 2 uses slowly building warm-toned light to ease you gently into morning the way a sunrise might. If the light alone doesn't do the trick, the clock can play the music of your choice from Spotify, Apple Music or other online music-streaming services. Beddi 2 can serve as a night-light and a white-noise generator as well. (A smartphone or tablet and a free Android or Apple app are required for initial setup and to customize the clock's settings.) $99.99. WittiDesign.com

• **Alarm clock that encourages little kids to stay in bed longer.** The Mella children's sleep trainer's cute digital "face" has eyes and a mouth—kids can judge by its open or shut eyes whether they should be up yet…or instead hang tight and let their parents or grandparents sleep a little longer. (The clock face changes color when it's time to rise, too.) The clock also serves as a night-light and white-noise machine, both conducive to longer sleep, and can function as a conventional alarm clock as well. $50. LittleHippo.com/products/mella

Back-Saving Chairs

Barbara Bergin, MD, an orthopedic surgeon at Texas Orthopedics, Sports & Rehabilitation Associates, Austin. She is also author of the blog "Sit Like a Man." DrBarbaraBergin.com

By now, we all know how detrimental sitting is for our health. And of course, we all tend to slouch when sitting at the usual desk chair, and that can lead to back pain.

Standing desks can negate some risk, but standing all day can hurt, too.

The following three unusual chairs offer a sensible middle ground between standing and traditional sitting. All count as active sitting, meaning that they require you to engage far more muscles than with a normal chair—so you can strengthen your core, burn extra calories and maybe even alleviate or avoid back pain.

Each one will take some time to get used to, so plan to feel a bit awkward at first. A good way to adapt to any of these chairs is to sit in one for just an hour at a time for a few days and then gradually increase from there. *Here are the best kinds of "active" chairs…*

•**Saddle stool.** These stools look a bit like oversized bike seats or saddles on top of office chairs. When you sit in one, it causes your hips to open and feet to spread almost as if you were riding a horse. This can help stave off a host of painful back and hip problems as well as plantar fasciitis, all of which can come from sitting prim and proper with your knees and feet together. When you sit in a saddle stool, your feet will naturally fall at 11:00 and 1:00, with hips rotated outward, which helps reduce stress across the hips and knees. The backless nature of this stool can improve your own back strength by requiring you to keep your core muscles engaged as you sit. However, if you find this too tiring or uncomfortable, you can purchase a saddle stool with a back.

Example: Jobri Betterposture Ergonomic Saddle Chair, $199.95. SitHealthier.com

•**Wobble stool.** This stool looks a bit like a bar stool on a sturdy base. The seat will wobble from the natural little movements a body makes when sitting, and this motion keeps your abdomen, back and leg muscles moving as you compensate. All of that extra movement may counteract the negative health impacts of extended sitting.

Example: Uncaged Ergonomics Wobble Stool, $99.99. UncagedErgonomics.com

•**Recumbent chair.** A standard chair makes slumping easy, but a recumbent, or kneeling, chair features a seat that slants by about 20 to 30 degrees. This makes it easier to maintain good posture and avoid back pain. And because a recumbent chair takes pressure off the lower back and buttocks, it can help sciatic pain, too.

Example: Relaxus Recumbent Chair, $159. RelaxusOnline.com

Note: Recumbent/kneeling chairs can be hard on the knees, so anyone with arthritis, patellar tendinitis, kneecap pain or a meniscus tear should avoid them. People with leg swelling should steer clear as well, as these chairs may restrict your circulation. For most people, this isn't a problem, but getting up every hour or so for a short break will make using this type of chair for extended periods more comfortable.

Product Sizes Keep Shrinking

Edgar Dworsky, a consumer attorney and former Massachusetts assistant attorney general. He is founder of the consumer-education websites ConsumerWorld. org and MousePrint.org.

Notice anything different about your orange juice lately? Several major producers, including Tropicana and Florida's Natural, shrank their containers from 59 to 52 ounces in the past year, a 12% decrease, without lowering prices. It wasn't so long ago that a carton of OJ contained 64 ounces.

Downsized products are nothing new—food makers have long known that supermarket shoppers are more likely to take note and change brands when prices increase than when package sizes decrease, so that's become a common way to boost bottom lines. But Tropicana was especially sneaky with its recent downsizing, switching to bottles that are narrower front to back but just as tall and wide as before, so they appear as large as ever through the supermarket cooler door. The quantity of juice in the container is hidden in small print at the very bottom of the label.

The makers of breakfast cereals sometimes use the same trick by shrinking boxes, making them narrower from front to back, the dimension most difficult to judge when the product is on store shelves. Meanwhile, Hershey's is replacing its soft plastic bags of individually wrapped chocolates with stand-up pouches. The candy is the same, but the amount in each package reportedly will decrease, boosting the price per ounce.

Over the years, toilet paper and paper towel makers have practiced a sneaky trick of their own. They don't just reduce the number of sheets per roll—as Bounty has done, for example—they reduce the dimensions of each sheet.

Example: Scott toilet paper has boasted "1,000 sheets per roll" for many years. But the size of each sheet slowly shrank from 4.5 inches square to 4.1 x 3.7 inches now. Consumers get 25% less toilet paper.

Additional product categories that seem to see more than their share of sometimes-sneaky product downsizings include coffee, ice cream, peanut butter, yogurt, toothpaste and shampoo.

What to do: Periodically compare the per unit, per ounce or per square foot price of the products you buy with those of competing products—even if the overall price is the same as ever. Be especially careful to do this when a product's packaging boasts of a new version, flavor, formula or some other improvement—manufacturers often make claims like these to distract from or explain away a smaller size.

GOOD TO KNOW...

Safer Food and Beverage Containers

BPA-free plastic products may be no safer than those containing BPA.

To be safe: Opt for glass and/or metal food and beverage containers, jars and bottles. If you do use plastic, avoid the dishwasher and microwave—heat accelerates chemical release. And if plastics show signs of damage such as haziness or cracks, discard them.

Patricia A. Hunt, PhD, Meyer Distinguished Professor in the School of Molecular Biosciences, Washington State University, Pullman, and leader of a study published in *Current Biology.*

Fruit Juice Alert

Fruit juice may contain lead and arsenic. These two harmful heavy metals—plus cadmium, which also is dangerous—showed up in 21 of 45 fruit juices tested by *Consumer Reports.* The juices checked were apple, grape, pear and fruit blend, and many brands tested were marketed to children. Drinking as little as four ounces a day of some of the juices could be cause for concern. Brands tested included Capri Sun, Gerber, Minute Maid, Mott's and Welch's.

Almost all of the tested juices had levels of heavy metal below what the Food and Drug Administration considers safe for human consumption. But *Consumer Reports* says that the levels should be lower, and its safety judgments were based on the levels it recommends.

Consumer Reports.

Get Better Service in Restaurants

Darron Cardosa, who has waited tables in the New York City area for more than 25 years. He is author of *The Bitchy Waiter: Tales, Tips & Trials from a Life in Food Service.* TheBitchyWaiter.com

Long waits, brusque waiters and bad tables can make dining out unsatisfying even when the food is fine. But restaurant patrons often have more control over the quality of the service they receive than they realize. Most waiters and waitresses want to provide stellar service—they make their living from tips. *Here's what you can do to increase the odds that you and your party will enjoy the dining-out experience...*

WHEN YOU RESERVE

• **Call to make your reservation, and when you do, effusively praise the restaurant's quality of service.** If you have eaten there before, tell how great the service was. If not, tell how you've heard about the great service. This sets the bar for service to you very high but does so in a way that's complimentary, not demanding. When people are told they're doing a great job, it makes them want to confirm that opinion.

If you are a repeat customer, the best way to use this strategy is to request a server *by name* when you call—and explain that you would like to sit in this person's section because he/she always does a wonderful job. Mention something specific that you appreciate about the service—"He's so friendly and attentive" or "She really made us feel welcome." Even if the server you request is not available, a smart host will deduce from this compliment that service is very important to you and perhaps make a note with your reservation to seat you with one of the restaurant's best servers. This reservations strategy is most likely to work at relatively upscale eateries because their reservation takers are most likely to have good customer service skills. But there's a version you can use even at lower-end places—ask to speak to the manager and offer your kind words to him instead.

• **If dining for a special occasion, use the implicit power of social media even if you don't plan to post about your visit.** Telling a restaurant that you're having an occasion such as a birthday or an anniversary has always been a good way to get a bit of special attention, but the age of social media has made it even more powerful. Savvy restaurateurs know that people often post online about their special occasions—and they know that making the occasion extra-wonderful for their guests can lead to some very flattering follow-up posts, which is excellent marketing for the restaurant. Your odds of receiving that special treatment are better if your occasion is entered into the restaurant's computerized reservation system than if you mention it only to your host or waiter when you arrive.

BEFORE YOU ORDER

• **Sit at the bar.** If you're a party of two or three, eating at the bar is an excellent way to get fast, personal service at many restaurants. Unlike a waiter, a bartender likely will be very close at hand throughout your meal...and because bartenders and bar patrons face one another, you're more likely to form a personal bond. It improves your odds of receiving complimentary drinks and other perks, too. And you often can get seated at the bar immediately even when there's a wait for a table.

Helpful: If you don't like the table you are offered at a restaurant, asking to sit at the bar may be preferable to asking for a different table. You may have been offered the original table because the waiter in that section had time to serve you. A different table might be served by a waiter who already is very busy.

• **Mention a tight timetable even if you're not trying to get out by a certain deadline,** such as by the start time of a play or movie. If you want a leisurely dining experience, you wouldn't do this, of course. But if you're concerned that things might drag, it's a way to get some extra insurance against slow service. (And don't wait until after you order to tell your server you're in a bit of a time crunch because at that point, there's less he can do to speed things up.)

Conversely, if your waiter is clearly very busy but you're in no hurry, say, "I can see you're busy. Don't worry too much about us—we're not in a rush." Your meal might end up taking a little longer, but you could earn the waiter's appreciation, which might result in perks such as complimentary drinks…or especially attentive service on future visits.

WHEN YOU ORDER AND EAT

•**Don't let an open menu keep your waiter away.** When your party is ready to order, confirm that everyone at your table has set his menu down and closed if it has a cover. If there's even one menu that looks like it's still being used, the waiter might think that the table is not ready to order, slowing your service. You can always pick up or reopen a menu when the waiter arrives if, for example, you want to remind yourself about food items.

•**Take simple steps that avoid annoying the waiter unnecessarily.** *Example:* If you want separate checks, tell the waiter before you begin ordering. With modern restaurant computer systems, it's not that difficult to provide separate checks…as long as your waiter knows you want them before he enters your meal into the system. And don't make your waiter stand around. It's perfectly fine to say you need more time to decide what to order and to ask the server to come back in a few minutes. But don't do what many people do—they say they're ready but then sit there perusing the menu while their server waits.

•**Ask for the waiter's help choosing between two items rather than asking, "What do you recommend?"** The standard "what do you recommend?" gives the waiter no hint about your personal tastes. It also lets the waiter recommend a dish that he was told to push because it's past its prime and the restaurant doesn't want to throw the food away.

•**Make requests when other people at your table are doing so, too.** Waiters hate it when they must make multiple trips to the same table because members of the group don't request such things as drink refills or additional utensils at the same time. Coordinate requests when you can. The easier you make the waiter's job, the more likely he will treat you well.

ANY TIME

•**Learn names.** Your waiter likely will tell you his name. Also ask the host or hostess's name and the busboy's name. If you're not great at remembering names, take a moment to jot them down. On future visits, call as many employees by name as possible. Knowing names is the key to being viewed as a regular—and being a regular is the key to receiving exceptional service.

•**Don't say, "I know the owner."** Patrons who say this are the subject of quiet mockery among the waitstaff, who inevitably assume that these patrons don't really know the owner (at least not well) and are lying or stretching the truth to get special treatment. If you really do know the restaurant's owner (or manager or chef), instead ask whether this person is in.

Example: "Is Jane Smith in today? If she has a second, could you tell her we'd love to say hi." That sends the message that you really do know this person…and if this restaurant VIP does stop by your table, this visit could indeed ensure attentive service from the waitstaff.

How to Get Discounts on New Clothes

Get discounts on new clothes by donating your old clothes. The following stores take in clothing at their retail locations, and some accept donations at outlet stores. Always call first to make sure that the store you're planning to visit accepts donations.

Examples: Eileen Fisher gives a $5 store card for each piece of its clothing…Levi's takes denim from any brand for recycling and offers 20% off one regular-price in-store item…Madewell accepts jeans—any brand—and gives $20 off a new pair for each pair you donate…The North Face takes clothing and footwear from any brand and gives a $10-off coupon for a purchase of $100 or more…Patagonia accepts its own good-condition items and gives a credit of up to $100.

Roundup of experts on what to do with old clothing, reported at MarketWatch.com.

New Ways to Save Money on Prescription Drugs

Charles B. Inlander, a consumer advocate and health-care consultant based in Fogelsville, Pennsylvania. He was founding president of the nonprofit People's Medical Society, a consumer-advocacy organization credited with key improvements in the quality of US health care, and is author or coauthor of more than 20 consumer-health books.

If it seems like prescription medication prices have risen nearly as fast as Bitcoin once did, you're not that far off. And it isn't just with exotic drugs. *Examples:* In recent years, the price of the heart drug *digoxin*, one of the oldest drugs on the market and historically very cheap, has been raised more than 600%...and the cost of insulin has tripled.

But there are strategies to control your drug costs so that you can afford what you need...

USE DISCOUNT APPS AND SITES

One of the few positive trends in the pharmaceutical business in recent years has been the rise of websites and apps that let you easily search for the lowest prices on prescription medication. None of these services accept insurance, but the prices offered are sometimes even lower than what many people would pay through their insurance plans.

Here are some of the best online drug discount programs (all are free to join)...

• **GoodRx.com** lists the price of any medicine at multiple pharmacies near you and posts coupons you can print out or send to your phone to reduce prices further. Consumers can save up to 80%.

• **RxPharmacyCoupons.com** can save you up to 90% on more than 20,000 name-brand and generic meds at more than 68,000 pharmacies.

• **BlinkHealth.com.** Buy your prescription at a discount online, then pick it up at your local pharmacy.

Many drug manufacturers also offer discount coupons. Search online for "discount coupons" and the name of the drug you need. These may not be usable along with your prescription drug coverage, so check with your plan.

LET COMPETITION WORK FOR YOU

You might be surprised to know that prescription prices can vary widely at different pharmacies—even within the same pharmacy chain. Before filling a prescription, call around to compare the price at your local mom-and-pop pharmacy and at nearby locations of major chains. This simple step can save you a bundle if you're paying cash or haven't met your drug plan's deductible.

Extra tip: Large-chain drugstores, such as CVS, Rite Aid and Walgreens, and large stores with pharmacies, such as Walmart, Costco and Target, are engaged in a price war over which one can charge the least for some of the most common generic drugs—so call around and take advantage when you have such a prescription to fill. Walmart, for instance, offers the blood pressure drug *atenolol*, the diabetes drug *glimepiride* and the cholesterol drug *atorvastatin* for just $4 a month each (or $10 for a three-month supply). Sam's Club fills some generic prescriptions for free for members. *Keep in mind:* Many chains offer drug discount cards, so sign up for them.

NEGOTIATE WITH YOUR PHARMACY

Most people think drug prices at pharmacies are fixed—but often they're not. Simply asking, "Is that your best price?" over the phone or in person is sometimes all it takes to get a discount. A good pharmacist may match a price you find online or search for discount programs or coupons that you can use to reduce the price. It can't hurt to ask—even at big pharmacies.

USE A MAIL-ORDER PHARMACY

If you are taking a medication to control a chronic condition long-term, there's no need to drive to the pharmacy or reorder every month. Mail-order pharmacies—and perhaps even your local one—deliver a 90-day supply to your door and can be set up to auto-refill prescriptions. And it's not merely convenient—it's often cheaper because you pay one dispensing fee for 90 days' worth of a drug, rather than one fee per month. People who have drug plans with participating mail-order pharmacies typically save as much as one-third compared with using a local pharmacy.

Caution: There are lots of unscrupulous businesses online that present themselves as legitimate pharmacies but that are not. Don't gamble on whether you will receive legitimate medicine. To ensure that you're getting the correct prescription when you buy drugs online, use only mail-order retailers that display the "VIPPS" symbol on their websites. This means the site is accredited by the Verified Internet Pharmacy Practice Sites (VIPPS) program from the National Association of Boards of Pharmacy. If you want to see whether an Internet pharmacy is accredited, you can look it up online at NABP.pharmacy/programs/vipps. An example of a good VIPPS-accredited mail-order pharmacy is HealthWarehouse.com. It does not take any insurance, but it's worth comparing prices with those you can get through your insurance plan—you might save money.

GRILL YOUR DOCTOR

Physicians are like the rest of us when they have a shiny new toy. When a promising new drug hits the market, they are likely to get excited and prescribe it instead of older alternatives. But what if the cost of this new name-brand drug is 10 times that of a time-tested generic or five times that of an older brand-name drug that might be equally effective? Your doctor might not consider the price difference.

Of course, if your condition requires a newer drug for which there's no cheaper equivalent, you should pony up. But whenever your doctor wants to prescribe you a new drug, make sure that you truly need it by grilling him/her about the pros and cons versus older drugs.

THE DANGER OF USING MULTIPLE PHARMACIES

While shopping around can cut your drug costs substantially, there is one potentially large drawback to purchasing your meds in multiple places—dangerous drug interactions. You might have multiple doctors prescribing you different medicines, with no one doctor knowing about everything you take. You should discuss with each of your doctors all the medications you take...but another line of defense against harmful drug interactions can be a pharmacist.

My advice: Make sure that each place that fills a prescription for you enters every med you take into its record on you...even meds that you get elsewhere. Ask a pharmacist to review this complete list every time you add a new prescription. This act of drug due diligence takes only a few extra minutes, and it will help ensure your safety.

Comparison Shop for Medications

Visit websites that list drug prices from various sellers so that you can comparison shop for the best deal...

• **PharmacyChecker.com** lists prices at online pharmacies in the US and abroad and can help users save up to 90%.

• **GoodRx.com** compares prices from more than 70,000 US pharmacies and says that its average user saves $276/yr.

• **BlinkHealth.com** negotiates prices with specific chains—you get reduced prices by buying from those chains through the site.

• **WeRx.org** lists local pharmacies and their discounted prices.

Also helpful: Go to the Food and Drug Administration's website, FDA.gov, and use the

---

> **TAKE NOTE...**
>
> ## Apps for Saving on Prescriptions
>
> •**Easy Drug Card** produces discounts of up to 80% if you do not have insurance or your insurance will not cover a medicine's costs—and it works for pet medicines, too.
>
> •**FamilyWize** works whether or not you have insurance and reduces prescription costs by an average of 40%.
>
> •**ScriptSave WellRX** does a similar price search and offers a savings card that can produce discounts up to 80%.
>
> Roundup of experts on medication costs, reported at WiseBread.com.

Drugs@FDA Database to find out about the generic equivalents of more expensive brand-name medicines.

MoneyTalksNews.com

Free Generics

Certain generic prescription drugs are free at supermarket chains…

• **Meijer** includes antibiotics such as *amoxicillin* and *ampicillin*, the cholesterol drug *atorvastatin*, the diabetes drug *metformin* and prenatal vitamins.

• **Price Chopper and ShopRite** include diabetes medications such as metformin and *glimepiride*.

• **Publix** includes the antibiotics amoxicillin and ampicillin plus the blood pressure drugs *amlodipine* and *lisinopril* and diabetes drug metformin.

• **Reasor's** includes several antibiotics plus prenatal and children's vitamins.

Prescriptions are required. Only certain dosages may be free.

Charles B. Inlander, a consumer advocate and healthcare consultant, Fogelsville, Pennsylvania.

A Dozen Ways to Save Money on Pet Care

Lauren Greutman, dog owner and author of The Recovering Spender: How to Live a Happy, Fulfilled, Debt-Free Life. She writes and speaks about frugal living and household finance on her website and on TV shows such as Today and Good Morning America. LaurenGreutman.com

Our furry friends (plus feathered friends and other pets, too) can be costly companions. *Example:* Add up the bills for pet food, veterinarian visits, kennels and other expenses, and the typical dog will cost its owner around $15,000 over the course of its lifetime, according to the ASPCA—much more if the animal experiences major medical problems. The average cat costs nearly as much, and even smaller pets such as guinea pigs, rabbits and birds can cost thousands of dollars to keep.

It's worth it, but wouldn't it be nice to spend less? *Here are a dozen ways to reduce the cost of pet ownership…*

VETERINARY CARE AND DRUGS

• **Buy pet medicines online or in affordable pharmacy chains.** Many veterinary practices add large markups to medicines. In nonemergency situations, check for lower prices on 1800PetMeds.com and PetCareRX.com—you might save as much as 50%. (For nonprescription pet medicines, also try Amazon.com, which recently purchased Wag.com.) Most Costco, Kroger and Walmart pharmacies sell veterinary medications at low prices, too, though they tend to stock only a modest selection of pet meds.

• **Buy pills meant for larger pets and cut them to size.** Because dogs vary greatly in size, dog medicines tend to be available in dramatically different dosages for large, medium and small animals. But while a pill meant for a 100-pound dog likely contains four times as much medicine as one meant for a 25-pound dog, it often costs only a little extra. With many drugs, it's safe to buy pills meant for a larger animal and use a pill splitter to divide them into the appropriate dosage for a smaller animal. Never do this, though, unless you have confirmed with your vet that it is safe to do with the specific medication.

• **Use the vet in a nearby small town.** Veterinarians in upscale cities and suburban areas often charge significantly more than those in more rural or economically modest areas. Call veterinary offices within a half-hour drive of your home, particularly those in areas with lower real estate prices, and ask their rates for basic checkups as a quick gauge of their overall prices. You might save $20 to $100 or more per visit. *Alternative:* If there's an accredited veterinary college in your area, it likely offers veterinary services at low rates. These services usually are provided by veterinary students, but those students are overseen by highly experienced veterinarians.

• **Ask local humane societies and SPCA chapters about affordable pet-vaccination**

programs in your area. Some pet-oriented nonprofits offer vaccinations on certain days of the year for less than a vet's office is likely to charge—often just $10 to $15 per vaccination, compared with $15 to $30 for the same vaccinations from the typical veterinary practice.

TRAINING AND BOARDING

• **Find affordable dog boarding, walking and sitting services on Rover.com.** This is the Uber of dog care—people make a few extra bucks by offering animal-care services through the website. In many areas, you can find people willing to walk a dog for as little as $15…or take a dog or cat into their homes (or dog/cat sit in your home) for as little as $20 or $30 per night, though rates vary. The site includes ratings and reviews of care providers from other pet owners so that you can select someone likely to take good care of your pet. Not only does that tend to be less expensive than kennels, it's great for pets that dislike kennels. *Alternative:* Make a deal with another animal lover in your area to take in each other's pets when you travel. Make sure all of the pets involved accept the presence of the others in a home before doing this.

• **Ask pet stores whether they offer special deals for owners of recently obtained pets.** If you get a new pet, there's a good chance that you can get some great deals from nearby pet-supply stores. Many stores, in particular chain stores, offer valuable coupon books to new pet owners in hopes of earning their ongoing business. *Example:* PetSmart's "Adoption Kit" includes a free private-training session…a free day of doggie day care…a free overnight boarding stay…a free bag of food… and a half-price grooming session.

• **Take training classes on YouTube.** Before you pay hundreds of dollars for pet-training classes or one-on-one sessions, try the free training videos on YouTube. Just type in the species of animal, the word "training" and the specific skill you are trying to teach or troubling behavior you are trying to stop.

PET FOOD AND TREATS

• **Choose pet food based on price per serving, not price per pound.** Inexpensive pet food is not a money saver if it's so full of "fillers" such as rice and corn that you have to give your pet larger-than-normal servings so that the pet gets the nourishment it needs. Dog- and cat-food packaging usually includes a "Recommended Daily Feeding Chart" that lists serving amounts for different-sized pets by weight. These guidelines report the amount of the food that an animal of a particular size is likely to need to obtain a balanced diet, according to the guidelines of the Association of American Feed Control Officials. Compare brands by comparing how many servings your pet would get for each dollar spent.

• **Price pet food online and in chains that beat grocery store prices.** Websites such as Amazon.com, Chewy.com and Walmart.com often undercut grocery store and pet-supply store prices on pet food by 10% to 20% and frequently offer free or low-cost shipping. (As a bonus, the potentially heavy bags of pet food will be delivered right to your door.) If you prefer to shop in brick-and-mortar stores, Walmart and Tractor Supply Co., a chain with 1,700 stores across the country, often charge less for pet food than do supermarkets and pet-supply stores. It's worth checking these sellers' pet food prices even if it's more convenient for you to buy from a nearby pet-supply store—some stores will match other retailers' lower prices.

• **Use a food dehydrator to make pet treats.** Most dogs and cats love dried meat treats, but these can be pricey in stores. With a food dehydrator, you can buy meat when it's on sale at your market and then make inexpensive dried meat treats at home. Enter the terms "dehydrator," "treats" and "dog" or "cat" into a search engine to find recipes.

PET TOYS AND ENCLOSURES

• **Purchase pet toys that were not meant to be pet toys.** If your dog plays with tennis balls, they're usually significantly cheaper in the sporting-goods section of a store than in the pet-supply section. If your pet likes to play with stuffed animals, you often can find these used at thrift stores for just 25 or 50 cents apiece. (Wash them before giving them to your pet.) Most cats would just as soon chase a piece of string tied to the end of a stick or the dot of light from a laser pointer as they would play with something that's marketed as a cat toy. Enter "cat toys" and "homemade" or "DIY" into a search engine to find many more options.

• **Buy fish tanks and animal cages at thrift stores…or look for postings on Craigslist.com.** Great deals on secondhand fish tanks usually are available—some families don't enjoy having fish as much as they expected or get rid of them when their children grow older…and others can't bring fish tanks with them when they move. Used animal cages can be good buys, too—just be sure to thoroughly clean any secondhand cage (or tank) before using it for your pet.

DON'T GET FOOLED…

Contractor Scams and How to Avoid Them

•**Pay-upfront scam.** The contractor insists on 30% to 50% of the project's cost in advance, saying that the money is needed for materials and equipment—but after you pay, your money disappears or the work gets started sloppily and you have nowhere else to go because of your investment. Unless you know you can trust the contractor, don't pay more than 10% of a job's cost in advance.

•**Verbal-agreement scam.** The contractor makes promises but does not put them in writing—then omits them from the job or demands extra money to do them.

Self-defense: Insist that a contract include everything you discuss.

•**Unforeseen-problems scam.** Near the job's end, the contractor demands more money, saying unexpected problems arose.

Self-defense: Hire a home inspector to determine whether the claim is legitimate.

HouseLogic.com

Don't Ignore Your TV's Update Requests

Modern smart TVs often ask viewers to allow updates—usually to improve securi-ty, provide new features or make existing ones better. Most updates take only a few minutes and are time well spent—if you dismiss them, your TV may develop issues that the updates would have fixed. Consider enabling automatic updates in your TV's settings—most smart TVs have this option.

Consumer Reports.

Apps That Give You More Storage on Your Phone

Apps to help save storage space on Android devices…

•**Google Photos.** This app automatically transfers your photos and videos to Google's servers. It gives you free unlimited storage, and Google won't compress images of up to 16 megapixels or HD videos of up to 1080p.

•**SD Maid.** After running a "clean," this app detects unneeded data from uninstalled apps and duplicate files saved in different places and lets you delete this unwanted data.

• **1 Tap Cleaner.** This program gives you a list of apps and how much space they are taking up and then helps you delete the ones you don't want. It also helps you delete call, text and Internet history to protect your privacy and free up extra storage space.

Komando.com

To Charge Your Smartphone Quickly…

• **Plug it into the wall, not a PC**—USB ports do not charge as quickly as wall outlets. Use a higher-amperage charger if you have one. *Example:* iPhones come with a one-amp charger, and the standard iPad charger's amperage is about twice that, so it will charge your phone faster than the charger that came with your phone.

•**Consider buying a fast charger**—there are several different fast-charging standards, so check your phone's manual or manufacturer website to find out what type will work for you.

Not necessary: Switching your phone off or to airplane mode. This makes little difference in charging time and can be an inconvenience because it can make your phone unavailable during charging.

The New York Times.

How to Outwit Robocallers

Jennifer Jolly, a *USA Today* columnist who has written extensively on combating robocalls. She runs the website Techish.com, which focuses on products and strategies to make consumer technology easier for people to use.

Y ou have tried and tried to stop those maddening robocalls that hawk lower mortgage rates…pretend to be the IRS claiming that you owe taxes…or promise to remove your computer viruses. Like millions of others, you've signed up for the National Do Not Call Registry, set your phone to block individual numbers and maybe even signed up with Nomorobo, which cancels calls from suspect phone numbers after the first ring. And of course, you generally ignore caller-ID numbers that you don't recognize. But the robocalls just keep increasing. About 4.2 billion robocalls were placed nationwide in August 2018 alone, up from 2.9 billion just a year earlier.

Some of these calls are legit, such as automated messages for flight delays and prescription refill reminders or legitimate debt-collection calls. But many are scams meant to draw you in so that a live operator can get on the line and convince you to hand over money or personal financial data. Here's why robocalls have proliferated and how you can step up your own war on robocallers.

WHY ROBOCALLS ARE OUT OF CONTROL

It's easy for scammers to collect millions of phone numbers, including yours, from online listings. And autodialing software lets con artists ring thousands of lines simultaneously at less than a penny per call through overseas servers that conceal their identities.

The National Do Not Call Registry deters legitimate marketers but has little effect on scammers. These robocallers use tricks to make their caller-ID different every time. Sometimes it appears as the number of a local police department or bank. Other times it's a number with the same area code and local exchange as the intended victim's, a practice known as "neighbor spoofing."

If you do pick up, robocall software can detect that a live voice has answered and mark you as a target for further calls.

Another devious innovation: When you pick up, you hear an "imitation of life" recording that sounds like an actual person on the other end of the phone. The idea is to get you to engage long enough to transfer you to an operator.

HOW TO FIGHT BACK

Robocalls will continue to be a problem, and there's no single solution. But using one or more of the following free or low-cost strategies can greatly reduce the frequency and volume of robocalls you receive. *To block robocalls from a smartphone or any phone using an Internet-based digital phone service such as Verizon Fios, Comcast Xfinity or Vonage…*

• **Get a third-party call-blocking app.** These apps can be downloaded to your smartphone, and you also can access them as part of your Internet-based phone service. They combine call-filtering software and vast databases of known bogus numbers to automatically block the calls or divert them to voice mail. Many people have been frustrated with the most popular of these services, Nomorobo, which doesn't always stop robocalls. If that's the case for you, try YouMail (YouMail.com). It analyzes each incoming call with "smart blocking" technology that uses historical call patterns, feedback from millions of its users and a constantly updated database of known robocallers before letting it ring on your phone. If the call is flagged as a robocaller, YouMail answers it instead with a recording, saying, "The number you've reached is out of service," which robocaller software can detect so that you are more likely to get removed from calling lists. YouMail does not work with traditional landlines.

Cost: Free. The company makes money by selling premium services for $5 to $10 per month that enhance your voice mailbox capabilities.

• **Use enhanced technology offered by your wireless carrier.** In 2017, the FCC issued new regulations allowing wireless carriers to intercept, analyze and even block calls to customers' phones that come from invalid numbers or those that show evidence of "spoofing" (altering the number that appears on your phone's caller-ID to disguise the robocaller's real number). Some major carriers provide spam-call protection that lets you block suspected incoming robocalls for free, depending on your wireless plan. Others offer a premium app with more sophisticated caller-ID features for a few dollars a month.

Robocall-blocking apps from the four biggest carriers…

• *AT&T Call Protect* is a free service available to eligible AT&T wireless customers. Call Protect provides automatic fraud blocking that stops suspicious calls from reaching your phone. For $3.99 a month, you can get Call Protect Plus enhanced caller-ID, which attempts to identify names and locations of callers not in your contacts list, and custom call blocking, which lets you choose the types of legitimate robocalls to allow, block or send to voice mail based on categories such as telemarketing agencies, doctor offices and political organizations.

• *T-Mobile Scam ID and Scam Block* are free services that alert you when an incoming call is likely a scam and/or prevent those calls from reaching you. For $4 a month per line, you also can get Name ID, which works similarly to AT&T Call Protect Plus, providing more in-depth caller-ID and management of the types of robocalls you want to receive.

• *Sprint Premium Caller ID* costs $2.99 a month and not only alerts you to robocalls but also provides a "threat level" indicator to give customers an idea of how suspicious calls are. Based on the threat level and settings you choose, the service can automatically block numbers or send them to voice mail.

• *Verizon Call Filter* is a premium service for $2.99 a month that alerts you if an incoming call is likely to be a robocall and

indicates whether it's a potential scam or a legitimate automated call.

To block robocalls from a traditional hard-wired landline phone…

• **Buy a device or order a service on your landline that screens calls** using "Caller Input." Whenever a call comes in, it is answered by the device or service, and an interactive recording is played that requires callers to enter a digit such as 0 or 1. If they don't enter this digit (robocallers can't), they are sent to voice mail or the call is disconnected. If they do enter the digit, the call is put through to you. You can set up a privileged list of callers who automatically bypass the screening. *Examples…*

• *Sentry 3.1 Call Screener* is a small stand-alone device that plugs into any landline. Callers who do not respond to the interactive message and who are not on your privileged list are disconnected. Available from Amazon.com and many electronics retailers. *Cost:* About $80.

• *"No Solicitation"* is a service from Century Link, a phone company that offers landline phone service in parts of 39 states. The free service screens calls using caller input. Call your landline service provider to ask whether it offers a similar service.

Online Shopping Warning

Fake online product listings sometimes show up for third-party sellers at popular websites such as Amazon.com and Walmart.com.

Self-defense: Check the manufacturer's website for a list of authorized third-party distributors—and beware if the seller's name is not on it. Be sure that the logos and packaging shown online are correct and look authentic—phony sites often have slight errors or specify that there is no packaging available. Be skeptical of an extremely low price—this often signals fraud. Other warning signs include a lack of a return policy, very long shipping times and very similar, overly positive reviews with many misspellings.

Kiplinger's Personal Finance.

12

Retirement Report

5 Mistakes to Avoid When Retiring Early

It is no accident that age 65 remains a popular retirement age. By that point, most retirees will have become eligible for both Social Security and Medicare, and any company pension payouts can begin. Even so, many people are drawn to the prospect of *early* retirement with its promise of decades' worth of time for travel or other passions. A recent survey found that 15% of adults in the US expect to retire before age 60, and 29% expect to retire between 60 and 65.

Early retirement might be wonderful if you can afford it...but there are some very dangerous ways that many early retirees sabotage their own retirements.

Making an early-retirement dream a reality requires even more careful planning than with a typical retirement. You have fewer years to save and a longer wait for government retirement benefits. What's more, recent economic trends could present additional challenges for early retirees. Health-care costs continue rising...inflation may be increasing as well...and some financial professionals are predicting an end to the stock bull market before long, which could threaten the value of retirement savings.

Because of these factors, anyone planning an early retirement must develop a disciplined strategy. *Here's how to avoid five common missteps people make when retiring in their 40s, 50s or early 60s...*

MISTAKE #1: **Not considering a phased retirement.** Many would-be early retirees simply pick an age at which they want to stop working and then try to figure out how much they'll need to save to reach that goal. But this black-and-white, by-the-numbers approach does not

---

Wes Moss, CFP, chief investment strategist and partner at Atlanta-based Capital Investment Advisors, author of the best seller *You Can Retire Sooner Than You Think* and host of the investment and personal finance radio show *Money Matters*. WesMoss.com

reflect the reality that retirement comes in many shades and can include a more gradual phase-out from your career, such as downshifting to part-time work...working more hours from home...or switching to a less stressful job.

This kind of transition helps bridge the potential financial and psychological gaps between a career and full retirement. To do this, rather than focusing on the day you'll stop working altogether, think about a period when you'll start working less, then envision possible scenarios to carry you to full retirement age.

Example: A 45-year-old making $100,000 per year is hoping to retire at age 55. To collect larger monthly benefits, he plans to wait until age 67 to start drawing from Social Security—five years after he becomes eligible. (Every year you wait to claim Social Security between age 62 and 70 results in roughly an 8% higher payout. See Mistake #3 for more Social Security advice.) This strategy might provide about $31,000 in Social Security benefits per year, though the exact figure would depend on his salary history. Rather than ceasing work entirely at age 55 and covering all expenses from savings until he collects Social Security, he could plan to gradually reduce his workload, generating wages of, say, $50,000 per year from age 55 to 59 and $30,000 from age 60 to 63. That way, he would have a much shorter period to rely solely on savings before claiming Social Security, and he would still be fully retired by age 63. Plus, he will retire with an extra $370,000.

To get an estimate of your Social Security benefit, go to SSA.gov and search "Social Security Detailed Calculator."

MISTAKE #2: **Failing to establish multiple income streams.** Preparing for early retirement involves more than just building a nest egg until it reaches a certain size and then tapping that money to pay living expenses. To maintain the retirement lifestyle you envision, it can be very helpful to have income from multiple sources—not just traditional retirement savings and investment accounts. *Reasons:* There is a psychological benefit from not having to depend on a single source of income. Also, investors can't begin taking withdrawals

from IRAs and 401(k)s before age 59½ without facing a 10% penalty on those withdrawals—reducing the net income you receive and creating greater risk that you'll deplete your savings during a long retirement.

Instead, develop a plan that includes additional sources of income that you can tap before age 59½. These might include taxable brokerage accounts that hold income-producing investments such as bonds and dividend-paying stocks...part-time work (discussed in Mistake #1)...and income-producing assets outside your retirement accounts, such as rental real estate.

Caution: Many early retirees tend to keep a large portion of their investments in stocks and other growth investments to help their savings last during a longer retirement. Although this approach can work very well as long as stocks do well, a sharp market downturn during the first few years of retirement can have a disproportionally damaging effect on your long-term wealth—a phenomenon known as sequence-of-returns risk. Making withdrawals from accounts that have declined in value due to market downturns requires you to liquidate more of your assets to maintain your desired income level.

What to do: Early retirees should plan to be flexible, based on market conditions, with the amount they withdraw from investment accounts each year.

MISTAKE #3: **Waiting too long to start collecting Social Security.** Waiting as long as possible to collect Social Security makes good financial sense for many retirees. The longer you wait up to age 70, the more you will collect each month for the rest of your life. (There's no benefit to waiting until after age 70 because age 70 is when your maximum possible benefit is reached.) For early retirees, however, it can make sense to start taking Social Security earlier to reduce your reliance on your other financial assets.

Consider your total income needs. If this amount would require you to withdraw more than 5% per year from your retirement account (which would increase your risk of draining the account prematurely), consider claiming Social Security at age 62—the current minimum eligibility age. If you retire at an age older than 62, consider claiming Social Security the year that you retire rather than waiting until you turn 70 (the age at which you can collect maximum benefits). Adding Social Security income early in retirement could reduce the risk of depleting your savings from excessive withdrawals even though you're receiving a smaller monthly benefit.

MISTAKE #4: **Failing to visit a health insurance specialist.** Most working adults get health insurance through their employers, while those who retire at age 65 or older are covered largely through Medicare. Early retirees fall between those groups and face a bewildering array of health insurance options—made even more confusing by current uncertainty in the health insurance landscape.

To help sort through these options, consider asking a financial adviser to recommend a health insurance specialist who can examine the options available in your state.

Examples: If your spouse continues to work, you could join his/her plan. Or you might examine your state's health-care exchange through the Affordable Care Act, which remains an option for at least the time being. Because your income might be lower after retirement, you might qualify for tax credits that help offset premium payments. Or consider Direct Primary Care, an alternative model for health insurance that charges a flat monthly fee covering routine primary care services. And you may want to consider buying long-term-care insurance before you retire, as the premiums increase based on the age at which you start a policy.

MISTAKE #5: **Failing to factor in the cost of supporting grown children.** Roughly 40% of parents are providing adult children some level of financial support. This financial burden falls especially heavily on early retirees, whose children are likely to be younger and even more dependent than average. It's not unusual for parents to spend more than $1,000 per month supporting their grown children, especially if more than one is dependent on them. If you plan to retire while your children are not financially independent, you must ei-

ther plan to cut them off when you retire or factor them in as an expense.

Helpful: Talk to your adult children before you retire to establish reasonable expectations for your support—both the amount of money you're willing to give them and how long you will keep giving it. These conversations can help prevent additional requests for money that might threaten your financial plan.

Retire Just a *Little* Later

John Shoven, PhD, the Charles R. Schwab Professor of Economics at Stanford University, Stanford, California. He is coauthor of the National Bureau of Economic Research study "The Power of Working Longer," which you can find at Siepr.Stanford.edu.

Working just a little longer past your planned retirement age can improve your standard of living for your entire retirement to a surprising extent.

Example: A new study from the National Bureau of Economic Research (NBER) has found that staying on the job just one additional year beyond age 66 would typically result in 8% more income annually. That 8% per year translates into enough dollars to make a difference—for example, it boosts an expected annual retirement income of $50,000 (from Social Security and savings) by $4,000…or an expected income of $125,000 by $10,000, every year for life. And working three extra years rather than one means nearly 25% more annual income.

Main reasons the effect of working another year or so is great: You take Social Security benefits later, so they'll be higher…and you contribute more to your 401(k) or other retirement account before you start tapping it. Also, if you want to buy an annuity for guaranteed steady income when you retire, you can get higher monthly payments for the same lump sum upfront because your remaining life expectancy is shorter.

Another surprisingly powerful benefit of delaying retirement: It can have as much of an impact on your retirement income as if you had saved more each year for a long time…and/or as if your investments had done much better while you were working.

Example: Someone who works just five months beyond age 66 would wind up with the same amount of annual income in retirement as if he had raised his annual 401(k) contributions by an additional percentage point of his salary 30 years earlier.

You Need a Plan B for Retirement

Robert Carlson, managing member, Carlson Wealth Advisors, LLC, reported by Harry Berkowitz, personal finance editor, *Bottom Line Personal*, BottomLineInc.com.

I'm primarily a financial editor, but I'll admit it—retirement planning is not my favorite way to spend a day. Numbers must be crunched, realities faced and tough choices made. It's not a chore I want to do again… but it's one I am going to do again, because many retirement plans eventually need to be retired—and replaced.

Creating a retirement plan means that we all have to make assumptions about the future of the markets, inflation, future priorities and our health over a period of many years. And most likely, "None of those assumptions are going to be correct," says Robert Carlson, managing member of Carlson Wealth Advisors, LLC, and editor of *Retirement Watch*, a monthly newsletter. "Some will be way off."

That doesn't mean retirement planning is wasted time. It means that the plan we have now is only Plan A. We should have a Plan B, too. If Plan A sets an annual retirement budget of $70,000, for example, Plan B might lay out how I could trim that to $50,000 if the stock market collapsed or a health crisis cuts into savings. Other potential Plan Bs might include ways that I could earn money in retirement if necessary…and where I could relocate if my initial retirement destination is not all that I had hoped.

I could put off constructing my Plan B until it's needed, but having a Plan B now reduces the odds that I'll react emotionally rather than thoughtfully if my Plan A doesn't materialize.

Looks like I can't retire from retirement planning just yet.

Tweak the 4% Rule for a Safer Retirement

Wes Moss, CFP, chief investment strategist and partner at Atlanta-based Capital Investment Advisors, author of the best seller *You Can Retire Sooner Than You Think* and host of the investment and personal finance radio show *Money Matters*. WesMoss.com

How much can you withdraw annually from your investment portfolio in retirement without ever running out of money? For more than two decades, 4% has been the widely accepted rule of thumb, assuming that you have a classic retirement asset allocation of half stocks and half bonds. But with inflation rising, plus the possibility of a recession and bear market in the next few years, you need to make some tweaks…

• **Start with the original approach.** During the first year of retirement, withdraw 4% of your portfolio. Every following year, withdraw the same initial dollar amount plus an increase for inflation. *Example:* If you have a $1 million portfolio, you withdraw $40,000 the first year…and if inflation that year is 3%, then the next year you withdraw $40,000 plus 3% of $40,000 ($1,200) for a total withdrawal of $41,200. You repeat these steps, using the previous year's total withdrawal and inflation rate, every year.

• **Veer from the original approach if your portfolio has a very bad or very good year.** *How to do it:* At the end of each year, divide the total amount of that year's withdrawals by the current value of your portfolio to get a percentage. If the withdrawals totaled 5% or more of the current value of the portfolio, you're in danger of burning through your savings too quickly, so you should reduce your total withdrawal amount for the next year to

4% of the portfolio's current value (instead of 4% of the original value) plus the usual adjustment for the previous year's inflation.

Example: Say that during the second year of retirement, you withdrew $41,200 based on your initial 4% amount plus the previous year's inflation. But at the end of that second year, you see that your portfolio value has dropped to $800,000. That means your withdrawals added up to 5.15% of the portfolio's current value—too much! So in the coming (third) year, withdraw no more than $32,000 (4% of the *current* portfolio value) plus a boost for inflation based on the inflation rate in the second year.

On the other hand, if your withdrawal amount over the past year came to 3% or less of the current value of your portfolio, you could splurge and take out more money in the third year using the same 4% formula—meaning, 4% of the current value of the portfolio plus an extra amount based on the previous year's inflation.

With these adjustments each year, over a 35-year period you would have greater than a 95% chance of not running out of money, based on historical returns of stocks and bonds.

TAKE NOTE...

For a Comfortable Retirement...

Many people need to at least double their savings rate for a comfortable retirement. Individuals ages 25 to 64 save an average of 6% to 8% of annual income. But for a middle-income earner ($53,000/year) to retire at age 65 with a 70% salary replacement rate, he/she needs to save 10% starting at age 25...15% starting at 35...or 27% starting at 45.

One solution: Work five years longer. Retiring at age 70 requires saving just 4% starting at 25...6% starting at 35...or 10% starting at 45.

Jialu Streeter, PhD, Stanford Center on Longevity in California, and coauthor of the study "Seeing Our Way to Financial Security in the Age of Increased Longevity." Longevity.Stanford.edu

Avoid These Costly Mistakes in Retirement Account Withdrawals

Ed Slott, CPA, president of Ed Slott & Company, a financial-consulting firm specializing in IRAs and retirement-distribution planning, Rockville Centre, New York. He is author of 12 books including *Ed Slott's Retirement Decisions Guide*. IRAHelp.com

---

Many people struggle with IRS rules concerning withdrawals from tax-deferred retirement accounts. Whether or not you actually are retired, when you turn 70½ you typically must begin to take required minimum distributions (RMDs) from those accounts each year. It's easy to make costly mistakes, including one you might make in the years leading up to age 70½. In the latest audit of retired taxpayers, from 2012, the federal government identified nearly 639,000 people with IRAs worth a total of $40.4 billion who may not have taken the correct RMDs. Penalties for making RMD mistakes are severe. If you fail to withdraw the required amount by the deadline, you could be fined 50% of the amount that you should have withdrawn.

The most important mistakes you need to avoid now...

BEFORE AGE 70½

MISTAKE: **Not tapping tax-deferred accounts until you start to take RMDs.** Many people draw on taxable savings early in retirement to let their tax-deferred savings grow as much as possible. But that strategy can hurt you in the long run because it increases the proportion of your assets that will later be subject to RMDs—perhaps even leading to RMDs in your 70s that are large enough to push you into a higher tax bracket. Also, an increase in your annual income from RMDs could trigger higher taxes on your Social Security benefits and a Medicare high-income surcharge.

Better: If you find that you have dropped into a lower tax bracket in your 60s after you retire, consider taking a series of distributions from tax-deferred accounts. Over time, these withdrawals will shrink the size of those accounts, resulting in lower eventual RMDs. If you don't need the distributions you take before age 70½ to live on, they can be converted to a Roth IRA, which never requires RMDs, or invested in a taxable investment account on which you will owe capital gains tax, not income tax, on profits.

AFTER AGE 70½

MISTAKE: **Postponing your first RMD.** Typically, the deadline to take RMDs each year is December 31 starting in the year in which you turn 70½. But the IRS gives you a cushion for the first one, allowing you to make your first withdrawal as late as April 1 of the year after the calendar year in which you turn 70½. Many people who want to put off starting RMDs opt to wait until this April 1 deadline. But that means you will be making two RMDs in a single year because your second RMD is due by December 31 of that year. Reporting two RMDs on your income taxes in the same year could bump you into a higher tax bracket for that year.

Better: Take your first RMD by December 31 of the year in which you turn 70½, not the following April 1. That way, you spread your first two distributions over two tax years.

MISTAKE: **Not understanding the different rules for taking RMDs from employee retirement plans such as 401(k) and 403(b) accounts versus IRA-based accounts such as traditional IRAs, SEP IRAs and SIMPLE IRAs.** The IRS requires you to calculate the RMDs and withdraw the money from your IRAs and employee retirement plans separately. This means that you can't, for example, take a distribution from an IRA to satisfy the RMD for your 401(k) account.

If you have multiple IRAs, the IRS allows you to take the entire RMD for all your IRAs from just one of the accounts if you wish. However, if you have more than one 401(k), you must calculate the RMD separately for each account and take the required amount from each one.

If you're still working at age 70½ and you do not own more than 5% of the company you work for, you aren't required to take RMDs from your retirement account in that current employer's plan. You are eligible for the "still-working" exemption, as it's known, even if you just work part-time. In fact, you can delay RMDs from that account until April 1 of the year after the year you stop working for the company.

Important: You are required to take RMDs from traditional IRAs and previous employers' 401(k)s even if you are still working.

MISTAKE: **Computing your RMD incorrectly.** Each year, you need to ask two questions to calculate how much you will need to withdraw…

What's the total value of my retirement accounts? Your RMDs are based on the balance in your accounts as of the end of the previous year.

What's my official life expectancy? To find out, consult the IRS table based on your current age. Most seniors use the Uniform Lifetime Table (Table III) in Appendix B of IRS Publication 590-B, *Distributions from Individual Retirement Arrangements* (IRAs). You divide the balance in your accounts as of the end of the previous year by your life-expectancy factor from this table to determine the minimum distribution you must take.

MISTAKE: **Not realizing that you might be able to get RMD penalties dismissed.** The IRS can waive part or all of the daunting 50% penalty on any shortfall in your RMDs for "reasonable" errors. In my experience, you have a good chance to get a waiver for errors that include bad or incorrect advice from a financial adviser, illness, a death in the family or a change of address that disrupted communication.

Steps to take to get a waiver: If you get an IRS notice of failure to meet your RMD, don't pay the penalty. Instead, double-check your RMD calculation to be sure it's accurate. Remove the shortfall amount from the appropriate retirement account or accounts as soon as possible. Then file Form 5329, *Additional Taxes on Qualified Retirement Plans (including IRAs) and Other Tax-Favored Accounts*, with the IRS and include a statement of explanation that includes a request that the penalty be waived.

MISTAKE: **Forgetting the "I" in "IRA."** Married couples often assume that because they file a joint tax return, they can choose from which spouse's IRA to take both their RMDs. But there's no such thing as a joint IRA or joint 401(k). RMDs must be calculated and withdrawn separately from each individual's account or accounts.

MISTAKE: **Thinking RMDs must be in cash.** The IRS allows you to take "in-kind" RMDs so that you are not forced to liquidate the assets just to raise cash for your distribution.

How it works: Say you own shares of stock, a fund or another security that has fallen greatly in value, but you expect it to recover. If you sell the stock in your retirement account and take a distribution, you have locked in your losses. Instead, set up a taxable brokerage account and have the shares transferred into it. You'll have to pay ordinary income tax rates on the value of the shares as of the day of distribution. But after you have held the shares in the taxable account for more than a year, any post-transfer appreciation will be treated as long-term capital gain with a tax rate as low as 0%, depending on your other income.

MISTAKE: **Thinking that you can withdraw amounts exceeding your annual RMD and get credit for next year.** You're allowed to take as large a distribution from your retirement accounts as you want. But the IRS allows you to fulfill your RMD requirements only one year at a time.

AN RMD TAX BREAK WHEN DONATING TO A CHARITY

One of the common mistakes involving RMDs occurs when you donate the money to charity—and you don't gift it in the most tax-efficient way.

People who take an RMD and then use it to make a charitable contribution may not be able to deduct it on their income taxes, especially if they opt to take the new, higher standard deduction this year.

Better: Take what is known as a qualified charitable distribution (QCD) to give up to $100,000 annually to charities. QCDs are available only to owners of traditional IRAs who are age 70½ or older.

You direct your IRA custodian to send a contribution directly to the charities of your choice. The distribution still counts toward your RMD for the year, but the amount is not included in your adjusted gross income. That gives you a chance to receive a tax benefit for your charitable gift even if you don't itemize.

Beware This Tempting Annuity

Scott Witt, president, Witt Actuarial Services, a fee-only consultant that analyzes life insurance policies and annuities for financial planners and affluent individuals, New Berlin, Wisconsin. WittActuarialServices.com

"**A**nnuity" is considered a dirty word by many investors because of the trickiness and complexity of many of these insurance contracts. So annuity providers introduce versions that seem more attractive and understandable. Among the most popular now is the *fixed-index annuity* (FIA).

The pitch: You enjoy a portion of the stock market's gains if stocks rise, and for safety, you won't lose any of your original investment even if the stock market plunges.

That's an intriguing offer at a time when many investors fear the 10-year-old bull market may end before long. Fixed-index annuity sales hit $58 billion in 2017, up 70% since 2012. *Problem:* The hidden costs and restrictions of these annuities mean that they often fall short of their big promises.

How FIAs work: You pay a lump sum to the insurance firm that provides the annuity. Your annual return is determined by a formula linked to a stock index such as the S&P 500. For example, you might earn 60% of the index's annual gain. And if the index's return is negative, your return for the year will be 0%, so your principal will remain safe.

The reality isn't nearly as good as the sales pitch for FIAs, which earn agents among the highest commissions in the annuity industry and tend to be mediocre investments. For starters, the formula used to calculate returns ignores stock dividends—it looks only at stock price gains. That can hurt. For the period from

1930 to 2017, dividend income contributed more than 40% of total S&P 500 returns, on average. In addition, FIAs typically cap annual returns in a range of 3% to 6%. So in 2017, when the S&P 500 returned 22%, your annuity account might have been credited with a 6% gain or less. Many FIAs lock up most of your money for 10 years, allowing you to withdraw no more than 10% of your account annually without penalty.

Finally, all withdrawals are taxed at your ordinary income tax rate, which may be higher than the capital gains rate you would pay on profits from investing in stocks directly.

In the past, the long-term returns of FIAs have been in the 3.5%-to-5% range. They may appeal to some investors who cannot stomach any annual stock losses. But you could get better results with only incrementally more risk with a portfolio of bank CDs (recently paying as high as a 3.39% annual yield for a seven-year term) and a small exposure to an S&P 500 exchange-traded fund (ETF).

An Annuity Gains Appeal

Stan Haithcock, a Florida-based annuity consultant who has authored six books on the topic of annuities. StanTheAnnuityMan.com

Annuities have long had a shady reputation—too complicated, too many fees. But a flood of retiring baby boomers who worry about outliving their assets are giving one particular type, called a deferred income annuity (DIA), another chance. Sales of DIAs soared to $2.3 billion in 2018, up from $200 million in 2011.

In exchange for a lump sum up front, these insurance contracts, which carry no annual fees, promise monthly pensionlike payments that the buyer can choose to start getting as soon as 13 months or as late as 40 years after the policy is issued. Payments continue for the rest of the buyer's life. The older you are when you start receiving the payments, the higher the payments are.

Another reason these annuities are popular now: Since 2014, IRS rules have permitted a special type of DIA called a qualified longevity annuity contract (QLAC) inside some 401(k)s and other tax-deferred retirement accounts. Buyers can postpone the start of payments up to age 85 and, until then, exclude the QLAC in calculating their required minimum distributions (RMDs) that start at age 70½, allowing those taxable distributions to be smaller.

Mistakes to avoid if you consider buying a deferred income annuity...

●**Getting too few price quotes.** Ask your insurance agent for five to 10 quotes. Major underwriters such as Lincoln National Life Insurance, MassMutual and New York Life Insurance all offer similar DIA and QLAC products, but payouts can vary because carriers often adjust their guarantees based on how much business they want to attract during a given period.

●**Waiting for interest rates to rise to get a better deal.** Although higher interest rates affect the level of payouts, postponing purchase of a DIA may mean less time until you start to draw on it, which tends to reduce payments.

How Rolling Over Your 401(k) Could Hurt You

Ric Lager, president of Lager & Company, which advises retirement plan participants about their options, Golden Valley, Minnesota. He is author of *Forget the Pie: Recipe for a Healthier 401(k)*. LagerCo.com

It's conventional wisdom to roll over your assets from a 401(k) plan into an Individual Retirement Account (IRA) whenever you leave a job. However, depending on your circumstances, as well as some big changes to retirement plans that Congress and the Trump administration have been considering at press time, it might be smarter to simply leave the money where it is or move it to a new employer's 401(k) plan. *Here's how to decide...*

THE ROLLOVER DILEMMA

The rollover of 401(k)s to IRAs accounted for more than 95% of the $2 trillion in total IRA contributions in 2017. But it also has led to accusations that investors are being coaxed into costly IRAs unnecessarily. The US Labor Department has launched an investigation into whether Wells Fargo & Co. made inappropriate recommendations to get participants in low-cost 401(k) plans to roll over assets into IRAs with big up-front fees.

The biggest knocks *against* keeping your money in an old 401(k)—high fees and limited investment choices—actually have diminished. Annual fees for 401(k) plans, including administrative fees, have dropped an average of nearly 15% since 2009. And 40% of all plans now offer "brokerage windows" with as many investment options as an IRA.

WHEN TO KEEP YOUR OLD 401(K)

If your employer offers 401(k) investment options that you like and that are low-cost (the average expense ratio of the mutual funds in the plan is 0.8% or less), it may make sense to stay put, especially if you can't re-create your portfolio in a brokerage IRA for less. Large employers often have the bargaining power to negotiate with investment providers to offer "institutional" shares of mutual funds that are cheaper than the "retail" versions available in brokerage IRAs. *Additional reasons to consider keeping your old 401(k)...*

• **Your 401(k) offers a self-directed brokerage window.** *How it works:* You get access to a major brokerage such as Fidelity or Charles Schwab, allowing you to choose from thousands of funds. Although you typically are charged an annual fee of around $50 to use the window, it gives you access to many investments not traditionally available in 401(k)s.

• **You may need protection from creditors and legal judgments.** That's especially important if you're a professional such as a doctor or lawyer. 401(k)s are protected by federal law and can't be touched by most creditors, even if you declare bankruptcy. Although a rollover IRA carries the same protection from creditors if you declare bankruptcy, it typically has much less protection in nonbankruptcy situations. If you lose a civil lawsuit in a malpractice case or because you injured someone, individual state laws determine whether creditors can go after your IRA accounts. For example, in nonbankruptcy proceedings, California protects only

enough of your IRA assets that a judge deems is necessary to support yourself when you retire.

WHEN TO SHIFT TO A NEW 401(K)

Many employers let employees transfer old 401(k) assets to their 401(k) plans. *Here's why it might make sense...*

• **Your new employer's 401(k) plan offers better features, investment options and fees than the old one.** You need to analyze each plan's "summary annual report" to compare details. You also can benefit from the simplicity of tracking all assets in one plan.

• **You are planning to retire early.** Normally, you must wait until age 59½ to make any withdrawals from a traditional 401(k) or traditional IRA—or withdrawals of profits from a Roth 401(k) or Roth IRA—without a 10% early-withdrawal penalty.* But if you leave your job at age 55 or later, the IRS allows you to start taking withdrawals from either type of 401(k) without a penalty. This applies only to a 401(k) at your current employer. (For a Roth 401(k), you must have started contributing at least five years earlier to qualify.)

• **You plan to work past age 70½.** Normally, at that age you must start taking required minimum distributions (RMDs) from your traditional and Roth 401(k)s and from traditional IRAs. But if you are working for an employer where you currently have a traditional 401(k) (which may include 401(k) assets from a prior employer's 401(k) plan) and you don't own more than 5% of the company, the IRS gives you a break. It doesn't require you to start taking RMDs for the traditional 401(k) until April 1 of the year after you retire, although you still must take RMDs for a Roth 401(k) starting at 70½. That means you can allow the assets to grow while postponing the RMD tax bite.

New development: The Treasury Department is reviewing RMD rules to see whether investors could be allowed to start RMDs later and/or RMDs could be reduced once they start.

*With a traditional 401(k) or a traditional IRA, you make contributions with pretax money and pay income on withdrawals. With a Roth 401(k) or Roth IRA, you make contributions with after-tax money...you never pay tax on withdrawals...and you never pay a penalty on withdrawals of your contributions.

WHEN TO ROLL OVER A 401(K) TO AN IRA

About 62% of employees roll over their 401(k) assets when they leave a job. If you work for a company with fewer than 100 employees, investment choices in the 401(k) typically are very limited and administrative expenses are high, making a rollover to an IRA a more attractive option. *Another reason to consider a rollover...*

• **You need a steady income in retirement.** While all 401(k) plans let you take distributions once you retire, many limit you to quarterly or annual withdrawals, making it difficult to customize an income stream that, say, fits your monthly budget. An IRA gives you flexibility to make your withdrawals at any time.

HOW NEW RULES MAY ENHANCE 401(K)s

New rules being considered at the time of press...

• **Pooled 401(k) plans.** Congress wants to allow small businesses across different industries to come together to form multiple-employer 401(k) plans. These large plans would be far more cost-effective and have lower administrative fees and investment costs. Separately, President Donald Trump has directed the Treasury and Labor departments to consider adopting new rules to accomplish this.

• **401(k) annuities.** Only about 9% of 401(k) plans now offer annuities, which provide pensionlike monthly payouts when you retire in exchange for a lump-sum initial payment. Annuities can help solve the challenge of creating a steady and reliable income stream in retirement. Congress wants to promote annuities by requiring 401(k) plan sponsors to show, in quarterly statements, how much income could be generated from an annuity.

GGOD TO KNOW...

Pension Assistance

Retirees and current workers can have their questions answered and problems addressed through a service of the Pension Rights Center at the website below. Free legal help may be available if needed.

PensionHelp.org

212

Answers to Tricky Social Security Questions from Widows and Widowers

Laurence J. Kotlikoff, PhD, professor of economics at Boston University and former senior economist with the President's Council of Economic Advisors. He is president of Economic Security Planning Inc., which develops financial-planning software, and coauthor of *Get What's Yours: The Secrets to Maxing Out Your Social Security.* MaximizeMySocialSecurity.com

---

The Social Security rule book is so long, complex and ever-changing that even Social Security employees don't understand it all. And among the trickiest questions are those related to the death of a spouse. So we went to one of the most knowledgeable Social Security experts in the country and asked for answers to some of the thorniest questions that widowed Social Security recipients often ask. *His answers can help you maximize your benefits without breaking tricky rules and potentially losing money...*

• **My wife died after I started my Social Security benefits.** Can I now suspend my benefits and claim widower's benefits based on my late wife's earnings so that my own benefits can increase until I claim them at age 70? (My benefits are larger than my wife's.)

These sorts of situations come up all the time. Unfortunately, in this case the answer is no—once you begin taking your own retirement benefits, you cannot suspend them and claim a widower's benefit instead.

There is one potential way around this. If no more than 12 months has passed since you began receiving your benefits, you have the option of withdrawing your application for retirement benefits by filing form SSA-521 and repaying all of the benefits you have thus far received (including any benefits paid to your children or late wife based on your earnings history). If you do that, it's like you never applied for your benefits in the first place, freeing you to claim widower's benefits until you reach age 70, at which point your own benefits will reach their maximum level (aside from future cost-of-living adjustments). You are limited to no more than one application withdrawal of this type for your entire life.

• **My husband died decades ago when we were quite young.** I'm now nearing retirement age. Can I collect widow's benefits based on his earnings even though he was in the workforce only a few years?

You probably can. This comes as a surprise to some people because wage earners typically need at least 10 years in the workforce to qualify for Social Security retirement benefits, but different rules apply with the benefits of a widow or widower. The younger the age at which the spouse died, the less work history that is required. The system for calculating this is complex, but as few as six "credits" can be all that's needed when a spouse dies young—and six credits can be earned in less than two full working years.

There are a few caveats worth noting, though. To be eligible for widow's benefits, you must have been married to your late spouse for at least nine months prior to his death. (This nine-month requirement is waived if the spouse died in active military service or under certain other circumstances.) And you must not currently be remarried unless you did not remarry until you were at least 60 years old.

• **I'm about to reach my full retirement age of 66, but I had been planning to wait until age 70 to start Social Security to get as much as possible each month.** However, my husband passed away, and my widow's benefit would be larger than my own benefit. Should I put off claiming my widow's benefit until age 70, too?

No. Unlike your own benefit, widow's benefits never grow any larger than they are when you reach your full retirement age. There is no upside to delaying claiming a widow's benefit any longer than that, and there is considerable downside to doing so—you would miss out on four years of monthly benefits.

• **I know my monthly Social Security retirement benefits will be less if I start collecting as soon as I become eligible at age 62 rather than wait until my full retirement age.** But if I switch to a widow's benefit based on my late husband's benefit when I reach full retirement age, will that be reduced,

---

REMINDER...

Don't Lose Track of Pensions and 401(k)s

More than 25 million US workers who changed jobs between 2004 and 2013 left at least one retirement account behind. The accounts can get harder to track over time as companies merge, go bankrupt or are spun off.

So keep all statements and other communications from all retirement plans...notify former employers and plan record-keepers of any changes in your contact information...and consider consolidating old 401(k) accounts into an IRA or your current employer's plan.

In the case of pension plans, you should hold on to your tax returns. If a plan claims it has sent you a payment but hasn't, an old tax return can prove that the plan owes you money.

Roundup of pension experts, reported at Kiplinger.com.

---

too, because I started my own benefit early? He waited until his full retirement age before claiming.

Your plan to claim your own benefits now and switch to widow's benefits later sounds reasonable. *Here's why:* If you were to claim your widow's benefit before you reach full retirement age, you would not receive your late husband's full benefit even though he waited until his full retirement age to start claiming. Instead, it would be permanently reduced because you took it early. By waiting until your full retirement age to claim the widow's benefit, you will receive his full benefit even though you started your own benefit early.

• **My first marriage ended with my husband's death, and my second ended in divorce.** Will I be able to claim a widow's benefit based on my first husband's earnings?

You probably can, as long as your first marriage lasted at least nine months. As you might already know, remarrying before you turn age 60 typically negates the right to claim a widow's benefit based on an earlier marriage. But if you are no longer married, you once again are entitled to receive your widow's benefit from your first marriage.

SOCIAL SECURITY MARITAL BENEFITS WITHOUT THE WEDDING

You might be entitled to widow's or spousal Social Security benefits even if you never actually wed your partner. The Social Security Administration recognizes common-law marriages—marriages where there was no official marriage ceremony or license but the couple lived together for an extended period as if married. But it does so only if the common-law marriage is recognized under the laws of the state where the Social Security recipient and his/her partner reside, or previously resided together, or if common-law marriages were recognized by the state when they lived there. Common-law marriages are recognized in Alabama, Colorado, the District of Columbia, Iowa, Kansas, Montana, Oklahoma, Rhode Island, South Carolina, Texas and Utah. In several other states, common-law marriages that were entered into before specified dates are recognized. (Go to bit.ly/2HiF2vc for the list.) The burden of proof will be on you to establish that the relationship qualifies (or qualified, in the case of widowhood) as a common-law marriage.

Bottom line: There are people who qualify for valuable spousal and widow's benefits despite the fact that they never officially wed—and many of them probably don't realize it.

How Social Security Misleads You with Its Language

Laurence J. Kotlikoff, PhD, professor of economics at Boston University and former senior economist with the President's Council of Economic Advisors. He is president of Economic Security Planning Inc., which develops financial-planning software, and coauthor of *Get What's Yours: The Secrets to Maxing Out Your Social Security.* MaximizeMySocialSecurity.com

The Social Security system is so complex that it has more rules than even the famously complicated tax code. And part of what makes Social Security so tricky is the language used by the Social Security Administration (SSA) and by others trying to explain what the SSA is trying to say.

After you have paid into the system for years, don't let the complexities of Social Security keep you from getting all the benefits you deserve. *Here are nine Social Security benefit terms that it pays to understand and that might mean something very different from what you think they do...*

• **"Full retirement age."** The word "full" usually means "maximum," so many people quite reasonably assume that full retirement age is the age at which the monthly Social Security retirement benefit reaches its maximum amount (other than for inflation adjustments).

What's tricky: Although it's true that your Social Security payments increase the longer after age 62 you wait to start collecting, those increases don't stop at full retirement age—which can better be thought of as "normal retirement age." They continue up to age 70. (However, certain types of benefits, such as "spousal benefits," reach their maximum at full retirement age...and at that age you can start earning as much income as you want without having any benefits withheld—more on these topics below.)

What to do: If your goal is to receive the highest-possible monthly Social Security benefit based on your own earnings history, you would have to wait until age 70 rather than claim at your full retirement age, which now is somewhere between age 66 and 67 depending on your year of birth. Of course, if you need the money sooner, either for spending or because you believe you would be better off investing it—or if you are convinced that you won't live much beyond 70—you may choose to start taking benefits sooner.

• **"Earnings test."** If you earn significant income ($17,640 or more as of 2019) during a year in which you receive Social Security retirement benefits but have not yet reached your "full" retirement age, SSA will withhold some or all of your payments for that year, depending on how much income you earn. (Go to SSA.gov, and search "Getting Benefits While Working" for details on how much.)

Such earnings also would reduce spousal benefits if your spouse has begun claiming them.

What's tricky: The withheld payments are not necessarily lost forever. Once you reach full retirement age, your monthly payments and any spousal benefits will be adjusted upward to start making up for the money withheld under the earnings test. If you live long enough, typically until around age 80, you can make up all of the withheld payments. But the fact that you are likely to get that money back often is not properly explained, making many Social Security recipients decide to forgo income opportunities and therefore reduce their wealth over time.

What to do: Consider both the reduction of current amounts received and the later upward adjustment in deciding whether it makes sense to claim Social Security benefits while you are working.

Exception: If you switch to a larger spousal or widow(er)s benefit at full retirement age, the upward adjustment of your retirement benefit will be of no value.

• **"Life expectancy."** If you use the calculators on the SSA website (or on many third-party financial websites), they will estimate how long you're likely to live based on factors such as your health and family history. Some calculators then will use this estimate to recommend when you should begin receiving your benefits.

What's tricky: Individuals don't die on schedule—they can outlive their life expectancies, potentially by many years. And if you make decisions about when to begin your benefits based on a retirement calculator that uses average life expectancies, you might undercut one of the best features of Social Security benefits—they continue for as long as you live, and the longer you live, the more it pays to have delayed starting benefits (up to age 70). Your widow(er) also will, potentially, enjoy higher benefits.

What to do: Do not claim your benefits before you turn 70 just because a retirement calculator featuring a life-expectancy estimate recommends that you do so. Think of Social Security as a form of longevity insurance that will protect you from outliving your savings.

• **"Spousal benefit."** Married people often are eligible for this benefit, which is based on a spouse's earnings history, assuming that the spouse already has started receiving his/her own benefit.

What's tricky: This is not an extra benefit you can claim on top of your own benefit—there's no way to receive benefits greater than the larger of the two at any time. The confusing way the SSA describes spousal benefits can make it seem otherwise, however—it implies that you can claim both at the same time. But if you try to claim both, you will receive your own benefit plus your "excess spousal benefit"—which is, roughly speaking, the portion of your spousal benefit that exceeds your own benefit. The total is not any greater than the larger of the two benefits.

In fact, depending on when you were born, it might not even be possible to start your spousal benefit without accidentally triggering the start of your own benefit, a detail that's easy to miss—and doing that could reduce your benefits for the rest of your life if you do it before your own benefit tops out at age 70.

What to do: If you were born on or before January 1, 1954, and your spouse is collecting his/her retirement benefits (or in some cases if you are divorced), you can file a "restricted application" to start only your spousal benefit when you reach your full retirement age—spousal benefits do not continue to increase beyond this point—while your own future benefit continues to increase, potentially up to age 70. If you were born after this date and/or have not yet reached full retirement age, do not file for spousal benefits unless you are willing to also start your own retirement benefit, which will prevent your own future benefit from continuing to increase. If you were widowed, it is possible to file for "survivors benefits" without automatically starting your own benefit regardless of your year of birth.

• **"Cost-of-living adjustment (COLA)."** You probably know that your Social Security benefits will be modified as needed to keep pace with inflation.

What's tricky: What's rarely mentioned is that these adjustments have historically fallen well short of increases in the actual cost of living. That's because health care and housing are a larger part of many seniors' expenses than they are for many younger people, and those expenses have been rising much faster than the overall rate of inflation.

What to do: Assume that your housing and health-care costs will rise significantly over the course of your retirement, and plan your retirement budget accordingly. Social Security's cost-of-living adjustments are very unlikely to keep pace.

• **"Retroactive benefits."** You might receive a call from a Social Security employee as you near your 70th birthday informing you that if you agree to start your benefits right then—before you turn 70—you can receive a check equal to six months of "retroactive benefits."

What's tricky: The SSA employee might imply that this check is extra money that you otherwise would not receive. In truth, if you accept this "extra" payment, the SSA will reduce your ongoing benefits as if you had started them six months earlier than the date you received the call.

What to do: If your plan has been to wait to age 70 to start receiving benefits, don't feel that you have to change your plan and jump at this offer.

• **"Tax-exempt interest."** Some government-issued bonds provide income that is not subject to federal income tax. That might not sound like it's related to your Social Security benefits, but it can be—and not in a good way.

MONEYWISE...

To Get the Most Money from Social Security

To collect the most possible from Social Security, be sure to work a full 35 years. Benefits are based on your 35 highest years of earnings—so if you work fewer than 35 years, the amount counted for each year without earnings is zero. That reduces your benefit permanently.

The Motley Fool, Fool.com.

What's tricky: The income produced by these bonds is itself tax-exempt, but receiving it makes it more likely that your Social Security benefits will be taxed. If for 2019, your non–Social Security taxable income plus this tax-exempt bond income plus half of your Social Security income exceed $25,000 ($32,000 for joint filers), up to half of your Social Security benefits might be taxable…and if it exceeds $34,000 ($44,000 for joint filers), up to 85% might be taxable.

What to do: If you invest in federally tax-exempt bonds, keep in mind that they might not be as appealing as you imagine during years when you receive Social Security benefits.

• **"Benefits estimate."** The SSA mails out statements to people age 60 and older not yet receiving benefits that include an estimate of future benefits.

What's tricky: The estimates can be wildly inaccurate—they often miss the mark by 20% or more.

What to do: Search online for a Social Security tool that adjusts for factors such as expected salary increases and estimated inflation.

• **"Supplemental Security Income."** Known as SSI for short, this is a program run by the Social Security Administration that provides income to certain low-income seniors and the disabled.

What's tricky: The Social Security Administration, itself known by the acronym SSA, administers programs known by the acronyms SSI and SSDI (that's Social Security Disability Insurance). All those similar acronyms can cause confusion. If you say the wrong acronym when you call the SSA or speak with a financial planner—or this person mishears you—you might receive the wrong advice. For example if you call the SSA and say, "I'm receiving SSI. Will my benefits change if I move to a different state?" you might be told that they could…but if you meant to ask about standard Social Security benefits, that answer is not correct.

What to do: When you speak with financial planners or the Social Security Administration, refer to programs by their full names rather than their acronyms to avoid misunderstandings.

Social Security Scam

Fraudsters are impersonating Social Security employees. They call potential victims and say that the Social Security number of the person being called has been suspended because of fraudulent activity and that immediate action is needed to fix the problem. The person is told to say the number to have it restored. Another version of this scam is when the criminals say government computers are down and the person being called must state his/her number to prevent it from being suspended. Variations on the scam use e-mail instead of phone calls. But Social Security will never call if it finds an account problem—it will send a letter through the US mail.

Social Security does send e-mails if you establish an online Social Security account. But you should never click links in any unexpected e-mail. If you see an e-mail demanding immediate action, go directly to SSA.gov to be sure that the message is legitimate.

Roundup of experts on Social Security scams, reported in RetirementWatch.com.

Best Ways to Earn a Few Extra Bucks (or a Lot) in Retirement

Nancy Collamer, career coach and consultant based in Old Greenwich, Connecticut. She is author of Second-Act Careers: 50+ Ways to Profit from Your Passions During Semi-Retirement. MyLifestyleCareer.com

Just because you want to retire doesn't mean that you're done working. Nearly one in five Americans age 65 and older is in the workforce, according to the Bureau of Labor Statistics. While 60% of that group has simply stayed on the job, the rest retired and later "unretired."

Some unretirees return to the workforce because they find retirement unfulfilling…others because they want to earn a few extra bucks, perhaps to take a special trip without bursting their retirement budgets…and still others because they suffered a financial setback and need to earn as much as possible.

Good news: Unemployment rates are so low right now that in many parts of the country, the odds of finding appealing work is very good even for retirees who have been out of the job market for years.

TARGET: $5,000 TO $15,000 PER YEAR

It might be possible to earn $5,000 to $15,000 per year without doing anything that takes up too much of your time—and/or without doing anything that even feels like work. *Three ways to earn a modest amount of income in a modest amount of time in retirement—and have a good time doing it…*

•**Be a dog walker, ride-share driver, Airbnb host or another sort of "gig" worker.** "Gig economy" companies such as ride-sharing firms Uber and Lyft are always in need of people who want to earn extra money through part-time freelance work. If you don't enjoy driving, alternative options include Rover.com, which arranges gigs as dog walkers/dog sitters…Jury Test and Online Verdict, which seeks people willing to serve as "mock jurors" so that lawyers can test their cases…Wyzant, which seeks tutors for students…and the well-known Airbnb, which helps people arrange short-term rentals of rooms or properties. Many retirees appreciate the flexibility of this sort of work—they take time off to travel and work only when they want. In many cases, the work is enjoyable, too.

Example: I know one retired corporate vice president who is earning $1,500 a month walking dogs through Rover.com. He doesn't need the money—he just loves dogs, and he considers it a good way to get exercise.

What to do: Visit $ideHusl, a website that provides ratings and details about gig-economy employers.

•**Be an adjunct professor.** A local college might be looking for someone to teach a class related to your area of professional expertise. These part-time professor positions tend to pay modestly—usually only a few thousand dollars per class—but that could add up to perhaps $10,000 a year if you teach a class or two per semester. Because the pay is minimal, colleges sometimes will hire people who don't have a PhD as long as they have relevant professional experience.

The main upside of this job isn't financial: Retirees often find it rewarding to pass along their knowledge to younger generations…and being a college professor conveys more prestige than most other low-paying part-time jobs.

What to do: Visit HigherEdJobs.com, which lists many jobs of this sort. Or look for a "jobs" or "employment" page on the websites of colleges within commuting distance of your home—especially nonelite schools such as community colleges.

•**Take a seasonal job someplace you would like to take a vacation.** Be a park ranger in a national park…or a guide at a fishing lodge…or a ski instructor at a ski slope. These jobs often pay little more than minimum wage, but they could include lodging and provide access to an incredible resort or a place of tremendous natural beauty. These employers often are happy to hire retirees—younger people who take these low-paying seasonal jobs tend to soon leave them for better-paying full-time positions, while many retirees prefer to work only a few months of the year.

What to do: Visit the website CoolWorks. com to find these opportunities…or contact the owners or managers of seasonal businesses where you would enjoy working.

TARGET: $20,000 TO $30,000 PER YEAR

If you always wanted to try a different career, an entry-level position in that field could pay in this range—if you were willing to take a full-time position. If you would prefer not to work full-time, returning to your former career on a part-time basis might be an option (more on returning to a former career below). But returning to your old career might not be the only part-time option that could pay you $20,000 or more. *You might be able to do something new that leverages your decades of experience in a new way, such as…*

•**Work for a recruiter.** If you retired relatively recently after decades in your field, there's a good chance that you have a broad network of contacts in the sector. These contacts could make you an appealing hire for a recruiter—you know who is worth hiring in the field. It might be possible to earn $20,000 or more working for a recruiter even if you take on only a few projects each year—recruiters can earn 20% or more of the first-year income of their placements. If you received half this fee when you take on a project for a recruiter, you could earn $20,000 by arranging just two hires with $100,000 salaries.

What to do: Contact recruiters who work in your sector—if you were recruited by a headhunter in recent years, that might be a good place to start. Explain that you are recently retired, have a wide range of contacts in your field and are interested in freelance recruiting opportunities. The job market is so hot these days that some recruiters—especially solo practitioners—are stretched thin and might be willing to give you a shot.

•**Become a consultant or trainer.** If you have a desirable business skill, employers might be willing to pay you to consult with them or train their employees. Skills in particular demand include sales, marketing and social media—but consulting/training is possible with any business-related skill. Your odds of success are highest if your résumé leaves no doubt that you truly were among the best at this skill during your career.

EASY TO DO…

3 Easy Ways to Make Some Extra Money

•**Share receipts.** Services such as Ibotta will pay you to scan and send receipts from items you buy. Ibotta sends you rebate offers from stores—you shop, use your smartphone to take a picture of the receipt, submit it using the Ibotta app and get a rebate within 48 hours.

•**Give your opinion.** Harris Poll Online pays for opinions on politics, products, customer service and more.

•**Take pictures.** Stock photography sites including Shutterstock.com always are looking for high-quality images.

MoneyTalksNews.com

Example: You won awards...or rose to an impressive level at a highly respected company.

Consulting or training can pay anywhere from $40 an hour to several hundred dollars an hour, depending on how in demand your skill is...how impressive your résumé is...and how good you are at marketing your services.

What to do: Let your network of contacts know that you are looking for consulting or training opportunities. Also, network with local business owners at area business association meetings and chamber of commerce meetings.

TO EARN $50,000 OR MORE

If you feel that you'll need to earn $50,000 or more a year, your best bet typically is to return to the sector where you worked prior to retirement—that's where your skill set and experience will be most valuable.

What to do: Learn as much as you can about what's going on in your former sector right now. What employers are pursuing what projects? What are the latest challenges? If you've been away for a while, you can catch up by reading the industry press and/or chatting or e-mailing informally with close friends and allies who still are in the sector. When you feel that you're up to date, brainstorm about specific ways that you and your skill set could help employers achieve their current goals.

Contact people in the field, say that you're looking to return to the workplace, ask if they know of openings and explain how you would help these employers achieve their goals. (The better job you do explaining how you can help an employer with its latest goals, the better the odds that it will want to hire you. This not only establishes that you would be useful, but it shows that you have remained in touch with the sector—something companies worry about when they hire unretirees.)

Two ways to contact people in the field...

• **Network one-on-one with your contacts.** Invite former colleagues who respect you to lunch or coffee.

• **Attend industry conferences.** These can be an effective and efficient way to meet large numbers of people in your former field.

Tip: Some people you meet with will no doubt wonder why you're unretiring, rather than unwinding on a beach somewhere. Explain that you enjoyed the relaxation of retirement but that the time away reminded you how much you enjoyed the challenges of the workplace, too.

Happiest Places to Retire in the US

Lynchburg, Virginia, tops the list as the happiest place to retire in the US with a well-being score of 64.9 on a scale of 0 to 100. The score is based on polled residents' ratings of five areas of their lives—purpose (do they like what they do), social (having supportive relationships), financial (being able to manage their budgets), community (how much they like the place where they live) and physical (being in good health).

The rest of the top 10 are Ann Arbor, Michigan, with a score of 64.4...Portland, Maine, 63.9 ...Carlsbad, California, 63.8...Durham, North Carolina, 63.6...Cape Coral, Florida, 63.6...Kennewick, Washington, 63.6...Provo, Utah, 63.2... Charleston, South Carolina, 63.1...Burlington, Vermont, 63.0.

Well-Being Index compiled by digital health company Sharecare, working with Gallup. WellBeingIndex. ShareCare.com

Least/Most Expensive States for Retirement

The least expensive US states in which to retire are Mississippi, whose annual average living expenses of $41,615 mean that you need $1,040,382 to retire and not run out of money if you draw down your savings by about 4% a year...Oklahoma, where you will require $1,093,640...and Michigan, which requires $1,098,594.

The most expensive retirement locations, because of high housing, tax, health-care and other costs are Hawaii, where you would need $2,307,419 to afford retirement…California, $1,746,356…New York, $1,658,418…and Alaska, $1,621,262.

Analysis by GoBankingRates.com.

Retiring Abroad Doesn't Have to Be Just a Dream

Dan Prescher, senior editor at *International Living* magazine and coauthor of *The International Living Guide to Retiring Overseas on a Budget*. He currently lives in Mexico and has previously lived in Panama, Nicaragua and Ecuador. InternationalLiving.com

Have you ever thought about retiring abroad? It's something many people consider and dream about. It can be a great way to stretch retirement savings and experience a different part of the world. But it's a dream that often is derailed by doubts—questions such as, *Is this really worth doing?…Is it practical?…Is it safe?…Would I be happy?*

An increasing number of retirees are concluding that the answers are all "yes"—more than 550,000 Americans now receive their Social Security benefits outside the US, a sharp increase from nearly 400,000 who did so in the year 2000.

The questions and doubts are not always easy to tackle. *To help you figure out whether retiring abroad would be great for you, here are answers to the big questions people often have about it…*

•**Won't I miss my family and friends?** The honest answer is, you might not miss loved ones any more than if you retired to a different part of the US—but it does depend on which country you choose. If you retire to Southeast Asia, for example, flying home can be a long haul. But if you retire to Latin America or Western Europe, coming back to see family isn't much harder or more time-consuming than flying around the US. Some people who retire to these regions fly back to the US multiple times a year…or even split the

year between the US and the foreign country. *Example:* Flights between Panama City and New York City are only around an hour longer, on average, than flights between Phoenix and New York City.

And video-calling services such as Skype and FaceTime allow you to call home as often as you like, as long as you have Internet service.

•**How much money will I save compared with living in the US?** In the popular expat enclaves of Latin America and Southeast Asia, your dollar might stretch nearly twice as far as in the US. Retired couples often can live very well for $2,000 to $2,500 a month…and sometimes even less. That, in essence, makes you quite a bit wealthier than you are in the US.

Don't expect to reap these savings from day one, however—it takes a few months to learn how to spend money efficiently in a foreign land. *Example:* Many retirees initially buy the products they used back home—but goods imported from the US can be pricey overseas. Soon they learn which local brands are just as good. For example, local beers, wines and liquors often are much cheaper than imports and they can be excellent.

On the other hand, if you retire to one of the big, famous cities of Western Europe, such as Paris or London, you'll likely spend more than you would in the US. But there are other, lesser known places in Europe that are affordable where you could retire on a modest budget. *Examples:* If you dream of retiring to France, affordable and appealing areas include the warm and beautiful Languedoc-Rousillon region near the Spanish border…the Rhône-Alpes region with its pristine lakes and Alpine views…and the pastoral Normandy region, a two-hour drive from Paris. Europe has excellent, affordable rail service, so you can visit any nearby big cities frequently. Or consider retiring to Spain and Portugal, which tend to be less expensive than other countries of Western Europe.

•**How will I get health care and health insurance?** Medicare will not pay your medical bills outside the US. But in the major retirement destinations of Western Europe and Latin America, health care is very affordable and very good. (In Latin America, health care often is up to US standards in big cities and towns. The farther you get from those population centers, the more limited the services are—something to keep in mind if you have specific health-care needs.) Prices might be one-third to one-fifth of what you would pay for comparable medical care in the US if you pay in cash—that is, without any insurance.

Many countries have national health-care systems with negligible fees that foreign residents are eligible to join. These programs can have long waits for nonemergency care, however, and in some cases, they do not provide access to the top hospitals. There often is a private health-care system as well. Insurance that covers this private system often costs just a few thousand dollars a year. *Example:* In Panama, private medical insurance can cost as little as $80 a month, but it typically is not available to people over age 65. People above this age can obtain a "hospital membership" for between $90 and $175 a month.

Smart: Keep your US Medicare coverage in effect even though you cannot use it outside the US. Medicare is relatively inexpensive, and if you keep it, you have the option of returning to the US to receive care for a major medical problem...or the option of moving back to the US later without paying the inflated Medicare premiums that follow a coverage lapse. It makes less sense to pay for a Medigap policy, which you buy from a private insurer to fill in coverage gaps that traditional Medicare leaves, if you expect to be out of the US for years. There's also no need to pay for Medi-

care Part D drug coverage because you can't use it when abroad...and you will not face a late penalty for signing up upon your return, as long as you do so within 63 days of moving back to the US.

• **Will I be allowed to set up residence anywhere I want to go?** Most countries are happy to have American retirees move in—US retirees bring dollars and don't take jobs away from locals. You might have to endure considerable paperwork and be required to prove that you have assets and income. *Examples:* Costa Rica's Pensionado program for expat retirees requires proof of monthly income of $1,000 or more from a pension or retirement fund. France does not have a program specifically for expat retirees, but expat retirees often can obtain a *carte de séjour visiteur* from a French consulate if they can show that they have the means to support themselves.

Buying real estate usually is possible, too—but don't be in a rush to do so. Rent for at least six months to make sure that you've truly found the place you want to live.

Helpful: If you decide to buy property, ask other expats in the area to recommend a lawyer who specializes in helping foreigners buy real estate—in many countries, the process is significantly different from that of the US.

• **Will my money be safe in a foreign bank?** Probably—most countries where retirees live have stable banking systems. Still, the banks may not have the rock-solid FDIC insurance of US banks, which is one reason many expat retirees keep most or all of their money in US bank accounts and in US investments. *Examples of US banks that do not impose currency-conversion fees or fees for foreign ATM use:* Capital One 360 Checking (CapitalOne.com) or Charles Schwab Bank High Yield Investor Checking (Schwab.com). Consider keeping a small amount of money in a local account in the country to which you have relocated.

• **Will I be safe in a foreign country?** If you retire to an area where there are lots of other Americans, the odds are good that you will be safe—if the area weren't safe, it wouldn't be so popular with Americans. That's true even in

TAKE NOTE...

Aging—It's All in the Mind

When brain scans were performed on adults (average age 71), those who reported feeling younger than their chronological ages had brains with structural characteristics that are more commonly found in younger people. The finding adds to the growing body of research into personal feelings about aging and their link to neurological changes.

Frontiers in Aging Neuroscience.

much of Mexico, a country that has well-publicized crime problems. The crime is largely concentrated in a few parts of that very large country—much of Mexico is as safe as the US. Safe, desirable and affordable areas include Mérida on the Yucatán Peninsula...and Lake Chapala in Mexico's central highlands.

For any country you are considering, the US State Department's Travel Advisories web page can be a useful resource for avoiding unsafe areas. (Go to Travel.state.gov, and click on the "Find International Travel Information" tab.)

•**Can I receive Social Security benefits abroad?** If you are a US citizen, you can receive your benefits in almost any country in the world. Cuba and North Korea are among the exceptions.

•**How will living abroad affect my taxes?** It will complicate them but not necessarily increase them. The US requires that its citizens file tax returns even when they live abroad, so you probably will have to file returns in two countries. But the US tax code includes a "foreign tax credit," so the amount in taxes you pay a foreign country generally can be offset from your US tax bill. Alternatively, you can claim an itemized deduction for foreign taxes.

You could avoid US income taxes entirely by renouncing your US citizenship, but very few expat retirees do this, for both patriotic and practical reasons. Keeping US citizenship guarantees that you can return to the US if necessary.

•**How hard is it if I don't speak the language?** If you choose a country where English is the official language, such as Belize or Ireland, this isn't an issue, of course. And you can get by speaking only English in other countries if you settle in a community with lots of American and Canadian expats. But why do that? You'll enjoy living abroad much more if you learn the national language, and it's fine—in fact, fun—to do that after you've arrived.

WHERE TO GO

Every year, *International Living* magazine rates foreign countries for Americans to retire to, based on a dozen criteria including climate, health care, safety—and affordability. Among the top-rated affordable countries for 2019 are Panama, Costa Rica, Mexico, Ecuador and Malaysia (list for 2020 was unavailable at press time). For more information, go to the website InternationalLiving.com/best-places-to-retire.

13

Travel Time

5 Travel Spending Mistakes Even Savvy Travelers Make

Travel savings are not always what they seem to be. That unbelievable $99 airfare to Europe? It may omit luggage fees, seat-selection charges and other costs. That tropical resort that's offering a half-off sale? Check the deal's dates—if it's the rainy season, you might spend more than half your trip stuck inside. It's not just the eye-catching advertised deals that can be deceptive, either—many travel costs are purposely made confusing by the travel industry.

You may be experienced enough to avoid some of the traps—such as the "low" hotel rates on third-party travel sites that often can be beat by going to a hotel's own website or calling the hotel directly. *But even many experienced travelers are making the following*

five mistakes when shopping for airfare...hotels...rental cars...and cruises...

***MISTAKE:* Booking nonrefundable hotel rooms or rental cars more than a month in advance.** The best deals on hotel rooms and rental cars often are not available until quite close to the travel date...and there is a way to give yourself an opportunity to get the best deal without the risk of simply waiting.

What to do: Book *refundable* hotel rooms and rental-car reservations approximately four to six weeks before your trip—that's often when the competitive prices begin to appear. Then, if you're sure of your travel plans, shop for lower *nonrefundable* prices during the week or so prior to your trip, when very attractive last-minute deals sometimes pop up. Keep checking nonrefundable prices right up to the final day and time when you can cancel the refundable reservation without a penalty.

Corey Sandler, veteran author and journalist based in Nantucket, Massachusetts. His latest book is *Bottom Line's Secrets of the Savvy Consumer*. CoreySandler.com

If you find a better nonrefundable price, grab it and then cancel your refundable reservation. *Example:* I recently saved $150 by canceling a refundable car-rental reservation one day before a trip and booking a nonrefundable last-minute deal instead.

Warning: This is not an effective strategy with airfare because refundable airline tickets are almost always much more expensive than nonrefundable tickets. As a rule of thumb, airfares tend to be lowest a few weeks prior to departure, though this can vary.

MISTAKE: **Paying one-way rental-car pricing for an extended trip.** Car-rental agencies often charge much steeper daily rates when travelers return cars to locations other than where the cars were picked up—potentially two to four times as much per day. If you are renting a car only to drive from one city to another, there might be no easy way to avoid these steep rates…but there is a better option if you intend to spend some days driving within a region, as well as some days driving from region to region.

What to do: When you intend to use a rental car within a region for one day or more and also to drive between cities, split the rental between two different cars. That way you pay the high one-way rate only for the day(s) when you actually are driving from town to town. *Example:* I needed a rental car to drive from Boston to New York City and then to drive around New York for a week. The best one-way rate I could find was slightly more than $150 per day—upward of $1,050 for the seven-day rental. But I found rates of just under $50 per day for an in-town New York City rental from the very same rental company. I rented a car in Boston for one day of one-way travel…dropped that car off at the New York rental desk…immediately picked up a different car…and saved more than $600.

MISTAKE: **Booking a flight through a discount travel site that doesn't provide key details until after you commit.** Some travelers are drawn to Priceline's Express Deals and Hotwire's Hot Rate Flight because these sites often offer lower airfares than can be found elsewhere—sometimes 10% or 20% less. The catch is that these sites require travelers to book nonrefundable fares before learning details such as which airline they will be flying and the departure and arrival times. (An eight-hour flight-departure window typically is provided instead.)

There's a reason these sites do not provide flight details before you book—their flights typically are among the least popular, least convenient flights around. If you're willing to take a chance to get a big discount, that's fine, especially if you can be very flexible. But if inconvenient flight times mean that you must use up a vacation day at each end of your trip getting where you're going, the savings may not be worth the trouble.

What to do: Consider skipping "blind offer" airfare sites.

MISTAKE: **Assuming that you must always book airline tickets online to avoid a phone-booking fee.** You may know that many airlines now impose a fee for booking a ticket over the phone rather than online—typically $25 per ticket. (Delta and Southwest do not currently charge a fee for phone booking.) But just because an airline charges this fee does not necessarily mean that you always must pay it to book by phone. Unlike with most airline fees, it often is possible to get phone-booking fees waived.

What to do: If there's a good reason that you want to book tickets over the phone, call the airline's reservations number and tell the representative why it would be difficult for you to book your ticket online. Is the airline's website giving you trouble? Is there something unusual about the tickets you are trying to book that makes them challenging to book through the website (such as booking two tickets but paying for one with frequent-flier miles and the other with a credit card)? Politely ask the rep if he/she will waive the phone-booking fee—more often than not, the rep will do so as long as the caller can point to an online-booking challenge. If a phone rep won't waive this fee, you haven't cost yourself anything except a few minutes of time—you can hang up and try to book online or call again and repeat your request to a different phone rep. *Exception:* Discount airlines in-

Best Time to Book for Low-Cost Plane Tickets

Booking an airline reservation 21 to 121 days before a flight is the best period for low price plus reasonable seat selection. Booking 169 to 319 days in advance costs an average of $50 more but, of course, offers the most flight and seat options. Booking 122 to 168 days in advance costs $20 more than in the lowest-cost period. Compared with the prime window, booking 14 to 20 days before a flight may save you a little money—depending on season and destination—but flight and seat options will likely be limited.

Booking seven to 13 days prior to a flight nearly guarantees both higher costs and fewer choices—fliers paid about $160 more for tickets in this time frame compared with the prime-booking period. And booking zero to six days before flying leads to an average increase of $208 over the prime-booking period—and the greatest likelihood of being in a center seat.

2018 Annual Airfare Study of 917 million airfares in more than 8,000 markets by CheapAir.com.

nard, Regent Seven Seas, Oceania and Viking are above average...AIDA, Carnival, Celebrity, Costa, Holland America, MSC, Norwegian, P&O, Princess, Pullmantur and Royal Caribbean are the next level down...and although there tend not to be budget cruise lines that are the equivalent of a budget hotel chain, older ships from some of the cruise lines in this last category tend to have lower rates, possibly because of less impressive amenities and/or less popular or shorter routes.

Helpful: Space-to-passenger ratio is one way to estimate the quality of a cruise ship. Divide the ship's "gross tonnage"—a measurement of a ship's usable space, not its weight—by the number of passengers it can carry. (Tonnage should be available on the cruise line's website. If not, call the cruise line and ask.) If the result is 30 or 40 or higher, it's likely a spacious, comfortable ship...if it's close to 20, it's likely a nice-but-not-luxurious ship...if it's around 10 or below, passengers probably are packed in like sardines.

cluding Allegiant, Frontier and Spirit rarely waive phone-booking fees.

MISTAKE: **Comparing cruise itineraries and prices but not cruise line and ship quality.** Travelers understand that a $100 room at a Comfort Inn is not necessarily a better deal than a $300 room at the Ritz-Carlton across town—the quality of these hotels will be very different. Yet novice cruisers often fail to consider differences in cruise-line quality when they compare cruise prices. (Some also fail to consider what's included in the price—some cruise prices include drinks, meals and even transit to and from the port...while others do not.)

What to do: Before booking, know whether you will be cruising on the Ritz-Carlton of cruise lines, on the Comfort Inn or on something in-between.

Examples: Crystal, Seabourn and Silversea are high-end cruise lines...Azamara, Cu-

Save on Baggage with This Credit Card Trick

You can save on baggage fees and other airline charges by booking travel with a credit card that waives the fees. The airline-branded cards often offer a checked bag for free when flights are purchased using the card. The free-bag offer frequently is extended to traveling companions as well. Some non-airline credit cards may refund other service fees, such as the cost of in-flight food and drinks.

An example: The PenFed Pathfinder Rewards card has no annual fee and refunds up to $100/year in incidental charges.

Kiplinger's Personal Finance.

Don't Get Stuck in Long Airport Security Lines

You can expect longer airport screening lines due to upgraded security measures. The Transportation Security Administration now is requiring travelers to remove any electronics bigger than a cell phone from carry-ons before X-ray screening.

To avoid getting stuck: Download the free *MiFlight* app for real-time reports from other passengers to estimate how long security checkpoint lines at an airport are taking. Bypass the longest lines by enrolling in TSA PreCheck (TSA.gov) or Global Entry (TTP.cbp.dhs.gov).

Christopher Elliott writes the "On Travel" column for *USA Today* and "The Navigator" column for *The Washington Post*. He is author of *How to Be the World's Smartest Traveler*. Elliott.org

Airports with Worst Wi-Fi Security

Travelers at some US airports are especially vulnerable to phone, laptop and tablet hacking. The Wi-Fi at these airports is weakly secured.

Least secure are San Diego International... John Wayne (Santa Ana, California)...William P. Hobby (Houston)...Southwest Florida International (Fort Myers)...and Newark Liberty International.

For protection, use cellular instead of Wi-Fi... avoid e-mail and financial accounts...and make sure you have the latest version of your device's operating system.

Dror Liwer, chief security officer of Coronet, a global cybersecurity firm with offices in Berlin, New York City and Tel Aviv. He oversaw a study of Wi-Fi security at 45 US airports. Coro.net

Avoid Jet Lag— 3 Ways That Work!

Michael J. Breus, PhD, clinical psychologist based in Manhattan Beach, California, diplomate of the American Board of Sleep Medicine and fellow of the American Academy of Sleep Medicine.

Wendy Bazilian, DrPH, RD, founder of Bazilian's Health Clinic in San Diego, where she has been helping clients with their health, nutrition and fitness goals for more than a decade. She is author of *Eat Clean, Stay Lean* and *The SuperFoods Rx Diet*.

Robin DiPasquale, ND, RH (AHG), doctor of naturopathic medicine and registered herbalist (American Herbalist Guild), in private practice at Red Lotus Healing Arts, Fort Collins, Colorado. Dr. DiPasquale has been practicing the healing arts for more than 30 years.

It's fun to see distant, exotic places, but if you're zoned out from jet lag, it's not nearly as much fun as it could be. Yes, eventually you adjust. But why lose precious vacation days (or productive workdays)? You don't have to.

Here are three top experts' favorite techniques to quickly sync your body clock to a new local time. *Bonus: You can use these strategies again when you get back home...*

TRY MELATONIN—THE RIGHT WAY

On average, our bodies tend to naturally adjust to time zones at a rate of one or two per day—so recovering from flying from Miami to Paris, six time zones away, can take up to five days. To shorten the recovery time, sleep specialist Michael J. Breus, PhD, recommends melatonin...taken in the right dose.

How it works: Melatonin is a sleep-enhancing hormone produced in the brain in step with Earth's 24-hour cycle of daylight and darkness. Levels are naturally highest at night (even if your body doesn't *think* it's night) and lowest upon exposure to sunlight in the morning (ditto). When you travel long distances, your body's rhythm gets confused by the external light and dark signals of your new location. The effect is especially pronounced when you travel more than three time zones eastward.

Try this: Melatonin is widely available as an over-the-counter supplement. To reduce jet lag, take 0.5 mg on the plane 90 minutes *be-*

fore bedtime in the place you're traveling to. A similar protocol was found to be remarkably effective in reducing jet lag for airline passengers, airline staff and military personnel who crossed five or more time zones in a UK study that compared oral melatonin with a placebo or medication.

Important: Although melatonin is sold in much higher doses than the 0.5 mg mentioned here, the smaller amount is just as effective—and less likely to cause side effects including headache, dizziness or stomach irritation. (You might have to buy a 1-mg form and split it in half, which is fine.) Because melatonin can have side effects, such as those described above, and can interact with other medications, such as antidepressants and blood pressure drugs, check with your health-care provider before taking melatonin.

CHERRY REMEDY

Would you rather eat a natural source of melatonin to reset your body clock? If so, tart cherries are one of the few foods known to contain the hormone and can be an effective remedy that is also tasty (albeit tart). Juice made from tart cherries also works. A study reported in *Journal of Nutrition, Health & Aging* found that, compared with a placebo drink, drinking tart cherry juice was better at increasing total nighttime sleep and reducing the number of awakenings.

Superfoods expert Wendy Bazilian, DrPH, RD, has found that staying hydrated, avoiding alcohol right before and during travel and getting regular daily exercise during your trip combined with the following protocol works against jet lag...

• **During the two days prior to departure,** drink six ounces of 100% tart cherry juice three times a day during each day. It doesn't matter whether you drink the juice straight or add it to another drink such as a smoothie, green tea, chamomile tea or sparkling water (all good combinations).

Another option: Instead of drinking cherry juice on these two days, eat three-quarters cup of dried tart cherries over the course of the day. These can be added to salad, cereal, trail mix, yogurt—or just eaten on their own.

Fruit-juice-sweetened dried cherries are best, but whether sweetened with fruit juice or sugar, dried tart cherries have a total amount of sugar that's comparable to most dried fruits, such as raisins.

• **On the day of travel,** if your flight leaves at 2 pm or later, drink six ounces of juice or eat one-quarter cup of dried tart cherries three times during the day, spaced out until your flight. For a flight earlier than 2 pm, drink six ounces of juice or eat one-quarter cup of tart cherries in the morning before leaving for the airport.

• **Once on board the plane,** eat one-quarter cup of dried tart cherries with at least eight ounces of plain or sparkling water.

Continue snacking on one-half to three-quarters cup of dried cherries each day in the days after landing. Also remember to stay well hydrated—which you can do not only by drinking water but also by eating water-rich foods such as soups and salads.

HELP FROM HOMEOPATHY

Homeopathy uses tiny, diluted doses of substances that in larger amounts typically *cause* particular symptoms but in tiny amounts provoke a healing response to those same symptoms. There is not enough scientific evidence to say with certainty that homeopathy is an effective treatment for jet lag, yet many users say it has worked for them.

For jet lag, naturopathic doctor Robin Di-Pasquale, ND, RH (AHG), typically prescribes for her patients *Blatta orientalis*, also known as Indian Cockroach. Homeopathic practitioners use the remedy prepared from this nocturnal insect to help diminish the effects of jet lag. Although homeopathic remedies are sold at many health-food stores, natural-food mar-

BETTER WAY...

Avoid Germs on a Plane

To avoid other people's germs on a plane, pick a window seat—that's where passengers tend to get the least exposure.

Study led by researchers at Georgia Institute of Technology, Atlanta, published in *Proceedings of the National Academy of Sciences.*

kets and drugstores, they are best prescribed by knowledgeable practitioners.

What to do: Regardless of what time of day or night it is when you land at your destination, take five pellets of 30c-potency homeopathic *Blatta orientalis*, placed under your tongue. Don't chew the pellets. Let them dissolve, and don't eat or drink anything for 10 minutes before and after. Repeat twice a day for two to three days. *Note:* While homeopathic *Blatta orientalis* is indeed derived from insects, the pellets themselves are tiny, white, sugary-tasting pills. There are no legs or antennae anywhere!

If you travel long distances frequently, the homeopathic remedy *Cocculus indicus*, made from the root of a climbing plant called Indian Cockle, may be more appropriate to address the extreme fatigue and exhaustion from continuous jet lag. Follow the same protocol as above.

Long Plane or Car Ride? This Supplement May Save Your Life

Fred Pescatore, MD, a practitioner of natural and integrative medicine in private practice in New York City. He is author of seven books including *The A-List Diet* and *The Hamptons Diet*. DrPescatore.com

Taking a long plane ride? Don't spend a lot of time worrying about crashing—the risk is extremely small. A much bigger risk is developing a life-threatening blood clot, aka *deep vein thrombosis* (DVT), in your leg during the flight. Most of these clots dissolve harmlessly, but they can instead break off and travel through your bloodstream to the lungs, causing a blockage called a *pulmonary embolism*, which can block blood flow and be fatal. And signs and symptoms of potential DVT, including swelling of the legs and/or ankles and leg pain, can be very uncomfortable.

The good news is that a simple herbal supplement can go a long way toward preventing swelling and reducing leg pain and, research

suggests, DVT. The supplement is Pycnogenol, a registered trademark for an extract from the bark of the French maritime pine.

PREVENTING DVT

Pycnogenol is a powerful antioxidant that improves circulation and reduces inflammation. In one recent study, 295 people who flew in economy class for more than eight hours were divided into three groups. One group took Pycnogenol, a second wore compression stockings (which help with circulation) and the third control group did nothing special.

Results: Members of the Pycnogenol group had the least leg/ankle swelling of the three groups and the least leg pain. There were two incidents of thrombosis in the control group but none in the Pycnogenol or stocking group.

My recommendation: Pycnogenol had a good showing in this study and makes sense as a blood-clot preventive on long trips—even long car rides. I typically recommend taking 100 milligrams of Pycnogenol twice a day for one week before a long flight, on the day of the flight and for one week afterward. While Pycnogenol generally is considered safe with few side effects, as with any supplement, consult your physician to make sure that it's right for you.

Best Credit Cards for Insuring Your Rental Car

WalletHub analyzed the coverage offered, types of vehicles covered, maximum number of days of coverage and how many countries the coverage is available in.

The best personal cards for rental-car insurance coverage are Citi cards, followed by Chase …Barclaycard…USAA…Capital One World Elite Mastercard…Wells Fargo Visa…Capital One Visa…American Express…U.S. Bank American Express…and Discover.

MoneyTalksNews.com

Hotel Discounts for Older Travelers

Many chains offer discounts even before you turn age 65.

• **Best Western** gives discounts of at least 10% for anyone age 55 or older.

• **Choice Hotels** offers up to 10% off for anyone age 60 or older—and for AARP members of any age, which can be as young as 50.

• **La Quinta** offers discounts of 10% for AARP members. Marriott starts its discounts—of at least 15%—at age 62.

• **Motel 6** gives 10% off the standard or lowest rate to anyone age 60 or older. Red Roof Inns offers 10% off to those age 59 and older.

The discounts usually will get you a better price than the standard rate, but discounts change frequently and vary due to many factors, so shop around.

MoneyTalksNews.com

Beware These Sneaky Hotel Tricks

Harry Berkowitz, personal finance editor, Bottom Line Personal, BottomLineInc.com.

Hotels are playing tricks to get more money from us. *Exhibit A:* I recently searched online for a room near Grand Central Terminal in New York City. I found what seemed to be a great one-night rate of $119 at the Royalton, a trendy hotel with customer ratings averaging four out of five stars and a bathroom described as a "sparkling and invigorating space that refreshes and restores."

I wasn't shocked that taxes added $21, but I was surprised to see in the fine print a "facility fee." For $34 for that one night, I could make phone calls and use the gym, Internet and business center—none of which I needed. When I called the hotel to opt out of that fee, I was told it's *mandatory*. I passed on that hotel.

After exploring many more possibilities online, I found a hotel called Club Quarters—rated *four and a half* out of five stars—touted at $129 on several hotel-search sites. OK! But on closer inspection, that price did not include this pool-free urban hotel's "resort fee" of $21.72 per night. I called Club Quarters and was told that by booking *direct* with the hotel, I would avoid this fee without losing any of its amenities, including free snacks. I booked direct...then called back a few days later when I noticed on the hotel's website a further reduced rate of $114, which the hotel granted me.

Lessons: Hotels are taking their cue from airlines and piling on sneaky fees. So read all the fine print...ask about any additional fees...call direct after searching online, and ask if there is an even lower rate...request that any extra fees be eliminated...and check back later for further reduced rates.

Airbnb Scam

A sophisticated Airbnb scam cheats victims out of thousands of dollars. The scammers

229

list properties on Airbnb and, when a victim expresses interest, quickly suggest communicating via e-mail, saying that it is more convenient. When the victim is ready to book, the crook sends the victim a link to a well-made but phony site that steals the booking fee.

Self-defense: Stay within the Airbnb website or app when negotiating and paying for a rental.

Steven J.J. Weisman, Esq., an attorney, author of *Identity Theft Alert* and founder of the scam-information website Scamicide.com.

Vacation-Rental Red Flags

WiseBread.com

• **Listings without photos**—or ones that show some rooms but not all.

• **Listings that do have photos**—but include some that show messy rooms.

• **Price far below market**—this is common in bait-and-switch scams.

• **Listings with poor grammar,** illogical sentences or disagreements between the ad title and the text.

• **Weasel words designed to distract from defects,** such as "quaint" for a place in need of extensive repair and "cozy" for one that is very small.

• **Requests to wire payment**—this is a common scam, since wire transfers are unnecessary and cannot be reversed.

• **Small number of reviews**—the reviews may not be genuine, especially if they all give the place a top rating.

• **Hard-to-reach owner**—this is another common indicator of a scam.

• **No address for the property**—thieves insist on receiving money before giving out the address.

• **Odd contract terms,** such as a nonrefundable security deposit.

230

Great Travel Destinations with Terrible Air Quality

Karen Cady-Pereira, senior staff scientist and manager for radiation and climate with Atmospheric and Environmental Research, a Lexington, Massachusetts, weather-and-climate-consulting company. She was lead author of a study of megacity air quality published in *Atmospheric Chemistry and Physics*. AER.com

Some of the most popular travel destinations in the world are also some of the most polluted. Below are five of those, including a key measure of their air quality—the mean concentration of particulate matter that is in excess of World Health Organization (WHO) guidelines. WHO tracks particles of two different sizes, and air that exceeds a certain level in either size is unhealthy.

• **Delhi, India,** is a popular tourist destination because of its history and culture, but its many vehicles, industrial clusters in and around the city, power plants and the use of fires to burn crop residue in surrounding agricultural lands have created some of the worst air quality in the world. The concentration of very fine particulate matter (PM) in the air is 14.3 times WHO guidelines for what is acceptable.

Two more Indian destinations with very poor air quality: Mumbai (PM 6.4 times guidelines) and Kolkata (PM 7.4 times guidelines).

• **Beijing, China,** is among the world's most dynamic cities and most memorable tourist destinations with a rich history dating back thousands of years. But dense traffic, heavy industry in the area and weather patterns that often trap smog over the city contribute to horrible air quality (PM 7.3 times guidelines). *Also:* Shanghai, China (PM 4.5 times guidelines)…and elsewhere in Asia, Bangkok, Thailand (PM 2.8 times guidelines).

• **Mexico City** has made strides in improving its air quality in recent decades, but issues remain due in part to a rapidly growing population with an enormous number of cars and trucks and a geographical "bowl" formed by a ring of surrounding mountains (PM 2.2 times guidelines).

• **Paris** is among the world's most popular tourist destinations, but its air quality is among the worst in Europe due in part to heavy industry in northern France and the city's severe traffic congestion (PM 1.4 times guidelines).

• **Los Angeles's** air-quality problems are not as bad as those in the other cities on this list, but it does have the worst air quality of any major travel destination in the US. That's due to terrible traffic congestion, a weather pattern creating a so-called "inversion" layer that acts as a lid and mountains to the north and east (PM 1.2 times guidelines). *Also:* Houston doesn't attract as many vacationers as LA, but its air quality is just as bad (PM 1.2 times guidelines).

No-Cost Cruise Ship Cabin Upgrades

A stateroom with a balcony can cost twice as much as a basic interior cabin, and a suite can cost three times as much. But if you take cruises regularly, you can earn loyalty points that, at the very highest levels, can get you free upgrades. *Other ways to earn a cabin upgrade…*

• **If you have high status with one cruise line**—and sometimes even with a hotel chain—you may be able to get that status transferred to a different cruise operator and get upgraded.

• **Cruise lines sometimes offer promotions of upgraded cabins**—or you may have to pay for an upgrade but will get onboard credits that offset the extra cost.

• **Some travel-reward credit cards** let you earn points toward a free cabin upgrade.

• **Some travel agents** have close ties to cruise lines and may be able to get you an upgrade.

WiseBread.com

Love to Eat and Travel? Great Food Festivals Around the World

Erik Wolf, executive director of the World Food Travel Association, which provides resources and training to help food and travel pros create culinary travel experiences. He has nearly three decades of experience in the travel industry and is author of *Have Fork Will Travel.* WorldFoodTravel.org

You may have a favorite food fair or festival that's worth traveling a few miles to reach, perhaps one that features barbecue, chili, pizza or even lobsters. But there are some food festivals so special that they are worth planning a big trip around. *Here are nine that stand out, stretching from Portland, Oregon, and Charleston, South Carolina, to Europe and Asia…*

• **Singapore Food Festival, Singapore, mid-July.*** Large sections of this bustling Asian city transform into an urban food festival each July. Singapore is something of a cultural melting pot, and its food draws influences from Chinese, Malaysian and Indian cooking, to name just a few. Expect a wide range of noodle and seafood dishes…distinctive spices and flavors…and interesting tropical fruits. As at most food festivals, there are meals made by chefs from top local restaurants, but here you also will find affordable and delicious street food. At "The 50 Cent Fest," for example, traditional snacks are sold for the equivalent of 37 US cents apiece, based on recent exchange rates. It's great fun. There's no entry fee for most venues and events. VisitSingapore.com

• **Krakow Pierogi Festival, Krakow, Poland, mid-August.** Pierogi—stuffed dumplings traditionally filled with ground meat, mushrooms, cheese, potato or sauerkraut—are among Poland's favorite comfort foods. At this festival you can sample dozens of regional variations and even try pierogi stuffed with atypical fillings such as seafood or venison. There are dessert pierogi stuffed with fruit

*All festivals occur annually except Terra Madre in Turin, Italy, which occurs every other year. Dates vary slightly from year to year. 2020 dates are provided when available.

and topped with sweet cream, too. Krakow's pierogi festival isn't as large or famous as most of the other festivals on this list, but the food and atmosphere are wonderful. It's a great reason to visit this beautiful, historic city. Admission is free, and the pierogi are extremely affordable—typically around 45 to 60 cents apiece at recent exchange rates. For more information, go to BiuroFestiwalowe.pl.

• **Feast Portland, Portland, Oregon, mid-September.** Since debuting in 2012, this has quickly become one of the most tempting food festivals in the US. There are more than 40 events, including a "Brunch Village," featuring breakfast from around the world…and a "Late, Late Show," featuring noodles. Feast Portland also provides "Hands-On" cooking classes…a "Smoked!" event featuring creative barbecue…wine, beer and cocktail tastings… and more. Ticket prices range from $35 to as much as $195 per event, so feasting at Feast Portland can get expensive—but no more so than indulging in this much fine food elsewhere in the US. FeastPortland.com

• **Terra Madre Salone del Gusto, Turin, Italy, September 14 to 18, 2020.** Nearly 1,000 farmers and food producers from approximately 150 countries are represented at this festival. There's no better single place to sample dishes and ingredients from around the world. The focus is small-scale farms and artisanal foods, not celebrity chefs and five-star dining. The festival is a favorite of the so-called "Slow Food" movement. A counterpoint to fast food, slow food features nutritious local ingredients produced by small farms and cooked fresh with great care. Explore spices from Asia…smoked meats from Scandinavia…artisanal gelato from Italy…cheeses from all around the world…and much more. If you miss this festival in 2020, you'll have to wait until 2022—unlike the other festivals on this list, this one is held every other year. Admission is about $11, and the food tends to be affordable. SaloneDelGusto.com/en

• **Oktoberfest, Munich, Germany, September 19 to October 4, 2020.** Oktoberfest is famous for beer, but it's a fun way to explore Germany's food, too. It's billed as the biggest festival in the world, attracting more than seven million guests each year—being part of this massive party is an unforgettable experience. There are parades, performances and, of course, beer tents of incredible size where you can down beers from mugs of equally impressive proportions. The food is not limited to bratwurst, Germany's famous sausage. There also are German classics such as *Schweinshaxe* (roasted ham hock)…*Brathendl* (roasted chicken)…*Steckerlfisch* (grilled fish)…and *Bratkartoffeln* (fried potatoes), plus desserts such as apple strudel and Black Forest cake. Admission is free, and meals tend to cost perhaps $14 to $25 at recent exchange rates. Oktoberfest.de/en

• **Eurochocolate in Perugia, Italy, mid-October.** Each October, approximately one million chocolate lovers sample sweets from more than 100 primarily Italian confectioners in this historic city in central Italy. The aroma alone is unforgettable. In addition to chocolate candy, there are chocolate desserts made by pastry chefs. It's a wonderful

---

TAKE NOTE…

Better Travel with a Food Allergy

If you have a food allergy, here are some helpful tips when traveling…

• **Carry a food-allergy card that lists your allergies in the languages spoken at your destinations**—the card should list exactly which foods you cannot eat. AllergyTranslation.com offers customizable cards starting at $8.

• **Be extra-cautious when ordering in restaurants**—soups may have shellfish broth… salad dressings may contain nut oils…and other possible allergens may turn up in unexpected places.

• **Pack plenty of your own snacks for your trip**—and a few meal replacements just in case you cannot find anything suitable when you arrive.

• **Consider staying in a hotel or Airbnb rental with a kitchen so that you can make your own meals**—and take your allergy card along when you shop for ingredients.

Roundup of experts on travel recommendations for people with food allergies, reported in The New York Times.

stop on an autumn driving tour of Italy—Perugia is roughly halfway between Florence and Rome. Admission is free, and the cost of samples varies widely. Eurochocolate.com

•**The South Beach Wine & Food Festival, Miami, Florida, February 19 to 23, 2020.** While much of the US is shivering in February cold, attendees at this food festival sip wine and sample expertly prepared food made by acclaimed chefs on the beach in Miami. The festival attracts top chefs from across the country—it has been called "spring break for chefs." The "Grand Tasting Village" is a highlight. Attendees can try foods from more than 50 restaurants under tents on Miami's beach for a single entry fee. A "Burger Bash," featuring upscale takes on the hamburger, is always very popular, too. Prices vary by event but are not low—expect to pay $85 to $250 per person per event. "Intimate Dinners" hosted by top chefs can cost as much as $350 per person. Sobewff.org

•**Charleston Wine + Food, Charleston, South Carolina, March 4 to 8, 2020.** Southern chefs, southern cooking and alcohol aplenty are the focus of this late-winter food festival in picturesque Charleston. But that doesn't mean the event is only for lovers of southern classics such as fried chicken and grits. This is where South Carolina's best chefs (and guest chefs from other parts of the country) come to show off their contemporary takes on the cuisine. There are more than 100 events, everything from wine tastings to barbecues to fancy sitdown "Signature Dinners" where high-end chefs curate multicourse meals. The "Culinary Village" is an annual highlight—attendees can spend up to five hours tasting foods and sampling drinks from dozens of restaurants for a single entry fee. (Current entry fee was unavailable at press time, but fee for 2019 was $135). CharlestonWineAndFood.com

•**Cooper's Hill Cheese Rolling Festival, just south of Brockworth, near Gloucester, UK, May, 25, 2020.** This isn't a food festival in the traditional sense, but it is among the world's most memorable annual food-related events. On England's spring bank holiday, competitors chase seven- or eight-pound wheels of locally made Double Gloucester cheese down a steep, grassy hill. The tradition has its roots in pagan fertility rites that date back centuries. Anyone can compete (the winners get to keep the cheese), but most attendees opt to pack picnic baskets and watch the fun. The region is home to charming Cotswold villages and natural beauty, and it's only about an hour away by car from Stratford-upon-Avon, birthplace of Shakespeare, and Oxford, home to England's great universities. It's a nice side trip if you'd like to escape London's bustle during a visit to England. Free.

Eat Like the Locals

Roundup of experts on eating during travel, reported in *The New York Times* and Orbitz.com.

To find the best local food when traveling, do basic research before leaving home to find out what an area is known for and to get the names of some restaurants. *Also…*

•**Sign up for a vacation package that includes a food tour,** or ask at your destination hotel or the local tourist office how to join such a tour.

•**Ask bar and restaurant staff for their recommendations**—people in the food and drink business will know the local scene.

•**Be sure to tip accordingly.**

•**Read reviews carefully**—and try to find reviews written by locals, not tourists, who tend to be too enthusiastic.

•**Read through reviews**—don't just trust the star rating of a place. If you're looking for a good meal and all the reviews are talking about a place's cocktails, you might want to keep looking.

•**Try street food when it is available,** especially if there is a crowd waiting to order—but make sure cold foods are kept cold and hot foods hot.

•**If asking a local for recommendations,** use your pretravel research to frame questions—ask about specific types of food and atmosphere, and if you want to try truly local dishes that are very different from those usually served to Western tourists, say so clearly.

Enjoy Eating When You Travel Alone

Janice Leith Waugh, founder of SoloTravelerWorld. com, which offers recommendations and links to special deals for solo travelers. Based in Toronto, Canada, she is author of *The Solo Traveler's Handbook.*

Solo travel, which is increasingly popular, has plenty of advantages, but eating alone in restaurants is the single most common source of anxiety for solo travelers, according to surveys. *Six ways to overcome this psychological challenge...*

• **Eat at food trucks or street food stands.** In many cities, these are a great way to try interesting local foods for a very reasonable price—and because these are not sit-down restaurants and there probably will be other people just grabbing and eating, you won't feel out of place or alone.

• **Eat at restaurants with communal tables.** To find restaurants that have large tables where patrons are supposed to dine together with strangers, search for the phrase "communal table" on foodie websites such as Yelp.com and Chowhound.com.

• **Eat at coffee shops.** Some coffee shops offer full menus. You're unlikely to feel out of place dining alone there because most coffee shops are full of solo customers reading newspapers, typing away at their computers or staring at their smartphones.

• **Eat at the bar.** Dining alone at a restaurant's bar doesn't feel as odd as dining alone at a table because you're not facing an empty chair. There sometimes are other patrons at the bar with whom you can chat...and if the bar is empty, the bartender might have time to chat.

• **Sign up for a cooking class or food tour.** You'll do most or all of your eating with your classmates or tour group.

• **Use the website/app VoulezVousDiner (VoulezVousDiner.com),** the AirBnB of dining, to find residents in the area who invite guests into their homes for shared meals, typically for a reasonable price. These gatherings tend to be friendly, and the food often is excellent. This website is especially popular in the major cities of France, but it offers dining opportunities all around the globe.

Best National Parks

The best national parks for the money, based on typical cost of round-trip airfare, a hotel for a week's stay, car rental, meals and entrance fees—plus experiences and amenities to make the trip worthwhile...

• **Rocky Mountain,** Colorado, $2,336 for a week's vacation for two people.

• **Great Smoky Mountains,** Tennessee and North Carolina, $2,297.

• **Zion,** Utah, also $2,297.

• **Death Valley,** California and Nevada, $2,193.

• **Yosemite,** California, $2,870.

• **Crater Lake,** Oregon, $2,243.

• **Hot Springs,** Arkansas, $2,211.

• **Saguaro,** Arizona, $2,527.

• **Great Basin,** Nevada, $1,715.

• **Voyageurs,** Minnesota, $1,999.

Analysis of the 61 US national parks by Money.com and travel website Kayak, reported at Money.com.

Small, Clever Ways to Make Travel Easier

• **Use pill containers to organize jewelry...** an eyeglass case for chargers and cords...and a binder clip to protect the heads of razors.

• **When booking flights and hotels online, always use private browsing**—websites track visitors, and some will raise prices when you return simply because you have been there before.

• **To keep pairs of earrings together,** put one through each hole of a two-hole button.

• **Whenever you start a new SD card on a digital camera, take a selfie first**—that way, if you lose the camera and need to claim it at a lost-and-found, you can prove that it is yours.

CanYouActually.com

Helpful Items When Traveling Abroad

Little things that mean a lot when traveling abroad…

• **A good pen**—always pack one to use when filling out immigration cards and other paperwork.

• **An unlocked phone** so that you can buy a country-specific SIM card for about $20 and have easy access to local maps, translation and more.

• **Digital downloads that let you use important travel features offline,** such as Google Maps and Google Translate. Digital upload services, such as iCloud or Google Photos, to save your photos automatically and protect them if your phone is lost or stolen.

• **A portable USB battery pack to allow on-the-go phone recharging.** A USB multi-charger that allows you to use one wall socket to charge several USB ports.

Roundup of experts on travel, reported in *The New York Times.*

Podcasts to Prepare You for Travel

One of the best ways to get in the mood for a trip—and make travel more special—is a podcast. *Here are six of the best travel podcasts available now…*

• **Zero to Travel** offers ideas and action plans for those interested in travel-related work, budget travel and putting travel at the center of their lives.

• **Amateur Traveler** helps people discover bucket-list destinations and find ways to get to them.

• **The Budget-Minded Traveler** is mainly for solo women travelers but includes ideas for anyone traveling alone.

• **Travel with Rick Steves** features little-known locations in Europe that can make an ordinary trip special.

• **Travel Wisdom Podcast** features guests who discuss their trips and say what they learned that other travelers can use.

• **As Told by Nomads** is for people interested in cultural immersion and using travel as an entry point to better understanding of world affairs.

Roundup of experts on travel podcasts, reported at WiseBread.com.

The Safe Way to Travel with Your Pet

Erin Ballinger, travel expert at BringFido.com, which provides pet-policy information for travel-related businesses. It has a toll-free phone number (877-411-FIDO) that pet owners can use to find pet-friendly businesses.

United Airlines temporarily suspended its pet-travel program in March 2018 following a series of troubling incidents that included the death of a dog stowed in an overhead bin. That incident called attention not only to United's missteps but to a growing travel trend—taking the family pet along on journeys. Despite United's problems, traveling with a pet can be safe, and it can be a money saver, too, when the cost of the pet's travel is less than the cost of a kennel. But traveling with your pet is worth considering only if you plan carefully and make smart travel choices.

Here's what you need to know to successfully and safely travel with your pet...

PETS ON PLANES

Whether your pet can travel with you in the cabin of an airplane or must be checked into the cargo compartment depends on the airline's rules and the animal's size. Typically, the pet must fit comfortably into a pet carrier that can fit under the seat in front of you for it to be able to travel in the cabin. Most airlines impose weight limits, too (usually 20 pounds).

For details about a specific airline's pet policies, call the airline or search for "pets" on its website.

Expect added fees whether your pet travels in the cabin or as cargo. These vary by airline but usually are $75 to $125 per direction traveled by the pet for cabin travel...or $100 to $200 per direction in the cargo hold.

Traveling in the cabin tends to be safer for pets than traveling in the cargo hold despite United's overhead-bin fiasco. In the cabin, there's no risk that the airline will misroute your pet...and the cabin and terminal are almost always climate-controlled. The cargo area often is not climate-controlled until the plane is in the air, so pets headed for cargo might wait in the heat or cold of the tarmac before loading.

But even the cargo hold is not tremendously dangerous—on most airlines. In 2017, US-based airlines transported animals more than half a million times, and the total number of deaths, lost animals and reported injuries came to just 40. But dig a little deeper into the animal air-travel data and you'll discover that pets faced more than twice the usual danger on one airline—United. (Delta has a poor record, too.)

Better: When possible, fly on Alaska Airlines or American Airlines if your pet will be traveling as cargo. These two airlines have done a significantly better-than-average job keeping animal passengers safe.

Six pet air-travel details worth knowing about...

•**Airlines that generally do not accept pets as cargo** include Frontier, JetBlue, Southwest and Spirit. Pets small enough to travel in the cabin usually can travel on these airlines, however. *Also:* Pets might not be permitted to travel in the cargo areas of other airlines, either, if the flight is longer than 12 hours or is to or from a location that is expected to have very hot or very cold temperatures.

•**Airlines generally require a "health certificate" signed by a veterinarian.** This form confirms that the pet's vaccines are up to date and that it is healthy. The vet might have to sign this certificate no more than 10 days before departure date.

•**If your pet travels in the cabin, it is likely to count as your carry-on item.** You will need an FAA-approved pet carrier that does not exceed the airline's (or the flight's) size limits. *Recommended:* The Snoozer Roll Around Travel Dog Carrier Backpack 4-in-1 ($119.95 to $129.95 depending on size, SnoozerPetProducts.com) has wheels so you can tow your pet through the airport, and it can convert into a backpack, dog bed and car seat.

•**Pets need reservations.** Airlines restrict the number of pets they accept per flight both in the cabin and in cargo. If you arrive at the airport with a pet that does not have a reservation and the flight's animal quota is full, you might have to take your pet back home—and potentially miss your flight.

•**Airlines do not necessarily transport pets of every species, breed or age.** Many accept only dogs and cats...and most will not accept snub-nosed dogs or cats in the cargo hold because of increased risk for potentially fatal respiratory problems. Animals that are younger than eight to 12 weeks might not be accepted either.

•**Don't give your pet antinausea or antianxiety medication before a flight** unless your vet recommends doing so. Some pets have adverse reactions to these medicines.

PETS IN TRAINS AND RENTAL CARS

Dogs and cats weighing up to 20 pounds now can travel on most Amtrak routes. The fee is $26, a bargain compared with the airlines. The pet must remain in a pet carrier no larger than 19 x 14 x 10.5 inches while onboard. (To get details online, go to Amtrak.com/on board/carry-on-pets.html.)

Most car-rental companies allow pets to ride in their cars with no official added pet fee. But these companies are notorious for tacking on steep cleaning fees when they find pet hair on car seats after cars are returned—potentially $100 or more.

Helpful: Pack an old sheet and put this over the backseat of the rental car if your pet will be traveling outside its carrier. Carefully inspect the car for hair and other pet-related issues before returning the vehicle.

PETS IN HOTELS

Four hotel chains that are particularly pet-friendly…

• **La Quinta Inns & Suites** allows guests to bring up to two dogs and/or cats with no additional fees or deposits at most of its 870-plus locations. (See LQ.com/en/landing/pet-policy for details.)

• **Red Roof Inn** allows guests to bring one pet weighing up to 80 pounds at most of its 500-plus locations. There are no additional pet fees or deposits. Pets cannot be left unattended in rooms, however. (See RedRoof.com/why-red-roof-inn/pet-friendly.)

• **Aloft Hotels,** part of the Starwood chain, not only allows dogs that are up to 40 pounds in size at most of its 100-plus locations with no fees or deposits, it also offers amenities such as dog beds and bowls at no charge. (Contact the specific Aloft property where you wish to stay to confirm that the location is dog-friendly…and/or to request permission to bring a dog larger than 40 pounds or a different species of pet.)

• **Kimpton Hotels** allows guests to bring any pet with no additional charges or deposits at most of its 60-plus locations. There are no official limits regarding pet species, quantity or size…except that the pet must fit through the hotel's doors. Pet beds, bowls and mats are available at no cost, and pets are welcome at Kimpton's nightly wine receptions.

Helpful: Rover.com can help you locate a doggie day care facility in the area you are visiting if your pet won't be joining you for all your vacation activities.

TAKING A PET TO A FOREIGN COUNTRY

Traveling abroad with an animal adds to the complications—you'll have to navigate the foreign country's animal-entry rules in addition to airline and hotel rules. These rules are becoming less onerous in most places—quarantines are no longer common—but expect plenty of paperwork, fees and other hassles. Don't leave this to the last minute because it can take weeks to sort it all out. *Five international animal travel tips worth knowing…*

• **Consult the US Department of Agriculture's website** to learn the rules for bringing a pet to a particular foreign country…and for bringing your pet back to the US (APHIS. USDA.gov/aphis/pet-travel). *Example:* A dog might need to be inspected for screwworm by a vet before you can return to the US from a country where that parasite is a problem. Affected countries are mainly in South and Central America, Asia and Africa. BringFido.com offers country-by-country guidance as well (BringFido.com/travel/international).

• **Vaccinations often must be administered well in advance of travel.** *Example:* Some countries will not allow an animal to enter unless it received its rabies vaccination at least 21 or 30 days prior to entry, depending on the country.

• **The European Union has a consolidated "EU pet passport" system** that allows animals to enter and travel through the region with relative ease. But there's a catch—these passports are issued only in the EU. If your pet doesn't yet have one, it will need an "EU Health Certificate" to enter the region. To obtain this, the animal will have to be examined by a "USDA-accredited" veterinarian, typically no more than 10 days prior to the trip. The certificate this vet issues then must be endorsed by a Department of Agriculture office. (Visit APHIS.USDA.gov/aphis/pet-travel and click "APHIS Veterinary Services Endorsement Offices" for help finding a vet who can do this in your area.) The fees for the exam, certificate and endorsement can easily top $200. (If you expect to bring your pet to the EU multiple times, it is worth obtaining a passport for it to make future trips simpler.)

237

•**Taking a pet from the US to Canada is comparatively straightforward.** You generally need only a certificate signed by a vet confirming that the animal has been vaccinated against rabies within the past three years. (Visit the US Department of Agriculture website for details.)

•**There's a chance that your pet might be denied entry despite your best efforts.** Occasionally, travelers spend weeks getting a pet all the paperwork and shots it needs...only to be told by a customs official at an airport in the foreign country that they've made some mistake. This can put travelers in a bind—they might have to leave their pet in quarantine, paying steep fees for the privilege...or get right back on a flight out of the country with their pet.

Bottom line: Follow the pet rules of the countries you visit to the letter.

Make Money While Traveling

Housesitting: Sites such as TrustedHouse Sitters.com/US let you look after someone's home, and sometimes the owner's pets, in exchange for free room and board.

Work-exchange programs: Workaway.info and HelpX.net provide opportunities ranging from work on family farms to babysitting or sheep and goat herding. Work and holiday visas from Australia, Canada, New Zealand and the UK allow visitors to work, usually for a year, teaching English as a Foreign Language (TEFL) can lead to opportunities in many countries.

Roundup of experts on ways to make money while traveling, reported at GoBankingRates.com.

Better Travel If You Have a Disability

•**Ask the airline for help.** Many will assign an employee to meet you when you arrive at the airport and provide assistance—and someone else to help after your flight lands.

•**Make plans with your hotel.** Be sure to explain what you need, such as a room with wider doors to accommodate a wheelchair.

•**Consider working with a travel agent** who specializes in planning trips for people with disabilities.

•**Book guides who are used to dealing with disabilities** and take the needs of travelers with disabilities into account in planning activities.

•**Consider a prearranged tour** specifically designed for people with disabilities.

•**Find out about accommodations at museums and other attractions**—special tours may be available but may require advance booking.

Roundup of experts on traveling with a disability, reported in *The New York Times*.

GOOD TO KNOW...

Take the Right-Length Vacation

On vacation, happiness tends to peak around the eighth day and then starts to decline. For peak happiness, take vacations that last a little more than a week.

Study by researchers at Behavioral Science Institute, Radboud University Nijmegan, the Netherlands, published in *Journal of Happiness Studies*.

14

Fun Finds

Great Streaming Channels That Are Free

There are many great streaming channels that are free (except for the burden of having to watch commercials). *Here are some of the best no-cost channels...*

•**For current TV shows—Yahoo! View** provides a few recent episodes of dozens of current network TV series (though not CBS shows). *Examples: The Good Place...This Is Us...The Tonight Show.* It has a small number of movies and basic cable shows, too. *Note:* Typically, you would watch Yahoo! View content on a PC or laptop or directly connect the PC or laptop to your TV. View.Yahoo.com

•**For TV shows from the 1950s, 1960s and 1970s—Shout! Factory TV** offers classic series such as *Car 54, Where Are You?...Route 66...*and *The Saint.* It has films, too, but they're mostly low-budget drive-in-movie fare. Shout!

Factory can be streamed on a PC, laptop or through the Pluto TV app. ShoutFactory.com

•**For free movies without commercial interruptions—Kanopy** offers more than 30,000 movies with no subscription fees or commercials. It has especially strong classic movies, art house films and documentaries. *Examples: To Catch a Thief...The 400 Blows...Seven Samurai.* To use it, you need to have a library card from one of the many libraries that offer Kanopy. Kanopy.com/wayf

Alternative: A rival service called Hoopla also offers free digital downloads of movies with no commercial breaks to cardholders of certain libraries. Its selection is less extensive than Kanopy's. HooplaDigital.com

•**For free movies from a pay movie service—Vudu** is best known as one of many services that rents and sells digital downloads

---

Jim Kimble, founder of The Cord Cutting Report, a website about streaming services and related topics. CordCuttingReport.com

of recent films on a per-film basis. But Vudu now also has a few dozen mainstream movies available for free at any given time—click the "Free" tab on its website. These are not the most recent releases, but there's often something worth watching. *Recent examples: The Terminator...Jerry MaGuire...Ace Ventura.* Vudu.com

• **For more free movies—Tubi TV** has partnered with movie studios Lionsgate, Paramount and MGM to offer some relatively recent mainstream films. *Recent example: The Homesman* (a 2014 Tommy Lee Jones and Hilary Swank drama). Tubi offers TV shows, too, though not many popular shows. TubiTV.com

• **For science fiction—Comet** offers classic sci-fi shows such as *The Outer Limits* and *Stargate SG-1.* It has sci-fi movies, too, but they're mainly drive-in-quality films. CometTV.com

• **For a TV-like flip-through-the-channels experience—Pluto TV** organizes a wide range of streaming content into a 100-plus channel grid that you can navigate as you would a cable provider's onscreen guide. Most of Pluto's content runs on a schedule as it does on conventional TV—but there also is an extensive on-demand menu of movies and a small selection of TV shows you can view if you're using the app. Pluto.TV

• **For national and world news—CBSN** is a 24-hour streaming news network offered by CBS (CBSNews.com/CBSN). *Alternative: Bloomberg Television* is a 24-hour global news channel that's free if you watch through Pluto TV.

• **For local news—NewsON** streams local newscasts from more than 175 stations in more than 114 US markets. Watch live or up to 48 hours after a newscast airs. NewsON.us

Big Discounts on Newspapers and Mags

• **DiscountedNewspapers.com** offers more than 400 newspapers at up to 92% off regular price.

• **Magazines.com** gives discounts up to 90%.

• **MercuryMagazines.com** offers free subscriptions to magazines that fit your professional profile—you fill out information on your job and industry and wait for matching offers.

• **The app Magzter** recently offered a year of unlimited reading of more than 5,000 magazines for $49.99.

• **Members of Amazon Prime** get access to free digital magazines. Kindle Unlimited offers newspaper and magazine access for $9.99/month.

MoneyTalksNews.com

RECENT FINDING...

How Much Do *You* Use the Internet?

A recent study says that people spend *one whole day per week* on the Internet. Since 2000, average time per week spent online has risen from 9.4 hours to 23.6—essentially one full day out of every seven. Online time is likely to increase as more everyday items become Internet-connected and the use of social media continues to grow.

Study by USC Annenberg Center for the Digital Future, Los Angeles, reported at CNET.com.

Great Freebies at the Library

• **If your library partners with the streaming service Kanopy,** you can get access to more than 30,000 commercial-free films from your home.

• **Some libraries offer free access to digital magazines, e-books and audiobooks** through apps such as Flipster and OverDrive.

• **Participating libraries provide free online courses** through LinkedIn Learning.

- **Some libraries offer self-improvement seminars and classes.** A few offer free passes to local museums and other attractions.

- **Some libraries offer loans of party supplies**—such as bakeware, fondue pots, pasta makers and chocolate fountains.

- **Libraries may offer study rooms** that can be used instead of renting a desk at a shared workspace…and meeting rooms for nonprofit groups.

Roundup of experts on library offerings, reported at MoneyTalksNews.com.

Your Old Family Photos Are Fading Away: How to Save Them

Jeff Wignall, a photographer and writer who has written more than 20 books about photography. He is a contributing editor with *Pro Photo Daily* and *Motion Arts Pro Daily* and a former "Camera" columnist for *The New York Times.* JeffWignall.com

The family photo album filled with old printed photos still is among our most valuable possessions because it is an irreplaceable history of our family and our ancestors and their times. Even if we create digital copies of these photos (a smart thing to do, see below), the original prints themselves always will resonate with us as precious objects, literally created and treasured by our ancestors, in a way that pixels on a screen never could. But time is not kind to print photos, and when they're gone, they're gone.

Problem: Many people keep these photos in albums that actually accelerate their deterioration. *Happily, there are simple steps you can take to preserve your cherished photos for generations to come…*

- **Move prints to archival storage.** The pages and glues in many photo albums contain acids and other chemicals that accelerate deterioration of photos. And popular "magnetic" albums, which let you easily move photos around, often have clear sheets that cover

each page—but over time these sheets stick to photos, ruining them.

Solution: Store your valued photographs in "archival," acid-free albums or boxes. Look for labels that show the product has passed the Photographic Activity Test (PAT). Reliable online sources include Light Impressions (LightImpressionsDirect.com) and Gaylord Archival (Gaylord.com).

Archival albums and boxes are more expensive than nonarchival types but are well worth the price. You can buy self-adhesive archival "corners" to mount on the pages to secure the images.

If the photos in your old family albums were placed there by the people who took the photos, be sure to maintain the order of the original photos on each page. Odds are your relatives knew the family time line and relationships and arranged photos accordingly—and even if they didn't, the way they displayed their photo treasures adds to the collection's authenticity. *Tip:* Use your smartphone to take snapshots of the original album pages before you transfer the photos to an archival album, then use these snapshots as a placement guide.

- **Scan originals to create digital files.** Since digital files don't fade, the only truly permanent solution to saving the images in your photos is to scan them and digitize them. It's easy to do on a flatbed scanner. The scanner on a basic all-in-one home printer usually does a very good job. No scanner? Your local library likely has one for free use. Local photo labs or photo studios may provide scanning services for a fee.

The correct scanner setting for photos is 300 pixels per inch (ppi)—it's a simple menu option. *Tip:* If you want to make a print that's larger than the original, simply increase the scanner setting. *Example:* If you double the resolution to 600 ppi during a scan and then reduce it back to 300 ppi when you go to print it from your computer, you can double the print size on the printing/editing software with no loss in quality. You even can triple the resolution to 900 ppi in a scan and then bring it down to 300 ppi in printing to triple the size of a printed photo.

If scanning your photos isn't appealing, use your phone. The quality won't be as good, but it's very convenient, and at least you'll have saved the images. *Useful app: Photomyne* for Android and iOS (limited use free trial; unlimited use app for $4.99). An account ($49.99/10 years) syncs your photos to other mobile devices and backs them up for safekeeping. It is geared specifically to turning print photos and albums into digital photo albums.

Important: Back up your new digital files onto DVDs or thumb drives, and store one copy at home and another in a safe-deposit box. *Alternative:* Back up digital files to the cloud.

• **Restore damaged prints.** Almost any amount of damage to an old paper photo can be magically repaired in digital editing. When the new digital image is printed, it will look like the old one—without the blemishes. You can master the basic skills (such as cropping and adjusting brightness and contrast) using a basic editing program—one great free one is GIMP (Gimp.org), but you'll want to turn to a pro for restoration to, say, hide a water stain or fix a torn photo (especially a tear through a face). I've seen photos that I thought were a total loss brought back almost as good as new. You'll still have the original for authenticity, but the new digitally enhanced print will be closer to how the original looked when it was taken.

Cost for pro restoration of old prints: $25 up to several hundreds of dollars, depending on the restorer and what's involved in the restoration.

• **Store your new archival albums safely.** The National Archives suggests storing print photos in a dark place (away from direct sunlight even in an album), at room temperature (60°F to 75°F) and with a relative humidity less than 65%, which means not in an attic or a basement.

Be a Better Bowler in Minutes

Michelle Mullen, former Team USA coach and USBC Gold Coach. Based in the Detroit area, she is author of *Bowling Fundamentals*. YourBowlingCoach.com

Bowling is very popular in the US—it's an immensely social sport, as many groups of bowling pals will tell you. But as with any sport, it's more fun when you get better at it. *Here, top bowling coach Michelle Mullen, shares three ways that almost every bowler can improve quickly…*

• **Let your *opposite* hand support the ball's weight in your stance and approach.** The secret to a consistently successful arm swing is keeping your arm loose and relaxed—but you can't do that when your arm muscles have to tighten up to support the weight of the ball. Instead, use your nonball hand to support the weight.

What to do: As you begin your approach, use your nonball hand to lift the ball up and out as far as feels somewhat natural…into a position where your swing arm can serve largely as a free-swinging pendulum, so its muscles never need to tense. Once you get comfortable with this natural pendulum swing, your delivery will become much easier to repeat than muscling the ball down the lane ever could be—physics is more reliable than muscle strength.

• **Stop bending at the waist as you release the ball.** It feels natural to bend, but it restricts your follow-through and leverage, reducing power and accuracy. Instead, keep your upper body fairly upright as you release the ball. Instead of bending at the waist, get low by bending your knees.

• **Use a ball that you don't have to squeeze.** As you swing, if you feel like you must squeeze

---

BETTER WAY...

Great Backyard Bird Photos

To easily capture close-up images of wild birds in your backyard, duct-tape a thin branch about a foot or so long to the pole or hook that holds your bird feeder. Prefocus your camera on this perch…and snap when birds use it.

Jeff Wignall, a photographer and author of more than 20 books about photography. JeffWignall.com

the ball with the fingers of your swing arm to prevent the ball from flying away, you're using the wrong ball. Squeezing forces you to more firmly engage the muscles of your hand and forearm—and using muscles this way makes a delivery difficult to repeat.

What to do: If you decide to buy your own ball, a reputable pro shop will determine the proper size and angles of the holes, as well as the distances between them, to create a good fit that allows you to use a light grip pressure. As a bonus, a light grip will reduce your risk for injury from overusing muscles. Don't be surprised if a pro recommends a ball lighter than the one you have been using—modern bowling balls can deliver plenty of force with less weight than the balls of decades past.

If you bowl only rarely and want to use a bowling-center ball that isn't custom-fit, look for one that you can get your fingers (including your thumb) all the way in but not so big that you have to squeeze the ball to keep your grip. The span should feel comfortable, too—not stretched or cramped.

It's Tee Time for Better Health!

Hitting the links increases longevity (by up to five years, according to one of the studies included in a recent meta-analysis) and improves risk for heart disease. Golf also is linked to better mental health, perhaps due to the social interactions and opportunities to connect with nature.

For the most benefits: Aim to get 150 or more minutes of playing time per week—and skip the cart and walk, if possible. Be sure to warm up before each round to prevent injury, and wear sunscreen to protect against skin cancer.

For more details, go to GolfandHealth.org.

Andrew Murray, MBChB, sports medicine consultant, University of Edinburgh, Scotland, UK.

TAKE NOTE...

To Retain a New Skill...

After learning a motor skill such as a tennis swing or playing a song, exercise vigorously for at least 15 minutes right away—and get enough sleep that night. The combo primes the brain for remembering.

Study by researchers at McGill University, Montreal, Canada, published in *NeuroImage*.

Happy Hobbies

Hobbies that boost life skills and happiness...

• **Cooking** requires planning and staying focused.

• **Hiking** helps clear your mind and improves physical health.

• **Painting** and sculpture can help you get a new perspective on life.

• **Writing** is good for self-expression and creativity.

• **Dancing** requires attention to routine and practice.

• **Yoga** helps you close off external thoughts and focus single-mindedly.

• **Reading** helps you learn new behaviors.

• **Video games** encourage focus, determination and trying to succeed within rules and guidelines.

LifeHack.org

How to Keep Your Garden Colorful All Summer Long

Teri Dunn Chace, a garden writer based in central New York who is author of more than 35 gardening titles, including *Seeing Flowers: Discover the Hidden Life of Flowers.* TeriChaceWriter.com

---

It happens every year. Spring arrives in a rainbow burst of tulips, daffodils and other fall-planted bulbs, but it fades away after a few short weeks. Meanwhile, trees and shrubs burst into colorful but brief bloom, then leaf out, and all that remains is green. Summer perennials and roses are growing but not yet blooming. It's an awkward *color gap*, occurring right when we're in the mood to be outdoors and want our yards to look great.

You can have lots of color during this time, though. Here are some tricks to get your garden and yard through the color gap in style. *The punch these plants provide improves the look of your yard for the in-between weeks of early to midsummer and often beyond...*

• **Install plants with colorful leaves.** Flowers don't have to be the only burst of color in your garden or yard. Splashy and patterned leaves of red, maroon, pink, white and cream can enliven any space. Coleus and caladium are good, affordable choices and widely available. (If you want these plants to liven up your garden in future years, bring them inside when summer is over. They don't like the cold and will otherwise die off.) Mix a few of these into your flower beds, and they'll distract as your spring flowers start to drop off and their leaves turn yellow, and still be around to highlight your midsummer blooms when those finally appear. You also can use perennials such as hosta, ivy and brunnera, which all come in variegated selections that help them stand out if your garden is going through a mostly green phase.

• **Choose double-duty flowers.** Look for ones that add a bit of interest even when they're not flowering. Try irises with yellow-striped foliage, gaura with white-edged leaves or an array of pretty purple, rose or even chartreuse heucheras. These selections look terrific even when not flowering. Any red-colored flower, such as impatiens, salvia or geranium, that you add will look amazing when paired with these leaves.

• **Don't play it too safe.** A blend of various complementary hues—created when you, say, plunk an entire flat of assorted marigolds or pansies into a bed—can get visually boring. With temporarily less competition for attention from other flowers, this is the time for annuals to shine. Aim for contrast. Pair strongly contrasting colors—yellow marigolds with purple

scaevola, red impatiens with white impatiens, blue salvia with orange zinnia.

• **Avoid planting "singletons."** A single, bold flowering plant doesn't give the eye a good chance to enjoy the rest of the garden because your gaze almost can't help but be drawn to it. And a color tends to make more of an impression if there's more of it. So plant the same or similarly colored flowers in groups of at least three.

In the "gap time," annuals are great for this purpose. A ribbon of white impatiens threaded through a perennial garden, for instance, or a section of purple-flowered salvia can be really dramatic without being overpowering.

• **Get maximum impact from potted plants.** Potted plants can be a beautiful and useful addition to your garden. Since they easily can be moved from spot to spot, just plop them down in whatever area needs a color boost. When choosing pots, don't settle for ordinary clay pots or plain window boxes. Use vibrant solid-color containers or patterned and painted ones. If you find a pot that you really like but it lacks necessary drainage holes, just "nest" a practical pot inside this decorative one.

Move those containers around! You can tuck a pot of, say, cheery geraniums into a flower bed that needs some color, then simply move it to another spot as the garden's other flowers come and go. Then put a fresh potted selection into that slot. In this way, you easily can swap out plants and ensure that your displays are always looking their best.

A "scene-stealer" is another good trick. Site a large pot, urn or other container in a prominent spot. Make it impressive, filling it to overflowing with your favorite colorful flowers and foliage plants. Nobody will notice that its surroundings aren't as exciting.

• **Don't forget garden décor.** It's not cheating to add nonplant items to take up the slack—it's practical and fun! The early-summer lull is actually an opportunity to take a good look at your yard and go shopping. Add a colorful gazing ball, a garden statue, pretty tiles or stepping stones, a bird house, a birdbath, a pretty flag, a bench or other garden furniture. Such items create a welcome distraction when your garden is not at peak color.

Also, the benefits of decorative garden items can outlast this gap period. These are objects that can give your garden a stable structure on which you can build beautiful displays year after year.

•**Look at the bigger picture.** The gap time also is a chance to look at what colors your home adds to the overall garden scene. What color is the trim, the front door, the garage door, the porch? Work with these colors, matching or contrasting them with flowers and containers.

If you don't work with your house's color (and style, for that matter), your landscaping may end up looking out of place or like a hodgepodge.

You might want to try going even bolder with your garden color. Why not paint an entire fence yellow, a trellis red, a gate purple? Garden color should be joyful, and a bold step such as that gets the party started!

How to Harvest and Dry Garden Herbs

Teri Dunn Chace, a garden writer based in central New York who is author of more than 35 gardening books, including *The Anxious Gardener's Book of Answers.* TeriChaceWriter.com

---

If you grow herbs in your garden, why not dry them so that you can savor them all year long? They'll make your cooking much more special than supermarket herbs. You even can give them as gifts. *How to do it right…*

PICK WHEN FLAVOR IS AT A PEAK

Herbs taste best when the plant is primarily producing foliage, not flowers. So pick them before they bloom or at least as soon as you see early blooms appear. Look carefully—herb flowers can be tiny and often not very colorful. *More tips…*

•**Harvest in late morning as soon as the dew is dry.** Levels of volatile oils, which give herbs their flavor and fragrance, peak early in the day.

•**Clip stems with sharp scissors or light pruners, not with your bare hands.** If you use your hands, it's easy to yank off a stem, disturb the roots, even pull out the whole plant. Plus, cutting cleanly is better for the plant.

•**Rinse off your harvest,** and pat dry thoroughly with paper towels.

DRY, DON'T ROT

Drying mistakes can lead to rot or mold. *Keys to success:* Moderately high heat (80°F to 90°F), and a dim or dark setting so light doesn't degrade the oils, and good air circulation to whisk away moisture. *Good options:* A spot in a hot, dry attic, garage, enclosed porch, shed, closet or cupboard. (None of the above if the air is humid!) *The best drying method? It depends on what you're drying…*

•**For large-leaved herbs such as basil, mint and comfrey—Screening.** Prop up a screen or rack so that air can circulate from below. Arrange stems or leaves in a single layer, not touching.

Warning: Do not use a galvanized metal screen—the metal can react with plant acids to form toxic compounds. But a regular household window screen should be fine—it usually is made of plastic or coated wire.

•**For medium-leaved herbs such as parsley, cilantro and sage or dill—Bundles.** Perhaps you've admired this technique somewhere—jaunty bundles of herbs hanging upside down. Your kitchen, alas, probably is not the right spot, because it's too bright. And dangling bundles along a wall won't allow enough air circulation. If you have rafters—especially in a hot, dry, dark spot such as an attic—that's perfect. Bundles of 10 to 12 stems work well, allowing the necessary air circulation. Secure firmly by the stems with rubber bands, then hang the bundles from a hook or nail.

•**For small-leaved herbs such as thyme and summer savory—Paper bags.** Place the herbs into lunch-size paper bags, and cinch the tops with a stapler. To allow air circulation, cut a few slits along the sides. It's already dark inside the bag, so any hot, dry area is fine.

Herbs usually dry in a week or two when conditions are correct. *Check them:* Leaves should be crumbly, not leathery. Store your home-dried herbs at room temperature in canisters with tight lids.

The Secret to Finding Great Cheap Wine

Jeff Siegel, the Wine Curmudgeon, a wine writer, wine critic and wine judge who specializes in inexpensive wine—the wine, he says, that most of us drink. He is author of *The Wine Curmudgeon's Guide to Cheap Wine* and oversees the award-winning Wine Curmudgeon website. WineCurmudgeon.com

---

Many of the world's great wines are too expensive for most of us. *Truly* great wines are so expensive that they're traded on their own stock exchange, called Liv-Ex. How about $5,400 for a bottle of the 2006 Château Cheval Blanc from Bordeaux in France?

Even if you're forking over "only" $50 or $100, you're likely paying a premium for publicity. Everyone knows about cabernet sauvignon from California's Napa Valley or bubbly from the Champagne region of France. It's the law of supply and demand. These regions produce a limited amount of wine, and so many people know about them that prices gravitate higher even before things such as quality and production costs come into play.

Great news: For those of us with more modest budgets, there's a way to buy cheap wines that share many delicious qualities with the great stuff—look for wines made in the same style but from less expensive parts of the world.

These cheaper wines—usually $15 or less—won't taste exactly like their $100 counterparts. But they're not supposed to. Rather, they're well-made in their own right, reflecting the part of the world they're from, a quality that wine geeks call *terroir*. And they are true to the essential characteristics of that particular grape, called *varietal correctness*. To my way of thinking, terroir and varietal correctness make the difference between grocery store plonk and quality cheap wine.

Tip: If a wine comes from a region of the world you've never heard of, you're on the right track. Of course, not all wines from obscure regions are good. You'll need to discover a few regions—and specific wines—that reliably deliver affordable quality for the kinds of wines that you like best.

So instead of expensive wines from overpriced regions, try these six lesser known wines to get you started. They all are inexpensive, and each reflects its terroir and its grape varietal beautifully.

RED BURGUNDY

Typical expensive wine: Bouchard Pere & Fils Gevrey-Chambertin, $60.

Our choice: Natura Pinot Noir, $10.

It's almost impossible to find quality red Burgundy—which has to come from the Burgundy region of France and be made with the pinot noir grape—for less than $50 a bottle.

Hence the Natura from Chile. Many Chilean wines offer tremendous value, and Natura goes one step further. It has the classic berry aromas of pinot noir plus a little spice, and more dark berry flavors become apparent as you drink it. This is a soft but not a simple wine. Yes, it's not as layered or as sophisticated as the Bouchard, and it doesn't have the latter's earthy, almost mushroomy flavor. But it's well-made and tastes like pinot noir, something uncommon at this price.

RED BORDEAUX

Typical expensive wine: Château Prieuré-Lichine, $60.

Our choice: Armas de Guerra Tinto Mencia, $13.

The Château Prieuré-Lichine is a legendary red blend of cabernet sauvignon and merlot from France's Bordeaux region with a history dating back to the mid-19th century. In other words, an expensive wine for a long time!

The Armas de Guerra Tinto, on the other hand, is made with the obscure mencia grape in Spain's even more obscure Bierzo area. The result, though, is a surprisingly similar wine—sort of savory and fresh with black fruit, and it smells of green herbs and a little black pepper. In this, it almost tastes more French than it does Spanish, which is as much appreciated as it is unusual.

WHITE BURGUNDY

Typical expensive wine: Domaine Christian Moreau Père et Fils Chablis Grand Cru, $100.

Our choice: Louis Latour Mâcon-Villages Chameroy, $15.

White Burgundy is chardonnay from the Burgundy region of France, and although it's not quite as expensive as red Burgundy or red Bordeaux, it's pricey enough. The $100 Moreau is a stunning wine, full of the minerality (a stony taste) and lemony citrus fruit that is typical of Chablis, a subregion of Burgundy.

The $15 Chameroy, oddly enough, also comes from Burgundy, but from a much less famous subregion, the Mâcon. Mâcon white wines usually are outstanding values—and the Latour Chameroy is one of the best. It has floral and honey aromas, ripe pear fruit and minerality on the finish. In this, it's softer and not as structured as the Moreau, but that it comes anywhere close is something every wine drinker should appreciate.

CHAMPAGNE

Typical expensive wine: Bruno Paillard Brut Première Cuvée, $50.

Our choice: Bodegas Pinord Dibón Brut Reserve, $10.

Champagne is sparkling wine from the Champagne region of France, and nothing else in the world can legally use that name. That translates into some of the highest wine prices in the world, and the Paillard—made in the classic style, with crisp citrus and green apple fruit and a hint of caramel in the back—is practically an entry-level product for $50.

Fortunately, we have cava, the sparkling wine made in Spain that uses the same production techniques as Champagne. So why the difference in price? Again, less respect for the region but also different and less known grapes—but as the Dibón demonstrates, this top-quality wine has layers of flavor and is made more in the style of Champagne than typical cava—creamy and caramel-like with candied pineapple in back and just a little tart apple. Plus, it has lots of the wonderfully tight

---

bubbles that are the hallmark of well-made sparkling wine.

SUPER TUSCAN

Typical expensive wine: Marchesi Antinori Solaia, $300.

Our choice: Monte Antico, $11.

Despite the name, a "super Tuscan" is not necessarily a super wine—it's just the Italian wine industry's term for a red blend typically made with sangiovese grapes in Tuscany that doesn't follow Italy's traditional rules for grapes allowed in making red wine in Tuscany.

Antinori made the first super Tuscan in 1971 and even today may do it better than anyone. The Solaia is a super wine and everything a super Tuscan is supposed to be—velvety, fresh and with full, already developed red fruit.

Then again, hardly anyone can afford it. That's where the Monte Antico comes in. It's also a super Tuscan. The difference is the grape quality, and the good news is that lesser quality doesn't mean poor quality. The Antico has rich and ripe cherry fruit and more traditional Italian earthiness. The latter gives the wine heft that too many Italian wines, desperate to please a focus group, don't have. And the fruit, which isn't overdone, is a counterpoint for the earthiness. It's a terrific value.

NAPA VALLEY CABERNET SAUVIGNON

Typical expensive wine: Caymus Cabernet Sauvignon, $80.

Our choice: Silver Totem Cabernet Sauvignon, $15.

The Wagner family has built an empire out of their Caymus wines and its flagship cabernet. It's the very definition of the current Napa style—soft and luxurious, almost too-ripe black fruit and so much oak aging that the wine tastes almost chocolatey.

The Silver Totem, from Washington State, shares the Caymus style. Everything is where it is supposed to be—some heft and tannins (acids that provide that characteristic astringent taste in the back of your mouth)…rich, dark fruit…enough acidity so that the wine is more than just smooth. I was surprised, at this price, that I enjoyed it as much as I did. Similarly priced American cabernets can taste sweet and syrupy and sometimes not even much like cabernet. This one is a standout.

Hold the Booze, Please: Recipes for Fantastic Alcohol-Free Cocktails

Tired of plain fruit juice and club soda? Looking to upgrade your Shirley Temple? Alcohol-free cocktails have become very popular of late, and mixologists across the country are shaking up the image of the "mocktail," keeping up with demand from patrons with a healthy respect for sobriety and a desire to sip a sophisticated drink.

We asked four drink experts to share their favorite no-alcohol cocktail recipes. They concurred that a well-crafted mocktail can offer complexities of flavor that make it well worth sipping and lingering over conversation—no alcohol needed.

The Douglas

From Danny Shapiro, managing partner, Scofflaw Group bar collective, and managing director, The Moonlighter, Chicago…

We tried many potential "signature" mocktails before declaring a winner for our new spot, The Moonlighter. This one started as a variation on *verdita*—a chilled shot of puréed fruit, veggies and herbs that's often served alongside shots of tequila. We finally arrived at this tasty, complex, unique drink.

- 1 cup pineapple juice
- ½ cup fresh-squeezed lime juice
- ½ cup simple syrup
- ½ large cucumber
- 10 fresh mint leaves
- 2-3 jalapeños, according to your taste, seeded and chopped
- ½ cup loosely packed fresh cilantro leaves
- ¾ teaspoon kosher salt
- 1 cup guava nectar
- 1 cup kiwi purée (three or four kiwis)

Put the pineapple juice and lime juice, simple syrup, cucumber, mint leaves, jalapeños, cilantro and salt in a blender, and process until smooth. Pour the mixture into a pitcher or large glass jar. Stir in the guava nectar and kiwi purée. Cover and refrigerate until chilled—the drink keeps for up to a week. To serve, pour into tall glasses and add ice. Makes six drinks.

Rhubarb-Plum Sparkler

From Frances Largeman-Roth, RDN, nutrition expert and author of *Eating in Color* and host of *The Milk Honey Kitchen with Frances* on YouTube…

I especially enjoy booze-free drinks that balance bitter or spicy with sweet. For this drink, you'll first make a syrup concentrate—this takes a little preparation, but you can then keep the syrup in a refrigerator for a few weeks and easily make a drink whenever you want.

For the syrup…
- 1 cup diced rhubarb (from about two stalks)
- 1 ripe plum, pitted and sliced into wedges
- 1 cup honey or light agave nectar
- 1¼ cups water

For each drink…
- ½ cup chilled sparkling water

In a medium saucepan, combine all the syrup ingredients and bring to a boil over high heat, stirring occasionally. Reduce to a simmer, and cook until there's a bright red syrup and the fruit has fallen apart, about five minutes.

Pour the syrup through a fine-mesh strainer, collecting the syrup in a bowl below. (The fruit can be discarded or eaten.) Allow the syrup to cool, then transfer it to a glass jar with a tight-fitting lid and refrigerate.

To make the drink: Pour one-quarter cup syrup into a champagne flute, then slowly pour sparkling water over the syrup. Makes eight drinks.

Rikki "Tiki" Tavi

From Mary Rich, executive producer, Spirit Savvy, a craft cocktail event company, Asheville, North Carolina…

I've learned a lot about combining flavors from working with wineries and distilleries around the country. To me, one sign of a great bartender is that he/she can craft a perfect mocktail. I like making *orgeat*—pronounced "or-zha"—for use in mocktails. This classic cocktail syrup is widely used in many tropical "tiki" drinks. It imparts a wonderful depth and richness when mixed with citrus.

For the orgeat syrup…

> 1   cup raw almonds
> 3   cups hot water
> Sugar

For the drink…

> 2   ounces orgeat syrup
> 3   ounces water
> 1   ounce fresh-squeezed lemon juice
> 1   orange blossom flower, thin orange slice or thin lemon slice, for garnish

Place the almonds in a bowl with enough cold water to cover. Let soak 30 minutes. Drain well, and place the almonds in a blender. Bring three cups of water to a boil in a medium saucepan. Once it has cooled slightly, add the water to the blender and process until the nuts are coarsely ground.

Line a large strainer with several layers of cheesecloth, and place it over a deep bowl. Slowly pour the almond mixture through the cheesecloth so that the nut milk drips through and is collected in the bowl beneath. After the nut milk drains for a minute, press down on the ground almonds to extract the last bit of liquid. Pour the nut milk back into the blender, then add an equal amount of sugar and blend. Let cool, then pour the mixture into a jar, cover and refrigerate until well-chilled. It can be kept for up to a month.

To make the drink: Combine the orgeat syrup, water and lemon juice in a cocktail shaker with ice. Cover, and shake until chilled. Strain into a Collins glass filled with ice. Garnish as desired. Makes eight drinks.

Tropical Haze

From Dianna Sanders, beverage director, The Promontory restaurant, Chicago…

What I love about this mocktail is that it's subtly smoky and just sweet enough. Also, the coconut milk gives it a silky texture. It definitely has an island vibe. The drink capitalizes on our restaurant's live-fire hearth to create smoked pineapple juice, but I've adapted the recipe to give you almost the same effect at home. The process is a bit labor-intensive but worth it!

> 2¼   cups chilled coconut water
> ½   cup canned coconut milk
> ½   cup smoked pineapple juice (see below)
> ½   cup pineapple juice
> ½   cup fresh-squeezed orange juice
> ½   cup simple syrup
> ¼   cup fresh-squeezed lime juice
> Grilled pineapple wedge and lime slice, for garnish

To make smoked pineapple juice: Prepare a charcoal grill for indirect heat by placing a small pile of charcoal on one side of the grill. Place about a dozen one-inch-thick pineapple slices on a grill rack on the opposite side of the coals. Once the coals are glowing red, drop a handful of wood chips on top of the coals, and close the lid. Allow about 15 minutes for cooking/smoking, flip the slices, then allow about another 15 minutes—the pineapple slices should be marked on both sides. Remove them from the grill, and transfer them to a bowl. Cover tightly with plastic wrap, and let cool completely. Once cool, uncover and press down firmly on the pineapple using a potato masher or squeeze by hand and collect the juice.

To make the drink: Pour all the ingredients over ice in a cocktail shaker, and shake well. Strain into a highball glass filled with ice, and garnish with pineapple and lime. Makes eight drinks.

Everyone Will Love These Holiday Treats— and They're Gluten-Free

Debby Maugans, a food writer based in Asheville, North Carolina. She is author of *Small-Batch Baking, Small-Batch Baking for Chocolate Lovers* and *Farmer & Chef Asheville*. FarmerAndChefSouth.com

If you're baking for the holiday season, here are two of our favorite crowd-pleasing gluten-free recipes so that everyone can enjoy your creations...including your sister who's gluten-free...your uncle who avoids all wheat...and your grandkids who think healthy desserts are icky. *Tip:* When buying all-purpose gluten-free flour mixes, check to see whether xanthan gum is an ingredient...if not, buy it separately and add it as instructed when using these flours.

Sweet Potato Scones

Canned sweet potato purée works fine for this easy recipe. Millet adds sweet, buttery, corn-like flavor...cassava flour adds body...and sweet rice flour lends a tender texture.

Try variations such as adding grated orange rind to the liquid ingredients or unsweetened dried cranberries to the flour.

Makes six scones.

- ⅔ cup cooked sweet potato, mashed
- 1 large egg
- 1½ Tablespoons whole milk
- 1 Tablespoon apple cider vinegar
- ⅔ cup cassava flour
- ½ cup sweet white rice flour, plus more for rolling
- ¼ cup millet flour
- 1 teaspoon xanthan gum
- ⅓ cup sugar plus one teaspoon, divided
- 1 Tablespoon baking powder
- 1 teaspoon baking soda
- ½ teaspoon freshly grated nutmeg, divided
- ½ teaspoon salt
- ¾ stick (6 Tablespoons) very cold unsalted butter

Preheat the oven to 425°F. Line a baking sheet with parchment paper.

Place the sweet potato, egg, milk and cider vinegar in a medium bowl. Whisk to blend until the mixture is smooth.

Combine the cassava flour, the half cup of sweet white rice flour, the millet flour, xanthan gum, one-third cup of the sugar, baking powder, baking soda, one-quarter teaspoon of the nutmeg and the salt in a medium bowl, and whisk to blend well. Grate the butter over the dry ingredients using the coarse holes of a box grater. With a fork or clean hands, toss the mixture briefly to coat the butter pieces with the dry ingredients. Use a spoon to push the ingredients to the sides of the bowl, creating a well in the center.

Scrape the sweet potato mixture into the well, and stir it with a spatula until it forms a soft dough. Turn the dough onto a surface sprinkled with additional rice flour, form it into a one-inch-thick disc and cut it into six triangular wedges. Then place the wedges one inch apart on the prepared baking sheet. Mix the remaining one teaspoon of sugar with the remaining one-quarter teaspoon of nutmeg, and sprinkle the mixture on top of the scones. Bake until lightly browned and a toothpick inserted in the centers of the scones comes out clean, about 18 minutes. Serve warm if possible.

Cranberry-Pear Croustade

A croustade is a free-form French tart made without a pie plate. This one is filled with wonderful flavors of the season—pears, cranberries and crystallized ginger.

Makes six servings.

For the crust...

- 1½ cups gluten-free all-purpose flour mix, plus more for rolling
- 2 teaspoons sugar
- ½ teaspoon salt
- ½ stick (4 Tablespoons) cold unsalted butter
- Yolk of one large egg, beaten
- About 5 to 8 Tablespoons ice water
- Cooking spray

For the filling...

- 1 pound ripe-but-firm Bartlett pears
- 2 Tablespoons fresh lemon juice
- ¼ cup sugar
- 1½ Tablespoons gluten-free all-purpose flour mix

½ cup fresh or frozen cranberries

3 Tablespoons finely minced crystallized ginger

Pinch of salt

Position the oven rack in the center of the oven. Preheat the oven to 400°F.

Prepare the crust: Combine the flour mix, sugar and salt in a large bowl. Lightly push the flour mix to the sides of the bowl, and grate the butter over the well you created. Use a spatula or your hands to gently toss the butter into the flour mix. Pour in the beaten egg yolk, and use a fork to mix the dough lightly until crumbly. Add the ice water, one tablespoon at a time, working it in with a fork until the dough holds together.

Sprinkle one tablespoon of the additional flour mix onto a large piece of parchment paper. Shape the dough into one disc, about six inches in diameter and one inch thick. Place it on the parchment paper.

Sprinkle about one teaspoon more of flour mix on top of the disc, and place another large piece of parchment paper on top. Using a rolling pin, roll the dough between the parchment paper into a disc that is 12 inches in diameter, picking up the top piece of parchment paper occasionally to keep it from sticking to the dough. When done rolling, carefully peel off the top piece of parchment, pinching any cracked pieces of dough back together.

Coat a baking sheet with cooking spray. Lift the bottom parchment paper with the dough, and carefully invert the dough onto the baking sheet. Gently loosen the parchment paper from the dough, but keep the dough covered loosely with it. Refrigerate while you prepare the filling.

Prepare the filling: Peel the pears, cut them in half, remove the cores and slice thinly. Toss with the lemon juice in a large bowl. Add the sugar, flour mix, cranberries, ginger and salt, and toss to coat well.

Spread the pear slices evenly in the center of the dough round, leaving two inches around the edge of the dough. Arrange the pear slices in any pattern you find attractive. Gently fold the edges over the pears to the extent that the edges reach, lightly crimping as you go.

Bake for 20 minutes in the preheated oven. Reduce the oven temperature to 375°F, and bake until the pastry is golden and the pears are tender, 15 to 20 minutes more. Serve warm or at room temperature.

Avoid These Holiday Pitfalls

•**Cramming in workouts**—squeezing in your usual 60-minute workout may seem like a good idea but may add too much stress at an already stressful time. Instead, try splitting up your routine with a short strength sequence in the morning, a walk at lunch and a yoga session before bed.

•**Stocking up on sleep**—you may be tempted to log some extra sleep if you have time off around the holidays, but straying from your normal sleep pattern can throw off your body clock and set you up for restless nights.

•**Brushing your teeth after red wine**—this might actually increase your risk of staining your teeth. Wine's acidity can weaken tooth enamel, and brushing right after drinking may contribute to erosion. Instead, rinse your mouth with water.

•**Making lots of "light" recipes**—when a food is healthier or lower-calorie, people tend to overindulge. You are better off fully enjoying a small serving of a full-fat, full-calorie favorite.

Health.com

HAPPIER HOLIDAYS...

Lift Holiday Moods with Scents

At your holiday table, use aromas to enhance everyone's state of mind—fresh-cut evergreen eases stress...peppermint increases energy... cinnamon sharpens focus...and vanilla inspires happiness.

Bottom Line research.

Make Your Christmas Tree Last Longer

Teri Dunn Chace, a garden writer based in central New York who is author of more than 35 gardening books, including *The Anxious Gardener's Book of Answers*. TeriChaceWriter.com

Putting a cut evergreen tree inside a dry, warm house isn't very practical, yet we invite nearly 30 million beautiful, fragrant real Christmas trees into our homes each year—to mixed results.

There are lots of myths about making a Christmas tree last longer—such as drilling holes in the base of the trunk to let in more water (it won't work and actually damages the tree's tiny capillaries that absorb water). *Here are the real ways to keep your tree fresh longer...*

LOOK, TOUCH, DROP

When you're shopping, look to make sure that your tree doesn't look wilted. Then touch to make sure the branches are flexible and springy, not stiff and brittle...and run your hand lightly along a branch toward you to see if the needles fall off. If a few drop, that's fine, but a lot isn't good. Now raise the tree a few inches, and drop it straight down on the bottom, cut portion of the trunk. If a shower of needles drops off, don't buy the tree.

Choose a tree that will fit into your base so that you won't need to hammer or whittle it (that damages capillaries, too). Get the seller to cut one-quarter inch off the base to expose fresh wood for better water uptake. Once home, place your tree away from any heat source (fireplace, heating duct, radiator).

BLEACH, ASPIRIN AND OTHER MYTHS

Your beautiful new tree is very thirsty, absorbing up to a gallon of water a day. Top off the water regularly, even daily, with cool tap water. Don't let the cut base be exposed to air.

What about additives to the water? A penny leaches copper, which is supposed to act as a preservative, but that's unproved. Nor will adding sugary soda or corn syrup "nourish" the tree—it's no longer alive.

Other additives kill germs—a bit of bleach, vodka, vinegar, lemon juice or an aspirin. But your tree drinks in water so quickly that the water won't get stagnant. And consider safety—do you want your pet or a small child around bleach water?

Here's what really makes a difference: Daily misting. Your tree will gratefully absorb the moisture through its needles. For safety, turn tree lights off first and leave them off for two or three hours after misting. And don't mist near delicate, fragile ornaments.

Tip: Turn off tree lights right before bedtime, mist and then turn them back on in the morning. Even those tiny lights emit heat that can dry out the tree.

Guys, You Could Look Much Better

Jennifer Mahoney, a wardrobe and personal-image consultant based in Chicago who works exclusively with male clients. She previously worked as a designer and merchandiser for men's apparel makers and has 20 years of experience in men's fashion. For more information, go to ASharpDressedMan.com.

If you're a man age 50 or older, there's a good chance you're not interested in keeping up with the latest fashion trends. But even if you don't hope to seem hip, you would do well to update your wardrobe from time to time. Fail to do so, and it isn't just your clothing that might be dismissed as out of date.

You don't have to spend a fortune to update your look—adding a relatively modest number of stylish pieces can make a big difference. And if you know which kinds of stores are the best to shop at—and which to avoid—you can buy good-looking, high-quality clothing for almost shockingly low prices.

Here are the items that almost every man age 50 or older should add to his wardrobe...

SHIRTS AND JACKETS

The clothes below will be an easy switch for you. They are nothing more than dress shirts and sport coats—just not the exact kind you've been wearing for decades!

• **Dress shirts with subtle check or plaid patterns.** Many men wear only solid white or blue dress shirts. If they own any patterned dress shirts, they're pinstripes—which were popular decades ago and now look dated. A check- or plaid-patterned dress shirt is a good way to look stylish while still dressing conservatively. Think *understated* here—the plaid or check should be subtle enough that the shirt's color looks essentially solid from a distance. Light pink and lavender checks or plaids are often-overlooked color choices that flatter most men.

The cut of a dress shirt makes a big difference—opt for the slimmest cut that fits you. Men who are carrying a few extra pounds often avoid close-fitting shirts, fearing that they will make the weight more obvious. In fact, it's loose-fitting dress shirts that balloon out from the body that inevitably are unflattering. If you wear an undershirt beneath a dress shirt, make sure that it fits close to your body, too, or it will ruin the look of even the best-fitting dress shirt.

Keep this in mind: "Slim fit" or "tailored-fit" clothing isn't only for slim men—all it means is that the clothing, when worn in the right size, fits close to the body.

Examples: Dress shirts appropriate for men who are not especially thin include Calvin Klein Slim Fit Dress Shirt and Bugatchi Plaid or Checked Shaped Fit Dress Shirt. Stylish dress shirts that flatter thin men include Ben Sherman Print Slim Fit Dress Shirt and Original Penguin Heritage Slim Fit Patterned Dress Shirt.

• **Sport coat with an unstructured cut.** If you're looking for one single garment that will help you look fashionable, a casual sport coat in navy or charcoal gray is the one to choose. You can wear this with anything from a dress shirt and dress pants to a T-shirt and jeans. Unlike most sport coats, a casual sport coat does not have much padding in the shoulders or other structure, so it won't seem formal when worn with informal garments. Also, a sport coat can be an effective way to hide a stomach that's expanded a bit over the years.

Examples: Banana Republic Slim Italian Wool Cotton Blazer or Indigo Blue Heritage Cotton-Blend Utility Blazer...Jachs NY Navy Woven Two-Button Notch Lapel Blazer.

PANTS

Many men opt for comfort over style when they select pants and end up looking baggy and frumpy. You can have comfort and style—just pick fairly close-fitting pants that have some stretch in the fabric, and you won't feel constrained.

• **Slim-fit sateen pants.** Don't let the word "sateen" turn you off. This kind of fabric weave is related to satin, but it doesn't look like satin. These are a more stylish replacement for khakis. They're cut more like slim-fit blue jeans than like baggy, unflattering khakis, but because the fabric has some stretch, they're comfortable.

Example: Calvin Klein Men's Slim Fit 4-Pocket Sateen Pants.

• **Slim-fit/straight-fit blue jeans with some stretch.** There's no avoiding it—men who want to look stylish in jeans should select a slim fit or straight fit (a little less slim than slim fit) that remains close to their legs. As noted above, you can have both that close fit and comfort if you buy jeans made from denim that has some stretchiness. In this category, smart shoppers can wear some beautifully made higher-end jeans that set you apart from the Levi's crowd without spending too much more.

Examples: Joe's Jeans Brixton Straight & Narrow...7 For All Mankind Standard or "Slimmy" Fit men's jeans.

SHOES AND SOCKS

Stylish shoes make a huge difference in how your overall look is perceived. They can be expensive, but they don't have to be.

• **Dark-color leather sneakers.** Men who want the comfort of sneakers during non-athletic activities should opt for stylish dark leather sneakers.

Example: The Ted Baker London Prinnc Leather Sneaker.

• **Monk-strap dress shoes.** These have a classic dress-shoe look, only with a buckle rather than laces. They're stylish without being showy.

Example: Cole Haan Kennedy Single Monk Strap Oxford.

• **Chukka boots.** These look like traditional Oxford dress shoes, but they're a bit taller, reaching the ankle. They're a stylish twist on a classic, conservative shoe.

Examples: Steve Madden Ivon Chukka Boot…English Laundry Ascot Wingtip Chukka Boot.

• **Socks that make a statement.** This isn't for every man, but if you want to inject some personal style and fun into your wardrobe without spending too much, distinctively patterned socks are one way to do it.

Example: Happy Socks offers dozens of distinctive patterns, most for $12 to $24 (Happy Socks.com).

ACCESSORIES

As most women know but most men never think about, little touches can make a big difference in looking good.

• **Leather (or faux leather) slide belt.** Slide belts have no belt holes but instead a hinged clasp, and most have classy, understated buckles. Unlike traditional belts, slide belts tend not to develop as obvious a line where the buckle rubs against the belt, so if you put on a few pounds and need to wear your belt a little looser, it won't be as apparent.

Example: SlideBelts Classic Black Belt ($38, SlideBelts.com).

• **Pocket square and/or flower pin.** Pocket squares are a stylish but not over-the-top way for men to add a little color to their outfits when they wear a suit or sport coat. Fabric lapel flower pins are in style these days, too. Your best bet is to get one that is less than two inches across and not too brightly colored, so it won't be too showy. The traditional option is to select ones that are (or include) a color that's in your tie, but you also could match the color of your socks or shirt…or for a bolder look, select a color that complements the color of the shirt rather than matches it, such as orange with blue.

Examples: Ben Sherman Tie, Pocket Square and Lapel Flower Stick Pin Sets…Original Penguin Hall Solid Pocket Square & Lapel Flower Pin Set. These are sold as sets, but you don't have to wear the pocket square and flower pin at the same time if that seems like too much.

WHERE TO SHOP FOR MEN'S CLOTHING

For a man seeking to update his wardrobe, it's best not to buy truly cheap clothing—such as most of the house-brand clothing sold at department stores—because the low-end materials and construction make it look cheap after just a few wearings, even if it looked good in the first place. *Much better…*

• **Shop at mid-tier clothing retailers** whose house brands are a cut (or two or three) above those of most department stores—these include stores such Brooks Brothers, Banana Republic and others mentioned above. And when these stores have sales, the price-to-quality ratio is extremely good.

• **Shop at the discount arms of high-end department stores,** where lots of initially expensive, very high-quality garments are marked way down because they did not sell during their first few months on store shelves. These include Nordstrom's Nordstrom Rack and Saks Fifth Avenue's "Off 5th." These stores also feature clothing made to the same high standards as the parent store's brand but in slightly different patterns or styles.

• **Try websites specializing in marked-down higher-end clothing.** Two that have especially good selections for men are Gilt.com and Zulily.com. You also can find some great deals at CalvinKlein.us/en/sale and Steve Madden.com's "Clearance" section.

Remember that if your goal is to look up to date, not trendy, last season's or last year's styles are a very good choice for both looks and price.

15

Car Care

Repair Your Old Car—or Replace It? How to Tell

Is it worth paying for a pricey repair on an old car with many miles on the odometer? That's a question worth asking, especially when the repair estimate is above $1,000 and the odometer is above 150,000 miles. There's nothing like a car that's already paid for—it's far and away the most cost-effective sort of vehicle to drive. But there's little point pouring thousands of dollars into a car if it isn't likely to give you many thousands more miles of relatively reliable service. At some point, it's time to say goodbye.

Here are the steps to take to gauge whether your car has reached that point when it has a problem…

1. Ask your mechanic to provide a quote on the repair. Request that this quote be broken down into parts and labor. If parts are a major slice of the price, check whether you could save a significant amount by using one or more used parts rather than the new ones your mechanic probably intended to use. You can search online for suppliers of the parts that your mechanic says you need.

Used parts aren't necessarily worse than new ones. They have some miles on them, but they're typically the original manufacturer parts, while new replacement parts often are aftermarket parts that might not be made as well—the quality of aftermarket parts varies. Some used-part sellers even test and warranty their parts—this isn't like the old days of heading down to the local salvage yard to pull parts off old cars yourself.

Warning: Do not buy used brake components, clutch components or a used fuel pump or water pump. These parts can wear out rap-

---

Russ Evans, ASE Master Certified Automotive Technician who manages Nordstrom's Installation and Diagnostic Center in Garretson, South Dakota. He is cohost of the syndicated radio show *Under the Hood*. UnderThe HoodShow.com

idly and could easily be on their last legs when you buy them. (And parts like these tend not to be offered with warranties.)

2. Look up how much cars like yours are selling for online. Sites where used-car prices can be found include Craigslist.com... eBay Motors (eBay.com/motors)...Edmunds. com...and KBB.com. Search for cars that are as similar to yours as possible in model, year and mileage. Their condition should be comparable to the condition your car would be in if you paid for the needed repair.

It's probably not wise to repair your car if you discover that you could purchase a very similar car for less than the price of the repair. (Remember that the prices you find online are likely to be asking prices—those cars probably could be purchased for at least a few hundred dollars less.)

If the repair price is fairly close to your car's value, consider your car's track record—if it has had a series of problems and you no longer trust it, it's probably time to move on...but if the vehicle was largely trouble-free until it experienced its current problem, it might be worth paying for the repair—after weighing the issues raised below.

Tip: It's more likely to be worth paying for a costly repair with a high-mileage full-size pickup truck than with a high-mileage car, SUV or small pickup. Full-size pickups tend to be built more solidly than other vehicles, so the odds are higher that if you repair the current problem, the truck will be able to provide many more miles of reliable service.

3. Check for additional problems (and pay your mechanic to do the same). Before you agree to a pricey repair on an old or high-mileage car, take a peek underneath. If you find significant rust on the frame or suspension, it's probably not worth repairing—there's a good chance that the car doesn't have a lot of miles left in it. This is especially common in the northern US, where car-corroding salt is spread on icy winter roads.

Ask your mechanic to put the car up on a lift before you agree to the repair so that he/she can check for major rust problems, too, as well as any other issues that could point to additional costly repairs soon. Ask him to start

the car to listen and look for potential issues (assuming that the car's current problem does not preclude starting it). Sometimes mechanics will do basic inspections like these for free, particularly for longtime customers. If not, offer to pay the mechanic's rate for a "used car inspection" on your own car. That's typically one hour at the garage's hourly rate, often $85 to $100, though potentially more at a dealership. It's money well-spent before investing thousands of dollars in a repair.

If the mechanic finds additional issues, ask how much those repairs would cost. Add that figure to the current repair estimate, and compare the total to what cars like yours are selling for online.

Also: Consider the condition of the car's tires (brakes, too). If they will need to be replaced soon, it could add hundreds of dollars to the price of keeping the car on the road. That might not be enough on its own to encourage you to move on from a car, but it could tip the balance if you're facing a close call.

4. Factor in your larger financial picture, your driving needs and your current car's fuel economy. Ask yourself these three questions if the repair-or-replace decision remains unclear...

Could you comfortably fit a monthly car payment into your budget or comfortably pay cash for a new (or reliable, low-mileage used) car? If upgrading to something significantly newer and more reliable would require a financial stretch, that's a reason to lean toward keeping your current car on the road a bit longer. Keeping the old car might lead to additional budget-taxing repair bills…but replacing this car definitely will take a bite out of your tight budget.

Do you drive long distances and/or depend on your car to get you somewhere that you absolutely must go regularly, such as a job? If so, lean toward replacing the car with something newer and more reliable. On the other hand, if you use your car only for short trips and you have family members or friends you can rely on for rides when your car is in the shop, then future breakdowns might not be as big of a deal for you.

What's your current car's fuel economy? Fuel economy has improved dramatically in recent years. For example, the base model of the 2018 Toyota Camry, a spacious, safe and reliable midsize sedan, gets 41 miles per gallon (mpg) on the highway, and the hybrid version of that car gets 53 mpg. If your current car is a fuel hog in comparison, replacing it might save you enough money at the pump to make that the smart decision.

For several years, infotainment systems in many vehicles have let you connect, or "pair," your smartphone wirelessly via Bluetooth or through a USB cable.

Problem: As drivers increasingly use car infotainment systems to send texts and e-mail, browse the Internet, log into mobile apps, get directions and even open garage doors, a vehicle's computer might store much of the data, which can be accessed easily by a tech-savvy thief.

What to do: When you sell a vehicle or return a leased one, wipe personal data from the computer. Many vehicles have a factory-reset option that returns the settings and data to their original state. Check the owner's manual or contact a dealer. Otherwise, delete information manually. Go to the infotainment system's main menu. Navigate to the list of paired devices, and follow the instructions to delete yours. If you used the vehicle's navigation system, clear your location history…and clear any garage-door codes.

For rental cars, doing a factory reset might violate a rental agreement requirement to not modify the vehicle's functionality. Instead, manually delete paired devices and location history. Ask rental-car personnel to walk you through the steps if you need help. If you visit a mechanic you don't trust not to snoop, delete your paired devices temporarily and reload your data when you get the vehicle back.

Hidden Danger in Your Car's Infotainment System

Nathan Wenzler, former chief security strategist at AsTech, an information-security consulting firm that helped Fortune 1,000 companies and their employees protect digital data. He is now with Moss Adams.

There's a hidden danger when you sell your vehicle…take it to a repair shop… reach the end of a lease…or return a rental car. The danger is in leaving detailed personal information in the auto's onboard computer, making you vulnerable to cybertheft.

5 Car Noises You Should Never Ignore

Jill Trotta, an ASE Certified Technician/Adviser who has more than 25 years of experience in the industry. She currently is director of the automotive group at RepairPal, a website that offers auto-repair information including repair-cost estimates and evaluations of more than 4,200 independent repair facilities nationwide. RepairPal.com

A 1960s TV series that featured a mother reincarnated as a talking car was played for laughs. But when your own car starts making unexpected sounds, it can be annoying, confusing or even frightening.

Should you ignore a car noise and hope it goes away, as they sometimes do? Rush to a mechanic? Or do something in between?

Here's how to interpret five common car noises and what prudent actions you should take when they occur...

• Hissing or sizzling from under the hood. This usually indicates that a fluid—most likely oil or coolant—is leaking onto a hot piece of metal, such as the engine or exhaust manifold, and being vaporized by the heat. You're most likely to hear this immediately after parking and turning off the engine because it usually is not loud enough to be heard over engine and road noise.

What to do: Immediately after turning off the engine, open the hood and look for smoke or steam—that's the easiest way to track down the leak. The leak either is very near the smoke or above it, where the fluid can drip down. If you don't see this, listen closely for the precise spot where the sound is coming from and look near and immediately above this. Meanwhile, use your nose to figure out what fluid is leaking. Burning oil smells acrid...burning coolant smells sweet.

If oil or coolant (or window-washer fluid or any other fluid) was added to the car within the past few days, there might not be any problem—a small amount of that fluid might have splashed when it was poured in. This will soon burn away, and the hissing or sizzling sound will cease.

Check the coolant and/or oil level. If either is below the marked minimum, add more before driving the vehicle any farther.

Warning: If the car has been driven recently, let it cool for at least 15 minutes before opening the radiator cap to avoid steam burns.

If fluid was not very recently added, however, take the car to a mechanic soon. An oil or coolant leak could ruin your engine if the fluid level gets very low. Oil leaking onto hot metal parts also creates a fire risk.

The cost of repairs can vary dramatically depending on the source of the leak. If an engine gasket or radiator must be replaced, your bill could be upward of $500 and potentially many times that if the head gasket must be replaced.* But if something simpler, such as a radiator hose, must be replaced, the bill might be $100 to $300, depending on the vehicle. (It generally is worth paying a mechanic to replace a radiator hose unless you are very good with auto repairs.)

• Squealing from under the hood, especially soon after you start the car or as you accelerate. An accessory belt probably is slipping. There are one or more rubber belts under the car's hood that transfer power from its engine to other components, such as the alternator, power steering pump and cooling fan. As these belts age, they become increasingly likely to slip and squeal. (Squealing also is common on very cold days.)

What to do: If your car dates to the 1990s or earlier, it likely has a belt or belts made from a type of rubber known as neoprene. You can visually inspect this type of belt for cracks or other signs of wear and replace the belt if you see significant cracks and gaps. You also can spray it with "belt dressing," available in auto-parts stores—if the noise stops after applying this dressing, the belt almost certainly is the problem and should be replaced soon. (Belt dressing is only a temporary fix.)

Newer cars have EPDM belts, which are made from a longer-lasting type of rubber. (If you're not sure what kind of belts you have, check with your car dealership or in your owner's manual.) These are less likely to show visible signs that they need to be replaced, and spraying belt dressing on EPDM belts can damage them. When you hear squealing from the belt of a car made since 2000, the best bet is to check its recommended service schedule in the owner's manual to see if a belt is due for replacement. If the belt isn't due for replacement—or you replace the belt and the squealing continues—something else could be causing the noise, such as a misaligned pulley or a bad bearing, and it's probably worth taking the car to a mechanic.

Some car owners can replace worn belts on their own, but it can be a frustrating chore.

*Repair prices can vary dramatically by vehicle and garage/dealership (new-car dealerships typically charge steeper rates). The prices cited in this article are average for most cars when taken to an independent garage.

For most people, it's well worth paying a mechanic $100 to $200.

• **Rattle under the car.** A part likely has come loose—but which part? Usually it's something that's easy to fix, such as a piece of the thin metal "heat shielding" that surrounds the exhaust pipe and other parts located under the car that get hot. But sometimes a rattle is something potentially serious such as a loose ball joint or tie rod—and if one of these steering components failed entirely, you could lose control of the car.

What to do: Park the car somewhere that you can safely lie next to it and peer underneath it. Visually scan for anything that obviously is hanging loose. If you don't see anything like that, reach under the car and feel for parts loose enough that they move when you touch them. (If you have recently driven the car, wait for its exhaust system to cool before touching it so you don't get burned. Cooling could take 30 to 60 minutes.) Follow along the exhaust pipe, feeling each exposed part from the engine to the tailpipe. If you find a loose part, fixing the rattle might be as simple as tightening or replacing the nut or bolt that is supposed to secure it. Or sometimes you can stop heat-shielding rattles by affixing hose clamps tightly around the rattling shielding, securing it firmly to the other nearby sections of heat shielding or whatever else the shielding was originally affixed to. (Hose clamps are inexpensive and available in hardware stores and home centers.)

If you cannot locate the rattle, bring the car to a mechanic soon. There is some chance that something crucial for control, such as a steering or suspension part, is failing—and those failures are tough to pin down unless a car is up on a lift.

• **Clicking, clunking or popping sound** from beneath the car when you turn the steering wheel. One or both of your outer constant-velocity joints might need to be replaced. Often called CV joints, these connect the transmission to the front wheels in a front- or all-wheel-drive car.

What to do: Take the car to a mechanic promptly. If one of your CV joints failed completely, your car could become uncontrollable.

Sometimes (but not always), when a CV joint is failing, at least one of your "boots"—the ringed rubber components that encase the axle right where it meets the inside of each front wheel—will be cracked or not securely connected to the inside of the wheel. It is easier to examine these boots if you turn the steering wheel completely to one side. Expect to pay perhaps $300 to $500 to have a CV joint replaced.

Warning: If your mechanic tells you that you need to replace only the boot, not the entire CV joint, ask for a quote for replacing the entire joint, too. You're likely to pay more for parts but less for labor if you replace the entire joint rather than just the boot, and your total bill is likely to be roughly the same either way. If there is no big price difference, replace the whole CV joint—when these boots fail, the CV joints they protect often sustain damage that might not be easily spotted but that could lead to additional problems down the road.

• **Squealing or grinding sound when you apply the brakes.** It's probably time for some sort of brake job. If you hear squealing, there's a good chance that you need only new brake pads—the squeal is generally produced by "wear indicators," small metal tabs designed to make this annoying noise to warn you that the pads are worn down.

Exception: If your brakes squeal only when you first start to drive each day and not later

GOOD TO KNOW...

No Need to Warm Up the Engine Anymore

Warming up your engine before driving made sense when engines used carburetors but not with today's fuel-injected engines. Modern engines warm up quickly. Letting them idle when cold can allow gasoline to mix with the oil, increasing engine wear. Simply start the car...be sure the windows are clear...and drive.

Clark.com

on, the noise likely is just moisture on the brake pads and does not mean the car has a problem. If you hear grinding, your brake pads are completely worn out and metal components of the braking system now are pressing against each other when you brake, damaging your brake rotors (the discs that the brake pads grab in a disc brake system). There's a good chance that in addition to needing new brake pads, you also will have to have your rotors "turned" (resurfaced) or replaced.

What to do: Get them checked very soon—the longer you wait, the greater the odds that the cost of the brake job will jump from $150 to $300 per axle to replace brake pads to $400 to $600 or more per axle to replace both pads and rotors.

Lifesaving Reminder

A sign in your garage may save your life if you have a car with a modern keyless ignition. It's easy to forget to push the button to turn the car off. The risk is even greater with hybrid cars, which are silent on battery power. Dozens of people have died from carbon monoxide fumes when cars were left on in a garage. And while some keyless cars shut off automatically, putting up a big sign may be the best reminder.

Robert Sinclair, Jr., manager of media relations for AAA Northeast, Garden City, New York.

Warning Light May Signal Problem with *Spare* Tire

Some modern vehicles, including many SUVs and pickups, monitor pressure in the spare as well as the other tires. Many drivers don't realize this and conclude that the monitoring system is malfunctioning when the light comes on but the tires in use seem fine.

Result: Drivers ignore the warning light, and their spares are flat when they need them.

Russ Evans, ASE Master Certified Automotive Technician and cohost of the syndicated radio show *Under the Hood.* UnderTheHoodShow.com

New Winter Tires May Be Old

Because recent winters have been fairly warm in many areas, some dealers still may be stocking tires manufactured three or more years ago. There are no laws limiting the time between manufacture and sale. To find the tire's date of manufacture, look for a number on the tire's sidewall. It gives the month and year of manufacture.

Example: The number 4117 means a tire was made in the 41st week of 2017.

Always try to buy the newest tires available, and steer clear of those made more than two years earlier.

Consumer Reports.

Gadgets That Make Driving Easier and Safer

Donna S. Stressel, occupational therapist at Sunnyview Rehabilitation Hospital in Schenectady, New York, a certified driver rehabilitation specialist and a driving instructor in the state of New York.

No longer being able to drive and losing your feeling of independence can be traumatic, and you're not likely to hang up your keys without a fight. Well, maybe you don't have to! If you're not as capable and confident behind the wheel as you used to be, whether due to a physical issue such as arthritis or to diminished vision, there are many devices that can help you stay on the road longer—safely.

We talked to Donna S. Stressel, an occupational therapist and certified driver rehabilitation specialist, who recommended products that can help remedy the most common issues facing older drivers, as well as drivers of any age with disabilities or mobility issues...

• **Larger mirrors.** If you have trouble turning your head or are regularly vexed by blind spots in your side-view or rearview mirrors, clip-on or replacement mirrors can help. Blind-spot side-view mirrors, available through Amazon and other online retailers, that attach on top of existing side-view mirrors are a good choice. With these add-on mirrors, you can continue to use the mirrors you are used to but expand their view. *Cost:* $20 to $50.

• **The HandyBar.** For anyone who has a mobility issue or is recovering from an injury, this assistive device provides support as you get in and out of your vehicle. It's especially helpful for people who have difficulty getting out of a low vehicle, such as a sedan, or getting into a high vehicle, such as an SUV or pickup truck. Available at Stander.com, the price is $34.99.

• **Steering-wheel cover.** A soft foam or leather cover can help when arthritis or carpal tunnel syndrome makes it difficult to hold the steering wheel properly. The most important consideration is that it fits the steering wheel of your vehicle's make and model—this is not as easy as it used to be because today's steering wheels tend to incorporate lots of unique contours and buttons, so read reviews about fit before purchasing. *Cost:* $10 to $20.

• **Seat cushion for height.** On average, people lose a half-inch of height every decade after age 40 and even more than that after age 70. If you don't have much height to spare when it comes to seeing over the steering wheel and dashboard, a seat cushion can help...and ensure that the center of the steering-wheel air bag is safely facing your chest and not your face. Visibility—your sight line—should be at least three inches above the steering wheel. A firm foam wedge-shape cushion (higher in the back and lower in the front) can increase your height without raising your legs too close to the steering wheel or too far from the pedals. An orthopedic gel cushion also can help with back or hip pain. These kinds of cushions can be found for about $13 to $80.

• **Swivel-seat cushion.** This type of cushion makes it easier for people with stiff joints or limited mobility to pivot to get in and out of the driver's seat. *Cost:* $15 to $60.

ADAPTIVE-DRIVING EQUIPMENT

These items should be prescribed by a certified driver rehabilitation specialist to be sure that you're getting the best equipment for your needs and can be trained in how to use it. This ensures that you'll be able to safely drive with the modifications and are compliant with all license-restriction procedures in your state. Only a certified mechanic specializing in installing adaptive equipment should make the modifications so that the equipment and installation meet all regulations. Note that not all vehicles can be modified in all ways, but if what you need is possible, the vendor will ensure that the appropriate equipment is used.

You can find a certified driver rehabilitation specialist through the Association for Driver Rehabilitation Specialists (ADED.net) or the American Occupational Therapist Association (AOTA.org)...and a certified installer through the National Mobility Equipment Dealers Association (NMEDA.com).

• **Swing-out swivel-seat replacement.** If a swivel cushion isn't enough of an accommodation, consider a swing-out or swivel-seat replacement. This involves completely replacing the seat that came with your car with a seat

---

TAKE NOTE...

For Better Posture After a Long Car Ride...

Help your posture after a long car ride with a five-minute, three-step workout...

Lunge stretch: From standing, step one foot forward, bend your front knee and hold for 15 seconds. Do three reps per side.

Scapular retractions: Put your hands on a wall, squeeze your shoulder blades, then release them. Do two sets of 10.

Rag-doll pose: Stand with your knees slightly bent, lean over and let your head hang down for 30 seconds. Do three reps.

Men's Health.

that stays anchored to the vehicle but moves in and out so that you can enter and exit without twisting or rotating. Cost can run several thousand dollars with installation.

• **Steering-wheel spinner.** This simple attachment, often a knob, is secured to a steering wheel to enable drivers with limited or no use of one arm to steer with their working arm. Price is about $100, including installation.

• **Left-foot accelerator.** People who have very limited or no use of their right leg, whether because of amputation, stroke or another condition, may be able to operate all the car pedals with their left leg. Prices range from about $500 to $2,000 depending on style (mechanical or electronic), including installation.

• **Pedal extenders.** If you can't comfortably reach the gas and/or brake pedal, professionally installed pedal extenders can help. They eliminate the need to sit too far forward in the seat, which can be dangerous. Price with installation is between $300 and $800 depending on the type of control.

• **Hand controls.** If you've lost the use of your legs from a condition such as paralysis, spinal stenosis or peripheral neuropathy, this device allows you to control the accelerator and brake using your hands. Prices start at about $1,500, including installation.

IF YOU'RE IN THE MARKET FOR A CAR...

Consider paying extra, if necessary, for certain features that will keep you more comfortable and safer on the road...

• **Power everything**—steering, windows, lift gate, door locks and seats that move up and down as well as forward and backward

• **Tilting and telescoping steering wheel**

• **Rearview camera** for backing up (now required on any new vehicle as of May 2018)

• **Factory-installed adjustable foot pedals** for the brake and accelerator

• **Large dashboard controls with buttons,** which are easier to manipulate than knobs

• **Warning systems to alert you to objects in blind spots,** especially while changing lanes, merging and parking

• **Lane-departure warning system** to warn you if your car is veering outside your lane

• **"Smart" headlights** with glare control that automatically pivot during turns and adjust the range and intensity of light based on oncoming vehicles

• **Crash-mitigation systems** that sense when you might be in danger of a collision and automatically stop the car.

Editor's note: Unless noted, the products mentioned in this article are available on Amazon, at department stores and through specialty automotive and assistive-device sites such as IndependentLiving.com and LiveOakMed. com. *Also:* The products typically are not covered by insurance but may be tax-deductible. See IRS Publication 502, *Medical and Dental Expenses*, for details.

Better Night Driving

Because of age-related changes to the eyes and diseases such as cataracts, diabetes or glaucoma, older people are susceptible to problems with night vision.

If you're an older driver, talk to your optometrist. You might be a candidate for prescription night-driving glasses even if you don't wear glasses during the day. If you're getting new glasses, consider an antireflective coating to help reduce glare, which can make driving at night much more comfortable. You also can ask your eye doctor if "high-definition" or yellow-tinted lenses, both of which can give you sharper vision and reduce glare, might be appropriate. If you are having cataract surgery—ask about getting an *aspheric intraocular lens*, which improves contrast sensitivity—though it's not covered by Medicare or insurance.

Other tips: When you are driving at night—make sure that your headlights, windows and mirrors are clean...use your window defoggers in bad weather...slow your speed...and turn on your high beams more often—but not in fog or oncoming traffic.

University of California, Berkeley Wellness Letter.

16

Happy Home

Save Your Marriage in Just Two Days

As a long-time marriage therapist with nearly 40 years of experience, I am one of a growing group of professionals who has found that the format of the traditional "60-minute" therapy session repeated week after week is impractical—even inherently flawed. Instead I, along with a growing number of my colleagues, now offer two-day couples intensives. But can you really turn your marriage around in two days? *Yes, you can.*

WHAT'S WRONG WITH THE THERAPY HOUR

When a couple starts traditional therapy, it often takes many sessions for the therapist to get enough information about underlying problems for reparative work to begin. Meanwhile, the problems persist, often adding to a deepening sense of hopelessness. Within each session,

it can be daunting to discuss profoundly personal subjects, so people often procrastinate, waiting until the end of a session to share their innermost thoughts and feelings. Ending sessions abruptly when people are in the throes of emotionally charged conversations doesn't bode well for the week ahead.

About 15 years ago, I started looking for better solutions for the on-the-brink-of-divorce couples who frequented my practice. They sincerely wanted help for their fragile marriages, and they didn't have time for "he said/she said" rehashing of marital woes or endless replays of "I'll change if you change first" mantras.

Two-day intensives—just you and your spouse or partner (for nonmarried couples) and a therapist—allow ample time to explore issues in depth, to deal with tough emotions

Michele Weiner-Davis, LCSW, founder of The Divorce Busting Center in Boulder, Colorado, which helps on-the-brink couples save their marriages. She is the best-selling author of eight books including *Healing from Infidelity, The Sex-Starved Marriage* and *Divorce Busting* and is a TEDx speaker. DivorceBusting.com

as they arise and, most important, to begin to find solutions to long-term problems.

The short time frame often helps get a reluctant spouse to participate.

Example: For one of my couples, married for 35 years, a key issue was the husband's long hours as a small-town physician. The wife felt unloved, and the husband felt misunderstood. But committing to months, perhaps years, of weekly therapy sessions was simply not feasible. A two-day format worked for both of them—and led to a breakthrough.

Bonus: Since two-day intensive marriage-therapy sessions are not available in every part of the country, many couples need to travel out of town to attend them. That allows couples to take a break from life's routines to focus exclusively on their relationships rather than careers and children—and to enjoy a bit of an adventure in a new place. Many also prefer the anonymity that seeking help away from home allows.

A DIFFERENT KIND OF THERAPY

The structure of these sessions stemmed from the work of a team I was on that developed an innovative approach called *solution-focused brief therapy* (SFBT) at the Brief Family Therapy Center in Milwaukee in the 1980s. Rather than focus on the past to understand why people are experiencing problems, SFBT focuses on the future, identifying the specific steps people must take to achieve their goals. It emphasizes people's strengths and resources rather than shortcomings. Couples are encouraged to shift from blame over what's going wrong—arguments, emotional distance, sarcasm—to overlooked times when things go a bit more smoothly…argument-free days…parenting differences handled collaboratively…unexpected friendly texts. Restoring positive feelings happens more readily when couples redirect their attention to their mates' positive actions and intentions because what you focus on expands. SFBT has been shown to be effective in many clinical studies and is offered around the world.

In a typical two-day session, each day starts at 9 am and ends around 4 pm, with a break for lunch. Instead of spending a great deal of time analyzing what caused problems, time is spent exploring the reasons couples are seeking help, their goals for their relationships and the concrete steps they need to take to stop fighting and achieve more love and connection in their lives. A portion of the sessions is devoted to teaching couples relevant relationship skills. For example, couples who complain, "We just can't communicate," learn specific skills to enable them to have productive conversations about heated topics such as dissimilarities in the handling of finances… levels of sexual desire…or beliefs about child-rearing or how free time should be spent.

Example: A couple married 32 years was trying to rebuild trust after the wife's affair. During their uninterrupted time together in two-day therapy, the husband for the first time had ample opportunity to openly express difficult feelings and ask questions in an environment where he felt safe to take risks. Rather than react defensively to his anger as she had previously, the wife learned to express her genuine remorse and desire to help the marriage (and her husband) heal. For the first time since the discovery of the affair, the husband felt that he and his wife were once again "on the same team," and they left thera-

---

GOOD TO KNOW...

How to Find a Therapist

If you can't get a word-of-mouth referral to a therapist who offers the type of sessions described in this article, search the therapist directory at AAMFT.org. Then explore therapists' websites to find one that offers this approach, and set up a time to talk—be sure to ask about the amount of experience a therapist has in conducting two-day intensive sessions.

When choosing a therapist, the most important factors include feeling comfortable and respected and feeling that the therapist has a good grasp of the issues you and your spouse are going through. Beyond that, be certain that your therapist is passionate about the merits of multiday intensive sessions versus weekly therapy-as-usual. That's someone who knows the difference two days can make.

py with a plan for rebuilding trust and restoring emotional and physical connection.

Many couples attending intensive sessions are at a crossroads—one spouse may be seriously considering divorce while the other is committed to working things out. While most couples wind up committing to staying together, in some cases during the therapy they decide to divorce. If this occurs, the focus of the therapy then turns to helping the spouse who is more committed accept the decision… to allowing each partner to gain insights into how he/she contributed to the breakdown of the marriage, which is key to not repeating those patterns in the future…and, if there are children, to discussing strategies for effective co-parenting once the marriage has ended.

Intensives help couples feel that they've left no stone unturned regardless of the outcome for the marriage, and that is important for many. Because intensives are geared toward the future, couples leave with clarity about their courses of action, often in the form of written plans. They frequently follow up with twice-monthly phone sessions with the therapist for several months, and some opt for a second in-person intensive six months later to further solidify and maintain the changes made during their time together.

The cost of two-day intensive couples therapy varies from about $1,500 to $5,000 a day depending on the location and the therapist's level of experience and skills.

Don't Let Money Fights Ruin Your Marriage

Olivia Mellan, a psychotherapist specializing in counseling couples on money, communications and conflict resolution, Washington, DC. Now retired, she is author of five books, including *Money Harmony: A Road Map for Individuals and Couples*. MoneyHarmony.com

If arguments over money leave you and your partner steaming and sulking, you're not alone—these financial tensions are one of the major sources of stress for couples, married or not. Among married couples, although they argue most often over children and chores, fights over money are more intense, last longer and are more likely to remain unresolved than fights about other topics, according to researchers at University of Wisconsin.

That's no way to have a love affair, is it?

For solutions, we turned to psychotherapist Olivia Mellan, an expert on money and relationships. Here is her explanation for why we really fight over finances—and her practical three-step plan to help any couple transcend these battles.

WHY WE FIGHT OVER MONEY

Our relationship with money is deeply emotional. Money both symbolizes and embodies freedom, security and control over our lives…and it can be strongly tied to self-worth and our judgments of others. We view money based on a lifetime of experience, including watching our parents handle—or mishandle—their finances when we were children.

When we find our romantic partners, it's really true that opposites attract. Spenders, who believe that spending is a way to show love, often wind up with savers who feel just as deeply that saving is the only way to be secure. Even if you didn't start out as opposites, chances are you'll eventually end up that way.

Example: Two spenders marry, and one of them eventually becomes a "super-spender" while the other becomes a saver (and planner). After all, someone has to take on that role!

Perception matters, too. Researchers from Brigham Young University and Kansas State University discovered that husbands who merely *thought* that their wives were too loose with money—whether or not their wives really were—had more money fights with their wives than husbands who didn't think so. It was true across all levels of income and all types of spending habits.

The key to achieving a more balanced and harmonious approach to money? Learn to stop seeing money as a *symbol* for love…power… security…control… freedom—and instead begin to see it as a *tool* for accomplishing life's goals together. *Here's how…*

STEP ONE: BRIDGE THE GAP BETWEEN MONEY STYLES

The first step is to understand, even appreciate, your partner's approach to money. *To do this...*

●**Acknowledge your secret envious feelings.** *If you are a spender,* you may marvel at a saver's skills at delaying gratification—but fear that if you admit this, your partner may rein in your spending even more tightly.

If you are a saver, you may be impressed with a spender's abilities to enjoy life—but worry that admitting this will encourage your partner to spend wildly.

Admitting your admiration for your partner's ways creates a sense of safety and good-will—tremendous goodwill—and helps you to start thinking about your money issues in a different way.

●**Play the opposite role.** Doing what does not come naturally increases empathy and understanding. Don't worry—you aren't committing to doing it forever!

Examples: If you're a saver, spend $25 or so each week on something nice but frivolous for yourself or your partner. If you're a spender, start squirreling away $25 a week or so in an envelope, earmarked for savings.

Do this "opposite" behavior for a few weeks, and write down how it feels. After a few weeks, you can stop—but be sure to treat yourself with a relatively small reward that feels more natural—a small savings for the saver...a small splurge for the spender.

STEP TWO: DIAL DOWN YOUR FINANCIAL DISCUSSIONS

It's easy to fly off the handle if, say, you are a saver and you see some big new Amazon charges on your shared credit card...or you are a spender and see "vacation" money suddenly put into savings.

Here's a better way: Schedule a time—when neither of you is particularly stressed—for the "structured communication" exercise described below. I've adapted it for money issues from the work of psychologist Harville Hendrix, PhD, author of *Getting the Love You Want.*

Get a kitchen timer, and set it for about 30 minutes. There are three elements to this exercise—mirroring...validation...and empathy. As an icebreaker, start by saying a few nice things about each other—they don't have to be about money—so that you both feel relatively calm and safe. *Now...*

●**Mirror.** Speak your piece about your partner's money move that upset or worried you. Pause every sentence or two so that your partner can repeat exactly what you just said and ask you, "Is there more?" If there is, continue. If not, move on to validating.

●**Validate.** Almost certainly you understand what your partner said, but now try to affirm it in a compassionate way.

Example: "It makes sense that you spent that money on Amazon. You felt flush with money because we already put an extra $250 into the emergency account." When you're done, ask, "Is there anything else you'd like to see validated?" If not, it is time to empathize.

●**Empathize.** If you have been sincere, you've been empathetic all along—but now be explicit. Name the emotion you think your partner is feeling without giving the cause. Use just one or two words such as "hurt"... "angry"..."hopeful"..."felt understood." Your partner can correct you if you're mistaken and tell you how he/she really feels.

Now switch roles—it's your partner's turn to mirror, validate and empathize.

This step helps build an empathetic bridge between your partner's world and your world. You should feel closer—and more able to negotiate a resolution.

Example: A spender who shops whenever he is anxious agrees to never spend above a certain amount without consultation—"I'll talk to you first before I make a purchase over $50." (If the conversation gets heated, though, go back to the mirroring step and start again.)

STEP THREE: GO OVER FINANCES TOGETHER...REGULARLY

Looking at your money together facilitates financial teamwork. Start holding meetings once a month, and always precede them with the structured communications exercise described above. You can go over your past, present and future spending, saving and investing—and your goals. After you get into the groove, you might have the get-togethers more often and for shorter amounts of time. But always use the structure so that you start from a place of intimacy instead of hostility.

If you are doing all these things and still cannot get on the same page financially, you may want to consult a financial therapist. Find one at FinancialTherapyAssociation.org.

Make Your Long-Distance Relationship Work Better

Michele Weiner-Davis, LCSW, founder of The Divorce Busting Center in Boulder, Colorado, which helps on-the-brink couples save their marriages. She is the best-selling author of eight books including *Healing from Infidelity, The Sex-Starved Marriage* and *Divorce Busting* and is a TEDx speaker. DivorceBusting.com

---

After Janet and Thomas's children left their California home for college, Janet was offered a great new position in Hawaii—and the couple jumped at the chance to try island living. But when their daughter, a college freshman, started to struggle with depression and took a leave from college, Thomas went back to California to lend her support—and wound up staying for nine months.

Long-distance relationships are increasingly common. The reasons are varied, although relocating for work, education or training often is a factor. They have their challenges, to be sure—but if you approach yours with the right attitude, tactics and plans, you can emerge with an even stronger relationship. *Here's how...*

SURPRISING BENEFITS DESPITE THE CHALLENGES

Spouses who live far apart often discover anew just how much they love each other—and become less likely to take each other for granted. When they connect on the phone or online, they share feelings of longing for each other more openly than ever before. When they are physically together, they find that instead of being irritated about each other's annoying habits, they focus on each other's strengths. Plus, having separate lives adds a bit of mystery, making sex, albeit rarer, more exciting.

But living apart also can be overwhelming—and intensely lonely. There's no one there to bring you a cup of coffee or rub your tense shoulders. And when finances or schedules prohibit frequent in-person visits, a couple's sex life can pass from the rare-and-exciting stage into a that-was-history stage.

You'll have to work harder to make it work out well. What's that entail? *Successful long-distance couples tend to do all or most of the following...*

• **Make living apart a joint decision.** Since good long-distance relationships require on-going collaboration, it's much better if both partners are on board from the start. Unilateral choices usually lead to resentment, anger—and sometimes worse. If one partner is extremely reticent about living apart, acknowledge the validity of this concern—even if you don't agree with or even understand your partner's reservations. Try brainstorming creative ideas for tackling your differences. To work, this must be a win-win situation.

• **Be clear about expectations.** Make sure that you have many open conversations about the nitty-gritty such as the intended duration of the separation, frequency of in-person visits, logistics of who visits whom, preferred methods for staying in contact and the best times to connect. Each couple is different—some enjoy having frequent contact throughout the day, while others find that distracting and invasive. And if you're already in a long-distance relationship and you never had these conversations, it's never too late!

• **Agree on relationship boundaries.** Anxiety about fidelity can be more of an issue when there's literal distance between you—it's human nature. Jealousy can be an issue, too. When you live apart, you will need to have a great deal of trust in your partner. Even if you think that you are on the same page regarding your expectations about monogamy and what constitutes betrayal, make sure that you have explicit conversations—and rules about what is and isn't acceptable to both of you.

More from Michele Weiner-Davis, LCSW...

Be Sure to Send Lots of Photos!

Whether it's the sights you discovered while touring a new city, silly selfies, the gourmet breakfast you made for yourself or the friends you encountered on your morning walk, sharing your experiences through photos is a powerful way to stay connected with your long-distance partner.

For example, few couples would have a problem if one partner had drinks with coworkers at a bar, but what about a nonbusiness dinner with just one attractive coworker? What about a new "friend" with whom you play tennis...go to movies...or even have dinner with at home? Talk about such possibilities when they are exactly that—possibilities.

●**Communicate often.** Be intentional about arranging frequent contact to discuss matters both big and small. If one person's need to communicate is greater than the other person's, compromise so that both partners' needs are honored.

●**Be flirty with each other.** Just because you are miles apart doesn't mean that you can't turn up the heat in your relationship—and heat is a tie that binds. Try spicy text messages...and talking on the phone about what you'd like to be doing if you were together. And when you are together, make sure that you make time to make love.

●**Don't overworry if every contact doesn't go well.** Although distance might make you feel pressured to make every conversation with each other wrinkle-free, that's an unrealistic expectation. For starters, all relationships have hills and valleys. Plus, when texts, phone calls and even video chats are the primary means of communication, meaning easily can be misconstrued. After an unpleasant exchange, take some time to calm down, and then nudge yourself to extend an olive branch as soon as possible.

●**Visit as often as finances and schedules will allow.** Even if your time apart goes without a hitch, it's still important to be together to touch, engage in mutually enjoyable activities, handle mundane tasks as a team and remind yourselves how nice it is to be part of each other's daily lives.

●**Parent together, wherever you are.** If you still have children at home, discuss which daily decisions the at-home parent will make...and which ones must be made mutually. When communicating with your kids, always back each other up. And even if you are both content with seeing each other fairly infrequently, the away parent should make spending time with the children—and grandchildren—a priority.

●**Monitor the plan.** It's important to regularly assess how well the new arrangement is working—for both of you. Identify and discuss what lets you feel comfortable with the separation...and the unsettling parts that need addressing. Discuss what each of you might do differently to feel more at ease with the distance.

In the end, the quality of a relationship is about much more than physical proximity. The truth is, many unhappy couples say that their loneliest moments are the ones spent *with* their partners. And many long-distance couples find that the experience strengthens their bonds. But it doesn't happen automatically. Whether you're living under the same roof or thousands of miles apart, relationship happiness takes commitment...sensitivity to your partner's desires...and yes, work.

Another Reason to Send the Kids Outside

Spending more time outdoors may make children less likely to require eyeglasses. First-graders who spent 40 additional minutes daily in outdoor activities for three years were less likely to be nearsighted at the end of the study than those whose routine did not include the extra outdoor time.

Study of 950 students at 12 schools led by researchers at Sun Yat-sen University, Guangzhou, China, published in *JAMA*.

Better Time-Outs

Time-outs must be carefully managed to be an effective discipline. *Some tips…*

• **They are only for children ages two to six**—older kids should have privileges revoked instead.

• **Time-outs should occur only in cases of specific behaviors** that parents and children discuss and agree upon in advance—for example, hitting and disobeying direct requests.

• **Toddler behavior that is less serious,** such as whining or begging, should be handled through compromise or by giving a simple explanation of why a particular behavior is not acceptable.

Ennio Cipani, PhD, clinical psychologist, Visalia, California, and author of the free e-book *Punishment on Trial,* quoted at LiveScience.com.

To Prevent Drinking Problems in Kids…

Letting children sip alcohol may lead to drinking problems later. Children under age 13 who were allowed to taste alcohol under parental supervision were more likely to have alcohol-related problems in late adolescence compared with those who weren't.

What adults can do: Do not give alcohol to children, and when they become teenagers, talk together about alcohol use so that they don't feel alone when facing drinking decisions.

Craig R. Colder, PhD, professor of psychology at University at Buffalo, New York, and leader of a study published in *Addictive Behaviors.*

Cleaning Products Contribute to Obesity

Everyday cleaners may make kids overweight. In homes where parents frequently used household disinfectants such as multisurface cleaners, babies three to four months old had lower levels of certain gut bacteria, compared with babies in households using ecofriendly cleaners. Scientists theorize that this altered gut bacteria may be a factor in obesity. Babies from homes using antibacterial products had higher body mass indexes at age three than babies from homes that did not use disinfectants frequently.

Study of 757 infants by researchers at University of Alberta, Canada, published in *CMAJ.*

Better Communication with Teens

Do not rehash problems with a teenager. While talking through a child's troubles can be helpful, excessively revisiting problems and asking numerous probing questions is often counterproductive. That causes teens to relive their worries and feelings instead of getting past them.

Parents should become aware of any tendency they themselves have to harp on problems or to discuss them repeatedly or at length. When conversations become overly focused on negative elements and come back to those negatives repeatedly, break the cycle by suggesting a distraction, such as taking a walk together.

Roundup of experts on parent-teen relationships, reported in *The Wall Street Journal.*

New Way to Help Teens Deal with Social Anxiety

Improv can help teens to handle fear and anxiety in social situations. School-based improvisational theater—with no script or preparation—may help to improve social phobias and anxiety disorders by giving teens a low-stigma, low-cost way to learn to overcome their fears. Improv may be particularly helpful for adolescents at poorer, lower-performing schools, since they may be less able to obtain standard medical and psychological treatment for social anxiety.

Study of 268 Detroit students by researchers at University of Michigan, Ann Arbor, published in *The Arts in Psychotherapy*.

How to Stand Up to Your Overbearing Parents

Susan Newman, PhD, a social psychologist based in the New York City area who specializes in parenting and family relationships. She is author of *The Book of No: 365 Ways to Say It and Mean It—and Stop People-Pleasing Forever.* SusanNewmanPhD.com

Do you wince when your parent weighs in yet again on your relationship… your career…your house and clothing…your diet…and other aspects of life that are really none of that parent's business?

The adult children of overbearing parents often endure this treatment for decades—they either feel powerless to stop it or feel that the emotional cost of doing so would be too high. Those who do stand up to an overbearing parent often do so by lashing out in anger and saying something hurtful that causes or deepens a rift in the relationship. (It is no fun to *be* the overbearing parent, either—see box on page 271.)

There is a better solution, explains social psychologist Susan Newman, PhD…

THE BIG SECRET OF OVERBEARING PARENTS

They may *say* or *think* otherwise, but in most cases, the adult children of overbearing parents are stuck in the parent-child relationships of their youths—it's as if they're still 10 years old and their parents still get to decide how they live.

The secret to breaking out of this unhappy pattern is to understand that you—the adult child—hold most of the power in the relationship—even though it might not feel that way. Sure, when you start to put limits on a parent's controlling behaviors, he/she likely will respond with anger or even the silent treatment. But when your parent realizes that you really mean it, he'll eventually accept limits.

Here's how to stand up to an overbearing parent, wrest back control of your life and build reasonable boundaries without doing unnecessary damage to your relationship with your parent…

FOUR WAYS TO RECLAIM CONTROL

1. Stop answering every call or text. Cell phones and text messaging mean that your mom or dad—or your spouse's mom or dad—has access to you 24/7. But in fact, it's you who are in control if you take that control.

What to do: If you have a parent who contacts you repeatedly over the course of a day and generally has nothing important to say, explain that you won't be repeatedly interrupting your other activities to answer these calls or texts right away, and offer a few good times when the two of you generally can talk.

Then as the nonvital texts and/or voice mails come rolling in, wait to respond until it's convenient for you. Not leaping to attention each time an intrusive parent tries to make contact is a crucial first step in rebalancing the relationship. This might feel uncomfortable for you at first, but within a few days or weeks, it will start to feel (and will in fact be) empowering.

Of course, if there is some reason to believe that a parent's message could be an emergency or a request for essential information, it's best to respond as quickly as possible.

2. Declare specific topics off-limits—and then express love. Overbearing parents often insert themselves into areas of their adult children's lives where their input is not welcome, such as advice about romantic partners, careers, cooking or homemaking skills, weight, spending decisions, wardrobe and grooming choices, child-rearing decisions and fertility problems.

What to do: Think about which topics truly annoy you when your parent weighs in on them. Then the next time the parent raises one of these topics, politely explain that you do not enjoy discussing the topic—and that you do not want to speak with him about it anymore. Before your parent can react to this, express your love for the parent and/or your

Are You an Overbearing Parent?

If your adult child is slow to respond to your messages or doesn't respond at all, you might be an overbearing parent. Other tip-offs are that your child is hard to pin down about dates or plans... gets together with you less often than before... uses schedule issues with your grandchildren or his/her spouse as an excuse...keeps reminding you how busy he is...acts annoyed or short-tempered when you do get together...balks at or dismisses your suggestions or ideas...criticizes you more often than before...has a grandchild or spouse call you instead of calling himself... seems more abrupt in conversations.

If these behaviors sound familiar, you can begin to remedy the situation by paying more attention to the subtleties in your interactions with your child—and then changing your behavior. Depending on the situation, you might try calling less often...be less demanding...be more flexible about plans (and less rigid about what you want)...accept that your adult child has a busy life. You also can ask your child directly what the problem is, although don't be surprised if he has trouble articulating it.

The truth is, by simply changing some behaviors and giving your child more space—being less intrusive, even less involved—you may find that your relationship improves.

appreciation for that parent's willingness to provide advice.

Example: "It really hurts me when you criticize my husband's career and his earnings. We are very comfortable with our decisions, and it doesn't make me feel good to have to defend them to you. But know that I love you and that I understand you want only what's best for me."

Adding an expression of love for your parent whenever you place a topic off-limits reduces the odds that the parent will react angrily. If your parent responds defensively—"I was only trying to help..."—say, "I know, and I love that you want to help me, but let's talk about something else." After you've done this once, you may find that it's easier in the future

to put other hot-button topics on the "do not discuss" list.

Chances are, you'll have to repeat your unwillingness to discuss a topic several times before your parent catches on that you're serious and that you're not backing down. Try not to express your frustration when you must repeat this request.

3. When your parent raises an off-limits topic by saying that he knows he isn't supposed to raise it, respond with gratitude. Once your overbearing parent gets the message that you are no longer willing to discuss a topic, don't be surprised if he raises it anyway by calling special attention to the fact that he is raising it.

Example: Your parent might see your new car and say, "I know I'm not supposed to discuss your spending habits..." and then trail off, making it clear that he does not approve of the purchase. These kinds of "noncomment comments" can be intensely annoying.

What to do: Rather than voice frustration, see this as a sign of progress and use positive reinforcement. That's more likely to encourage the truly desired behavior (not raising it at all) in the future.

Example: "Thank you so much for respecting my wishes about not raising that subject. It really means a lot to me that you're willing to treat me as an adult as I asked you to."

4. Inform your parent that you cannot continue with family traditions or rituals that no longer fit your schedule. Overbearing parents often consider the time they spend with their adult children "tradition"—and they might have lots of these traditions!

Examples: We always have Sunday dinner together—it's a family tradition...we always spend two weeks each summer together at the lake—it's a family tradition...etc.

To an overbearing parent, an adult child is behaving irresponsibly each time he fails to maintain these traditions. But these frequent obligations can become burdensome as your life changes—especially if you have a hectic career, live far away and/or have children of your own who have numerous activities and commitments.

What to do: If a "tradition" has become a burden, don't just apologetically skip it now and then. That avoidance doesn't empower you or reset the relationship—it just lets your parent make you feel guilty each time. Instead, acknowledge the tradition, but clearly state that your participation in it must change.

Example: "I know we have a tradition of getting together every Sunday, but we're not going to be able to do that anymore. The kids just have too many things going on for us to keep that up every week." Once there is no longer an expectation, you may opt to participate in the activity with the parent when it makes sense for you…with much less stress and no guilt.

Helpful: If there is more than one tradition you wish to break, spread this out over several months or longer. Ending numerous traditions all at once might make your parent fear that you are planning to break off all contact.

When a Loved One with Dementia Is Hard to Handle…

Deborah Bier, PhD, a dementia behavior expert in private practice in Lancaster, Massachusetts. She offers in-person coaching and online training and coping tools on her website, FromCrisisToCalm.com. She is also author of *From Crisis to Calm: A Practical Guide to Family Dementia Trouble.*

Caregiving for a dementia patient—whether it's your spouse, parent or some other loved one—is not easy. But the right mind-set will help you defuse and even prevent the troubling behaviors that often occur.

Whether your loved one repeatedly loads and unloads the dishwasher…has conversations with an imaginary friend…or hides the daily mail, you need to respond in a way that will help you *change* the behavior. You won't get anywhere trying to reason with the person.

You need to dig deep to uncover the hidden meaning of what's going on—in the dementia patient's mind there is always a "reason" for even the strangest behaviors.

What to do: Step back and do a little detective work by reviewing the "Five Ws"— who, what, when, where and why.

For example, let's say a woman with dementia starts screaming in fear whenever she uses the bathroom at night. She insists that an "old woman" is watching her, but her daughter checks and there's no one else in the bathroom or at the window. *Ask yourself…*

• **Who are the people involved in the problem behavior?** Is the behavior triggered by one particular person? Does it only happen when the person is alone? In the example above, the screaming happens only when the mother is alone.

• **What is the exact behavior to be addressed?** Break down large problems into smaller pieces that can be easier to fix. The behavior described above is the woman's fright reaction to seeing or imagining a voyeur.

• **When does the behavior occur?** Look for patterns in terms of time and antecedents. What's going on in the environment just before the behavior…a nursing shift change…boredom…seeing others leave the building? Does it happen only at night, or only when it is time to take medication? The woman above screams only at night when sundowning (also known as late-day confusion) is common.

• **Where does the problematic behavior occur?** Is it only in the bedroom, at a doctor's office, outdoors, etc.? The woman's screaming occurs only in the bathroom, specifically when she is sitting on the toilet.

• **Why is the behavior happening?** This is often the toughest question to answer because it requires delving into the mind of the person with dementia. Is your loved one uncomfortable, frightened, lonely or looking for a purpose? When the daughter of the screaming woman recreated the scene for herself, she realized that the bathroom mirror is directly opposite the toilet. Her mother was seeing her own reflection…but didn't recognize the "old woman" as herself, which is common in the later stages of dementia.

The solution to this problem was not to attempt to convince the mother she was seeing her own reflection. Instead, the daughter simply covered the mirror each night (when the woman's sundowning caused mental confusion).

Important: Medication can often cause or worsen dementia symptoms. Be sure to factor that possibility into any troubling behavior—and consult a doctor for advice.

4 KEY STEPS

When interacting with a person with dementia, try these "rules"…

• **Nurture positive emotions.** Leave your emotional baggage at the door. Let go of anger, guilt or resentment when you are dealing with your loved one with dementia. This is not always easy between family members, but you will be motivated to do this when you see how much it improves dementia behaviors. For example, people with dementia are attuned to body language and tone of voice, so it's very helpful if you are able to remain upbeat and loving.

Also, begin each interaction by "bringing the sweetness." Start with a warm moment—bringing a cup of cocoa in the morning, sitting and holding hands, reading a funny story—before every care task or interaction. It only takes a minute, and it will end up saving you time with the dementia behaviors it prevents or improves.

• **Work with your loved one's still-present abilities.** Rather than dwelling on what your loved one can no longer do, reconnect with what he/she still can do. For example, people with Alzheimer's disease tend to lose fine motor control first—making it difficult to button a shirt, for example—but your loved one can still walk. This means you still can take walks with your loved one and perhaps observe trees, flowers and other elements of nature.

• **Think when you communicate.** Talking to someone with dementia demands attention to details. *You need to…*

Remember that body language and emotions often speak louder than words.

*Use simple sentences…*and slow down. Allow time for words to be processed. Make sure you have your loved one's attention before you begin speaking by catching and maintaining eye contact.

Speak on the same physical level—sitting or standing—and approach the person from the front, not from the back or side, which can startle your loved one.

• **Be aware of sensory changes.** Dementia changes the way our senses work, which can trigger problems. Understanding these changes will often help you explain the "why" of a particular behavior. *For example…*

Vision changes can make it difficult to clearly see and identify objects. Brighter lights and contrasting colors are needed. Also be sure that your loved one wears all sensory aides, such as eyeglasses and hearing aids.

Sounds of favorite music can stimulate memory and keep people with dementia engaged. But ambient noise—traffic or construction—can be irritating and distracting. *Helpful*: Sit down and listen to the music with your loved one so you can share the experience. If he previously played a musical instrument—even years ago—encourage him to pick it up again.

Senses of smell and taste can change and are known to become less acute with normal aging—even more so with dementia. Throwing plates of food or refusing to eat may be due to a changing ability to taste, rather than petulance. Eating with another person may help him mimic the proper actions of eating, and the social interaction of breaking bread together is often an encouragement to eat.

The takeaway: By thoughtfully changing the way you interact with your loved one, you can nudge behaviors in a more peaceful direction, allowing the two of you to reconnect emotionally.

HELPFUL WEBSITE…

Caregiving Guide

At this website, get practical information on behavioral, financial, housing, legal and medical issues. Topics include self-care for caregivers…medication management…handling dementia…coping with hoarding, sundowning and other problems…etc.

DailyCaring.com

Protect a Parent from Caregiver Abuse

Sandra D. Glazier, Esq., a Bloomfield Hills, Michigan–based partner at Lipson Neilson PC. She specializes in family law and estate planning. LipsonNeilson.com

I s the person who takes care of your parent taking advantage of that parent instead? Sometimes there are obvious solutions, such as replacing the caregiver or discussing your concerns with your parent (or the parent's spouse). But what if the caregiver is your sibling…or the parent trusts the caregiver?

Here's what to do if a caregiver might be robbing your parent of his/her freedom or assets…

• **Confirm your suspicions.** Is it suddenly difficult to contact your parent? When you do reach him, is the caregiver always nearby monitoring the conversation? As a start, ask the parent's other relatives and friends whether their observations match yours.

Next: Visit your parent in his home. Controlling caregivers often isolate their victims to deepen their dependence—so observe whether your parent has time outside the caregiver's presence (ideally with friends) and whether he is housebound despite being mobile. Also check whether valuables are missing…and whether the parent has access to all of his own mail. (And scan that mail to make sure that he still is receiving his bank, credit card and investment statements—abusive caregivers often change addresses on file so that mail is sent to them.)

• **Focus outside eyes on your parent's situation.** To do this, offer to pay for visits from a professional care manager. This person will coordinate your parent's care—and watch for signs of elder abuse. The local Area Agency on Aging or the Aging Life Care Association likely can help you find a care manager. Expect to pay $100 to $200 per hour.

Also ask your parent whether he stays in touch with a financial adviser. If not, suggest that he do so. You can alert a financial adviser (or estate planner) to watch for suspicious transactions.

• **Consider corrective steps.** If you determine that a caregiver is exerting undue control and your family cannot remedy the situation on its own, report your concerns to the Adult Protective Services department in your parent's state. This agency can assess the situation and might take steps to protect your parent.

• **Hire an attorney to petition for your guardianship or conservatorship (depending on the state) of your parent.** This is an option if the parent is no longer capable of looking after his own affairs. The bar association in your parent's home state may direct you to appropriate attorneys. This can be a lengthy and expensive process and usually is a last resort, but it's needed in some cases to stop an abusive caregiver.

For Lower Funeral Costs…

L ower the cost of a cremation or funeral by joining a nonprofit memorial society. To find one in your state, go to Funerals.org and locate your local affiliate of the Funeral Consumers Alliance (FCA). Visit the local affiliate's website to find out how to join—this can be done online for about $35. FCA affiliates have agreements with licensed funeral directors to provide cremation or burial services for a predetermined maximum cost that is almost always lower than the price paid by the general public. *Example:* In one state, FCA members paid $995 for direct cremation instead of the quoted-to-the-public price of $2,695, a saving of $1,700… and $1,495 for direct cremation with memorial service, compared with a cost to the public at large of $4,570, a saving of $3,075.

Contact FCA for help if you live in one of the states without an FCA affiliate: Alabama, Alaska, Hawaii, Iowa, Mississippi, Montana, Nebraska, New Hampshire, New Mexico, North Dakota, Oregon, West Virginia or Wyoming.

Clark.com

Anxiety: Don't Get Stuck in This Hidden Trap of Grief

Claire Bidwell Smith, LCPC, a Los Angeles–based licensed therapist specializing in grief. Her latest book is *Anxiety: The Missing Stage of Grief.* She also is author of *The Rules of Inheritance* and *After This: When Life Is Over Where Do We Go?* ClaireBidwellSmith.com

Most of us do not like to think about grief. But when we do, what often comes to mind are the well-known "stages of grief"—denial, anger, bargaining, depression and acceptance—coined by the late Elisabeth Kübler-Ross.

Never mind that the Swiss-born psychiatrist originally intended her stages to describe the experiences of people facing their own deaths, not grieving someone else's. Or that she eventually made clear that not everyone goes through all the stages or in the same predictable order.

The missing stage: What's become increasingly clear is that one extremely common and often debilitating stage of grief is not included. That stage is anxiety.

One landmark study published in *American Journal of Psychiatry* found that the onset of generalized anxiety disorder is strongly associated, especially after age 40, with the unexpected death of a loved one. Beyond that, there's little research on how many people become anxious—or more anxious—after a death, yet it's something grief counselors see all the time.

It makes sense. When someone close to you dies, one of your worst fears comes true. You are reminded that your own life will end some day, that bad things happen and that you are not always in control.

And maybe you were anxious already. Nearly one in five adults has suffered from anxiety in the past year, and nearly one in three has experienced an anxiety disorder sometime in their lives, according to the National Institute of Mental Health.

If you are one of those people, you may be especially vulnerable to renewed or intensified anxiety when a loved one dies. You may feel constantly worried, fearful, restless, jittery and irritable and may experience physical symptoms, such as a pounding heart, shortness of breath, muscle tension and sleeplessness.

For some people, the first undeniable sign is a panic attack—a sudden sense of impending doom that can be accompanied by rapid heartbeat, sweating, nausea, shaking, choking and a fear that you are going crazy or are about to die.

People often say that anxiety symptoms "come out of the blue." But here's what's often going on—a buildup of suppressed stress and emotion has finally found a way to get your attention. You can try in vain to push the feelings back down…or deal with them—and work past the anxiety. *Here are some of the most effective ways to do that…*

STEP #1: **Tell your story.** If you are fortunate, you will have a safe friend or family member who is willing to listen to your story—including your regrets and fears—without judgment or advice.

Many people find it helpful to see a professional grief counselor or attend a bereavement support group. Many hospitals and hospice organizations offer them, and finding one

---

WHAT TO DO…

The Antidote to Loneliness

The death of a spouse is a major cause of loneliness in older adults…and loneliness is associated with more depression and earlier death.

Recent research: Widowed adults who began volunteering at least two hours weekly reduced their loneliness to the same level as that of people who were married, according to data collected on 5,882 adults over an eight-year period.

Theory: The act of engaging in new social interactions helps ease the transition to widowhood—even for those who have the support of friends and family.

Visit VolunteerMatch.org to find opportunities in your area.

Ben Kail, PhD, assistant professor of sociology, Georgia State University, Atlanta.

near you is likely just a Google search away. Many groups are organized by age or type of loss (for example, the loss of a spouse, parent or child or a loss due to suicide). Online grief forums can sometimes be valuable as well.

***STEP #2*: Hear (or read) others' stories**. While it can be difficult at first, many people eventually find comfort in hearing or reading about the losses others have experienced. It can help you to feel less alone and less anxious. You can find that fellowship in a support group and by reading about others' experiences in online forums and books.

Some good memoirs to consider include: *Wild* by Cheryl Strayed (who lost her mother)...*The Year of Magical Thinking* by Joan Didion (who lost her spouse)...*Her* by Christa Parravani (who lost a sibling)...and *Truth & Beauty* by Ann Patchett (who lost a friend). There are many more. If reading is difficult for you at this time, consider listening to an audio version of the book.

***STEP #3*: Release yourself through writing.** Many people are filled with regrets and a sense of guilt after a significant loss. Maybe they were not there when their loved one died. Or they think they said the wrong thing to the dying person.

One way to deal with such feelings: Write a letter to your deceased loved one. Apologize, if you feel the need, or say goodbye in the way you missed out on before. Some people also write letters to themselves—forgiving themselves, with kindness and compassion, for any perceived mistakes.

You can use writing to probe any feeling—including those you might be reluctant to admit to others (such as relief that a loved one who was suffering has died). Get a beautiful blank journal and try to use it for even just five to 10 minutes each day for as long as you feel the need. You can start by just writing what you are feeling—something like "I'm lonely" or "I'm scared," and then just keep writing for 10 minutes. If you're intimidated by the thought of writing out your feelings, you can dictate your feelings into your smartphone.

***STEP #4*: Consider using some cognitive behavioral therapy (CBT) techniques.** CBT is a short-term treatment often used for anxiety. It is a practical approach that helps people recognize and change thoughts and beliefs that contribute to their distress. While some people need the help of a therapist, there are CBT techniques you can try on your own. *The Anxiety & Worry Workbook* by the renowned American psychiatrist Aaron T. Beck, MD, is an excellent resource for this, as well as apps you can use on your smartphone.

Among the things you might try: Writing a list of your anxious thoughts (like *I'm afraid I might have cancer*)...noting the physical symptoms (such as a rapid heartbeat) and cognitive symptoms (such as an underlying fear that you will die just like your loved one did)...and observing the way you behave as a result (avoiding doctor appointments or seeking reassurance online).

Becoming aware of such links is a step toward breaking these negative patterns. But this can be hard—if you feel your anxiety is out of control and interfering with your life, be sure to seek professional treatment.

***STEP #5*: Try meditating.** Like CBT, meditation is, at its core, a technique for helping you notice your thoughts—and break free from those working against you. Your mind may be humming with worries about the future, but you can learn to live in the present. It can be as simple as taking a few minutes each day to sit and focus on your breath moving in and out of your body, letting your thoughts come and go without judgment.

Skeptical? Just give it a chance. You might start with a class or workshop or get a good guidebook, such as *Wherever You Go, There You Are: Mindfulness Meditation in Everyday Life* by professor and meditation teacher Jon Kabat-Zinn, PhD.

***STEP #6*: Start planning your own death.** It might sound counterintuitive to think about your own death when you're grieving the loss of someone dear to you. But remember this— the root of anxiety is uncertainty. Planning for your eventual death can help set your mind at ease…and lessen the anxieties of those we leave behind.

So get your own affairs in order—write (or update) your will…decide on a health-care proxy…create your advance directive…make your funeral wishes known…and let your friends and family members know what you would like them to have when you are gone. This can be scary, so take your time and enlist the support of a professional and/or friends and family members. But facing your fears can help you put them in their place and get on with life.

FUN FINDING…

Professor Fido

The presence of a friendly dog improves the speed and accuracy with which young children handle mental and physical tasks, including reading. Dogs seem to reduce anxiety while building motivation, confidence and feelings of support—helping children who have difficulty with reading.

Sophie Hall, PhD, research fellow, School of Life Sciences, University of Lincoln, UK, and leader of a study published in *PLOS ONE*.

How to Make Your Pet a Social Media Star

Roundup of experts on pets on social media, reported at MSN.com.

• **Decide why anyone would want to follow your pet**—unusual appearance, activities or tricks, for example.

• **Post only photos of your pet doing whatever makes it interesting**—no other photos.

• **Use hashtags to help fans easily find your content**—they work especially well on Instagram.

• **Once people start showing up and commenting, interact with them** and "like" their comments.

• **As your audience grows, start a website for your pet** so that potential sponsors can reach you and so that you can sell pet-related merchandise.

• **Watch for companies that send free products once you attract a big enough following**—make deals only when products match your pet's personality.

• **Consider creating your own products as your pet's following grows**—calendars, stuffed toys and more.

Does Your Dog Have an Allergy?

A common allergy symptom in dogs is scratching, often along with vomiting or diarrhea. If you notice these, see a veterinary dermatologist to find out whether your dog is allergic to something in the air. If so, your pet may need medicated shampoo and possibly medicine. Some people assume that stomach problems and itching are caused by food allergies, but dogs are rarely allergic to specific foods. It is more common for them to react to airborne substances such as pollen, mold or dust mites—and these allergies can cause gastrointestinal disturbance.

Your Dog.

Little-Known Sign of Arthritis in Dogs

A dult dogs that develop fear of loud noises may have musculoskeletal pain, not a behavioral issue. Dogs for which the fear is behavioral usually develop it early. But if a dog has become afraid of noises later in life, the cause may be pain from a condition such as arthritis. In older dogs, becoming startled or tensing up in reaction to noise may worsen pain that already is there so that the dog develops an association between the noise and bodily pain. If a dog without previous fear of loud sounds develops this fear, talk to your veterinarian—medicine to relieve the pain may help, or antianxiety medication may be useful.

Your Dog.

Don't Let Your Cat Make You Sick

Cat-scratch disease is a bacterial infection that happens when a cat bites or scratches hard enough to break a person's skin or licks an open wound. The bacteria that cause the disease are found in 40% of cats. Felines rarely have symptoms, but affected people can have swollen lymph nodes for months and may need antibiotic treatment or even hospitalization.

Self-defense: Wash your hands after any contact with a cat. Keep cats' claws trimmed.

Wash any bites or scratches well with soap and running water. In case of any bite, seek medical attention.

HealthLetter.MayoClinic.com

Why Cats Should Work for Their Food

In the wild, cats would need to catch about 10 small mammals a day to get the energy they need. Feeding cats from a bowl undermines basic cat-hunting instincts, reducing problem-solving behavior and physical exercise.

What to do: Try a puzzle feeder—a device that the cat must manipulate in some way to get the food. It stimulates the cat mentally while encouraging it to eat small amounts frequently as it would in a hunting existence in the wild.

Sarah Ellis, PhD, feline behavior specialist, quoted online at ICatCare.org, the website of International Cat Care, Tisbury, UK.

17

Household Hacks

How to Motivate Yourself to Declutter *Now!*

Sometimes, the best way to tackle a big task is to change the way you think about it. That's the genius behind the popular decluttering movement from Sweden called "death cleaning."

The idea: Leave your home neat and orderly to make life easier for people who live on after you're gone.

Thinking about such a thing may not immediately appeal to Americans, who tend to avoid talking about death or contemplating their mortality at any cost. But just like creating a will or an advanced directive, decluttering your home is a gift you can give to the people you love. It's also a gift to yourself—a way to keep what you really want and give away what others might benefit from now... and rid yourself of everything else.

No matter what your age, death cleaning can help you live a happier life in a clutter-free home. So we asked Jennifer L. Fitzpatrick, an expert on gerontology and caregiving, for her advice on how *anyone* can use this Swedish decluttering solution...and how our readers might inspire their loved ones to consider using it, too.

***CHALLENGE:* Who will deal with what you leave behind?** Think about the people who will have to clean up your home after you are gone. When my grandmother died, she owned some jewelry. She didn't leave behind instructions for whom she wanted to have what. Fortunately, my aunts graciously decided how to distribute these keepsakes and there was no friction. But that's rare. Often situations such as this cause major rifts

---

Jennifer L. Fitzpatrick, MSW, LCSW-C, founder, Jenerations Health Education, a consulting company for health-care professionals and caregivers (JenerationsHealth.com), and gerontology instructor at Johns Hopkins University, Baltimore. She is also author of *Cruising Through Caregiving: Reducing the Stress of Caring for Your Loved One.*

and even estrangements in families.

Swedish solution: Put yourself in your grown child's shoes—or your grandchild's, your best friend's or whoever is likely to be left with the task. Imagine putting this person in the position of having to decide with each of your possessions which to keep, which to sell, which to give away to relatives and friends, and which to donate to charity or throw away. When *you* are in charge of clearing out your possessions, you make the choices.

CHALLENGE: **How do I get started?** Most of us want to live in a clutter-free home. It's so much easier to take care of, and it just feels good. But we generally think about it…think about it some more…and then never actually do it.

Swedish solution: Take advantage of any "life change" by using it as your springboard—a child going off to college…repair or remodeling work being done on your home…a milestone birthday…out-of-town visitors coming to stay with you…or even recovery from an illness that makes you contemplate the future a little more intently.

Beware: Don't use some (real or imagined) life event in the distant future as an excuse to procrastinate. The best time to start is right now!

CHALLENGE: **Knowing which belongings to start with.** When some people start to declutter, the first thing they do is head straight for the possessions that they haven't seen or touched for the longest time—but these often turn out to be items with great emotional resonance such as old letters and photos, military badges and decorations, clothing of long-deceased family members and other very personal memorabilia.

Result: They get bogged down with too many memories, and the project grinds to a halt.

Swedish solution: Start with the things that have little-to-no personal significance but that clutter many homes—old electronic equipment, lamps with no shades (and shades with no lamps), unneeded office supplies, unneeded tools, etc. Begin with things that are clearly broken or obsolete, and ask yourself,

MONEY SMARTS…

Big Home Upgrades at a Small Cost

For less than $100, there are a variety of home improvements you can make. *For example, you can…*

●**Buy paint and rollers** and change the look of a room.

●**Organize clutter** by buying baskets or a low-cost closet system.

●**Get plants** to change your home's outdoor look or to freshen up the interior.

●**Buy low-cost patterned fabrics** and use them to make curtain panels or chair cushions.

●**Cover an accent wall** with reclaimed wood planks, such as old barn siding.

●**Upgrade front-door hardware** with new locks, knobs and handles.

●**Hang a mirror** from a consignment store or discount shop over a buffet or dresser.

●**Print, frame and hang some of your favorite photos.**

WiseBread.com

Does this have sentimental value? Could someone else find a good use for it if I took it to a thrift shop? Or does it really belong in the trash? Then work your way up toward the possessions that may mean more to you—things such as books and birthday and anniversary cards, letters and photos and even your kids' or grandchildren's school-age artwork. Once you get to the more emotional stuff, you'll have developed the decluttering skills and momentum to carry you through.

CHALLENGE: **Thinking, *Someone in the family might want this one day*.** A big impediment to reducing our possessions is the worry that we are somehow shortchanging family members—we might not even know *which* family members—who would one day love to have these possessions. This is particularly so for pieces with sentimental value to you—such as the sideboard that your mother got from her mother or a set of china—but the truth is, there probably are no younger members of the family who feel this way. Your emotional attachment makes you think these possessions are important to others.

Swedish solution: Ask among your family if you wish, but if no one steps up to claim a possession, know that selling it or giving it to charity now would bring someone you don't know joy right away…and you'll be saving your family the hassle of getting rid of it or trying to sell it later.

CHALLENGE: **Too much time on your hands makes you complacent.** If you aren't naturally the "do it now" type, having too much time on your hands can be as bad as having too little. If you're retired or working part-time, you can easily tell yourself that you'll clean out that closet (or the whole house) next week or the week after—again and again.

Swedish solution: Give yourself a deadline. One way to do this is to call Goodwill, the Salvation Army or a similar organization and schedule a pickup in two weeks' time. Then set a goal for how much you'll have when the truck comes to collect your stuff—five boxes of clothing and shoes, for instance, or all the china, silverware and kitchen gadgets you never use.

CHALLENGE: **You make progress but then lose steam.** Decluttering can be emotionally and physically challenging, and it's easy to lose your motivation even if you started with the best intentions.

Swedish solution: Enlist a professional or a hard-nosed pal. Professional organizers can make thinning out your possessions less emotional. They also are helpful if you suffer from anxiety or hoarding tendencies and cannot bring yourself to toss much of anything. And they know of services that can efficiently help you with physical removal of large items. If your budget doesn't allow for a pro, ask for help from a friend who you know will give you the tough love you need to stay on task and not coddle you. A friend, family member or hired help also can be invaluable if you have any physical limitations that prevent you from lifting boxes, standing on a step stool or navigating an attic stairway.

More Efficient Use of Kitchen Appliances

Microwave: Use round containers to heat food more uniformly—in rectangular ones, the corners usually attract more energy, overcooking some of the food.

Oven broiler: Keep the oven door slightly open to vent steam and help food develop crustiness.

Slow cooker: Avoid opening it until there is less than an hour to go to be sure that your dish cooks properly.

Dishwasher: Put dishes with starchy stains in the middle of the racks, where the strongest spray of water goes.

Blender: To prevent stalling, first put in the liquid or yogurt base of whatever you are blending, then layer ingredients from smallest to largest, keeping ice and other tough-to-blend items at the top.

Roundup of experts on kitchen appliances, quoted in *Reader's Digest*.

Never Put These Items in the Dishwasher!

• **Cast-iron skillets,** which require special care and seasoning.

• **Wooden cutting boards,** which can warp and crack because of heat and water.

• **Brass, bronze and pewter,** which can become discolored.

• **High-quality knives,** including ones with wood handles or carbon-steel blades, which easily can be damaged.

• **Fancy china,** which can discolor or fade.

• **Aluminum bakeware** that does not specify that it is dishwasher-safe.

• **Crystal barware,** which can shatter.

• **Gold-plated cutlery,** whose coating can wear off.

- **Anything repaired with glue,** since heat may loosen the glue.
- **Items with printed words or measurements that can become illegible.**
- **Nonstick pans,** whose coatings can wear off or become damaged.

Roundup of experts on proper cleaning of household items, reported at Today.com.

Help for a Smelly Dishwasher

De-stink a foul-smelling dishwasher with vinegar and baking soda. *What to do...*

Detach your dishwasher's filter, soak it for 10 minutes in sudsy water, then replace it. Pour one cup of white vinegar into the bottom of the dishwasher, and run the heavy cleaning cycle. When that's done, sprinkle baking soda along the bottom of the dishwasher and leave it overnight before running another heavy cleaning cycle.

USA Today.

To Remove Mildew Odor from a Front-Load Washer...

First, use a towel to dry the rubber gasket around the opening. Then spray the gasket with a mixture of bleach and water, scrub with an old toothbrush and use a rag to wipe away any remaining solution. Next, fill the detergent dispenser with white vinegar, and run the washer, empty, on the hottest cycle.

To prevent mildew: Keep the gasket dry, and leave the washer's door open when not using the machine. Repeat the vinegar wash monthly as needed.

Better Homes & Gardens.

Get Rid of Those Dust Mites

The best ways to reduce dust mites, which can worsen allergies and asthma...

- **Reduce humidity,** which dust mites like—keep home humidity at 30% to 50% by using a dehumidifier or central air-conditioning.
- **Use dust- or allergen-blocking covers on mattresses and pillows.**
- **Wash sheets and blankets weekly,** in hot water if possible or in cool or warm water with bleach.
- **Vacuum carpets and fabric-covered furniture** at least weekly using a vacuum cleaner with a HEPA filter.
- **Clean surfaces with a damp mop or cloth,** not dry tools, to avoid stirring up dust.
- **Replace carpets with hard surfaces such as wood or tile** if you are especially sensitive to dust mites—and replace curtains with blinds that can be cleaned.

HealthLetter.MayoClinic.com

Cleaning Your House Can Harm Your Lungs

Philip J. Landrigan, MD, dean for global health and professor in the departments of pediatrics and environmental medicine and public health, Icahn School of Medicine at Mount Sinai in New York City.

You might expect people who clean houses or offices for a living to develop lung problems from harsh cleaning products. But it happens even to people who regularly clean just their own homes.

So finds a new study published in *American Journal of Respiratory and Critical Care Medicine* that followed more than 6,200 adults for 20 years. Compared with people who didn't clean their own homes, those who did so at least weekly scored significantly lower on a measure of overall lung function. In this one measure, the decline was similar to that found in people who have been smoking cigarettes for years.

To learn more, we spoke with environmental expert Philip J. Landrigan, MD, of the Icahn School of Medicine at Mount Sinai in New York City. *His advice to keep your lungs from being harmed…*

• **Use your nose.** Ammonia and bleach are known irritants that can, over time, impair lung function even when inhaled in low concentrations. You can tell just by opening a product and giving it a sniff that it is irritating—avoid those products.

• **Buy safe.** Choose gentler products. While labels are no guarantee—they're not regulated—look for products that use terms such as "gentle," "nontoxic" and "ecofriendly."

• **Make your own.** For total control over what you breathe in when you clean your house, use ingredients such as distilled white vinegar or borax to make your own safe cleaning products.

Example: Mix three-quarters cup of vinegar with three-quarters cup of water in a spray bottle to clean windows and mirrors.

No matter how long a person has been using irritant chemicals, there are health benefits that come from stopping their use. Some will be immediate…others take months or years…but all the results are positive.

EASY TO DO…

Let the Sun Shine In

Sunlight reduces harmful bacteria inside your house. The study showed that sunlit rooms have about half the viable bacteria that dark rooms have. To keep the accumulation of potentially unhealthy bacteria in your home low, open the curtains or shades and let in the sunshine.

Kevin Van Den Wymelenberg, PhD, director of the Energy Studies in Buildings Laboratory at University of Oregon, Eugene and Portland, and coauthor of a study published in *Microbiome.*

Natural, Chemical-Free Cleaners

Multipurpose spray: Three tablespoons of Castile soap in one-and-a-half cups of hot water.

Scrub: Three-quarters cup of baking soda and one-quarter cup of Castile soap mixed with one tablespoon of warm water.

Window cleaner: One tablespoon of cornstarch, one-quarter cup of white vinegar and one-quarter cup of rubbing alcohol in two cups of warm water.

Carpet stain remover: One tablespoon of Castile soap and one tablespoon of white vinegar in two cups of warm water.

Better Homes & Gardens.

Surprising Household Items That Can Go Bad

Save money by buying only as much of these items as you will use before they go bad…

• **Cleaning supplies start to degrade once they're opened**—laundry detergent retains full power for just six to 12 months, dish soap 12 to 18 months.

• **Motor oil breaks down when stored for a long time**—the shelf life depends on the manufacturer.

• **Toiletries and cosmetics may go bad quickly**—mascara in three months, oil-free foundation in a year, lipstick in two to three years, deodorant in three years.

• **Wood stains, whether oil-based or water-based, typically are good for only a year** after opening.

MoneyTalksNews.com

Little-Known Uses for Plain White Toothpaste

Shine jewelry: Brush diamonds and other jewelry instead of using jewelry cleaner.

Get rid of car-interior smells: Smear toothpaste on a paper towel, fold the towel and place it underneath car seats while the vehicle is parked in sunlight—as the car heats up, the paste will give it a fresh, minty odor.

Scrub nail stains caused by dark polishes: Use a nailbrush or unused toothbrush.

Deodorize hands and containers: Scrub hands with toothpaste. If a container has a residual smell, put some toothpaste in it before scrubbing it.

Remove table rings caused by placing glasses on wood: Rub out the stain using toothpaste on a soft cloth, then finish the job using furniture polish or oil.

Roundup of experts on uses of toothpaste, reported at FamilyHandyman.com.

Move Over Olive Oil! These Oils Deserve a Place at the Table

Torey Armul, MS, RD, LD, a registered dietitian in private practice in Columbus, Ohio, media spokesperson for the Academy of Nutrition & Dietetics and author of *Bun Appétit: A Simple Guide to Eating Right During Pregnancy.*

You've heard that olive oil is best for health. But is it best for all different cooking methods? And what if you want a subtler flavor?

You may be surprised to learn that there are other tasty and nutritious choices. This doesn't mean it's time to ditch your olive oil, but these four oils deserve shelf space for their versatility as well as their health benefits.

Note: Healthy oils play an important role in satiety and flavor of food, but they are still calorie-dense, so portion control counts. Aim for a daily total of one to two tablespoons and maximize their nutritional impact by using a variety of oils.

AVOCADO OIL

Pressed from creamy avocados, avocado oil stands out because of its slightly buttery flavor—great for smoothies, sauces and baked goods.

It's also a top choice for high-heat cooking. That's because it has the highest smoke point of all oils, at 520°F. Smoke point is the temperature an oil can withstand before breaking down. Oil heated beyond its smoke point loses nutritional value and may create harmful carcinogens. (As a point of reference, generic olive oil in general has a medium smoke point of 320°F, which makes it best for sautéing and cooking at low heat. Extra-virgin olive oil's smoke point, however, is higher at 405°F.)

Choose avocado oil for high-heat cooking methods like searing, roasting, barbecuing and frying.

Health benefits: Avocado oil is high in healthy monounsaturated fats, especially *oleic acid.* These improve blood cholesterol levels, which can reduce the risk for heart disease. Avocado oil's anti-inflammatory nutrients also may help ease inflammation, joint pain and stiffness from arthritis.

SESAME OIL

Sesame oil, pressed from sesame seeds, is very versatile. Just read labels carefully. "Pure" sesame oil has a light, nutty flavor and, with a medium-high smoke point of 350°F, can be used for light sautéing. "Toasted" sesame oil, on the other hand, has a very bold taste and is used as a seasoning, not as a cooking oil, to complement the flavors of Indian, African and Asian dishes.

Health benefits: Sesame oil is equally rich in polyunsaturated and monounsaturated fats. Although the ideal amount to have in your diet is not yet known, research shows it can promote heart health by decreasing LDL cholesterol and reducing blood pressure.

FLAXSEED OIL

Flaxseed oil has a smooth and slightly nutty taste. With a very low smoke point of 225°F,

More from Torey Armul, MS, RD, LD...

Cooking Oil Tips

When shopping for cooking oil, look for cold-pressed or unrefined oils. While more expensive, this method extracts oil by putting the fruits or seeds through a press. Refined oils are usually processed with chemicals and undergo bleaching and/or deodorizing. Store flaxseed and sesame oils in the fridge. The other oils may be kept in the fridge or in a dark cabinet, away from heat. Let refrigerated oils come to room temperature before using. All of these oils should be stored in dark, airtight containers.

it's most suitable for cold preparations such as salad dressings and dips or as an addition to smoothies and precooked foods.

Health benefits: Flaxseed oil is the best vegetarian source of *alpha-linolenic acid* (ALA), one of the omega-3 fats known for improving cholesterol levels, lowering triglyceride levels and blood pressure, reducing inflammation and decreasing the risk for certain types of cancer. (Fatty fish contain the other omega-3s—EPA and DHA.) Just one tablespoon provides at least four times the daily recommended amount of ALA.

WALNUT OIL

Walnut oil is another excellent source of ALA—one tablespoon provides the recommended daily amount. Unrefined walnut oil has a medium smoke point of 320°F. It becomes slightly bitter when heated, so use it for salad dressings or for adding flavor to cooked pasta, poultry, fish or even smoothies.

Health benefits: According to research published in *Journal of the American College of Nutrition*, healthy men and women who substituted 1.3 ounces of walnuts and one tablespoon of walnut oil for other fats in their diets for six weeks had lower resting blood pressure and lower stress-induced blood pressure than those who ate a more typical American diet, despite their calorie intakes being equal.

Better Beef Stew

Cook stew at 275°F to 300°F rather than the more typical 325°F to 350°F. At this lower temperature range, the meat softens without collapsing or becoming stringy. This also helps the liquid and aromatics blend into the tastiest possible sauce. Expect it to take three to five hours to make stew this way. Use a heavy pot with a heavy lid, such as a Dutch oven.

Julia Moskin, food writer and reporter, writing in *The New York Times.*

One-Pan Dinners That Will Wow the Crowd

Debby Maugans, a food writer based in Asheville, North Carolina. She is author of *Small-Batch Baking, Small-Batch Baking for Chocolate Lovers* and *Farmer & Chef Asheville.*

An entire meal roasts to perfection in minutes. It's healthy and delicious—and there's hardly any cleanup. Welcome to the sheet-pan dinner solution.

You won't sacrifice taste for convenience, either—roasting at high temperatures for short periods browns the surfaces of food, resulting in rich, caramelized flavors. Meats, poultry and fish stay moist inside, and vegetables turn out crisp on the outside but tender inside.

All you need is a good sheet pan. Don't try this with your cookie pan—it's too thin for good roasting. You'll want a heavy-gauge aluminum or steel sheet pan with one-inch-high sides. It has to be large enough that all the foods you put on it fit in a single layer without touching. If they get too close together, foods will start to steam. These recipes were prepared on a 17-inch-by-12-inch heavy-gauge steel sheet pan, but there are many sizes available depending on how many servings you want to make.

Cleanup is a cinch whether you line the pan with foil or parchment paper...or cook the food directly on the pan (better for browning). It's true that if you use your sheet pan often, it won't stay shiny. But a little wear gives it character!

Here are three easy, tasty, complete sheet-pan dinners for you to enjoy. Each recipe makes four servings.

Roast Chicken and Vegetables with Harissa Vinaigrette

You can try this recipe with many different vegetables beyond the carrots, zucchini and tomatoes listed. Experiment with root vegetables (sweet potatoes, red potatoes, turnips and parsnips)…broccoli florets…cauliflower florets…eggplant…yellow squash.

Cut root vegetables and eggplant into one-inch cubes, and slice yellow squash into one-inch-thick slices to make about four or five cups in total.

Harissa is a smoky, spicy North African condiment, a paste or purée made from a variety of dried roasted red peppers, tomatoes, vinegar and toasted spices including caraway and cumin. It adds a depth of aniselike, earthy flavor to foods ranging from eggs to sandwiches and roasted meats and poultry. I like Organic Harissa by Les Moulins Mahjoub, available online for about $15 for a 6.5-ounce jar. You also can look for harissa in jars, cans or tubes in the international foods sections of supermarkets.

Serve with a slice of crusty whole-wheat bread such as a boule.

  2 Tablespoons plus 1 teaspoon extra-virgin olive oil, divided
  4 (four-ounce) skinless, boneless chicken thighs (or chicken breast halves, cut in half crosswise)
  ½ teaspoon ground cumin
  ¾ teaspoon salt, divided
Grated zest and juice of one lemon
  2 Tablespoons harissa
  2 teaspoons grated fresh ginger (optional)
Olive oil cooking spray
  10 cherry tomatoes
  4 or 5 medium carrots, cut into three-inch pieces and halved lengthwise
  2 medium zucchini, sliced into ¾-inch-to-one-inch pieces

Preheat the oven to 400°F. Place a rimmed sheet pan in the oven to heat.

Brush two teaspoons of the olive oil on the chicken. Combine the cumin and one-half teaspoon of the salt in a small bowl. Mix well, and sprinkle on the chicken.

Combine one tablespoon of the remaining olive oil, lemon zest and juice, harissa and ginger (if using) in a small bowl. Whisk to blend.

Remove the hot baking sheet from the oven, and coat with cooking spray. Place the cherry tomatoes, carrots and zucchini on the baking sheet. Drizzle with two teaspoons of the olive oil, and sprinkle with salt. Use a wide spatula to turn the vegetables, and coat with olive oil and salt, then spread in a single layer, spacing one-quarter-inch to one-half-inch apart. Add the chicken pieces. Brush the chicken and vegetables with some of the harissa mixture.

Bake 10 minutes. Remove the pan from the oven, and brush the chicken and vegetables again with the harissa mixture. Continue baking until the chicken is cooked, about 10 more minutes (a meat thermometer inserted in the center of the chicken should read 165°F).

Roast Pork Chops with Sweet Potatoes and Kale

Make this with bone-in center-cut pork rib chops—meat always tastes better when it's cooked on the bone.

  2 Tablespoons honey
  2 Tablespoons soy sauce
  1 teaspoon dried thyme
  ½ teaspoon salt, divided
  ¾ teaspoon freshly ground pepper, divided
  4 (1¼-inch-thick) bone-in center-cut pork rib chops (about six ounces each), trimmed of excess fat
Olive oil cooking spray
  2 (eight-ounce) sweet potatoes, washed, peel on
Bunch kale (six ounces), trimmed, washed and torn (about five packed cups)

Mix the honey, soy sauce, thyme, one-quarter teaspoon of the salt and one-half teaspoon of the pepper in a small bowl. Measure out one tablespoon and set aside. Brush the remaining mixture all over the pork chops.

Preheat the oven to 425°F. Place a rimmed sheet pan in the oven to heat.

Meanwhile, trim the ends of the sweet potatoes, and cut lengthwise into one-inch slices. Toss with the reserved tablespoon of the honey mixture.

Remove the hot baking sheet from the oven. Spray with cooking spray. Arrange the pork chops on the baking sheet, then arrange the sweet potato wedges around the chops. Roast for 10 minutes.

Remove the pan from the oven, and scatter torn kale around and on top of the pork and sweet potatoes—this is an exception to the sheet-pan dinner "don't let foods touch" rule—they'll still roast.

Sprinkle the remaining one-quarter teaspoon of salt on the kale. Roast for five minutes or until a meat thermometer inserted through the side of a chop into the center reads 145°F.

Mirin/Miso-Glazed Salmon with Baby Bok Choy

This recipe calls for an intact single side of salmon—I spied a deep-red side of wild salmon about the right size in my local market and couldn't resist, and it turned out great. If you prefer to cook individual portions, use five-ounce fillets and reduce the cooking time by about a minute.

Mirin is a subtly sweet Japanese rice wine vinegar that adds a tangy richness—as does miso, a salty fermented soybean paste. You can find both mirin and miso in the international section of most supermarkets near the soy sauce.

¼ cup mirin

2 Tablespoons red miso paste

2 Tablespoons soy sauce

1 Tablespoon grated fresh ginger

1 side of salmon (1¼ pounds—about 20 ounces) or 4 (five-ounce) center-cut salmon fillets

2 baby bok choy (about four ounces each), halved lengthwise

1 cup fresh or frozen corn kernels (if using fresh, about two ears' worth) (optional)

3 Tablespoons sliced scallions

Preheat the oven to 400°F. Line a rimmed sheet pan with parchment paper.

Combine the mirin, miso, soy sauce and ginger in a small, deep bowl, and whisk until smooth.

Place the salmon on the parchment-lined sheet pan, and brush half the mirin/soy sauce/ginger mixture on the salmon. Place in the center of the oven, and roast 10 minutes.

Remove the pan from the oven, and arrange the baby bok choy halves, cut sides up, and corn kernels, if using them, around the salmon. Lightly brush one tablespoon of the mirin/soy sauce/ginger mixture onto the cut edges of the baby bok choy and onto the corn. Sprinkle sliced scallions over the fish. Continue roasting three to five minutes or until the salmon is just translucent in the center and the outside edges flake with a fork. (The fish will continue to "cook" slightly after you remove it from the oven.)

Remove the pan from the oven, and let stand five minutes. If you are using a whole salmon, "flake" it—gently pull the cooked fish apart so that it separates into equal-sized pieces—and place on serving plates with portions of baby bok choy halves and corn.

GOOD TO KNOW...

Tricks to Make Hard-Boiled Eggs Easier to Peel

To make hard-boiled eggs easier to peel, add baking soda to the water in which you boil the eggs—one-half teaspoon per quart of water. This makes the water more alkaline and the shells come off more quickly.

Also: Roll the hard-boiled egg back and forth until small cracks appear all over the shell, then start peeling from the larger end of the egg.

Or: Put the cooked egg in a small, strong glass with a little bit of water, cover the top of the glass with your hand and shake vigorously until the eggshell has dozens of cracks—the shell should slip right off.

Prevention.com

Barbecue Bliss: Grilled Meat with Grilled Fruit

Debby Maugans, a food writer based in Asheville, North Carolina. She is author of *Small-Batch Baking, Small-Batch Baking for Chocolate Lovers* and *Farmer & Chef Asheville.*

Firing up the grill? Be sure to make your steak, chicken and other meats memorable by also grilling fruit! Grilling caramelizes fruits' natural sugars, adding complex sweetness that complements the savory, salty flavors of grilled meats—while brightening plates with beautiful colors. *Start with these three recipes…*

Grilled Balsamic Pork Loin with Pineapple

The sweetness of pineapple and the tangy taste of marinated pork are quite different. But when you grill them, the smoky caramelized flavors that emerge meld the flavors beautifully. Marinate the pork for at least an hour beforehand—and you could even prep the day before and refrigerate overnight.

- ¼ cup balsamic vinegar
- 3 Tablespoons extra-virgin olive oil
- 2 Tablespoons Dijon mustard
- 1 Tablespoon packed light brown sugar
- 1 Tablespoon finely chopped fresh thyme
- ½ teaspoon kosher salt
- ½ teaspoon freshly ground pepper
- 1 (1-pound) piece boneless pork loin
- 1 fresh pineapple, trimmed, core removed, cut into 14 slices (about ¾-inch-thick)

Combine the vinegar, olive oil, mustard, brown sugar, thyme and the salt and pepper in a resealable plastic bag. Seal the bag, and shake to blend the ingredients. Measure out six tablespoons of marinade, and reserve the rest for the pineapple. Place the pork in the bag with the marinade. Seal the bag, and turn to coat with marinade. Refrigerate for at least one hour.

Prepare the grill for indirect medium-high heat. Brush the pineapple slices with two tablespoons of the reserved marinade. Place the pork on the grill over indirect heat, cover and grill for 20 minutes. Baste the pork with some of the remaining reserved mixture, then turn and baste again. Arrange the pineapple slices over direct heat.

Cover and grill, basting the pork occasionally, until it is cooked through and a thermometer inserted in the center of the pork registers 145°F—about 20 minutes more. Grill the pineapple until it's well-marked, turning once, about 15 minutes.

Transfer the pork to a cutting board, and let stand 10 minutes before slicing and serving with the pineapple slices. Makes four servings.

Mediterranean Flat-Iron Steak and Watermelon Salad

"Flat iron" steak has an unusually rich beef flavor that is both tamed and complemented by the juicy, sweet watermelon. It's perfect for grilling—flat and rectangular so that it cooks evenly. It needs to be marinated, though, or it can be tough, so plan for at least six hours of marinating in the fridge. *Note*: You can substitute flank steak or skirt steak—just cook a minute or two less than the instructions below call for.

- ⅓ cup fresh lemon juice
- ¼ cup extra-virgin olive oil
- 1½ teaspoons dried oregano
- 1 clove garlic, crushed and finely minced
- ¼ teaspoon salt
- ¼ teaspoon freshly ground pepper
- 1 pound flat iron steak
- 2 (¾-to-1-inch-thick) slices watermelon. (Round "baby" watermelons, with their dense flesh and seeds, work great on the grill.)
- 4 cups watercress or arugula
- ¼ cup thinly sliced red onion
- 16 cherry or grape tomatoes
- ¼ cup crumbled feta cheese, optional

Combine the lemon juice, olive oil, oregano, garlic, salt and freshly ground pepper in a small bowl, and whisk to blend. Place the steak in a sealable plastic bag, pour in half the dressing and seal the bag. Turn the meat in the bag to coat, and refrigerate at least six hours or up to overnight, turning the bag occasionally. Reserve the remaining dressing. (Cover and refrigerate it overnight.)

Prepare the grill for direct medium-high heat. Brush the watermelon slices with about one tablespoon of the reserved dressing. Place the watermelon and steak directly over the coals on a lightly oiled grill rack. Grill the watermelon slices until well-marked, about two minutes on each side. Grill the steak until desired degree of doneness, about 10 minutes for medium, turning once. Transfer the steak to a cutting board, and let stand 10 minutes.

Cut each slice of watermelon into four triangles. Thinly slice the steak against the grain.

To serve, arrange the watercress or arugula and steak slices on serving plates. Whisk the reserved dressing, and drizzle it over the steak and watercress. Place two wedges of watermelon on each plate, arrange onion slices and tomatoes on each plate, and sprinkle with feta cheese if desired. Makes four servings.

Grilled Chicken and Skewered Peach Salad

The golden caramelized sweet juices of the peaches add fresh summery flavor to the grilled chicken. *Note*: While any skewers will work for grilling, you'll get best results with parallel skewers—there's one handle but two skewers. They make food easier to turn over.

- 3 Tablespoons sherry vinegar or white wine vinegar
- 3 Tablespoons avocado oil or extra-virgin olive oil
- 2 Tablespoons minced shallots
- ½ teaspoon curry powder
- ¼ teaspoon salt
- ½ teaspoon freshly ground pepper
- 3 (4-ounce) chicken breast halves
- 2 large, ripe peaches
- 4 cups mixed greens or spinach
- ¼ cup chopped, unsalted, roasted almonds
- 2 ounces crumbled goat cheese, blue cheese or, if preferred, any mild soft cheese

Combine the sherry vinegar, avocado oil, shallots, curry powder, salt and pepper in a small bowl, and whisk to blend.

Pound each half chicken breast to an even thickness between pieces of waxed paper. Whisk the vinaigrette, measure out two tablespoons, drizzle it over the chicken and spread

evenly. Preheat the grill for direct medium-high heat.

Cut the peaches in half, remove the pits, then cut each half into four wedges. Thread the peach slices on two parallel skewers for easier grilling. Whisk the vinaigrette again, measure out one tablespoon and brush or otherwise spread it on the peach slices.

Place the chicken and peach slices on the grill rack. Grill the peach slices until well-marked on each side, about one minute per side. Grill the chicken until cooked through, about five or six minutes on each side. Transfer the chicken to a cutting board, and let stand five minutes before slicing.

Arrange the greens, chicken and peaches on serving plates. Drizzle with the remaining vinaigrette, and sprinkle with almonds and cheese. Makes four servings.

INDIRECT VS. DIRECT GRILLING

These recipes call for direct and indirect heat.

For *direct* heat…

Charcoal grill: Evenly distribute hot, ash-colored coals in an even layer, sides touching, on the charcoal grate. (If you want high heat, add an additional layer of hot coals.) Position the cooking grate over the coals, and lightly brush vegetable oil on the cooking grate just before adding food.

Gas grill: Set all burners to the heat level directed in the recipe. Lightly brush vegetable oil on the cooking grate just before adding food.

For *indirect* heat…

Charcoal grill: Arrange hot, ash-colored coals on one half of the charcoal grate, piling them in an even layer. Position the cooking grate over the coals, brush vegetable oil on the grate just before adding food, and place food over the half with no coals underneath.

Gas grill: Set burners to the heat level in the recipe. Brush vegetable oil on the cooking grate, and turn off two or more burners before placing food. Keep these burners turned off.

Peanut Butter "Fat Balls"

Containing nuts, chia and hemp seeds, and omega-3 fatty acids, these "fat balls" make tasty and healthy snacks.

To make them, mix one-half cup of smooth peanut butter with one-third cup each of chia and hemp seeds and one tablespoon of coconut butter. Refrigerate until firm, then scoop out one tablespoon of the mixture at a time, and form each into a ball. Roll the balls in one-quarter cup of cocoa powder. Serve immediately, or place in an airtight container in the refrigerator for up to four days. Each vegan, gluten-free ball contains about 100 calories.

Health.com

Cinnamon-Toast Chickpeas

Drain and rinse a can of chickpeas. Dry them on a paper towel. Preheat the oven to 375°F, and put parchment paper on a baking sheet. Spread the chickpeas on the sheet in a single layer, and bake for about 35 to 45 minutes or until crispy. While they are still warm, toss them in a bowl containing one tablespoon of olive oil, one tablespoon of honey, and cinnamon to taste. Spread them back on the baking sheet, and bake another 10 minutes or until caramelized.

Shape.com

Way Beyond Pie— Delicious Apple Recipes

Linda Gassenheimer, an award-winning author of several cookbooks, including *The 12-Week Diabetes Cookbook* and *Delicious One-Pot Dishes*, and the *Food, News and Views* podcast on 880thebiz.com. She also writes the syndicated newspaper column "Dinner in Minutes." DinnerInMinutes.com

Here are some new ways to enjoy apples beyond eating them or using them in salads or baked in a pie. The apples in the recipes below are commonly available in the autumn and winter in most markets.

But before we get to the delicious recipes, here's a quick guide to how best to use some popular apples...

Apples that hold their shape when cooked: Fuji add an intriguing zing to quiche...Granny Smith are very tart with a high acid content that makes them good for baking.

Apples for snacking and salads: Cortland is good for salads or instead of crackers with dips...Gala can be used in salads, fruit salsas, relishes and chutneys...McIntosh's tender white flesh cooks down quickly.

Apples for snacking but not for salads: Red Delicious are best eaten fresh—they don't hold their shape when cooked, and the flesh turns brown quickly.

Each recipe makes two servings, but it is easy to multiply if you want to serve more...

Curried Soup with Crunchy Apples

Curry powder, ginger and coconut milk flavor this warm and inviting soup. The Cortland apples used are crisp, blending with sautéed onion, lentils, almonds and cilantro and adding a pleasant contrast in texture and flavor.

- 2 teaspoons canola oil
- 1 cup sliced onion
- ½ cup sliced carrot
- ½ cup sliced celery
- 2 teaspoons curry powder
- 1 Tablespoon flour
- 1 teaspoon ground ginger
- 2½ cups low-sodium chicken broth
- ¾ cup light coconut milk
- ½ cup dried lentils

Salt and freshly ground black pepper

- 1 Cortland apple, cored, unpeeled, cut into small cubes (about one cup)
- ¼ cup slivered almonds, toasted
- 2 Tablespoons chopped fresh cilantro
- 2 lemon wedges

Heat the canola oil in a large saucepan over medium-high heat. Add the onion, carrot and celery. Sauté for five minutes, stirring occasionally. Add the curry powder, flour and ginger, and sauté for about 30 seconds. Stir in the chicken broth and coconut milk. Bring to a boil, and add the lentils. Reduce the heat to a simmer and cover. Cook for 20 minutes. Add salt and pepper to taste. To serve, divide the apple cubes and almonds between two bowls, and ladle the soup over them. Sprinkle with cilantro, and place lemon wedges on the side.

Fall Harvest Sausage Stew

Fall harvest sweet potatoes, tomatoes and apples are combined with turkey sausage to make this a tasty autumn stew that also works well any time of the year. Cooking the ingredients in beer adds an intriguing depth of flavor.

There are several types of turkey sausage available at most supermarkets. I prefer the mild ones for this dinner, but if you like your stews with a kick, buy the ones marked hot.

    2 teaspoons canola oil
    2 low-fat turkey sausages, cut into two-inch
      pieces
    ½ pound sweet potato, peeled and cubed
      (about 1⅓ cups)
    1 medium onion, sliced
    1 green bell pepper, sliced
    1 Golden Delicious apple, unpeeled, seeded
      and sliced
    2 cups (approximately one 14.5-ounce can)
      canned low-sodium, no-sugar-added diced
      tomatoes, undrained
    1 bottle (12 ounces) beer (any type)
    2 teaspoons fennel seeds
    Salt and freshly ground black pepper
    ¼ cup broken walnuts

Heat the canola oil in a large saucepan over medium-high heat. Add the sausages, sweet potato, onion and green pepper, and sauté for five minutes, stirring occasionally. Add the apple, tomatoes, beer and fennel seeds. Bring to a simmer, lower the heat, cover with a lid, and simmer gently for 15 minutes. Add salt and pepper to taste. Divide the stew between two large soup bowls, and sprinkle with walnuts.

Goat Cheese, Apple and Pecan Flatbread

Fuji or Golden Delicious apples work well for this dish. The sweet flavor mixed with onion, cheese and arugula creates a sweet, tangy flatbread.

Look for ready-made flatbread in the supermarket. This recipe uses flatbread that measures 7 x 10 inches—a very thin pizza crust also works.

    2 flatbreads
    2 Tablespoons olive oil (divided use)

    1 cup shredded part-skim mozzarella cheese
    1 Fuji apple, unpeeled and thinly sliced
      (about 2 cups)
    ½ medium sweet onion (such as Vidalia),
      thinly sliced
    ½ cup broken pecan pieces
    4 ounces soft goat cheese
    2 cups loosely packed arugula (about half a
      5-ounce package)

Preheat the oven to 400°F. Line a baking tray with foil. Place the flatbreads on the foil. Spread one-half tablespoon of the olive oil over each flatbread. Evenly spread one-half cup mozzarella cheese over the olive oil. Arrange the apple slices overlapping in a spiral over the cheese. Place the onion slices over the apples. Sprinkle the pecans on top. Cut the goat cheese into small pieces (about one inch each), and evenly place them on top of the flatbreads. Bake in the preheated oven for 15 minutes. The apples will be soft but will hold their shape. Top each flatbread with one cup of the arugula, and drizzle the remaining olive oil over the arugula.

Apple Fluff

This light, fresh dessert is like biting into an apple-cinnamon cloud. It calls for McIntosh apples, which are sweet and tangy with tender white flesh and cook down easily to make a purée.

    1 large McIntosh apple, peeled and cored,
      cut into one-inch pieces (about 2 cups)
    1 cup water
    2 Tablespoons honey
    4 teaspoons sugar
    2 teaspoons vanilla extract
    1 teaspoon ground cinnamon
    4 egg whites, separated from whole pasteur-
      ized eggs
    2 Tablespoons unsalted walnut pieces

Add the apple pieces to a saucepan with the water, honey and sugar. Stir to combine ingredients. Place over medium heat, bring to a simmer, lower the heat and cover. The apples should be soft after about five minutes. Simmer for one or two minutes longer if needed. Strain and purée the apples in a food processor or sieve. Mix in the vanilla extract and cinnamon, and set aside to cool. Beat the egg whites to stiff peaks, and gently fold in the apple purée. Spoon into two small bowls. Sprinkle walnuts on top. Serve immediately.

get about. If you can see the food—in a glass container, for instance—you're more likely to notice it and use it before it spoils.

Toby Amidor, RD, certified dietitian nutritionist and author of *Smart Meal Prep for Beginners*, quoted at Insider.com.

Best Ways to Freeze Produce

Whether you buy your fruits and vegetables from farmer's markets or supermarkets or pick them from your own garden, sometimes you have too much! *Solution:* Prepare produce right, and freeze in individual-serving-size freezer bags. *Here's how to freeze popular vegetables so that they'll taste farm-fresh throughout the winter…*

Kale: Cook, pack and freeze.

Broccoli: Cut into florets, blanch for 30 seconds, plunge into ice water and drain before freezing.

Cauliflower: Cut into florets, blanch for up to a minute, drain, dry and freeze.

Spinach: Blanch, cool, drain, squeeze out excess moisture and pack and freeze.

Tomatoes: Quarter and freeze in bags, or blanch whole in boiling water, then freeze.

Roundup of experts on food storage, reported at GoBankingRates.com.

Food-Storage Mistakes

• **Keeping any raw meat, chicken or fish on a refrigerator shelf above any ready-to-eat or prepared foods.** This might let raw, possibly contaminated, juices drip into the ready-to-eat or prepared foods—so always store raw food at the bottom of the refrigerator.

• **Keeping eggs in the refrigerator door.** Food stored in the refrigerator door is exposed to a lot of changes in temperature, which can make it go bad faster.

• **Storing food in opaque containers.** Food in non-see-through containers is easy to for-

Easy Ways to Keep Food Fresh Longer

The average American family of four wastes up to $2,275 each year by throwing away spoiled foods. *Here's what you can do to stop that…*

• **Lightly butter the exposed side of a cheese block,** wrap the block in waxed paper and put it in a plastic bag.

• **Puncture the plastic bags in which you bring home produce from the store** to avoid trapping moisture that causes spoilage.

• **Freeze fruits and vegetables that you will not use quickly.**

• **Wrap the crown of a bunch of bananas with plastic wrap**—this helps to slow the release of ethylene gas, which causes ripening.

• **Bundle herbs and keep them in a vase or glass of water rather than the refrigerator**—trim the stems first, as you would with flowers.

• **Store counter items away from windows** —sunlight causes faster ripening.

• **Wrap lettuce, broccoli and celery in aluminum foil before refrigerating them.**

• **Keep mushrooms in paper bags, not plastic.**

• **Keep tomatoes upside (stem side) down on the counter** so that air does not get into the top opening and speed ripening.

MoneyTalksNews.com

Food "Garbage" You Can Use

Food parts you usually throw away but actually should keep…

• **Pineapple cores contain the beneficial enzyme bromelain, which aids digestion**—finely chop the core, and add it to fruit salad, slaw, chutney or a stir-fry, or blend it in smoothies.

• **Kiwi skin has more fiber than the rest of the fruit**—simply eat kiwis whole, or peel them and add the rind to a smoothie.

• **Onion skins contain high levels of the anti-inflammatory antioxidant quercetin**—add them to soup, stock or sauce, then discard the skin before eating.

• **Watermelon rind and seeds contain several nutrients**—add rind to fruit salads, salsas or chutneys, mix into soups or pickle it…toss seeds in olive oil and salt, then roast at 350°F for 10 to 15 minutes, and sprinkle on salads or add to trail mix.

Roundup of experts on food use, reported in Reader's Digest. RD.com

How Long Can Takeout Stay in the Fridge?

Some takeout food can be refrigerated for longer than many people assume, so you don't have to throw it away. *Amount of time popular takeout stays safe to eat in the fridge…*

Four days: Pizza without seafood toppings can remain safe and tasty if refrigerated within two hours of being prepared…rotisserie chicken, deboned once it has cooled and placed in a small container.

Three to four days: Some Mexican foods such as quesadillas and burritos if refrigerated within two hours…salads, if dressing is on the side, but only one day if dressed.

Two to three days: Chinese food—although seafood may become unappetizing after a day.

Two days: Sandwiches or burgers if kept condiment-free—with condiments, they usually will not be appetizing for more than a day.

Exception: Sushi—eat it the day you buy it, since it becomes slimy or sticky quickly.

Roundup of experts on takeout food, reported at MarketWatch.com.

Make Cut Garden Flowers Last

Teri Dunn Chace, a garden writer based in central New York who is author of more than 35 gardening books, including *Seeing Flowers: Discover the Hidden Life of Flowers.* TeriChaceWriter.com

A bouquet of homegrown flowers is one of the great joys of gardening—whether you proudly display it in your house or give it as a gift.

But if you want to make your homegrown cut flowers last as long as florist flowers often do, forget that romantic image of laying flower stems gently in a pretty basket slung over your arm as you gather them.

Here's why: When a plant stem is severed from a plant, not only is its source of moisture cut off but air bubbles can form in the stem's base, slowing or preventing water uptake later. By the time you get the plant inside and plunk your flowers inside a vase, it may be too late. The result? Limp flowers mighty soon. *Here's a better way…*

IN YOUR GARDEN

• **Fill a bucket with a few inches of lukewarm water.**

• **Use a sharp, clean cutting tool such as a knife or garden shears**—sharp so that the stems do not get mashed…and clean so that harmful bacteria don't invade the plant tissue.

• **For flower stems, cut on a slant,** allowing maximum surface area for water uptake.

• **For slender flowering shrub or tree branches,** make a square (perpendicular to the branch) cut.

Immediately after cutting, place stems in the bucket with water.

IN YOUR HOME

Relax if you can't or don't want to arrange your flowers in a vase immediately after cutting them. They'll be soaking up water from the bucket and getting plump. Just put the bucket in a cool, dark place. Overnight is fine.

When it's time to put the flowers in a vase, work on a table or counter close to a sink. Fill a clean vase about halfway—you can always add more water later.

Next, recut each flower stem under water (while still in the bucket) with a sharp, clean knife—a half inch or more above the garden cut. This may feel awkward at first, but you'll master it after a few stems. For the woody stems that you cut square, recut them and then slit them up the middle about one inch up.

That's it! Now you've done what good florists do to make their flowers look great and last long. If you want flowers to last even longer, recut them and refill the vase with fresh water every day.

I don't know if DIY cut-flower preservatives such as an aspirin or a few drops of lemon juice help, but here's one final tip that really will make a difference. At night, or when you're not home, move the flowers, vase and all, to the fridge or just some cool, dark spot—and then return it to the display spot the next day.

How to Grow Houseplants...from Food

Janet Loughrey, a horticulture photographer, writer and master gardener based in Portland, Oregon. Her work has been featured in Garden Design, Sunset *and* Better Homes & Gardens *as well as in numerous books. LoughreyPhoto.com*

Remember the third grade, when your teacher suspended an avocado pit with toothpicks in a jar and put it on a windowsill? It's still a great way to create a beau-

tiful houseplant. But that's just the beginning. Here are three even more beautiful houseplants you can grow from parts of fruits and vegetables that you would otherwise throw out...

• **Pineapples.** Pineapples are easy to grow and, with patience, produce fruit. *Here's how:* Twist off the leafy crown and peel off a few rows of leaves at the base to expose about one inch of stem. Let the crown dry for a day or two, then plant in an eight-inch-diameter pot filled with potting soil and place in a sunny location.

Pineapple plants like hot temps (65°F to 85°F) and moist soil. As the plant grows, repot it to roomier pots. *To encourage fruiting:* After about a year, cover the pot and plant and an apple with a large plastic bag (the apple gives off ethylene gas, which hastens blossoming). Move the bagged plant out of the sun for about a week, then remove the bag and apple and put the pot back in a sunny spot. With luck, you'll see a baby pineapple in a few months.

• **Gingerroot.** Gingerroot creates an exotic-looking houseplant with tall, grassy stems and plenty of new roots (technically, rhizomes). *Tip:* Some supermarket ginger may be treated to prevent sprouting, so use organic ginger. *Here's how:* Snap a piece of ginger, using the normal joint lines, into several pieces about two-inches square each, and push each piece about an inch deep into an eight-inch-diameter or larger pot filled loosely with potting soil. Water and place in a warm, sunny location. Keep moist. Sprouts will emerge in two to four weeks and will grow two feet or more in a few months. Cuttings are great to flavor soups! Harvest gingerroot in eight months to a year by pulling up the stalks.

●**Citrus fruits.** Lemons, limes, oranges and other citrus seeds all will produce lovely houseplants, although they may not fruit. *Here's how:* Harvest seeds from fresh fruit. Carefully snip the pointy tip of the seed casing with a sharp knife or small sewing scissors, and peel back to remove the seed within. Place seeds on a dampened paper towel, fold that in half, seal in a zipper bag and place in a dark, warm corner. If the towel starts to look dry, spritz it with water to keep it damp. Roots should emerge in about a week. Plant rooted seeds in damp potting soil, and move to a bright windowsill. Leaves will start to grow in a week or two.

The Best Time to Fix Your Lawn's Bare and Thin Spots

Teri Dunn Chace, a garden writer based in central New York who is author of more than 35 gardening books, including *The Anxious Gardener's Book of Answers*. TeriChaceWriter.com

When autumn arrives, it's easy to take a break from your lawn. It's growing more slowly, so it needs less mowing—maybe less watering, too. Time to kick back until spring, right? Big mistake.

It may sound counterintuitive, but if ever you are going to reseed your lawn, the fall is the time. The ground in the fall actually is warmer than in spring, so seeds germinate more quickly. Plus, cooler weather slows the growth of weeds, so your baby grass won't have as much competition as it would in spring. Repairing bare patches isn't a lot of work—but it's easy to make mistakes that undermine your efforts. *Here are common pitfalls—and what to do instead…*

MISTAKE: Procrastinating. This is especially important if you live in an area with cold winters—your window of opportunity to sow is only a month or two after summer's heat subsides and before the first frost. Do it in autumn and your baby grass will "get its feet under it," that is, establish a root system and settle in before winter's cold.

What to do: Start by identifying places where your lawn hasn't thrived. These are the places you want to seed. *Tip:* If you have bare patches due to foot traffic, maybe it's time to be pragmatic, give up on grass in those locations and put an actual path of stepping stones, gravel or even paving.

MISTAKE: Picking the wrong type of grass seed.

What to do: Shop carefully—you'll discover that there are many different kinds, including mixtures. Don't be daunted—narrowing down is easier than you think. "Cool-season" grass seed is right for most of the country, including the Northeast, Mid-Atlantic and much of the Midwest and Plains States. If the area doesn't get much sun, use shade-tolerant blends. Discuss your options with an experienced nursery person.

MISTAKE: Seeding without preparing an area's soil. The new grass won't thrive, or it might not grow at all!

What to do: Tug or dig out the disappointing grass—and any weeds—to a depth of at least four inches to be sure that you've removed most or all of the root systems of unwanted or struggling plants. Sprinkle in topsoil and organic matter (compost or dehydrated cow manure) in a 50:50 ratio. Then rake the area level to prepare it for sowing (you don't want little hills or hollows).

MISTAKE: Waiting to plant too long after you prep. When you've dug out an area, it's an open invitation for rain and wind—and digging dogs—to take fresh soil away. Plus, weeds can invade.

What to do: If you don't have time to seed right away after you prep an area, cover it with a tarp secured with rocks or bricks until you are ready.

MISTAKE: Sowing on dry ground. When you water after planting, you move the seeds around and cause clumping.

What to do: Before you start sowing, sprinkle the area until it is damp but not soggy.

MISTAKE: Sowing unevenly. When seeds

295

clump, they still will germinate, but the little grass plants will compete with one another for root space, sun and air. Plus, it doesn't look nice to have uneven grass growth.

What to do: Follow your seed packaging's directions about amount per area, and spread the seed evenly. Hand-broadcasting is easy to do (see below), but if you're sowing a large area, it's easier to use a spreader.

To hand-broadcast seed: Take a small handful of seed and release it as you walk backward. That way, you don't walk on your work!

Tip: Freshly sown grass seed will grow better if you help it get in better contact with the soil. After sowing, you can pat it down with the back of a shovel, rake or garden fork. An old-fashioned lawn roller also does a fine job.

MISTAKE: **Skipping mulch.** Grass seed and baby grass need a several-week commitment.

What to do: Lightly spread mulch on all freshly seeded areas with straw. Just scatter it evenly over the surface but not densely, which would block water and light from reaching germinating seeds. Mulch helps prevent water runoff from washing your seeds away.

Water daily, if it doesn't rain, with a gentle sprinkler. Depending on the type of seed, the grass should sprout (germinate) in a week to several weeks. Cooler weather slows it down—another reason to get started earlier in fall rather than later.

THE SOD OPTION

If you want an alternative to the work of reseeding described above, you can always buy a bit of sod. *Granted, it's more expensive, but there are times when it makes good sense...*

• **You are trying to establish grass on a slope.** Seed sown on a hill tends to wash down—very frustrating. Sod will stay!

• **Weeds have been a constant problem.** Sod is not only weed-free but also thick enough that when laid down, weeds aren't able to break through.

• **You're in a hurry.** Perhaps you aren't willing or able to babysit freshly sown grass seed.

Sod, while convenient, is not a "drop and go" project—as some people have found out the hard way. *For best results...*

• **Just as with seeding, you must prepare an area.** Dig down to clear out any existing vegetation (weeds, disappointing patchy grass) and rocks, as deep as necessary for the sod to lie flush with a walkway, driveway or adjacent lawn.

• **Water the area before and after setting the sod in place.** Sod doesn't come with a lot of soil attached, and if you neglect to water the ground beforehand, the roots will struggle.

• **If rainfall is sparse, water daily for the first few weeks.** If sod dries out, it dies—it cannot be revived as established lawn grass can.

• **Sod doesn't need to be mulched.**

Whether you use seed or sod, as cold weather approaches, the burgeoning young grass patch will slow down and go dormant, just like the rest of your lawn. But its roots now will have a head start, and you will be gratified to see the green results of your efforts when spring returns.

WHEN SPRING SEEDING IS BETTER

If you live in a really hot and/or dry part of the country such as Florida, the Gulf Coast, the Southwest or southern California, spring actually is better than fall for reseeding. In spring, start with "warm-season" grass such as St. Augustine, Bahiagrass or Bermudagrass so that it has maximum time with warm weather before winter comes.

What you can do now: Apply lawn fertilizer. No need to wait for spring for this. *Tip*: Don't use "garden" fertilizer. Instead, buy separate "lawn" fertilizer—it's high in nitrogen, which lawns especially need. Wait until the weather cools down to apply.

How to Plant a Tree So It Thrives

Teri Dunn Chace, a garden writer based in central New York who is author of more than 35 gardening books, including *The Anxious Gardener's Book of Answers*. TeriChaceWriter.com

D o you really know how to plant a tree so that it survives and thrives? Probably not! Many individuals make mistakes when planting a tree. In recent years, pros who study tree growth have learned new information and have changed the standard planting advice.

Here, based on the latest scientific knowledge, are the common mistakes to avoid…

MISTAKE: **Digging the planting hole too deep.** If it's too deep, the tree's roots could rot. Instead of measuring from where the trunk visibly meets the root-ball to the bottom of the root-ball, measure from the "first root flare" (the spot where the first lateral roots start) to the bottom of the root-ball. That's how deep your planting hole should be.

MISTAKE: **Not allowing for root expansion.** Make your hole at least a foot wider than the root-ball on all sides. Tree roots grow outward, and you want them to—they will stabilize and anchor your tree over time.

MISTAKE: **Holding your tree by the trunk.** Yanking a trunk can break roots near the center of the root-ball or scuff tender bark (which invites disease and insects). Move your tree only by hefting the root-ball.

To get a tree from your vehicle to the planting site, use a wheelbarrow or put it on a tarp and drag the tarp over. Gently maneuver the tree into the hole before snipping off any twine or carefully tugging away burlap (leaving it on until then protects the root-ball from damage or drying out).

MISTAKE: **Adding organic matter.** Current thinking is to not add organic matter (such as compost, peat moss or dehydrated manure) to the hole when planting a tree. Research has shown that this causes the roots to stay right in the area and can stunt growth. Refill the hole with the soil you dug to make it.

MISTAKE: **Hasty hole-filling.** Shoveling the soil back in all at once, without taking time to water, is bad for the young tree. In the following days, vulnerable roots may dry out in air pockets and the tree may lean or fall over because it's not securely settled.

Instead, just after you position the tree, fill the hole about halfway, firmly tamping the soil with your hands or the back of the shovel as you do so. Then fill the hole with water, and let it soak in. Continue adding soil to fill the hole completely. Water again, pressing in more soil.

MISTAKE: **Allowing water to run off.** Water delivered directly to the root system is critical to getting a young tree off to a good start. After the tree is planted and watered for the first time, as described above, use your hands to construct a basin—that is, a several-inch-high dirt berm in a circle around the planting hole's outer edge. Fill with water, and watch it soak in right where it is needed. Do this daily, unless it rains, for the first several weeks of its new life.

MISTAKE: **Skipping mulch.** Mulch holds in soil moisture, moderates soil-temperature fluctuations and keeps out competing weeds. So on planting day, lay down bark mulch that is three-to-five-inches high over the previously described basin—but an inch or two away from the trunk to avoid bark decay.

MISTAKE: **Staking unnecessarily.** Unless your tree is in a very windy spot or especially top-heavy, anchoring it with stakes and lines—which many people automatically do when planting trees—actually can do more harm than good. The ties holding the lines to the trunk can abrade bark, inviting disease…and the tree may not grow as strong because it will depend instead on the support of the lines.

You Can Profit from a Tree You No Longer Want

Roger Cook, who has been the landscaping contractor for the Emmy award–winning home-improvement show *This Old House* since 1982. The program airs on PBS. He also is owner of K&R Tree and Landscaping, Burlington, Massachusetts, which he founded with his wife, Kathleen.

If your yard is home to a large, healthy, mature tree that you may love but no longer want, read on before you call a tree-removal service to cut it down and take it away in pieces. You just might be able to give that old majestic giant a new life in a new yard with a new family that will appreciate it just as much as you have—and you could make a pretty penny doing it.

WHY SELL—AND WHO'S BUYING?

There are various reasons why a tree may no longer be appropriate for your property. Many home owners, and even plenty of landscapers, make the mistake of planting young trees too close to the house or too close to other trees. As they mature and soar, their roots and branches crowd the home and one another, forcing the home owner to part with a perfectly good tree. In other cases, the tree simply grows too large, casts too much shade or requires too much work in the way of raking, pruning and other upkeep.

Most people pay a tree-removal service a good chunk of change to safely cut the tree down, cart it away and bury, grind down or otherwise destroy the stump. That's because they don't know that another option exists. In many cases, a specialty landscaper will pay you for the opportunity to remove the living tree, roots and all…store it…find a buyer…and transplant it to a new yard. These landscapers pay a premium for good trees because they're not buying just wood and leaves—they're buying time. An impressive mature tree may have taken 10, 20, 30 years or more to get that way— and if you can provide decades of growth in just one afternoon, you can expect to collect.

WHAT'S YOUR TREE WORTH?

If you're thinking of selling a tree, it's likely that your first consideration is how much you can get for it. The short answer is that it depends. There are many variables—including the type of tree, its age, height, health, branch structure and root structure, what region you're in and other factors. Trees have sold for $500—and they have sold for up to $5,000.

What you'll need to do is contact one (or better yet, several) landscapers who buy large trees and ask for offers (at no charge to you). The expert providing the valuation will want to see whether your tree has been properly sheared or radically pruned and whether it's well-developed or attractive on only one side. The ease of getting to the roots also plays a role, as does the presence or lack of underground utilities.

Some types of trees are typically in higher demand than others and therefore are easier to sell and tend to fetch better prices. Flowering trees such as dogwoods and magnolias are especially popular, as are beech trees, Japanese maple trees (particularly the big, red ones), Japanese umbrella pines and heritage river birches. But any large, healthy tree has a chance of selling.

WHAT'S INVOLVED IN REMOVAL

There are various ways to remove a tree, all of which involve large, heavy specialty equipment designed to create and secure a movable root-ball. In some cases, landscapers will dig a trench around the roots. In other cases, they'll "evacuate" the roots by blasting away dirt with pressurized air. A massive, bladed machine called a tree spade gathers the root-ball and transports the tree. It's difficult, invasive work, but reputable companies prep the area with protective materials to prevent damage to the driveway, sidewalk, lawn, house and other surroundings.

Under ideal circumstances with the proper access, the whole process can be done in a single afternoon. It's important to note that this is never a do-it-yourself project even if your neighbor 50 feet away is ready to pay you for your tree. You're almost certain to kill the tree and—between water, gas and electric utilities, the powerful specialty equipment you'd have to rent and the massive, unstable tree itself—you're likely also to hurt yourself or damage your property. To find a company that performs this work, search online for "selling mature tree," "tree relocation" or "tree movers," along with your zip code.

TAKE NOTE…

Make the Birds Happy

At this website, you can learn how to create a bird-friendly yard…which plants are most desirable for your property…top choices for container gardens…more.

Audubon.org/PlantsForBirds

Danger of Extended-Control Herbicides

Extended-control herbicides containing the compounds *imazapyr* or *imazapic* can severely damage trees and shrubs—even kill them—when applied to weeds nearby. Commonly known as weed killers, they are used to control persistent plants such as crabgrass, dandelion and poison ivy for up to one year and are available at hardware stores, Lowe's, The Home Depot and other retail outlets. These compounds are water-soluble and persist in the soil, which is why such products can affect plants near the ones onto which they are applied.

Bartlett Tree Experts, Blog.Bartlett.com.

Destroy the Creepy Crawlies Plaguing Your Trees and Bushes

David Deardorff, PhD, a plant pathologist, former professor and researcher at University of Hawaii and Washington State University. He is coauthor of several books about plants, including *What's Wrong with My Plant? (And How Do I Fix It?)*. KathrynAndDavid.com

The toxic chemicals frequently used to treat common plant problems can be bad for people and animals. They can get into water supplies, be ingested by pets and wildlife or get inhaled when we apply them. But these chemicals are not the only solutions for the pests and diseases that can plague bushes and trees. Here are safe solutions to four problems that many home owners face. In most cases these are affordable, practical do-it-yourself solutions, though in the case of taller trees, you might need to enlist an arborist with equipment that can reach high enough.

APHIDS

These tiny sap-sucking insects attack an extremely wide range of trees, bushes and other plants. Often the first sign of an aphid infestation noticed by home owners is that anything left outside under the branches of the tree or bush ends up coated in a sticky, varnishlike coating—that's aphid excrement raining down.

A few other insects, such as white flies, excrete a similar sticky varnish. To confirm that aphids are the pest in question, check the undersides of the tree's or bush's leaves for large numbers of very small insects that have relatively long antennae.

What to do: Spray an insecticidal soap liberally onto the leaves of affected trees and bushes. These soaps are deadly to aphids but safe for people and animals. *Example*: A brand called Safer Insect Killing Soap (around $10 for 32 ounces). Apply about every seven days when aphids are present. (Despite what you might hear from a neighbor or online, spraying diluted dishwashing soap is not a good idea—although it can indeed kill aphids, the detergents in these products are bad for plants.)

When you spray for aphids, also check whether there are large numbers of ants on and around the tree or bush. Some ant species herd aphids onto plants so that they can feast on the waste that the aphids produce—it's full of sugar. Get rid of these ants by wrapping a "sticky tree band" around the trunk of the tree or bush—an adhesive product such as Tanglefoot Insect Barrier spread onto a narrow, paperlike band that's wrapped around the trunk (about $17 for a kit). When ants try to climb the tree, they get stuck and die.

Also sprinkle diatomaceous earth around the trunk of the affected plant. This is a powder derived from the fossils of ancient marine algae. It is not at all harmful to people or animals, but on a microscopic level, it's sharp enough to slice into bugs' bodies if they walk across it.

POWDERY MILDEW FUNGUS

This fungal disease makes affected plants look as if their leaves have been dusted with flour. Rub a leaf gently with your finger—if powdery mildew fungus is the issue, the powder will rub off easily.

This fungus probably won't kill your trees and bushes, but it can cause deformed, discolored leaves. That doesn't just detract from the plants' appearance, it also weakens them by inhibiting their ability to collect sunlight for photosynthesis. (Powdery mildew fungus actually is not a single species—perhaps 200 different funguses are grouped together under this name.)

What to do: Make a mix of one tablespoon baking soda and one tablespoon liquid hand soap—not dishwashing liquid—per gallon of water. Then spray a generous amount of this mixture onto the leaves of affected trees and bushes as well as surrounding plants. The baking soda raises the pH of plant leaves, which can kill fungus. The soap acts as a spreader and stabilizer—without it, the baking soda/water solution would bead up on leaves and roll off. Apply once a week, and reapply following rain.

CATERPILLARS

Caterpillars eat the leaves of trees and bushes, and some types of caterpillars eat other parts of plants as well, such as the flowers, seeds or fruits. Their voracious appetites can do enormous harm—in large numbers caterpillars can virtually defoliate trees or bushes.

What to do: If you see lots of caterpillars in one of your trees or bushes—or many of the plant's leaves are riddled with holes where caterpillars have dined—spray a bacteriological parasite known as *Bacillus thuringiensis,* often called "Bt," onto the plant. This bacterium is deadly to almost all common types of caterpillars, but when used as directed, it is harmless to people and animals. Brand names include DiPel (about $25 for a one-pound bag of DiPel Pro DF) and Thuricide (about $9 for an eight-ounce bottle).

ROOT WEEVILS AND OTHER SOIL-DWELLING PESTS

Root weevils are beetles, but they start life under the soil as larvae feeding on plant roots, often doing tremendous damage. Adult root weevils climb up the plants to feed on their leaves—you may notice notches along leaf edges. Bushes and trees that can be victimized include azalea, hemlock, lilac, privet, rhododendron, spruce, yew and many more.

Unlike with many beetles, with weevils you're more likely to notice the notches they eat out of leaf edges than you are to see the insects themselves—even the adults live in the soil and come out mainly at night.

What to do: Apply beneficial nematodes to the soil surrounding affected trees and bushes, ideally in the spring. These are microscopic roundworms that get inside the gut of certain soil-dwelling insects including root weevils and then release a type of bacteria that's deadly to these pests but harmless to people and animals. Purchase nematodes from an established seller such as Arbico Organics ($36 for NemaSeek, which contains five million nematodes—enough to treat up to 218 square feet) or Orcon (about $48 for seven million). Confirm that the product you select specifically lists weevils among the pests it can control—different beneficial nematodes kill different insects.

A LANDSCAPING SOLUTION TO PESTS AND DISEASES

There's one strategy that will greatly reduce the risk to your trees and bushes from an extremely wide range of different pests and diseases—but it's a solution that's best implemented before your plants are even in the ground.

Position trees and bushes so that their branches will not touch other trees and bushes of the same species even when they reach their full, mature size. (The nursery where you purchase your trees and bushes, or your landscaper, can tell you how wide a particular tree or shrub will grow.) Or better yet, don't position plants of the same species anywhere near one another in your yard.

Many pests and diseases affect only a very small percentage of plants. As long as a tree or shrub is not near another of the same type, pest and disease problems tend to remain contained—one of your plants might develop a problem, but it's unlikely to spread to the rest of your landscaping.

18

Life Lessons

Mister Rogers' Valuable Advice Is Still Spot on Today

Hi, Neighbor. If you'd forgotten the smiling face and gentle voice of the man who offered this greeting daily after he donned his signature cardigan and sneakers, recent reminders have cropped up everywhere. Fred Rogers, who died in 2003, made a posthumous comeback in the popular documentary, *Won't You Be My Neighbor?*...the recently released biography, *The Good Neighbor: The Life and Work of Fred Rogers*...and the movie, *You Are My Friend*, which stars Tom Hanks.

Why Fred Rogers, and why now? Well, 2018 marked the 50th anniversary of the Presbyterian minister's children's show, *Mister Rogers' Neighborhood*, which aired from 1968 to 2001. But this is about so much more than an anniversary. It's about a legacy that only continues to grow and resonate with people of all ages. If you consider the eerie similarities of then and now, it's easy to see why. In 1968, political and racial tensions were at an all-time high. Assassinations, riots and terror attacks were happening both at home and internationally. Friends and family were at odds over everything from the Vietnam War to rock music. Then, as now, Fred Rogers modeled the best in all of us and reminded everyone of the good and positive in life. At the root of all his lessons is one simple, guiding principle—always be kind, or as he would put it, "Be a good neighbor." *Here are five more gems for grown-ups from Mister Rogers...*

***LESSON 1*: Like yourself.**

Tres Roeder, MBA, founder and president of Roeder Consulting, a Cleveland-based project-management firm that works with midsize and Fortune 500 companies. He grew up watching *Mister Rogers' Neighborhood*, and the lessons he learned shaped his attitudes and informed his business life. Roeder is author of two best-selling books on communication and interpersonal skills in the workplace—*Managing Project Stakeholders* and *A Sixth Sense for Project Management*. RoederConsulting.com

Mister Rogers said: "One of the greatest gifts you can give anybody is the gift of your honest self."

Fred Rogers instructed each of us to conduct our lives in our own unique way and also in a way that works harmoniously alongside others. He told children in every episode, "I like you just the way you are."

The not-so-hidden message: You need to like yourself, too. In one episode, he illustrated this message by drawing a hasty picture with crayons and holding it up for his pint-size audience, saying, "I'm not very good at it, but it doesn't matter. It feels good to have made something." If you love and accept yourself along with your imperfections, you'll be kind to yourself. Both self-acceptance and kindness give you a strong foundation for confidence and compassion, which makes it much easier to be kind to other people.

LESSON 2: Talk about your feelings.

Mister Rogers said: "People have said, 'Don't cry,' to other people for years and years, and all it has ever meant is, 'I'm too uncomfortable when you show your feelings.' I'd rather have them say, 'Go ahead and cry. I'm here to be with you.'"

Fred Rogers didn't minimize problems. He acknowledged that there are times when everything isn't fine—that it's OK to be sad, scared or hurt. That acknowledgment gives others a safe space to talk through their feelings, whether it's about something personal—a divorce, illness—or professional, such as upheaval at work. Change is scary and often painful, even when it's not something big and personal such as a divorce or illness. Regardless of the setting, it's important to be patient with others. Listen and let them talk through their feelings without passing judgment. This helps people find acceptance about what is happening inside themselves.

LESSON 3: Have faith in humanity.

Mister Rogers said: "One of the greatest dignities of humankind is that each successive generation is invested in the welfare of each new generation."

Rogers was the master of framing life in realistic but still positive and constructive terms.

He was fond of sharing what his mother said whenever he saw scary things on the news. "Look for the helpers. You will always find people who are helping." As adults, we are wise to remember this when we see a heartbreaking school shooting or natural disaster. Focusing on the first responders and Good Samaritans who step up in the face of tragedy reminds us that there are caring people in the world and helps restore our faith in humanity.

Recently in my community there was a major fire at a beloved school. At first, everyone at the scene was filled with anger, sadness and frustration that this could happen. Then some of the parents began to create thank-you posters for all the different fire companies that responded to show the community's gratitude. They were able to channel those negative emotions into something positive.

BETTER WAY...

Appreciate the Good in Your Life!

Here's how to be sure you appreciate the good in your life…

●**Share your feelings.** When something positive happens—even something as small as having a laugh with friends or seeing a beautiful nature scene—express your appreciation.

●**Take a mental photo.** Consciously tell yourself when you're enjoying something, and decide how you want to remember the moment.

●**Congratulate yourself when things are going well,** and give yourself credit for what you have done.

●**Take extra time to be in touch with your senses during enjoyable experiences**—for instance, by slowing down and carefully experiencing the flavors in each sip of wine.

●**Be demonstrative**—when something good happens, laugh out loud and shout for joy. Stop yourself from focusing on the negative.

●**When bad things happen, remind yourself how much worse things could be**—for example, if traffic makes you late for work, remember that some people do not have jobs at all.

Fred Bryant, PhD, social psychologist, Loyola University, Chicago, and coauthor of Savoring: A New Model of Positive Experience, *quoted at GreaterGood.Berkeley.edu.*

LESSON 4: Control what you can—you.

Mister Rogers said: "In times of stress, the best thing we can do for each other is to listen with our ears and our hearts and to be assured that our questions are just as important as our answers."

At a time when it seems like there are all kinds of madness in the world, the one thing everyone can do is stay calm and in control of himself/herself. Say you're late and stuck in highway traffic and someone flies by on the shoulder. The natural reaction is to get angry, and that's OK—denying what happened is not the answer. Instead, Fred Rogers would suggest that you keep control by imagining what valid reasons a person might have for doing that. Perhaps the woman in the passenger seat needed to get to the hospital. That reframing of the situation makes you see the behavior as acceptable. Instead of blood flowing to the emotional part of your brain, you've rerouted it to the thinking part and calmed yourself down in the process.

LESSON 5: Get your point across with respect.

Mister Rogers said: "Love and trust, in the space between what's said and what's heard in our life, can make all the difference in this world."

Fred Rogers helped people find the desire within themselves to be better. For example, if a doctor admonishes someone with a heart problem to stop smoking and exercise more to increase his odds of living longer, the patient may feel offended and often won't take the advice. But if the doctor says, "If you stop smoking and exercise more, you'll be able to play with your grandchildren longer without becoming short of breath and needing to rest," the patient will be more likely to want to change his unhealthy behavior. The doctor phrasing the request like this appeals to the patient's love of his grandchildren and comes off as less judgmental and more supportive.

Whenever it comes to a sticky or polarizing issue, if you challenge someone aggressively, that person is going to feel even more strongly about his own opinion, even if it is wrong, because emotions override the facts. Instead, Rogers believed that by discussing differences of opinion in a respectful way, people can get to a better place together. If you get your point across in a civil, diplomatic way, you can change the chemistry in the room and bring everyone to a level of common human understanding and decency.

Secrets from the World's Happiness Superpowers

Meik Wiking, CEO of The Happiness Research Institute, based in Denmark. Wiking has written many books and reports on happiness, including *The Little Book of Hygge* and *The Little Book of Lykke*.

Can the happiness of different countries be *measured?* And if so, can it help make *you* happier?

An initiative of the United Nations releases a *World Happiness Report* each year that lists the countries whose citizens are deemed the happiest. This ranking is based on six key factors—trust (in government and business)…health…gross domestic product (GDP) per capita…generosity…freedom to make life decisions…and social support (or a sense of community). *Secrets of five super-happy countries that can help make you happier, too…*

DENMARK

The secret: Bring your community together.

Why it makes you happy: Lykke (pronounced loo-kah) is the Danish word for happiness, and it's vital to life in Denmark. Most uniquely, the Danish people have pioneered the concept of *hygge* (pronounced hoo-ga), creating cozy contentment and well-being through simple acts like spending time with friends and curling up on the couch with a mug of hot tea and a good book.

About 50,000 Danes live in a type of cohousing, called *bofællesskab,* in which several independent houses are clustered around a large common house and garden. It's attractive to families with young children (no need to hire babysitters!) and older adults, who often become socially isolated. In research published last year, having supportive friends in older age was found to be an even stronger predictor of well-being than strong family connections.

Anything that increases the sense of community will echo the spirit of Danish communal living—build a community garden…start a book-sharing program in your neighborhood or religious institution…organize a block party, etc.

BHUTAN

The secret: Brain-brushing.

Why it makes you happy: While most countries emphasize financial measures like gross national product, the Bhutanese focus on a "Gross National Happiness Index." In Bhutan, the school day begins and ends with a short mindfulness exercise called brain-brushing, an emotionally balancing meditation so named to help children view it as routine as brushing teeth.

Want to try a form of brain-brushing? Loving-kindness meditation, in which one silently repeats phrases such as *May you be happy* or *May you be free from suffering* when thinking about somebody else, has been shown to be effective at promoting positive emotions.

Helpful: The *Calm* app, for instance, offers guidance in loving-kindness meditation for iOS and Android platforms.

JAPAN

The secret: Forest-bathing.

Why it makes you happy: Called *Shinrin-yoku*, forest-bathing is the act of spending time outdoors and soaking up the sights, smells and sounds of nature. You breathe in the earthy scents and take time to appreciate the contrasting colors of leaves, sky, earth and water.

Forest-bathing has been linked to lower blood pressure and lower levels of the stress hormone cortisol (after only 20 minutes!).

One theory, beyond just the fact that it's relaxing: Trees release aromatic compounds called *phytoncides,* and inhaling these compounds may curb the production of stress hormones.

So get out into nature. *An easy way to do it:* Visit the same natural spot often throughout the year, mindfully noting each seasonal change, like the sound of the leaves rustling in the wind in fall…and then the absence of that sound in the winter.

COLOMBIA

The secret: Bike when you can.

Why it makes you happy: Besides the physical health benefits, exercise in general improves mood, boosts self-esteem and protects against depression. In fact, a 2018 study published in *The American Journal of Psychiatry* estimated that 12% of future cases of depression could be prevented if adults were physically active for just one hour total each week…less than nine minutes a day!

BRAZIL

The secret: Help strangers.

Why it makes you happy: A study published in 2003 in *American Scientist* that explored people's willingness to help someone during a chance street encounter found that a whopping 100% of Rio de Janeiro residents offered to assist a stranger who dropped a pen or who appeared blind. Helping people has science-backed health and happiness benefits. People who volunteer, for example, tend to live longer, are less likely to become depressed later in life and have better self-esteem. So give back—to a cause, to a friend, to a stranger.

The Power of Gratitude

Genuine expressions of thanks are more highly valued by the people who receive them than the senders think they will be. In a recent study, senders expected thank-you notes that they had written to generate a happiness rating in the recipients of three on a scale of one to five, with five indicating the most happiness. But recipients reported their happiness as a four, on average.

The notes were not simple thanks for a gift—they were letters of gratitude to people who had affected the senders in some positive way. The quality of writing did not affect recipients' appreciation—they cared about how warm and genuine the notes were.

Amit Kumar, PhD, assistant professor, department of marketing, University of Texas at Austin, and coauthor of a study published in *Psychological Science.*

TAKE NOTE...

How to Accept a Compliment Gracefully

When you get a compliment, say thank you and then connect with the person who gave it by engaging in small talk. In the US, a compliment is an invitation to chat, not a statement to be accepted with only a thank you. After saying thanks, find a way to engage the other person by commenting on something that you both have in common or by extending the discussion into a new area.

Example: If someone compliments your outfit, say thank you and tell him/her about the store where you found it.

The New York Times.

The Basics of a Better Apology

• **Genuine remorse**—specifically saying how sorry you are.

• **Expecting unpleasant but deserved consequences**—something you must do or undertake to show that you truly are sorry for what happened or what you said.

• **Resolution not to commit the same error again**—stated directly and without qualifications.

• **Sincere effort to avoid the situation in the future that led to the error** in the first place.

The New York Times.

Eye Contact Discourages Lying

Simply making eye contact with someone renders that person less likely to lie to you—you do not have to say something like, "Look me in the eye and tell me..." In a recent study, even when lying was encouraged to win a game, participants were about 9% less likely to lie if their opponents looked directly at their eyes.

Jari K. Hietanen, PhD, heads the Human Information Processing Laboratory at University of Tampere, Finland, and is coauthor of a study published in Consciousness and Cognition.

How to Make Life's Biggest Decisions

Rabbi Sherre Hirsch, author of Thresholds: How to Thrive Through Life's Transitions to Live Fearlessly and Regret-Free. She serves as the Senior Rabbinic Scholar for Hillel International, which serves Jewish students at more than 550 universities around the world. She also counsels private clients and leads retreats on grieving and living well. SherreHirsch.com

Should I change careers? Should I relocate? Should I divorce...or marry? These and other big decisions are difficult for almost everyone. They demand that we step into the unknown, which can be disorienting, unsettling...even terrifying.

Here are four ways to improve your odds of making smart decisions...

• **Strive for a B+ result when making big decisions.** It's natural to search for perfect A+ options. Of course, you want an A+ job where you are fulfilled and well-compensated...an A+ relationship where everything goes smoothly with your partner...and an A+ retirement where you stroll along the beach looking as happy as those TV-commercial retirees. The trouble is, A+ options don't always exist, and if you target these, you might end up missing out on perfectly good B+ options. Or you might continue pushing yourself to build that A+ retirement nest egg or afford that A+ house when you would be much happier if you decided the B+ nest egg or house was good enough and gave yourself permission to relax.

What to do: When you struggle to find an option that seems perfect, remind yourself that a B+ is really good. A B+ (or an A–) is a whole lot better than average...and it's a whole lot better than never choosing an option and wasting months or years searching for an A+

305

that doesn't exist. And if you are a person who tends to judge your life largely by others' lives, keep in mind that most people who seem to be in A+ situations actually aren't—it's just that you don't know the troubles they have!

●**Don't turn down an option because you're not certain it's a step forward.** When people consider the opportunities and options that come their way, they often think in terms of forward progress and upward mobility. Would accepting this job be a rung up or a rung down for my career? Would going back to school or relocating be a step forward or a step back? Often the answer isn't clear, and that lack of clarity can lead to inaction and missed chances…or to regret when an option we select turns out to be the wrong one.

What to do: Visualize your options as openings in a maze, not rungs on a ladder. If you reach an opening as you walk through a hedge maze, you wouldn't expect to be able to see far ahead or know for sure which path was correct—you would just decide based on the knowledge that you have and move forward. That's all anyone can really hope to do with many life decisions. When you look back years later, it might seem obvious which choices you should have made, but there's a good chance that this was unknowable at the time.

Helpful: When you need a reminder that you can never make decisions with perfect foreknowledge, reread Robert Frost's poem *"The Road Not Taken."* Its concluding lines are among the best known in American poetry and among the most misunderstood…

Two roads diverged in a wood, and I—
I took the one less traveled by,
And that has made all the difference.

Read the poem, and you'll see that its protagonist is not extolling his wise decision or advising us to choose an unconventional life—he is admitting that at the time he made his biggest decision, he really didn't know how to choose between his options and eventually did so essentially by chance.

●**Live in your decision for a day.** Most people have had the experience of making a decision and then waking in the middle of the night convinced that they made the wrong

BETTER WAY…

It's Time to Speak Out!

What stops you from speaking your mind, and what you can do about it…

●**Being unwilling to get somewhat uncomfortable—**understand that the discomfort disappears over time. You may feel it initially, but after speaking up several times, it will become less or disappear.

●**Fear of being criticized in return—**accept that this can happen, but it should not stop you from saying what you feel.

●**Fear of damaging relationships—**if you remain respectful and clear in what you say, your demeanor should be seen in a positive light.

●**Not knowing exactly what you want—**think through what you want to accomplish, and clarify your feelings before speaking.

●**Being uncomfortable when disagreeing with others—**realize that you need the courage to express a difference of opinion… consider seeing a therapist if you cannot accept this.

Roundup of experts on assertiveness, reported in The New York Times.

decision. Sometimes there's no turning back once you've committed.

What to do: Before you finalize a major decision, tell yourself you've already done so and then live with this for 24 hours, time permitting. If you've made a good choice based on what you know and can reasonably expect, it probably still will feel good throughout this day.

If your decision nags at you during this day, dig into the nagging feelings. If they are feelings of discomfort or fear, that does not mean your decision is incorrect—it's perfectly normal to experience discomfort and fear when making major choices. But if what you feel is something more akin to regret or dismay, it's worth reevaluating your decision. To do this, tell yourself you have made a different choice—whichever option was in second place—and live with that decision for a day. If you get through this day without feeling regret or dismay, this might be the better choice for you.

Example: A writer was offered a prestigious position. But after living for a day with the decision to accept it, he realized it wasn't something he wanted to do but rather something he felt he was expected to do. Turning down the position felt right.

If every option you consider triggers feelings of regret or dismay, stop searching for the option that feels right and instead consider which feels least wrong. Sometimes in life we must settle for our least-bad option for the time being. And you never know—you may find out that it was a great decision all along and you were making yourself suffer unnecessarily.

• **Ask yourself if there is a "normal" to go back to.** When people are faced with a potentially life-altering choice, most lean toward one option above all others—the option to "get back to normal." They favor this not because it's their best choice but because it feels safe. But there's usually a problem with the "back to normal" option that they have failed to consider—the "normal" they are trying to return to may no longer exist.

Examples: Moving back to your former hometown is an option when you are deciding where to relocate or retire—but that town may no longer be the place you remember, and you are no longer the same. You still may love the town, but consider how much has changed since you lived there. Taking back your spouse might be an option after a separation—but the relationship may be different after the split and reunion.

Even when there is an option that does get life somewhat back to normal, this feeling will not last forever. Staying put in your current job rather than taking a new one is fine, but as time passes, your colleagues will change, your responsibilities will change and/or you may no longer find the job fulfilling.

What to do: It's fine to include a familiar place, person or position among your options—returning to something can be a reasonable choice—but evaluate this option just as you would a brand-new opportunity. Ask the same probing questions about it...and employ the same vetting process with it.

Example: If you rent a home for a month in each of the towns where you are thinking of retiring, do so in your former hometown if you are considering it as well—don't assume that you already know this place.

Whenever you experience warm, comfortable thoughts about any kind of "back to normal" option, ask yourself, *In what ways might this option be different and less comfortable than it used to be?* You then might comfortably choose a new path in the maze!

To Solve Modern Life's 6 Biggest Problems: Learn from the Ancient Greeks

Massimo Pigliucci, PhD, the KD Irani Professor of Philosophy at City College and professor of philosophy at the Graduate Center of the City University of New York, both in New York City. His latest book is *How to Be a Stoic: Ancient Wisdom for Modern Living*.

If you're looking for a practical, good-for-you guide to keeping your sanity in our complicated, overstimulated society, look back...*way back*...to the ancient Greco-Roman philosophy of Stoicism. You'll be in good company. Stoicism is all the rage in Silicon Valley, on Wall Street—Warren Buffett, Jeff Bezos and Bill Gates often are described as following Stoic principles—and in books, online courses and live events.

Why follow a way of approaching life that dates back to around 300 BCE? Human nature still is pretty much the same—people want love, wealth, children and respect, and they still are afraid of disease, natural disasters, poverty and being spoken ill of. As much as ever, people today need a framework to orient themselves, set priorities, appreciate the good and handle the bad.

Stoicism may sound simple, but once you start to apply its principles every day, it's remarkably liberating.

Stoicism is not about suppressing emotion (à la *Star Trek's* Mr. Spock) or being so self-reliant that you don't need anyone. What it is about, fundamentally, is recognizing that each of us can control only our own judgments, decisions, intentions and behaviors—we can't control outcomes. If you're not successful, learn from it and move on. It's that two-part approach—living in the moment but always striving to become a better person—that gives this philosophy its edge. When making major decisions, Stoics consider the following four "cardinal virtues"...

• **Practical wisdom**—the knowledge of what is good and bad, and what needs to be done.

• **Courage**—not just physical courage but also the moral courage to face daily challenges with clarity and integrity.

• **Temperance**—the exercise of self-restraint and moderation in all aspects of life.

• **Justice**—treating others fairly even when they have done wrong.

At the root of Stoicism is respect for other humans. The ancient Stoics were the only major group of free people at the time who were openly opposed to slavery and who thought that women were full-fledged human beings. *Here's how classic Stoicism might help you approach some very modern challenges...*

Modern challenge: "I'm under constant stress."

Stoic approach: Stress is not something that is placed upon you—it comes from your own misguided expectations, from being too attached to certain outcomes and from trying to control things that are not within your control.

Say, for example, that you wanted to finish preparing a room in your house for your aging parents to move into and you didn't get it done by your deadline. Accept that, and don't wallow in regret—remember that you can't always control outcomes. But at the same time, learn from the experience.

There's a key Stoic practice that can help—end each day by writing answers to three questions in a diary: *What did I do wrong today? What did I do right today? What could I have done differently today?*

Modern challenge: "I have relentless demands on my time."

Stoic approach: Recognize that time is your most precious resource. Don't easily give it away—it can never be paid back—and don't fritter it away. Learn to say "no" when people ask for more time than you can comfortably give. *Look at it this way:* If a friend asked to borrow $10,000 but you had only $5,000 to spare, that's all you could offer. In the same way, don't "steal" time from people who really matter to you. Remember—Stoics place a strong emphasis on responsibility to family and friends.

Modern challenge: "I waste time on the Internet and feel bad about myself."

Stoic approach: Technology is neither good nor bad. It is what it is. But how you use it—what's under your control—can make you a *better person.*

I am active on Twitter for my job. I curate, share other people's work, follow people who make interesting suggestions, etc. But I can't engage with all my 25,000 followers—and when a follower is insulting or aggressive, I exercise my Stoic virtues of temperance, courage and justice by not responding...deleting a post...and/or unfollowing. In fact, digital technology is like being in a "virtue gym"—it gives you constant opportunities to exercise your ethics and character.

Modern challenge: "Even though I've done OK financially, I'm never content with my wealth and possessions."

EASY TO DO...

Anxious? Sniff Some Lavender

Sniffing lavender for anxiety may be as effective as taking a drug. In a recent animal study, the scent of linalool, an alcohol component in lavender, induced an antianxiety response in mice similar to that of antianxiety medications. The effect has not yet been tested on humans, but it could prove to be very similar.

Hideki Kashiwadani, PhD, a physiologist and neuroscientist at Kagoshima University, Kagoshima, Japan, and lead author of a study published in *Frontiers in Behavioral Neuroscience.*

Stoic approach: There is nothing in Stoicism that says wealth is bad or that you shouldn't use it to live a good life—ancient Stoics ran the financial gamut from slaves to emperors. But money is very consciously recognized in Stoicism as a great *temptation*—the more people have, the more they become focused on possessions and expensive experiences...always wanting more.

How to free yourself? Recognize that possessions are external objects that you can lose—you're lucky to have them, but that luck can turn at any moment. That may sound scary, but it's actually quite liberating. You've already mentally accepted the worst possible outcome...which actually is unlikely to take place. Some Stoics periodically "practice" not having things they do have. Why? To get used to the idea that everything they think they own actually is borrowed from the universe, so to speak.

Examples: They regularly fast for a day or more to better appreciate the next meal... take cold showers to remember what a privilege it is to be able to take a hot one. Did your favorite mug break? Even 10 seconds of upset is unnecessary. Tell yourself, *It was a mug. I knew it could break.*

Modern challenge: "I'm getting older, and I constantly feel worried about my health."

Stoic approach: Recognize what you can control and what you can't—and let go of the desire to control outcomes. You can eat right, exercise, avoid cigarettes, etc., and make medical decisions based on empirical evidence, but you can't truly control whether you get sick or what the outcome of any illness is. In a sense, worrying too much about ourselves is a form of narcissism, an attitude that Stoics avoided by reminding themselves of their place in the infinity of space and time, a meditation practice known as "the view from above."

Modern challenge: "I'm afraid of dying."

Stoic approach: Death is natural and inevitable, and we need to accept it or we will not be truly happy during life. Part of accepting death is preparing for it, yet many Americans have no will, no power of attorney, no do-not-resuscitate order. Stoics consider it courageous to prepare for the end of life, and it can be a refreshing exercise. And according to Seneca, one of the great Stoic philosophers, the ultimate test of character is how one handles the last moments of life.

6 Clever Strategies for Ending Bad Habits...and Starting Good Ones

James Clear, a consultant and speaker based in Columbus, Ohio, who has worked with Fortune 500 companies and sports teams. He is founder of The Habits Academy online course and author of *Atomic Habits: An Easy & Proven Way to Build Good Habits & Break Bad Ones*. HabitsAcademy.com

We tell ourselves that we will cut out fast food and eat healthy...but then find ourselves eating a cheeseburger. We tell ourselves we'll get work done first thing every morning...then find ourselves sleeping in. No doubt about it, bad habits are hard to break and good ones are hard to start. But maybe that's because of the flawed ways we go about trying to break and start them.

When I was in high school, I was hit in the face with a baseball bat that had slipped out of a teammate's hands. I ended up in a coma. After coming out of the coma, I experienced months of seizures and serious vision problems—I literally couldn't see straight. Yet six years later, I was named the top male athlete at my college, I was the captain of the baseball team, and I was one of 33 students nationwide named to the ESPN Academic All-America team.

There wasn't some miracle solution that suddenly solved my physical challenges. In addition to going through extensive physical therapy, I achieved what I did partly by developing healthy habits day in and day out—good sleep habits, good study habits and good fitness habits. I didn't set out to have great habits, I just knew I'd have to work hard every day to overcome my injury.

In the years since then, I've made a study of habits, keeping up with the latest academic research and reading about the habits of successful people and organizations. Eventually I started a website about habits and then began training other people in ways to improve their habits.

Six surprising ways to form good habits and break bad ones...

• **To change your habits, change your identity.** How we see ourselves can dramatically affect our habits. A paper published in 2011 by a team of Harvard and Stanford researchers found that people were significantly more likely to vote if they were asked prior to the election, "How important is it to you to be a voter?"...and less likely to vote if they were asked, "How important is it to you to vote?"

What's the difference? The first question makes people think about their identity—not just about an action they might or might not take. Once someone identifies himself/herself as "a voter," he no longer has to force himself to get to the polling station on election day—it becomes a natural thing to do.

What to do: Label yourself as someone who already has the habit you want...or who doesn't have the habit you want to break. *Example*: If you would like to stop smoking and you're offered a cigarette, don't say, "No thanks, I'm trying to quit"...say, "No thanks, I'm not a smoker." If you want to exercise regularly, don't tell yourself when you wake up in the morning, *I've got to get out of bed and go for a bike ride*...tell yourself, *I'm a biker*.

Conversely, if you already have assigned yourself a negative identity, reassure yourself that it need not be permanent. Refer back to a time before this was your identity, if possible. *Example*: If you often tell yourself, *I can't get in shape, I'm just built this way,* remind yourself that there was a time back in childhood or early adulthood when you were fitter and more active.

• **Stack the new habit you want on top of a habit you already have.** Many of our habits come in series, with one leading automatically to the next. In the morning, perhaps you shower...comb your hair...brush your teeth... get dressed...then brew coffee. You don't have to force yourself to brush your teeth—you

pick up your toothbrush without thinking as soon as you put down your hairbrush. This phenomenon can be used to instill new habits using a strategy called Tiny Habits developed by Stanford University behavior scientist BJ Fogg, PhD.

What to do: When you want to instill a new habit, don't just decide to do it—decide to do it immediately following a habit that you already have. If the new habit is something you wish to do every morning, such as 10 minutes of stretching, you might stack it on your morning-coffee-brewing habit—get the coffee going, do your stretching, then return to the kitchen to find your coffee waiting for you. At first, you'll have to remind yourself to exercise after starting the coffee—a note left by the coffeepot will help—but within a week or two, it will become a habit that you do without thinking, such as brushing your teeth.

• **Focus on the simple act that sets the stage for the challenging habit.** Do you belong to a gym but rarely manage to get there to exercise? Stop focusing on the exercising, and focus instead on the getting there. Committing to working out for 60 minutes four times a week is daunting—so don't do it. Commit instead to putting on your workout clothes and driving to the gym. Those are both easy things to do. Once you're at the gym in your exercise clothes, you might discover that the workout happens almost automatically.

What to do: When the habit you want to establish seems daunting, instead get in the habit of completing the initial simple step that sets the stage for this habit. Often that's enough to get the ball rolling. *Example*: If you struggle to get in the habit of writing a book, instead get in the habit of sitting at your computer with a word-processing program open (and potential distractions such as e-mail alerts and Internet-browsing programs closed).

• **Stop focusing on goals.** When people resolve to establish or abolish a habit, the first thing they tend to do is set a goal. *Examples: I'm going to quit smoking…I'm going to stop watching so much TV and read books instead.*

But when we focus on a goal, we often revert back to our old ways soon after achieving that goal (or after realizing that we will fall short of the goal). Someone who resolves to lose 20 pounds might successfully shed that weight…only to gain it right back.

What to do: It's fine to have a goal—goals sometimes provide useful initial motivation. But after you set a goal, set that goal aside and focus instead on establishing a system that will get you where you want to be. Systems are much more important than goals because goals tend to be short-term targets, while systems can become lasting habits. *Example*: Rather than focusing on the goal "save money for retirement," focus instead on creating a system that trims your ongoing spending so that savings happen automatically.

• **Point at and call out your bad habits.** One reason bad habits are so hard to break is that they can become so ingrained that we barely notice we're doing them. The Japanese railway system has developed a very effective solution for this lack-of-attention problem—it's known as "pointing and calling." When a train approaches a green light along the track, Japanese train drivers point at the light and say, "Signal is green." When pulling into a station, they point at the speedometer and say their current speed. Train conductors do the same when they can see signals or speed. It may sound silly for someone to do this day after day, but it forces the person to be aware of things that might otherwise have occurred with little notice. It is credited with reducing errors by 85% and accidents by 30%.

What to do: Literally point at and call out the habits you wish to break or create. If you waste too much time staring at your cell phone, point at the phone and say, "Wasting time," when you catch yourself doing so. If you chronically forget your wallet when you go out, point at the wallet and say, "Wallet," as you head for the door. Soon you'll discover that you're paying more attention to the behavior you want to change and heading off the bad habit before it occurs most of the time.

• **Praise yourself for your bad-effort days.** There will be days when it's especially difficult to follow through with a new habit because you're under the weather, unusually busy, distracted by new concerns or for any number of reasons.

What to do: Make a very modest effort on these days. Is your habit doing 50 push-ups? Do five. Reading one chapter of a textbook? Read one page. Put a positive mental spin on these minimal efforts by telling yourself, *Even when I'm feeling my worst, I still don't miss a day.*

How to Motivate Yourself to Start a Project

• **If you are putting a project off because you are afraid you will do it poorly,** adopt a prevention focus—for example, think of how completing the project will prevent your boss from getting angry or thinking less of you.

• **If you are delaying because you just do not feel like doing something,** ask yourself why you need to feel like doing something in order to start doing it—this will help you realize that your feelings are just getting in the way of your accomplishment.

• **If you are not getting started because something is hard or boring,** create an if-then plan to make yourself decide to get going. *Examples*: If I haven't started the report by 2 pm, then when 2 pm rolls around, I stop whatever I am doing and start it…if the boss does not bring up my request for a raise the next time we meet, then I will bring it up myself.

Heidi Grant, PhD, social psychologist and associate director, Motivations Science Center at Columbia University, New York City, writing in *Harvard Business Review*.

Surprising Way to Deal with a Stressful Task

Brynne DiMenichi, PhD, Learning and Decision Making Lab, Rutgers University, Newark, New Jersey, and author of study.

Next time you face a stressful task, think back to a time when you confronted a challenge—and failed. You'll be more likely to succeed. So finds a study published in *Frontiers in Behavioral Neuroscience*. One group of participants wrote about past failures...a second group wrote about unrelated topics.

Both groups then were given the same stressful challenge—writing a speech in six minutes about why they should get a dream job...presenting it in five minutes to a chilly "recruiter"...and then counting down by 13s from 2063. They then tried a new task requiring persistent attention.

Results: Participants who had reflected on past failures handled the new task with better physiological responses and less unnecessary rushing, leading to significantly better performance.

It's all about how much stress your brain creates. Stress makes our bodies release the hormone *cortisol*, triggering the "fight or flight" response. That is great when you need to, say, run away from a tiger but counterproductive when you need to focus.

Why would focusing on a past failure reduce stress? It's the comparison. You might realize that the new challenge seems less daunting than one that laid you low in the past.

To harness the power of past failures before a new challenge, spend perhaps 10 minutes writing or thinking about one of your failures. It should be specific, painful, personal—and, if possible, related to the challenge. For example, before a job interview, you might write about a past job interview that went wrong. Far from undermining your confidence, doing this exercise could help you keep cool under pressure.

People with Mild Autism Are All Around You: How to Connect

Janet Lintala, DC, an autism mother and author of *The Un-Prescription for Autism*. She is also a chiropractor in private practice in Beckley, West Virginia. LoveAutismHealth.com

You probably know someone who has a mild form of autism. You might not know for sure, and, indeed, that person might not even know. It could be your neighbor, a coworker, a friend's child or an acquaintance in, say, your book club or bowling league. Maybe it's not readily apparent at first, but over time, you realize that it's tough to make small talk with this person. It is socially awkward, so you stop trying. Maybe you've written him/her off for being rude.

While most attention goes to children, many adults with *autism spectrum disorder* (ASD) have never been diagnosed with it—partly because we are so much more knowledgeable about it now than we were even 15 years ago. So they have never received help in understanding themselves and communicating in a mostly nonautistic world. And that world often doesn't have a clue how to interact with them.

That's where your understanding comes in. Don't worry—you don't have to know for sure that someone has ASD to improve your approach. The truth is, it's never a bad idea to reach out to anyone who is struggling in social situations or can't seem to fit in at, say, the office.

DO YOU UNDERSTAND ASD?

Autism is a developmental disability that can affect a person's ability to communicate, socialize and behave appropriately. People on the spectrum can range from those who are not verbal at all to those who have sophisticated vocabulary and strong language skills, yet still struggle with everyday banter.

Common misconception: Many people believe that people with ASD don't need friends—that they're introverts who are happy being alone. This couldn't be further from the truth—most people with autism are socially motivated. They just need your understanding when they reach out. *Here's how...*

YOUR NEW CONVERSATION SKILLS

Although communication skills vary greatly in people with ASD, in general such people have a hard time engaging in what we consider ordinary conversation.

What that looks like: A person with ASD may find it hard to put words together to form longer sentences...to keep up with the rapid-fire exchanges of a spirited conversation...to ask follow-up questions to keep the back-and-forth going...to stay focused on what people are saying. Many with ASD have trouble establishing or maintaining eye contact even during one-on-one conversation. They also may take words literally when the words are not intended literally (which is often)...and misunderstand the meaning of slang phrases. Humor often relies on a play on words, so someone on the spectrum might completely miss a joke. And a nearly universal trait of people with ASD is difficulty picking up nonverbal cues, such as facial expressions, tone of voice or body language.

Result: The conversation never really gets started...peters out quickly...or ends in misunderstanding and maybe even annoyance on the part of the nonautistic person. *Tips for better conversations...*

• **Be patient.** People with ASD frequently have trouble processing spoken words and need time to figure out what you are saying. To help, slow down when you speak...and give them time to come up with a response.

• **Be kind.** Don't assume that someone who doesn't dive into typical conversation is self-centered or aloof. He may have trouble focusing because he's overwhelmed by sensory stimulation—people with ASD find many environments to be too loud, bright and/or smelly. They're not being judgmental—they literally experience these sensory inputs in ways that are different.

• **Be very clear.** Because of their difficulty picking up nonverbal cues, people on the spectrum may have difficulty detecting and understanding sarcasm, irony, innuendo or inside jokes. So be as direct and concrete as you

can, and don't take offense when the other person keeps asking questions to clarify what you mean.

• **Be understanding.** People with ASD also can have an anxiety disorder or be nervous around others, often because they were bullied and laughed at when they were younger. That's another reason that they may take longer to answer a question—they're afraid of saying the wrong thing.

MANAGE SOCIAL INTERACTIONS BETTER

Two common behavioral features of autism are intensity and repetitive behavior. A child with autism, for example, may carefully line up his toys again and again—and have meltdowns when he's asked to do something else. Autistic adults, too, may have more trouble than you would expect shifting from the topic or task at hand.

What that looks like: If he's part of a conversation, a person on the spectrum might get very animated chatting about, say, the Beatles—but be utterly unable to chime in when the talk shifts to, say, the Rolling Stones. He may get very anxious when asked to multitask. *How to interact more smoothly...*

• **Manage expectations.** We are used to people looking us in the eye and nodding their heads to show that they are paying attention to our conversation. Your bowling partner with ASD might not look up when you speak, but it doesn't mean that she's not listening.

• **Find creative solutions—and translate them into concrete steps.** Sure, it's irritating when someone in your book club highjacks the discussion about *Emma* to go on about 19th-century fashion. Instead of banning her from the book club, find a work-around that's good for everyone. *Example:* Institute a rule that everyone gets to express her ideas for 10 minutes and then has to relinquish the discussion to the next person.

• **Give everyone a way to contribute.** Your fellow choir member may not be verbally quick enough to share his song suggestions for the upcoming concert when everyone else is brainstorming out loud. So you can propose that members also e-mail their ideas later—or bring them to the next meeting.

Once you're thinking along these lines, you'll get in the habit of solving these little glitches easily.

LIVING AS NEIGHBORS AND FRIENDS

Autism is a spectrum. Some people diagnosed as children may need help with activities of daily living throughout their lives. But many learn to function well in society with a little help.

We often assume that people with disabilities such as ASD can't lead fulfilling lives or fall in love, get married or make lifelong friends. But many can. Many do—and they are all around you. We can help by becoming more knowledgeable about this common disorder and showing empathy as they work on its challenges. We might even find that we've developed new friends.

DEALING WITH AUTISM IN THE OFFICE

Given their challenges in making small talk, understanding typical instructions and deviating from routine, adults with autism spectrum disorder (ASD) often struggle on the job. Many have trouble finding work and keeping it. *Here's what can help make the workplace more kind, inclusive and, yes, more productive…*

•**Promote an atmosphere of understanding.** Share what you have learned about autism with your colleagues. Things will go much smoother around the office if coworkers aren't surprised by someone's ASD-related behavior.

•**Speak concretely whenever possible.** Avoid slang, and use simple, direct language instead.

•**Explain the culture.** There may be unofficial customs that a typical person would simply "pick up," but a person with ASD won't. So tell your coworker if it's the custom that everyone chips in for snacks…and that it's fruitless talking to Jane in accounting before she's had her coffee.

•**Put it in writing.** If you need to give your coworker a set of instructions, e-mail her or write the instructions on paper instead of telling her verbally. Ditto for schedule changes.

•**Be clear about performance expectations.** Let's say that there is an urgent deadline. It might suffice for most people if you hint that this means a little sacrifice, but it's better to say, "For the next three weeks, each of us will need to stay an extra hour each night or work at our desks at lunch to make this happen." Otherwise, your coworker with ASD might take an hour-long lunch—because that's what the employee handbook says.

•**Ask for input.** Many of your coworkers may enjoy grabbing a beer after work occasionally, but the person with ASD may find the tumult of the bar overwhelming. To be more inclusive, offer everyone the opportunity to suggest different venues for out-of-office get-togethers, such as lunch in the park, a potluck at someone's house or drinks at a quiet bar.

You Can Be Surrounded by People and Still Be Lonely: What Helps

Julianne Holt-Lunstad, PhD, professor of psychology and neuroscience at Brigham Young University, Provo, Utah. Her research focuses on the long-term health effects of social connections and includes a meta-analysis on the effects of loneliness and social isolation on mortality.

We tend to think of loneliness as a negative feeling of being disconnected and alone. *But here's some good news:* Loneliness also can be a powerful motivator—even a biological urge—to reconnect. We are social animals, after all, and the urge to have strong bonds with others is a powerful one.

You don't have to be lonely. And neither do any of your loved ones.

Loneliness is such an epidemic in the US that social scientists have been digging deep to find ways to help people overcome it. *Unfortunate fact:* The prevalence of loneliness has more than doubled in the US since the 1970s. It now affects an estimated 42 million Americans over age 45.

The truth is, what helps one person leave loneliness behind may be different from what helps another. It may take trial and error to stop feeling lonely or to help someone do so. But there are now evidence-backed approaches that can help many people feel less lonely—and improve their health. To find out more, we spoke with Julianne Holt-Lunstad, PhD, a professor of psychology and neuroscience at Brigham Young University.

LONELY IN A CROWD

What is loneliness? It's a gap—between the kind of social relations you want and what you actually have. It's a *perception* of social isolation that doesn't always have to do with how many people surround you. You can be lonely with colleagues, with friends…and in a marriage. If most of our dealings with our friends and relatives are superficial or filled with conflict, we will feel disconnected no matter how big our social network is.

Conversely, you can feel just fine even when you are totally alone—that's the positive experience called solitude. That's why, to transcend loneliness, you need to have people who you can trust and who understand you—people who you are working with to manage life's challenges and truly thrive.

AS UNHEALTHY AS OBESITY

Loneliness is a hot topic in social science these days because of growing scientific evidence that a lonely life is an unhealthy one. It's truly a killer.

Sobering finding: A meta-analysis of 70 studies found that loneliness increases the risk for an early death by 26%. That makes it about as great a public health threat as obesity.

Feeling isolated increases the risk for chronic body-wide inflammation, which can lead to a host of diseases including high blood pressure, diabetes and cancer. Loneliness also is strongly linked to increased risk for cognitive decline and, for people with Alzheimer's, a faster progression of the disease. It's not just biology, either. Good relationships improve our satisfaction with life and enhance a sense of meaning and purpose—and that in turn makes it more likely we'll take good care of ourselves. Close bonds also help us cope with stress and minimize the risk for depression.

THE PATH TOWARD LONELY

If we have such a strong drive to be socially connected, why are so many people becoming lonely? Research has revealed a common psychological trap that many people fall into.

People don't start to become lonely voluntarily. Rather, there may be some kind of disruption—moving away, retiring, a death or divorce or even a new marriage—that takes you away from most or all of your social support system. Health issues, such as hearing loss or vision loss, can make it hard to hold a conversation, and injury or poor health can make it hard to get out of the house. And while we tend to associate older people with these risk factors and more isolation, studies show that loneliness powerfully affects all age groups, even college students who are literally surrounded by peers their own age.

Faced with isolation, many people feel a strong need to connect with others. *Problem:* Loneliness that is deep enough also makes people so desperate for connection—and makes the stakes of social interaction so high—that they become hypersensitive to people around them. Of course, social sensitivity can be a strength, making you more empathetic, which draws people to you. But social hypersensitivity can make you more likely to misinterpret offhand remarks or behavior or worry too much about how other people see you, causing you to feel anxious, act awkwardly, withdraw from social situations and/or ruminate excessively about perceived slights. That can turn into a vicious cycle—less connection, more hypersensitivity and therefore even less connection.

SOLUTIONS FOR LONELY

If you see yourself in some of what's described above, consider all of the following suggestions…

• **Reframe your thinking.** If you find yourself feeling lonely despite being around others, your first step should be to reframe/replace negative thoughts that you have about and in social situations—*He really doesn't like me if he walked right past me without saying hello!*—with nonjudgmental interpretations such as, *He might have been in a rush, so not saying hello doesn't necessarily mean he doesn't* *like me.* Reframing your thoughts takes practice—indeed, it's a key part of the popular and effective talk therapy called *cognitive behavioral therapy*, or CBT. There are many highly qualified therapists who use CBT, so if you want a professional to guide you, consider one-on-one visits or group sessions for people with social anxiety.

• **Visit people face-to-face.** There is robust evidence that visiting with people in person is particularly powerful—so do what's needed to make it happen! Using social media isn't nearly the same thing.

Exception: Digital connections can deter loneliness if they help you get together with friends or find like-minded groups to join—especially if these groups meet in the "real" world.

• **Lend a hand.** When you hear, "It's better to give than to receive," whom do you think it's better for? The answer is—the giver. Evidence shows that volunteering, with the focus on helping others rather than oneself, makes people feel less lonely. It bolsters both social connections and a sense of purpose—you're helping people, and they're depending on you.

• **Renew the bonds that already exist.** The friends and family members we're emotionally closest to have the greatest influence on our health, research shows. Make a special effort to nurture those relationships. Set a reminder on your phone to call those folks regularly, and make concrete plans to get together. If you've had a falling out with a friend or family member and think the relationship could be retrievable without too much stress, see what you can do to make amends.

• **If you are in a relationship, be more responsive to your partner's needs.** There is a lot of loneliness within marriages—even reasonably good marriages. You may feel a distance between what you want your relationship to be and what it actually is. A love relationship is complicated, no doubt, but one thing that can make a lonely partner less lonely is for that partner to increase his/her responsiveness to the other partner. That means, for example, that you not only listen when your spouse is venting about a looming

work deadline, but you also offer to lighten her load at home so she can meet it—and then follow through even if you're both eating takeout for a week. When partners acknowledge each other's needs and desires, both of them are less likely to feel disconnected and frustrated with their marriage.

WHAT WILL HELP HEAL OUR SOCIETY

One reason loneliness has become a virtual epidemic is that there is shame and stigma attached to this emotion. We might not hesitate to tell others we are *angry*, for example, but many people refuse to admit—even to themselves—that they feel disconnected. The realization that loneliness is a health risk as serious as obesity can help change that.

We can create a national dialogue around it. Students can learn about the health benefits of good relationships...doctors can talk to their patients about loneliness and do risk assessments...and perhaps workplaces could institute policies that would encourage a work-life balance.

Even government policy can help. *Example:* We now know that untreated hearing loss puts older people at greater risk of becoming isolated and lonely. And a new federal law allowing hearing aids to be sold over the counter rather than only by prescription—making them more affordable—was passed partly to address just that problem. It is too early to know whether this law will reduce isolation, but it aims to address one risk factor—and it's a start.

The Perks of Being Alone

After interviewing 295 people about their reasons for spending time alone, researchers found that those who spend time alone because they enjoy solitude report high levels of creativity.

However: Alone time is not healthy when it is due to shyness or a dislike of social interaction—both of which are linked to higher levels of psychological distress and low levels of creativity.

Julie Bowker, PhD, associate professor of psychology, University at Buffalo, The State University of New York.

Feeling Down? That's OK!

People who acknowledge and accept feeling depressed or anxious—without berating themselves—feel better than people who ignore their emotions or judge them as negative, according to a study of 1,300 adults. Study participants, who reported feelings after journaling or delivering a three-minute videotaped test, had lower levels of distress and fewer symptoms of depression if they accepted these feelings.

Iris Mauss, PhD, associate professor of psychology, University of California, Berkeley.

6 Tips to Fight Loneliness

Take action against loneliness, which is detrimental to both mental and physical health...

• **Make small talk with strangers**—simply chatting in person, not online, boosts well-being.

• **Have as much face-to-face contact with friends and family as possible**—use video conferencing if distance or health issues make that impossible.

• **Use social media such as Facebook to create your own social networks,** such as a book club where you share personal reactions with other readers.

• **Invite neighbors over for coffee,** and help them with small chores when you can.

• **Try throwing a dinner party**—eating together is a long-established method of connecting with people.

• **Creative group endeavors,** from crafts nights to choral singing, also can improve connection with others.

Roundup of experts on preventing loneliness, reported in *Psychology Today.*

How to Find a Good Therapist

• **Ask for references from health-care professionals you already know and trust,** and if you're comfortable with it, ask friends and family for recommendations.

• **Call each recommended practitioner, and ask both about costs and about whether he/she has helped people like you in the past.** That may mean explaining your biggest issue briefly and asking whether the therapist can help with it.

• **Ask whether the therapy would focus mainly on solving the current problem or delving into the habits and patterns that contribute to it.** This will give you an insight into the kind of therapy he practices and whether or not that works for you.

• **Get an idea of how long the therapy might last** by asking how the practitioner knows when the therapy is finished. There's no right or wrong answer to this question, but you'll get some idea of how the therapist's process works and whether you feel you're compatible with the therapist.

Roundup of experts on finding a therapist, reported in *Men's Health.*

Apps to Help Your Mental Health Can Backfire

Lisa Parker, PhD, postdoctoral research associate at University of Sydney, Australia, and lead author of the study titled "Mental Health Messages in Prominent Mental Health Apps," published in *Annals of Family Medicine*.

S earch the term "anxiety" or "depression" in the Apple App Store or Google Play store, and dozens of self-help mental-health apps appear. But do they work?

The truth is, few have been rigorously tested—and many encourage expectations that actually may harm mental health. So finds an analysis of the marketing used to promote 61 top-rated mental-health apps available in the US, UK, Canada and Australia. *Results…*

• **Many apps invoked vague scientific authority** with phrases such as "clinically proven" but didn't cite any research.

• **Apps often framed mental-health problems as present in everyone** and characterized normal, healthy responses to stress as abnormal.

• **Many encouraged frequent and excessive self-monitoring**—which can make certain mental-health conditions worse.

To be sure, some apps have been shown to be beneficial. Researchers cite another large-scale study published in *World Psychiatry* that found that there is evidence that some smartphone apps can help improve moods and reduce depressive symptoms.

Examples: The meditation app *Headspace* ($12.99 per month)…*SuperBetter* (free), which helps users confront tough challenges and reduce symptoms of anxiety and depression…and *PTSD Coach* (free), an app to help with post-traumatic stress disorder developed by the Departments of Defense and Veterans Affairs. All are available for both iOS and Android.

But even evidence-based apps still may encourage constant checking, which can undermine mental health. It's fine to use a meditation app such as *Headspace* on your own, but apps designed to treat depression or anxiety are best used along with a therapist. A self-help app should be just one part of your support system for mental health.

INTERESTING FINDING…

Sour Foods Can Lead to More Risk-Taking

People who consume something with a sour taste, such as a piece of sour candy, are more likely to engage in behaviors carrying some risk. This means that people who have anxiety disorders or depression—conditions that make them especially risk-averse—may benefit from consuming sour foods.

Chi Thanh Vi, PhD, research fellow in multisensory experiences, Sussex Computer-Human Interaction Lab, University of Sussex, Brighton, UK, and leader of a study published in *Scientific Reports*.

19

Business Brainstorm

New Rules for Breakthrough Résumés

Applying for jobs? Bringing your résumé up to date must include more than adding your latest work experience. Today's job hunters need to construct résumés that work equally well for three different types of readers and include several key features that appeal to the different readers. These readers include employers sorting through massive stacks of candidates and giving each just a cursory glance…employers taking a closer look at the résumés of the most promising candidates…and increasingly sophisticated software called "applicant tracking systems" that employers use to sort through résumés instead of humans doing it. These software systems have become extremely widespread. Creating a résumé that works for all of these audiences requires some finesse.

Here are the eight things you must do before you submit your résumé…

•**Make a key degree part of your name.** An employer flipping through a stack of résumés might not read yours closely enough to notice that you have an advanced degree or certification.

What to do: If you have an important credential, cite this after your name on the first line of your résumé where it can't be missed. *Examples*: Jane Smith, MBA…John Jones, EdD…Mary Johnson, CPA.

•**Eject the objective.** Modern résumés no longer include an "Objective" statement—a subhead summarizing the applicant's career goals. The single focus of a résumé today should be what the applicant can provide to the employer, rather than what the applicant wants from the employer.

Amanda Augustine, career-advice expert, TopResume, the world's largest résumé-writing service. Based in New York City, she is a certified professional career coach (CPCC) and certified professional résumé writer (CPRW). TopResume.com

What to do: Replace the objective section with a "Professional Summary." This summary should mention your most important skills...note how you have used those skills to help former employers...and describe how you will use them to help your next employer—all in just a few sentences. Including this summary improves the odds that an employer reading your résumé quickly will see enough of the highlights to include you in the stack of applicants deserving further consideration—employers often read less than one-third of a résumé before making this initial decision.

•**Mention the specific skills and attributes that employers most value for the position you are seeking.** Employers use software to search résumés for these. What are the skills and attributes? You don't have to guess—employers usually include them in their job listings.

What to do: Read job listings not only for positions you intend to apply for but also for similar positions that you don't expect to apply for because they are far from where you live. The words that appear in multiple listings are the words employers are most likely to search for in your résumé—which means that they're words you must include in your résumé. These words might include position titles, software programs or equipment names, specific tasks...and general workplace traits and attributes.

•**Link skills and traits to prior jobs.** Many of the keywords you cite in your résumé can be included in the professional summary and/or a "Skills" section. But also work as many of them as possible into your descriptions of prior work experience. This shows that you're not just claiming to be able to do these things—you've actually done them. *Example:* If you list "team management" among your skills, your work history should cite examples of times you led teams to quantifiable successes.

If a skill is relevant to several of your prior positions and you don't want to cite it over and over on your résumé—that would become repetitive—include it in your description of a recent job and/or a job you held for a significant duration. The software that scans your résumé for this keyword might give you less

credit for it if it's listed only under a job you held for a short period or years ago.

•**Don't bury your accomplishments with bullets.** Traditionally, many résumés have been structured as a series of bullet-point lists. *Example*: Every previous position would be marked with a bullet...as well as every cited skill. Bullets can be an effective way to highlight key info on a résumé—but when so many listings have bullets, nothing seems special.

What to do: Use bullets to call attention to your bragging points—the information that most likely will land you the job interview—including career-making achievements and prestigious honors.

•**Let go of the past.** Employers rarely put much stock in job experience from long ago—it isn't considered very relevant. In fact, given today's constantly changing technology, having a long work history often is taken as evidence that an applicant is out of date, even though it is not supposed to.

What to do: Describe in detail only your past 15 years of work experience. Condense all earlier jobs into a total of no more than a few lines under the heading "Earlier Work Experience." List only company, title and loca-

TAKE NOTE...

Better Cover Letters

•**Avoid saying you don't have experience even if that is true**—focus on what you have done that is relevant to the job.

•**Never copy and paste the same letter**—tailor each to the company and job.

•**Avoid slang, jokes and informal phrases.**

•**Be confident but not cocky**—let your experience and knowledge speak for you.

•**Do not make offhand suggestions about improving the company**—they can be insulting.

•**Send in all information and required materials.**

•**Proofread and spell-check everything.**

Money.com

tion for these earlier jobs...or describe all of your earlier experience in a sentence or two.

Exception: If you held an especially prestigious or notable position earlier in your career, it makes sense to include an additional sentence or two about that. And if you've been out of the workforce for much of the past 15 years, including the older experience might be necessary—but also obtain training or seek part-time work so that you have something recent on your résumé as well.

•**The latest word-processing software makes it easy to construct creative, distinctive résumé designs—but you shouldn't do that.** Yes, you could arrange your résumé into columns of text...add graphics and photos...and include some shaded sections or multiple-color fonts—but doing any of these things would be a mistake. "Creative" résumé designs could prevent applicant-tracking software from reading your résumé properly...and frustrate humans trying to find information on it, too.

What to do: Design a résumé that looks like a résumé. There are appropriate résumé templates available for free online. If you want to show off your creative side or design skills, include a link/web address on your résumé to an online portfolio of your work.

•**Two résumés are too many.** It used to be fairly common for people to have two quite different résumés (and sometimes more), each structured for a different potential career path. The omnipresence of LinkedIn has ended that. Virtually all employers now visit applicants' LinkedIn pages before deciding whom to interview. If your LinkedIn page does not seem in line with the résumé you submitted and with the job being offered, you probably won't get an interview. (And you definitely need a LinkedIn page these days.)

What to do: It's OK to tweak your résumé slightly to focus on the experience or skills most appropriate for a particular job opening, but the résumé must still be in step with information in your LinkedIn profile.

Résumé-Killing Cliché

Saying that you're "Proficient in Microsoft Office suite" or "Proficient in Microsoft Word" on your resume could be a mistake. This proficiency is basic for anyone doing any sort of office work, so listing it makes it seem as if you have only the most basic skills.

Exception: If an ad specifically asks for Microsoft Office expertise or mentions the specific programs within the suite, draw attention to your skill in whatever is required to be sure that the potential employer's software finds the keywords it is programmed to seek.

Roundup of experts on writing résumés, reported at Money.com.

Best US Cities for Job Hunters

Pittsburgh tops the list. It has a median base salary of $46,500 and job satisfaction rated 3.2 out of 5. It was followed by St. Louis, $48,000 and 3.5...Indianapolis, $45,000 and 3.4...Cincinnati, $45,000 and 3.3...Hartford, Connecticut, $55,000 and 3.3...Boston, $62,000 and 3.5...Memphis, $43,900 and 3.5...Raleigh, North Carolina, $50,000 and 3.4...Cleveland, $46,000 and 3.2...Detroit, $50,000 and 3.3.

The list is based on a proprietary scoring system that looks at hiring opportunity, cost of living and reported job satisfaction.

Survey and analysis by Glassdoor.com.

The Robo Job Interview

Automated phone interviews are becoming more common as companies try to streamline the hiring process. The computer asks standard questions about work history, prior successes, most difficult challenges and so forth and records the answers. The process is like leaving a series of voice-mail messages. Applicants provide answers that later may be reviewed by hiring managers, who then follow up directly.

Among the large companies using automated interviews are lab-test provider Quest Diagnostics…hospital operator HCA Healthcare…insurer Allstate…trash hauler Waste Management…and many others. Even some smaller companies now use them.

The companies say that the system lets applicants provide information at their convenience and without needing computer or smartphone access. But some job seekers say that the highly impersonal arrangement, which does not allow them to ask questions, is off-putting.

Roundup of experts on automated job interviews, reported in The Wall Street Journal.

Job-Interview Blunders

Don't make any of these six mistakes in a job interview…

• **Asking what the company does**—do research in advance.

• **Asking the interviewer anything personal**—stay professional at all times.

• **Saying that you expect to move on in a few years**—the interviewer likely will prefer someone who seems to have a stronger commitment.

• **Commenting that this is not your top choice**—the interviewer needs to feel that you value the organization to which you are applying.

• **Asking whether the firm monitors e-mail or Internet use**—the answer is yes, and you should not have to ask.

• **Saying that you hated your last boss or company**—it is best to always put a positive spin on your experience.

BusinessInsider.com

Best Jobs in the US

The best job in the US now is software developer. It is followed by statistician, physician assistant and dentist. Fifth place is shared by orthodontist and nurse anesthetist.

The ratings are based on seven factors, including salary, employment rate and stress level. Health care is the field with the best combination of high salaries and low unemployment.

Considered just from the viewpoint of pay, all five top jobs are medical: Anesthesiologist, surgeon, oral/maxillofacial surgeon, obstetrician/gynecologist and orthodontist.

For a look at the best jobs in 15 categories, go to the website, Money.USNews.com/careers/best-jobs/rankings.

2019 Best Jobs ranking by US News & World Report.

Worst Jobs for the Future

The worst job for the future is watch repairer. The profession is expected to decline 27% between 2017 and 2027 as people increasingly turn away from watches for telling time.

Other fast-fading jobs: Textile-machine operator, expected to fall 23.6%…logging worker, down 17%…paper hanger, down 12.6%…photo processor, down 12.3%…telephone operator, down 10.7%…prefab-home builder, down 7.8%…shoe-machine operator, down 7.3%…projectionist, down 6.4%…fabric mender, down 2.1%.

Good news: The skills for some of these jobs may be useful in others.

Example: Telephone operators could apply similar skills as police, fire or ambulance dispatchers—a field that is expected to grow 9% over the next decade.

Analysis by Emsi, a labor-market research firm, Moscow, Idaho.

Reignite Your Career with a "Senior Internship"

Carol Fishman Cohen, both chair and cofounder of iRelaunch, a career-reentry consulting firm based near Boston. iRelaunch.com

In the movie *The Intern*, Robert De Niro plays a 70-year-old retiree who becomes an intern at an online fashion business. The plot was fictional, but there actually are internships designed for experienced employees who have been out of the workforce. If you have put your career on hold to raise kids, care for an ill family member or just try out retirement, one of these "senior" internships could jump-start your career again, fill the gap in your résumé and convince an employer to hire you.

These eight-week-to-six-month senior internship programs are very different from the fetch-the-coffee internships meant for college kids. They tend to be for people who spent at least five to seven years—or possibly much longer—in the workforce before a career break. Many of the programs pay wages in line with interns' experience, and a few even offer benefits.

Example: The Boeing Return Flight program offers a 401(k) retirement account, health and dental insurance and more.

Companies that offer these programs consider it a low-risk way to try out an underutilized pool of experienced workers. Trying out employees who have been out of the job market makes particular sense for employers these days because low unemployment is making it hard for them to recruit the skilled people they need.

When these internships end, at least half of the interns typically are offered permanent positions (this varies by company, sector and year). And these permanent positions do not tend to be entry level—in fact, it isn't very unusual for an older intern to be offered a job at the vice-president level.

FINDING AN INTERNSHIP

To locate senior internships suitable for you…

• **Explore the list of ongoing programs at iRelaunch.com.** Click the "For Relaunchers" tab, and then select "Paid Corporate Return to Work Programs Around the World." This list features programs from a wide variety of companies including Dell, Deloitte, Fidelity, Ford, Goldman Sachs, Johnson & Johnson, Mastercard, MetLife, Microsoft, Morgan Stanley, Northrop Grumman, PayPal, PepsiCo, Texas Instruments, United Technologies, Visa, Whirlpool and more.

Helpful: Also click "Career Re-entry Programs" under the "For Employers" tab on iRelaunch.com. This longer list includes experienced-employee internships and other career-reentry programs known to have been offered in the past in addition to ongoing programs. Some of these programs might not currently be accepting applicants, but there's no harm in reaching out to ask.

Also, peruse free tools and resources at iRelaunch.com, including the 3,2,1 iRelaunch podcast, which offers advice, strategies and success stories for returning to work after a career break.

• **Contact the career services office at your alma mater.** Explain that you're a graduate hoping to return to the workplace following a career break, and ask what services the office offers. These may include free or discounted access to career assessments and, in some cases, coaching to help interpret the results…as well as mock interview practice.

APPLYING FOR AN INTERNSHIP

Once you've located internships that you may want to apply for, take the following steps for the best chance of landing one…

• **Signal to employers that you're chomping at the bit to return to work.** Before applying for an internship, take a technical course or certification course relevant to your field, and/or volunteer in a relevant role.

Example: Mentor young entrepreneurs in your sector through the Service Corps of Retired Executives. Check out CatchAFire.org,

GOOD TO KNOW...

Black Is Best for the Interview

Seventy percent of candidates who were hired wore mostly black clothing when they were interviewed—and only 33% of rejected candidates wore black.

Black clothing apparently helps hiring managers make positive judgments more quickly. Fifty percent of employers say that they can decide in the first five minutes of an interview whether a candidate will be a good fit for the position.

MoneyTalksNews.com

Idealist.org and VolunteerMatch.org for volunteer projects and roles.

●**Catch up on the latest news and thinking in your field.** Ask people you know who still are active in the sector which blogs, podcasts and books will help you catch up on the latest developments. Reading these will help you become an expert on the subject matter all over again, which will give you confidence when you go for interviews.

●**Network in search of company insiders.** Ask people you know in the sector—including recent retirees—whom they know who works at a company offering an internship of interest. If you can convince someone who works there to put in a good word for you, it will greatly improve your odds of moving forward in the selection process. LinkedIn can be a useful networking tool for identifying these individuals.

●**If a company doesn't offer a senior internship program, suggest one.** Although these programs are proliferating, most companies still don't offer them. Don't hesitate to suggest a special project, contract consulting arrangement or other short-term work opportunity that allows you to engage with a company on a temporary basis. If the company is intrigued by you and your background but hung up on the fact that you took a career break, a short-term work opportunity may be the perfect solution.

Career-Boosting College Courses

College courses that will benefit career development...

●**Business writing** to help you create better memos, e-mails, reports, grant applications and more.

●**Communication and public speaking** for more effective interaction and better presentations.

●**Digital communication and electronic marketing** to understand social media better and use the sites more effectively.

●**Computer software skills** for enhanced spreadsheets and document processing.

●**Web development and programming** that covers languages such as Python and HTML5 and shows how to build websites and improve portfolios and résumés.

●**Entrepreneurship** to focus on the practical aspects of creating and growing a start-up.

●**Professional skills classes** that combine elements such as teamwork, leadership, self-awareness and networking.

WiseBread.com

Flexible Jobs

Top industries offering work-from-home jobs include education, health care, human resources, pharmaceuticals, research and the nonprofit sector.

Jobs commonly advertised: Coder, customer service representative, editor, interpreter, tutor, writer.

The top-10 companies offering part-time, telecommuting and freelance positions: Kaplan, Active Network, K12, Grand Canyon University, Edmentum, Connections Education, GreatAuPair, Houghton Mifflin Harcourt, Language Line Solutions, Alere.

For the full list: Go to MoneyTalksNews.com and search for "25 Best Remote Jobs."

Ranking by job-search site FlexJobs.com, reported at MoneyTalksNews.com.

Would You Work Well from Home?

Working from home is not beneficial for everyone.

Background: The flexibility to work from home is thought to reduce stress.

New research: Remote workers who have naturally high levels of emotional stability (meaning that they are not overly reactive to difficult situations) do better at home than workers who are less emotionally stable.

Theory: Workers with higher emotional stability are better at finding ways to connect with others and accomplish work even when isolated from coworkers and resources.

Sara Perry, PhD, assistant professor of management at Baylor University, Waco, Texas.

Great Work-from-Home Opportunities

GoBankingRates.com

Legitimate opportunities to work from home are offered by a variety of major companies. *Top 10 companies and opportunities they offer...*

• **Amazon.com**—software developers and digital-marketing experts.

• **Intuit**—tax specialists.

• **Aetna**—account executives and clinical case managers in specific states.

• **UnitedHealth Group**—care managers, senior coders, Medicare consultants.

• **Salesforce**—software engineers, product managers.

• **Williams-Sonoma**—call-center customer reps.

• **Anthem**—account and program directors, marketing director.

• **Walden University**—full-time faculty and academic program directors.

• **Conduent**—call-center customer reps in specific states.

• **Xerox**—salespeople, account operations managers.

For a list of 40 companies offering legitimate work-at-home opportunities, go to GoBanking Rates.com/making-money/jobs/companies-that-pay-you-to-work-from-home.

GoBankingRates.com

Where to Earn Quick Money If You're a Writer

Websites for writers trying to earn money fast...

• **Contently.net** connects companies such as Walmart and Facebook with writers. These companies often pay between $1 and $2 per word.

• **ClearVoice.com** allows you to set a minimum rate for your articles and sends you only opportunities that meet your pay requirements.

• **SkyWord.com** works with companies such as Overstock and Lending Tree and features analysis software that connects with your social-media profiles so that you can track your articles. Rates range from $40 to $150 per article.

• **eByline.com** has a job board where writers can pitch ideas to outlets such as Purdue University, PetCo, Los Angeles Times and more. If an outlet is interested, it can contact you for an assignment.

WiseBread.com

Better Management of a Family Business

• **Don't force a new generation into the business**—it often is better for them to get professional experience elsewhere, then join the family firm.

• **Separate business and personal life clearly,** and never let personal issues invade the office.

- **Write job descriptions so that family members know what is expected of them.**

- **Do not overmanage**—establish a clear line between mentoring and watching a family member's every move.

- **Be flexible**—everyone should be open to ideas from everyone else.

CNN.com/business

Top Small-Business Credit Cards

- **TD Business Solutions,** no annual or foreign transaction fees and 0% introductory APR.

- **American Express Blue for Business,** double rewards points for the first $50,000 of purchases each year.

- **Bank of America Business Advantage Cash Rewards,** $300 statement credit with $3,000 in purchases within 90 days, no annual fee.

- **BBVA Compass Visa Business Rewards,** lets you choose one reward category—such as office supplies, gas, etc.—for triple points and one for double.

- **Capital One Spark Miles Select for Business,** 20,000 bonus miles (worth $200) with $3,000 spent in three months on eligible purchases, no annual fee.

- **Chase Ink Business Cash Credit,** $500 cash back with $3,000 in purchases within three months.

Roundup of experts on small-business credit cards, reported at GoBankingRates.com.

Better Small-Business Marketing

- **Use e-mail to keep your name in front of prospects and customers**—get them to opt in by offering them something of val-ue, then set up regular, automatic mailings through services such as Constant Contact, VerticalResponse or Mailchimp.

- **Plan to spend time on social media**—check in occasionally all week, respond to comments, write posts, choose pictures and use a scheduling tool such as Hootsuite or TweetDeck. Pick social-media platforms based on your content—highly visual material goes well on Facebook and Instagram…creative items are good at Pinterest…and business-to-business marketing is best at LinkedIn.

- **Do not confine your marketing to online efforts**—face-to-face talks are valuable, so join a local organization and attend meetings regularly.

Rhonda Abrams, author of *Successful Business Plan: Secrets & Strategies*, quoted at USAToday.com.

BETTER MEETINGS…

Dos and Don'ts When Leading a Meeting

For much better meeting management…

- **Do start on time** to show that you respect attendees' schedules.

- **Don't go past the planned end time** unless you encounter a genuinely critical issue that cannot wait.

- **Do call on people by name,** and be sure that everyone contributes.

- **Don't invite anyone to a meeting who will not be able to take part in a useful way.**

- **Do stick to the meeting's topic.** Don't go into something else just because the group is together.

- **Do acknowledge any off-topic comments,** but say that they will need to be discussed at a later time.

- **Don't dismiss ideas out of hand**—ask the person to explain his/her thought process.

- **Do explain your own reasoning when introducing your own ideas.**

Roundup of experts on leading meetings, reported at GoBankingRates.com.

How Anxiety Can Help You Get It Done

Some anxiety is normal and useful. It provides a burst of energy that improves functioning. *Example:* Anxiety about meeting a deadline can produce enough energy to improve focus so that you can meet the deadline.

Roundup of experts on anxiety, reported in *The New York Times*.

Land That Promotion

Don't sabotage your promotion chances. *Good advice…*

• **Do not apply for all jobs throughout the organization**—watch for opportunities that interest you and fit your qualifications.

• **If you are denied a promotion, don't complain to others or claim to be the victim of office politics**—this shows weakness of character and can affect future possibilities.

• **Keep in touch with management about your goals, asking how to be more successful and move ahead**—and request feedback if you are passed over for a promotion so that you have a better chance next time.

USNews.com

What Bosses Want to Know from Employees

Things most bosses want an employee to tell them…

• **You want to be challenged more often**—decide what you want to be doing beyond your everyday work, and ask.

• **There are major issues with other employees**—if you can document them.

• **What the current state of employee morale is**—whether positive or negative.

• **How you think you are doing**—say honestly what is going well and what is not, and ask for what you need to do better.

• **What you like and do not like about the job**—such as projects that motivate you and others that just seem like busywork.

• **How you could be a better employee**—if it would help the company to give you more training, let you attend a conference or participate in a workshop.

Roundup of experts on employee empowerment, reported at WiseBread.com.

Better Performance-Review Prep

To prepare for your next job-performance review…

• **Understand the review process**—ask for details if you are not sure how reviews are handled.

• **Keep a daily journal of what you have done, highlighting major tasks.** Be prepared to present accomplishments that further company goals—for example, how much client contact you have per day.

• **Create your own goals or objectives for the next 12 months.** Anticipate ways your boss may critique your work habits, and be prepared with responses.

• **Have some discussion points of your own so that the review becomes two-way.**

• **Be prepared to give the boss feedback**—be candid but careful in how you express concerns.

MoneyTalksNews.com

Best Way to Quit a Job

The most googled work query is *How to quit a job*. That was searched far more often in 2018 than any other job-related question…followed by users asking what job they should have, which jobs pay the most and how to turn down a job offer. The strong economy may be the reason more people are looking for ways to quit work.

To leave on good terms: Give at least two weeks' notice…meet in private with your boss to resign…be positive, thanking the company for the lessons you learned and the opportunities you had…be respectful if asked for feedback…offer to train your replacement…and stay on good terms with ex-colleagues and bosses, in case you need them for references.

Roundup of experts on quitting a job, reported at MarketWatch.com.

Very Good Reasons Not to Work Those Extra Hours…

• **Working more than 40 hours a week makes job burnout more likely,** and burnout is the main reason for employee turnover.

• **Overtime hours are less productive than regular ones,** so you are stressing yourself while getting less done.

• **Significant extra hours**—55 or more per week—were found in one study to increase the chance of developing cardiovascular problems.

• **Another study found that people who worked more than 52 hours a week** had increased suicidal thoughts.

Bottom line: Companies that expect work during off-hours are harming themselves. The health issues associated with the extra work and stress are leading to more employee absences and higher health-care costs.

Roundup of experts on work and health, reported at BusinessInsider.com.

GOOD ADVICE…

Take Your Vacation Days!

Americans take only half their allowed vacation days. Research shows that vacationing boosts productivity afterward—and even planning a vacation increases happiness.

Study by employment information and recruiting site Glassdoor.com.

Get More Fit While You Sit

Craig Horswill, PhD, clinical associate professor of kinesiology and nutrition, University of Illinois at Chicago.

Sitting for long stretches—in particular more than 60 to 90 minutes at a time—is bad news for your health. In fact, one study linked 7% of all deaths in adults age 45 and older (even for those who exercise regularly) to excessive sitting.

Many people—and companies—have spent a lot of money to equip offices with standing desks and desks connected to treadmills so that workers can stay more physically active while they work.

Latest development: A new product, tested by scientists at the University of Illinois at Chicago, helps sedentary workers burn calories by increasing movement—while sitting. The HOVR is a movable footrest that is installed on the underside of a desk to help counter the negative effects of sitting by allowing users to swing or twist their legs while working. (Another version has a floor stand that eliminates the need for installation.)

How it works: The aim is to increase non-exercise activity thermogenesis—that is, the calories you burn in non-sportslike activity, such as typing, fidgeting or climbing a flight of stairs.

In a study, the HOVR raised users' metabolic rates (the rate at which your body burns calories while at rest) by 17%, compared with 7% for those standing at a desk. The increase in metabolic rate is probably less than that for an under-desk Exercycle or treadmill desk, although the HOVR may be less distracting.

Where to buy: SitFlow.com (This device is now called SitFlow.)

Cost: About $59 for the desk-mount swing and $119 for the floor stand version.

Note: There are similar types of products available online.

20
Safety Survey

It's 10 feet deep!

Smart Ways to Use Urgent Care

It wasn't that long ago that you had two choices if you needed prompt or emergency medical care—your doctor's office or a hospital emergency room. But now a third option has come on the scene in a big way—urgent care centers. In fact, there are now more than 7,600 urgent care facilities in the US, and the numbers are growing. Some are owned by hospitals, others by physicians and still others by private corporations (including drugstore and grocery store chains). But they are all a viable alternative to an emergency room or your doctor's office when a minor accident happens or if an illness develops after normal business hours—and they can save you money and time as well. *Smart ways to use urgent care...*

• **Don't make it a one-stop center.** There's no such thing as one place where you can get all your medical care. If your doctor's office is nearby, it's still the place to go for conditions that do not need to be addressed immediately, such as annual or routine exams, rashes, colds and flu, and prescription refill authorizations. If you're having symptoms of a heart attack (such as difficulty breathing and/or chest pain)...a head injury or uncontrollable bleeding...symptoms of a stroke (such as numbness or weakness on one side of the body and/or trouble speaking)...intense pain or seizures... or loss of consciousness, you should always get to an emergency room (or, even better, call 911 and let an ambulance take you there).

Insider tip: Consider using an urgent care center if your doctor's office is closed and you have a non-life-threatening condition such as

Charles B. Inlander, a consumer advocate and health-care consultant based in Fogelsville, Pennsylvania. He was founding president of the nonprofit People's Medical Society, a consumer-advocacy organization credited with key improvements in the quality of US health care, and is author or coauthor of more than 20 consumer-health books.

a cut or other superficial wound, moderate burn, sprain or respiratory infection.

• **Know what to expect.** Most urgent care centers are open 12 to 18 hours a day. Some offer 24-hour services. You do not need an appointment, and the industry average is less than a 30-minute wait for care versus the longer times that are typical of ERs. Most urgent care centers accept health insurance, including Medicare. There is usually a doctor present during all open hours, although in some instances you may be seen or treated by a nurse practitioner or physician assistant. All of these health professionals tend to have good experience with the type of issues they treat in urgent care centers.

Insider tip: About 13% of urgent care centers now provide ongoing primary care to local patients. This is especially useful if you live in an area with few primary care doctors or need more available hours to see a physician.

• **Check out your local urgent care facility.** Unlike hospitals, urgent care facilities are generally not licensed by the state. However, if they are owned by a hospital, they are considered part of the hospital's licensed operation and are subject to inspection and review by state medical-licensing boards. Otherwise, the only government oversight of urgent care facilities is confirming that the doctors, nurses, physician assistants and technical staff are

properly licensed by the state. But you can—and should—find out more.

Insider tips: Before you need to use an urgent care center, ask your primary care doctor or specialist to recommend one in your area. Check the website of the Better Business Bureau, BBB.org, for any complaints against a facility. You can even drop in on a facility and ask for a tour and list of services. Also, make sure that the center accepts your insurance. And don't forget to check with your friends or relatives—word-of-mouth recommendations from people you trust often are good sources of information.

When "Simple" Surgeries Turn Deadly

Frank Overdyk, MD, a patient-safety advocate and anesthesiologist in Charleston, South Carolina. Dr. Overdyk is a member of the board of advisors of the Physician-Patient Alliance for Health & Safety, PPAHS.org. He received the 2018 AAMI (Association for the Advancement of Medical Instrumentation) & Becton Dickinson Patient Safety Award.

Some surgeries and procedures are considered "minor" when compared with lengthy, invasive operations such as heart or brain surgery…or a hip or knee replacement.

The so-called simple procedures—performed about 40 million times each year in the US—often take place in ambulatory surgery centers (ASCs), where you're sent home in a few hours. But what happens when simple surgeries go wrong—or even turn deadly?

NOT SO SIMPLE AFTER ALL

Since their introduction in the US in the 1970s, ASCs have been a valuable resource, helping patients avoid hospital-acquired infections and speeding recovery at home in more comfortable surroundings.

However, the risks are real. Deaths resulting from treatment at ASCs are not officially tracked, but according to a recent investigative report published by *USA Today Network* and *Kaiser Health News*, more than 260 ASC patients died from surgical complications (such as internal bleeding and cardiac arrest) over

GOOD TO KNOW...

Lifesaving Smartphones

The Medical ID feature or app on smartphones lets first responders get access to emergency contacts and medical information without a passcode. They simply tap Emergency on the home screen or password-prompt screen.

To set up on iPhones: Find the built-in Health app, tap "Medical ID," then tap "Create Medical ID" and fill in your information.

On Android phones: Download the free Medical ID app. Open the app, tap "Edit" to modify the basic profile supplied, then tap the check mark.

Reader's Digest, RD.com.

the last five years. *Some key risks—and how to protect yourself...*

COSMETIC SURGERY (SUCH AS A FACE-LIFT)

What can go wrong: Particularly during any type of cosmetic surgery, in which a surgeon is operating near the mouth, nose, vocal cords or neck, general anesthesia (the use of a drug to make the patient unresponsive and unconscious) or "deep sedation" (similar to general anesthesia but often does not involve a breathing tube) can interfere with a patient's ability to breathe.

To protect yourself: If your surgeon plans to use deep sedation, ask whether a dedicated sedation provider will be involved (by law, general anesthesia requires an anesthesiologist, nurse-anesthetist and/or anesthesiologist assistant). Or ask whether the surgeon can use local anesthesia or a nerve block instead. With a nerve block, local anesthetic is injected near nerves and specific body parts that will be affected by the surgery. Nerve blocks have different risks from general anesthesia and deep sedation but usually don't impede your ability to breathe or your level of consciousness.

TONSILLECTOMY

Nearly 300,000 tonsil-removal surgeries are performed each year in adults—often prompted by frequent sore throats. But chronically swollen tonsils also contribute to sleep apnea, which raises risks for serious conditions, such as heart attack and stroke.

What can go wrong: Tonsillectomy involves the airway and blood vessels. Persistent bleeding in the airway after tonsillectomy is an infrequent but serious complication that requires immediate attention and can arise hours after the procedure...long after the ASC closes.

To protect yourself: Ask to be the first case of the day. This is the best time to schedule any procedure—but especially this one. Scheduling early in the day gives the most time for any complication to be addressed on-site.

BUNIONECTOMY

What can go wrong: Recovery from bunion removal can be very painful, and opioid pain relievers often are prescribed for the immediate post-op period and beyond. This can be dangerous, especially for patients with sleep apnea, obesity or advanced age. In addition to depressed breathing, opioids can trigger a variety of side effects, including nausea/vomiting and urinary dysfunction.

To protect yourself: Before your procedure, discuss the plan for post-op pain management. Ask your doctor how you can limit opioid use by instead relying on alternatives, including nonsteroidal anti-inflammatory drugs (NSAIDs) and the COX-2 inhibitor *celecoxib* (Celebrex). These drugs target enzymes responsible for inflammation and pain without such a high risk for side effects.

ENDOSCOPY

What can go wrong: With endoscopy, which involves the use of deep sedation, both the doctor performing the procedure and the anesthesia provider are working inside your airway. This means that contents from your stomach could get into your lungs (aspiration).

To protect yourself: Make sure you are a suitable candidate and without an acute illness.

ARE YOU AN ASC CANDIDATE?

If you're elderly and/or have chronic health problems that increase your risk for complications during or after your surgery—such as moderate-to-severe sleep apnea, morbid obesity or chronic obstructive pulmonary disease (COPD), discuss with your primary care doctor and the doctor performing the procedure whether you're a suitable candidate for outpatient surgery at an ASC.

Also, if you have a cold, the flu or a fever, call to notify your outpatient facility—you may be asked to reschedule the procedure to a time when you are well. Similarly, if your blood sugar or blood pressure is high or unstable...or you have shortness of breath from asthma or heart failure, notify the doctor performing the procedure and get advice on the best plan of action.

OTHER SAFEGUARDS YOU NEED

Before undergoing treatment at an ASC, also make sure that...

• **The facility only rarely needs to transfer a patient to a hospital for more advanced care.** The hospital also should be relatively close.

• **There will be electronic monitors and "crash carts" on-site.**

• **A dedicated anesthesiologist,** nurse-anesthetist or anesthesiologist assistant will be on hand during the procedure. This is crucial if you will be receiving general anesthesia or deep sedation. Deep sedation carries greater risks than "conscious sedation," during which the patient is able to respond to verbal prompts and commands.

Note: If you are comfortable with taking oral medication for anxiety and prefer not to take the additional risks associated with deep sedation, ask for conscious sedation, and make sure your consent form indicates this.

• **Your oxygen saturation and exhaled carbon dioxide** ("capnography") will be continuously monitored by the dedicated provider mentioned above during all procedures requiring deep sedation or general anesthesia. Oxygen saturation also should be monitored continuously during recovery from deep sedation or general anesthesia. The recovery area should be staffed by a qualified professional trained in basic and advanced cardio life support.

• **The doctor performing the procedure has board certification** by a board that is a member of the American Board of Medical Specialties, ABMS.org. This credential is highly recommended and offers an added layer of safety.

How to Deal with an Aggressive Dog— Yours or Someone Else's

Marc Bekoff, PhD, professor emeritus of ecology and evolutionary biology at University of Colorado, Boulder. He's a fellow of the Animal Behavior Society and author of *Canine Confidential: Why Dogs Do What They Do.* MarcBekoff.com

---

Man's "best friend" isn't always friendly. Sometimes dogs snarl, bark menacingly, lunge or bite. *Here's what to do if a dog—yours or someone else's—acts aggressively...*

IF A DOG ACTS AGGRESSIVELY TOWARD YOU

Resist the urge to turn and run—that might prompt the dog to pursue, a race the dog almost certainly will win. Instead, break off eye contact with the dog—eye contact increases the unease of some agitated dogs. If you see that the dog's owner is nearby, stand still and wait for the owner to restrain the pet or calmly call to the owner if he/she appears unaware. If the owner doesn't seem to be nearby, slowly back away. If possible, back away in a direction that opens up an obvious escape route for the dog, decreasing any sense that the dog has of being cornered. If the dog has you cornered and you can't back away, slowly and calmly walk sideways until you're in the open.

As you back away, keep your hands low and open, with your palms facing the dog. Some dogs interpret fists or hands above the dog's head as threats. You can try talking to the dog in a calm, low and relaxed tone—your tone is more important in this situation than what you say.

Warning: A wagging tail does not always signal a friendly dog. A rapid, staccato wag often indicates nervousness, which could suddenly become aggression. Other potential signs of a nervous dog include ears pinned back...tail tucked between the legs...and/or a low, barely audible growl.

IF YOUR DOG ACTS AGGRESSIVELY TOWARD SOMEONE ELSE

If your dog is on a leash when it becomes aggressive, slowly and gently (but firmly) pull it to your side while speaking calmly. Do not yank the leash or yell at your dog—that could increase your dog's stress level and aggressiveness.

If your dog is not on a leash, call the dog to you. To increase the odds that the dog will come to you, get in the habit beforehand of providing a small treat each time it comes when called. If your dog doesn't come to you, walk slowly and calmly to it and take it by the collar, attaching the leash if you have it. Do not rush at your dog or yell at it to stop—these signs that you are anxious will only add to your dog's anxiety.

If your dog frequently is aggressive, find a trainer to help you and the dog learn to control this behavior.

When Ice Cream Turns Deadly

F. Perry Wilson, MD, assistant professor of medicine at Yale University School of Medicine, New Haven, Connecticut. MethodsMan.com

A "safe" food additive may be very dangerous for some people. The finding solves a medical mystery—why are so many people suddenly getting seriously ill from *Clostridium difficile* (C. diff) infections? The intestinal bacteria can cause severe, intractable bouts of diarrhea and lead to dangerous—even fatal—colon inflammation. It often is resistant to antibiotics. About a half million people get sick from this infection every year in the US—and 15,000 die. But serious *C. diff* infections were much rarer before the year 2000. Why the upsurge?

A POPULAR NEW ADDITIVE

Trehalose is a sugar that is found naturally in minuscule amounts in certain foods such as honey. But since a commercially produced version was approved as a food additive by the FDA—in the year 2000—larger amounts have flowed into our foods. It enhances flavor, reduces bitterness and adds sweetness to foods as varied as ice cream, baked goods, pastas and candies.

But trehalose also nourishes *C. diff*. A 2018 study published in Nature found that the two most virulent and deadly strains of *C. diff* metabolize trehalose and grow better than on other sugars. When researchers gave trehalose to mice infected with *C. diff*, the fatality rate of those mice tripled.

For people who acquire a *C. diff* infection—common in hospitals and other health-care settings—this means that having trehalose in your diet might give these especially dangerous, antibiotic-resistant strains an extra source of food. So they multiply.

WHEN TO AVOID TREHALOSE

For most people most of the time, there's no need to avoid foods containing trehalose. Under normal circumstances, helpful bacteria in your gut outcompete *C. diff*, preventing illness.

But a great danger exists when you have a serious infection treated with "broad-spectrum" antibiotics, especially the kind that is serious enough to land you in the hospital. Those antibiotics wipe out helpful gut bacteria.

Take action: Read ingredients lists on all packaged foods you eat, and avoid any that include trehalose while you are taking such antibiotics and for several weeks afterward. And avoid trehalose if you have or have recently recovered from a *C. diff* infection.

TAKE NOTE...

Know the Real Signs of Drowning

The real signs of drowning are not what TV and movies show. There's actually little splashing and no waving or calling for help. *For example...*

●**Drowning people can't call for help** because the respiratory system is tied up trying to breathe.

●**Drowning people's mouths sink below the water surface, then reappear.**

●**They can't wave for help**—their arms instinctively extend and press down on the water's surface, and the movements cannot be controlled.

●**When people are drowning, their bodies remain upright in the water**—they can struggle for only 20 to 60 seconds before going under.

If you are not sure what is going on, ask someone in the water if he/she is all right. If you get no answer, the person needs to be rescued.

SoundingsOnline.com, a boating website.

Better Pedestrian Safety

Every day, 430 pedestrians are treated in ERs for traffic-related mishaps in the US… and more than 15 die each day from their injuries. In total, pedestrian fatalities have shot up 46% since 2009.

Some of the blame goes to our love affair with SUVs. The supersized behemoths cause more deaths than any other type of vehicle.

Other risks: Jaywalking…poor nighttime visibility…walking while intoxicated…or ignoring traffic while sending a text.

So what can you do to stay safer?

Smart strategies: Be sure to wear bright-colored clothes when walking during the day. At nighttime, increase your visibility by carrying a flashlight and/or wearing reflective clothing—you can buy reflective vests online for less than $10. Walking sober is a no-brainer.

Also: Be sure to watch for turning vehicles—and always walk on the sidewalk (if there isn't one, walk facing traffic). And avoid distractions. Texting can wait…a driver might not.

Rebecca Shannonhouse, editor in chief, *Bottom Line Health*, BottomLineInc.com.

Better Home Security

In addition to installing exterior lighting and asking neighbors to watch your house when you are away, remember that most break-ins happen through ground-level windows and doors, so strengthen them. Window bars are the strongest window security and almost impossible to get past, but ask local police if they recommend them.

Also, most burglaries occur between 10 am and 3 pm, not at night—and many thieves get in through unlocked doors or windows—so stay alert if you are home during the day, and lock everything when going out.

Roundup of experts on home security, reported at FamilyHandyman.com.

GOOD ADVICE...

Where to Hide Valuables in Your Home

●**Put cash and important papers in an envelope,** and tape it to the back or underside of a drawer.

●**Cash also can be stored in a marker after you remove the ink cartridge** or inside the spring bar that holds toilet paper.

●**Small items can be kept inside the case of a wall clock or mantel clock** as long as the clock itself is not worth stealing. Or a small box of valuables can be put into a larger box containing other things, such as old sweaters.

●**If the exterior hood for your dryer vent is accessible, you can hide a spare house key inside it**—just glue a magnet to the key and tuck the key up out of sight. If the vent hood is aluminum or plastic, glue a magnet to the inside of it and another magnet to the key.

FamilyHandyman.com

Inexpensive Lifesavers

Each of these lifesaving items can be bought for $15 or less…

●**Baking soda** can put out small fires, especially grease fires.

●**A car hammer** is specially designed to break window glass if your car is ever submerged in water.

●**A personal water filter** can remove potentially harmful organisms from lake or river water in case you run out of water while hiking or camping.

●**An emergency blanket** can protect against sun, wind and water during a hiking or camping trip, can be turned into a makeshift shelter and can be hung as a distress flag.

Roundup of experts reported at MoneyTalksNews.com.

Index